Functions 11

Exercise and Homework Book

AUTHOR

Antonietta Lenjosek
B.Sc., B.Ed.
Ottawa Catholic School Board

REVIEWERS

Kirsten Boucher
Durham District School Board

Barbara Canton
Limestone District School Board

Rob Gleeson
Bluewater District School Board

Bryce Bates
Toronto District School Board

NELSON

NELSON

Functions 11 Exercise and Homework Book

ISBN-13: 978-0-07-031875-5
ISBN-10: 0-07-031875-1

2 3 4 5 21 20 19 18

Printed and bound in Canada

The Geometer's Sketchpad®, Key Curriculum Press, 1150 65th Street, Emeryville, CA 94608, 1-800-995-MATH.

PUBLISHER: Linda Allison
ASSOCIATE PUBLISHER: Kristi Clark
PROJECT MANAGER: Janice Dyer
DEVELOPMENTAL EDITORS: Jackie Lacoursiere, Susan Lishman, Paul McNulty
COPYEDITOR: Linda Jenkins
ANSWER CHECKER: Daniela Spiroska
MANAGER, EDITORIAL SERVICES: Crystal Shortt
SUPERVISING EDITOR: Janie Deneau
EDITORIAL ASSISTANT: Erin Hartley
MANAGER, PRODUCTION SERVICES: Yolanda Pigden
PRODUCTION COORDINATOR: Paula Brown
COVER DESIGN: Michelle Losier
ELECTRONIC PAGE MAKE-UP: Laserwords
COVER IMAGE: © Andrew Kornylak/Getty Images

Contents

Chapter 4 Trigonometry

Chapter 5 Trigonometric Functions

Chapter 6 Discrete Functions

Chapter 7 Financial Applications of Sequences and Series

Overview

Functions play an important role in many activities, from business and economics to the social, medical, and physical sciences. *McGraw-Hill Ryerson Functions 11 Exercise and Homework Book* is designed for students planning to qualify for college or university. It is designed to complement the *McGraw-Hill Ryerson Functions 11* student book.

Exercise and Homework Book Organization

- Chapter 1 distinguishes between functions and relations, including the use of the vertical line test. You will find the domain and range of functions and relations. You will examine various representations of functions, including graphical, function notation, mapping notation, and mapping diagrams. You will identify a variety of methods for determining the minimum and maximum of quadratic functions, and then apply these functions to solve related real world problems. You will practise the skills required for work with radicals. You will use the role of the discriminant to determine the number of solutions for a quadratic equation. You will determine equations of quadratic functions based on their roots and given information. The chapter ends with solving linear-quadratic systems.

- Chapter 2 extends your knowledge of transformations related to quadratic functions (grade 10 math) to general transformations of key base functions. You will then apply the transformation concepts established in this chapter to exponential functions in chapter 3 and trigonometric functions in chapter 5. The chapter begins with methods for identifying equivalent algebraic expressions. You will practise operations with rational expressions, including finding the restrictions on variables. Then, you will explore transformations of functions, including horizontal and vertical translations, reflections, and stretches and compressions. You will also examine combinations of transformations. The chapter ends with determining the inverse of a function graphically and algebraically.

- Chapter 3 introduces a new function, the exponential function. The chapter begins by studying exponential growth in populations and other real-life situations. Then, you will examine exponential decay in relation to half-life and radioactive materials. These concepts are connected to the meaning and applications of negative exponents and rational exponents. You will investigate properties and characteristics of exponential functions, as well as the impact of transformations on the graphs of exponential functions. The final section of this chapter examines mathematical modelling with exponential functions, including solving problems using the functions.

- Chapter 4 extends your knowledge of trigonometry studied in grade 10. The chapter begins by identifying special angles and triangles in terms of the unit circle. You will determine exact values of special angles, co-terminal and related angles, in degree measure, using the primary and reciprocal trigonometric ratios. The latter part of the chapter focuses on solving a variety of two dimensional and three dimensional problems involving right triangles and oblique triangles, including the ambiguous case of the sine law. In the last section of the chapter, you will work on proofs of trigonometric identities, which require the use of the Pythagorean, quotient, and reciprocal identities.

- Chapter 5 applies the concepts from chapter 4 to analyse the graphs of trigonometric functions. In the first section of the chapter, you will examine mathematical modelling with periodic functions. Then, you will graph the sine and cosine functions and identify their properties. You will investigate transformations of the sine and cosine functions and explore mathematical modelling with transformed functions. In the latter part of the chapter, you will collect data representing periodic behaviour and determine equations representing a variety of periodic situations. You will then solve related problems, including those that do not involve angles.

- Chapter 6 introduces discrete functions. The start of this chapter explores sequences as discrete functions and then examines recursive procedures. You will study Pascal's triangle and patterns in Pascal's triangle, as well as applications of the triangle. You will then explore arithmetic and geometric sequences and series and solve a variety of problems involving their application.

- Chapter 7 relates the concepts of discrete functions from chapter 6 to a focus on financial applications. The beginning of the chapter identifies and compares simple and compound interest. Then, you will explore present value, and finally, you will investigate and define ordinary annuities and the present value of an annuity. Throughout the chapter, you will solve a variety of real-world problems involving applications of these concepts, both algebraically and using technology.

Study Guide Features

- Each section begins with Key Concepts that summarize the concepts needed to complete the exercises.
- The sections continue with a worked example that guides you through the skills needed to complete the exercises.
- Exercises are organized into three sections: A (practice), B (connect and apply), and C (extend and challenge).
- A review of all the sections is included at the end of each chapter.
- Each chapter includes Math Contest questions that cover the concepts in the chapter, as well as extend your thinking and combine concepts from previous chapters.
- Selected questions in each section are marked by a star that indicates that full worked solutions are provided at the back of the book. Answers to all other questions are also provided.
- A practice exam at the end of the study guide gives you the opportunity to determine if you are ready for the final examination.

Symbols

SYMBOLS

$\mathbb{R}$	real numbers
$\mathbb{N}$	natural numbers
$\mathbb{Z}$	integers
∞	infinity
$\in$	belongs to
$[a,b]$	$a \leq x \leq b$ (closed interval)
(a,b)	$a < x < b$ (open interval)

GREEK LOWER CASE LETTERS

α	alpha (a)
β	beta (b)
γ	gamma (g)
δ	delta (d) lower case
Δ	delta (d) upper case
λ	lamda (l)
ρ	rho (r)
θ	theta (th)
τ	tau (t)
π	pi (p)
ω	omega (o)

Formulas

ALGEBRA

Factoring Special Polynomials	$x^2 \pm 2xy + y^2 = (x \pm y)^2$ $x^3 \pm y^3 = (x \pm y)(x^2 \mp xy + y^2)$ $x^2 - y^2 = (x - y)(x + y)$
Quadratic Formula	If $ax^2 + bx + c = 0$, then $x = \dfrac{-b \pm \sqrt{b^2 - 4ac}}{2a}$
Discriminant	Determine the number of solutions to a quadratic equation and the number of zeros of the related quadratic function by using the discriminant. If $b^2 - 4ac > 0$, there are two solutions (two distinct real roots). 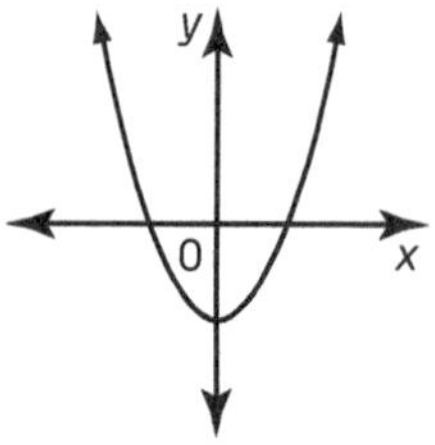 If $b^2 - 4ac = 0$, there is one solution (two equal real roots). 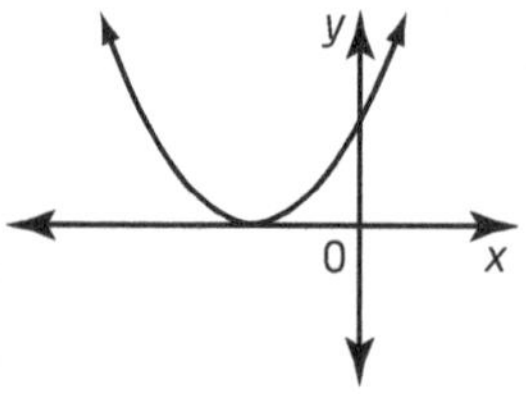 If $b^2 - 4ac < 0$, there are no real solutions. 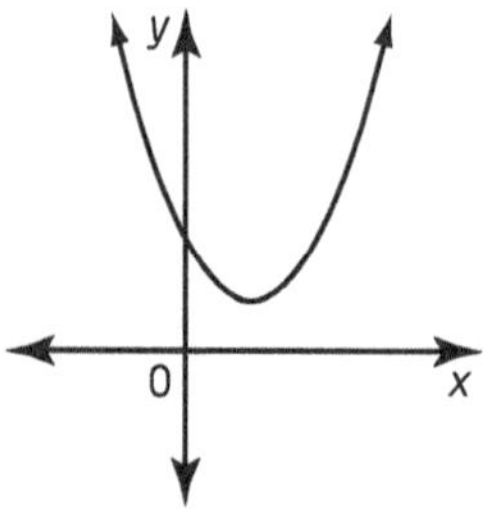

RULES FOR EXPONENTS

Product	$(x^a)(x^b) = x^{a+b}$
Quotient	$\dfrac{x^a}{x^b} = x^{a-b}$
Power	$(x^a)^b = x^{ab}$
Power of a Product	$(xy)^a = x^a y^a$
Rational Exponent	$x^{\frac{1}{a}} = \sqrt[a]{x}$
Negative Exponent	$x^{-a} = \dfrac{1}{x^a}$

ANALYTIC GEOMETRY

Distance between Two Points Distance between two points $P_1(x_1, y_1)$ and $P_2(x_2, y_2)$	$P_1P_2 = \sqrt{(x_2 - x_1)^2 + (y_1 - y_2)^2}$
Linear Function For a line through the points $P_1(x_1, y_1)$ and $P_2(x_2, y_2)$	Slope: $m = \frac{y_2 - y_1}{x_2 - x_1}$ Slope y-intercept form of equation: $y = mx + b$, where b is the y-intercept Point-slope form of equation: $y - y_1 = m(x - x_1)$
Quadratic Function Equation for a parabola with vertex (p, q)	$y = a(x - p)^2 + q$ Find the vertex of a quadratic function by – graphing – completing the square: for $f(x) = a(x - h)^2 + k$, the vertex is (h, k) – partial factoring: for $f(x) = ax\left(x + \frac{b}{a}\right) + k$, the x-coordinate of the vertex is $-\frac{b}{2a}$
Circle Equation for a circle centre (h, k) and radius r	$(x - h)^2 + (y - k)^2 = r^2$

MEASUREMENT

In the following, P represents perimeter, C the circumference, A the area, V the volume, and SA the surface area.

Triangle	c, h, a, b $P = a + b + c$ $A = \frac{1}{2}bh$
Cylinder	r $V = \pi r^2 h$ $SA = 2\pi rh + 2\pi r^2$

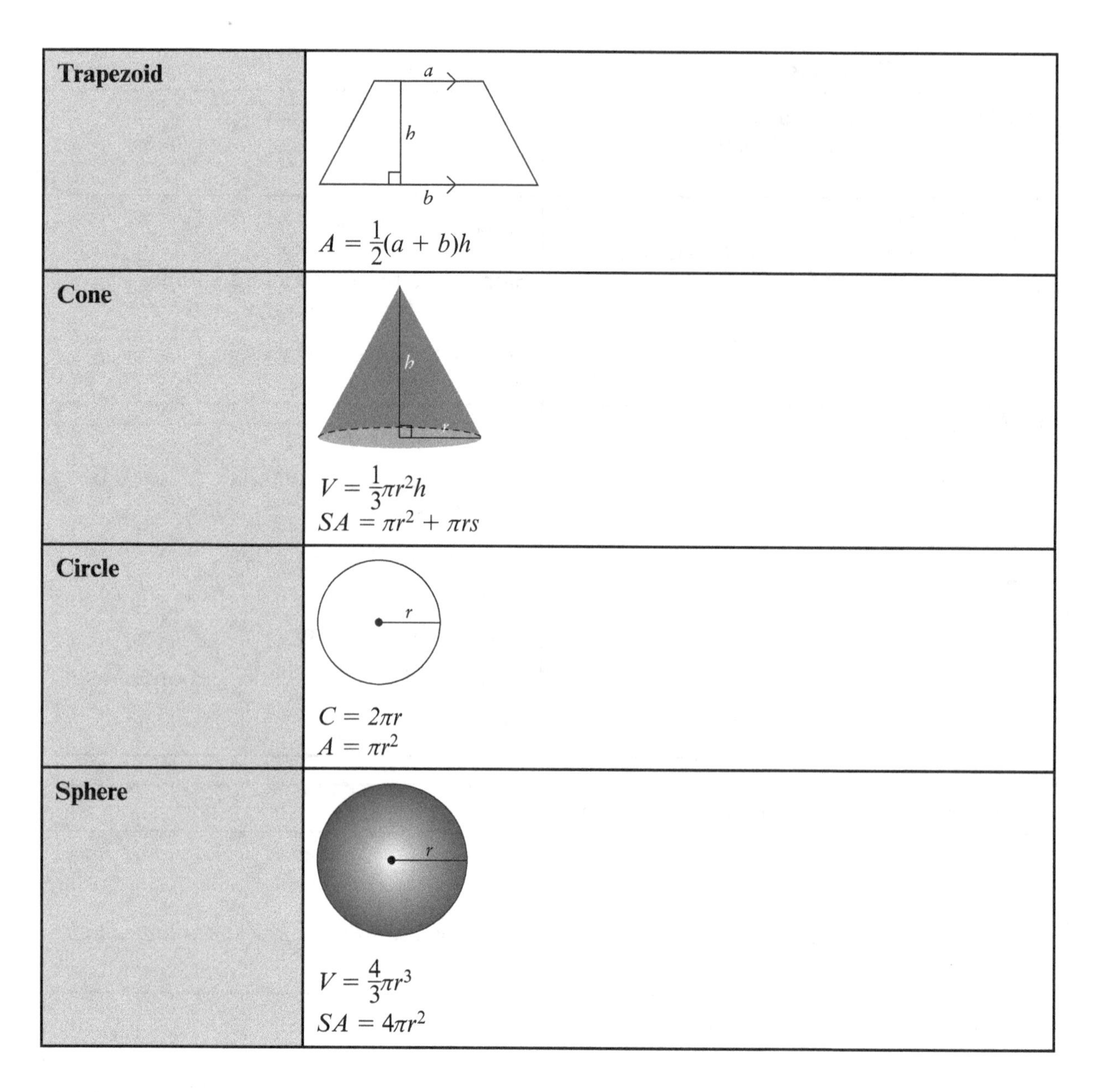

Trapezoid	$A = \frac{1}{2}(a + b)h$
Cone	$V = \frac{1}{3}\pi r^2 h$ $SA = \pi r^2 + \pi rs$
Circle	$C = 2\pi r$ $A = \pi r^2$
Sphere	$V = \frac{4}{3}\pi r^3$ $SA = 4\pi r^2$

TRIGONOMETRY

Primary Trigonometric Ratios hypotenuse, opposite, θ, adjacent	$\sin \theta = \frac{\text{opposite}}{\text{hypotenuse}}$	$\cos \theta = \frac{\text{adjacent}}{\text{hypotenuse}}$	$\tan \theta = \frac{\text{opposite}}{\text{adjacent}}$
y, r, (x, y), θ, 0, x	$\sin \theta = \frac{y}{r}$	$\cos \theta = \frac{x}{r}$	$\tan \theta = \frac{y}{x}$

Sine Law	$\frac{\sin A}{a} = \frac{\sin B}{b} = \frac{\sin C}{c}$	$\frac{a}{\sin A} = \frac{b}{\sin B} = \frac{c}{\sin C}$	
Cosine Law	$a^2 = b^2 + c^2 - 2bc \cos A$	$b^2 = a^2 + c^2 - 2ac \cos B$	$c^2 = a^2 + b^2 - 2ab \cos C$
Fundamental Identities	$\sin^2 \theta + \cos^2 \theta = 1$ $\tan \theta = \frac{\sin \theta}{\cos \theta}$	$1 + \cot^2 \theta = \csc^2 \theta$ $\cot \theta = \frac{\cos \theta}{\sin \theta}$	$\tan^2 \theta + 1 = \sec^2 \theta$
Reciprocal Identities	$\csc \theta = \frac{1}{\sin \theta}$ $\sec \theta = \frac{1}{\cos \theta}$	$\cot \theta = \frac{1}{\tan \theta}$ $\sin \theta = \frac{1}{\csc \theta}$	$\cos \theta = \frac{1}{\sec \theta}$ $\tan \theta = \frac{1}{\cot \theta}$
Unit Circle	The coordinates of the point (x, y) on a unit circle are related to θ such that $x = \cos \theta$ and $y = \sin \theta$. $\tan \theta = \frac{y}{x}$ Exactly two angles between 0° and 360° have the same sine ratio. Exactly two angles between 0° and 360° have the same cosine ratio. Exactly two angles between 0° and 360° have the same tangent ratio. Find pairs of related angles using the coordinates of the endpoints of their terminal arms. Use a reference angle in the first quadrant.		
Special Triangles	Determine exact trigonometric ratios for special angles using special triangles: The exact trignometric ratios for 45° are $\sin 45° = \frac{1}{\sqrt{2}}$, $\cos 45° = \frac{1}{\sqrt{2}}$, and $\tan 45° = 1$.		

TRANSFORMATIONS

Vertical and Horizontal Translations	The graph of $g(x) = f(x) + c$ is a vertical translation of the graph of $f(x)$ by c units. If $c > 0$, the graph moves up c units. If $c < 0$, the graph moves down c units. The graph of $g(x) = f(x - d)$ is a horizondal translation of the graph of $f(x)$ by d units. If $d > 0$, the graph moves to the right d units. If $d < 0$, the graph moves to the left d units. Create a sketch of the graph of any transformed function by transforming the related base function. In general, determine the domain and range of a function of the form $g(x) = f(x - d) + c$ by adding the d-value and the c-value to restrictions on the domain and range, respectively, of the base function.
Reflections	$y = f(-x)$ A point (x, y) becomes $(-x, y)$. The graph is reflected in the y-axis. 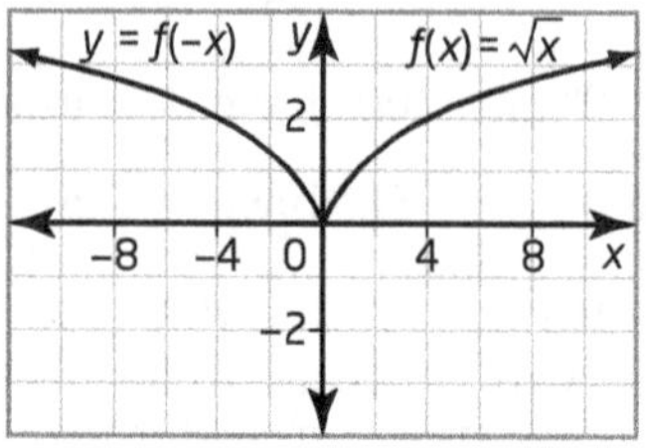 $y = f(-x)$ y $f(x) = \sqrt{x}$ 2 −8 −4 0 4 8 x −2 Replace x with $-x$ in the expression.
	$y = -f(x)$ A point (x, y) becomes $(x, -y)$. The graph is reflected in the x-axis. 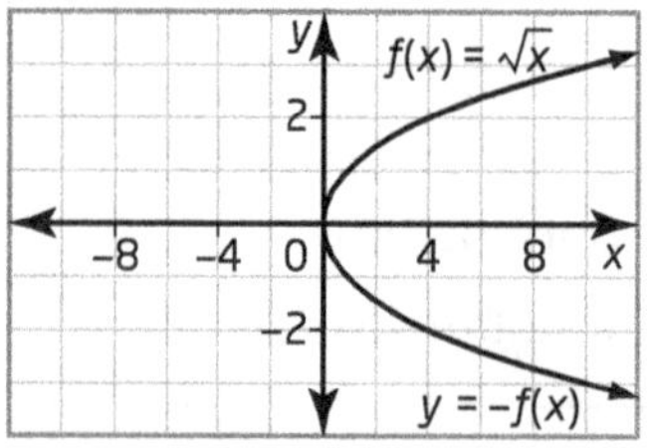 y $f(x) = \sqrt{x}$ 2 −8 −4 0 4 8 x −2 $y = -f(x)$ Multiply the entire expression by −1.

	$y = -f(-x)$ A point (x, y) becomes $(-x, -y)$. The graph is reflected in one axis and then the other. First replace x with $-x$ in the expression, then multiply the entire expression by -1.
Stretches	The graph of $g(x) = af(x)$, $a > 0$, is a vertical stretch or a vertical compression of the graph of $f(x)$ by a factor of a. If $a > 1$, the graph is vertically stretched by a factor of a. If $0 < a < 1$, the graph is vertically compressed by a factor of a. The graph of $g(x) = f(kx)$, $k > 0$, is a horizontal stretch or a horizontal compression of the graph of $f(x)$ by a factor of $\frac{1}{k}$. If $k > 1$, the graph is horizontally compressed by a factor of $\frac{1}{k}$. If $0 < k < 1$, the graph is horizontally stretched by a factor of $\frac{1}{k}$.
Combinations of Transformations	The parameters a, k, d, and c in the function $y = af[k(x - d)] + c$ correspond to the following transformations: – a: vertical stretch or compression and, if $a < 0$, a reflection in the x-axis – k: a horizontal stretch or compression and, if $k < 0$, a reflection in the y-axis – d: a horizontal translation to the right or left – c: a vertical translation up or down

DISCRETE FUNCTIONS

Sequences	Given the explicit formula for the nth term, t_n or $f(n)$, of a sequence, write the terms by substituting the term numbers for n. Examples: $t_n = 3n + 2$ and $f(n) = 5n + 3$. An explicit formula for the nth term of a sequence can sometimes be determined by finding a pattern among the terms.

Recursive	A recursion formula shows the relationship between the terms of a sequence. Represent a sequence by a pattern, an explicit formula, or a recursion formula. Write formulas using function notation. For example: Pattern: 1, 3, 5, 7, ... Explicit formula: $t_n = 2n - 1$ or $f(n) = 2n - 1$ Recursion formula: $t_1 = 1, t_n = t_{n-1} + 2$, or $f(1) = 1, f(n) = f(n-1) + 2$
Arithmetic Sequences	$t_n = a + (n - 1)d$ $a =$ the first term $d =$ the common difference $n =$ the term number
Geometric Sequences	$t_n = a(r)^{n-1}$ $a =$ the first term $r =$ the common ratio $n =$ the term number
Pascal's Triangle	$t_{n,r} = t_{n-1,r-1} + t_{n-1,r}$ $n =$ the horizontal row number $r =$ the diagonal row number
Arithmetic Series	Given the first term, the last term, and the number of terms of an arithmetic series, find the sum of the series using the formula $S_n = \frac{n}{2}(a + t_n)$ or the formula $S_n = \frac{n}{2}[2a + (n - 1)d]$. Given the first terms of an arithmetic series, find the sum of the first n terms using the formula $S_n = \frac{n}{2}[2a + (n - 1)d]$.
Geometric Series	The formula for the sum of the first n terms of a geometric series with first term a and common ratio r is $S_n = \frac{a(r^n - 1)}{r - 1}, r \neq 1$.

FINANCIAL APPLICATIONS

Interest	$I = Prt$ $P =$ principal, in dollars $r =$ annual interest rate, as a decimal $t =$ time, in years $A = P + I$ $A =$ amount of an account earning simple interest
Compound Interest	$A = P(1 + i)^n$ $P =$ principal $i =$ interest rate per compounding period $n =$ number of compounding periods

Present Value	$PV = \frac{FV}{(1 + i)^n}$ FV = future value n = number of compounding periods i = interest rate, as a decimal per compounding period
Annuities	$A = \frac{R[(1 + i)^n - 1]}{i}$ R = regular payment i = interest rate per compounding period, as a decimal n = compounding periods
Present Value of an Annuity	$PV = \frac{R[1 - (1 + i)^{-n}]}{i}$ R = regular withdrawal i = interest rate per compounding period, as a decimal n = number of compounding periods

Tips for Success in MATH

IN CLASS

- **Listen** carefully to your teacher.
- **Focus** and **pay attention** to examples and their solutions.
- **Copy** all notes and examples. **Think** about the solutions.
- **Ask** questions when you don't understand.
- Use class time **efficiently**. Begin homework when time is given in class.
- Use **proper form** when solving questions. Don't skip key steps.
- **Ask** about homework questions you had difficulty with. Copy solutions to questions you didn't understand.
- **Concentrate**, think, pay attention, ask questions, and focus on the given examples in class.
- Create a **Math Vocabulary/Formula List** section in your notebook to record all important words, definitions, and formulas.
- Read the **instructions** to a question so that you are familiar with the wording.

AT HOME

- **Complete** your math homework **every night**. Try **every** question assigned. Refer to the text and class example solutions to help you.
- **Check** your answers with those at the back of the book. Highlight homework questions that you had **difficulty** with or **could** not do.
- **Review** examples and notes. Use them to help you with your homework.
- **Memorize** all formulas, definitions, vocabulary, and steps/procedures for solving longer questions.
- For each lesson and chapter **prepare a summary study sheet** that contains: important **formulas, definitions, vocabulary, procedures for solutions**, and **solutions** to questions from the homework that **you** found to be difficult.
- **Update** your study sheet after each lesson. This will save time when studying for tests and the exam.

PREPARING FOR A TEST

- Begin studying and reviewing at least **3 days prior** to a test. **Don't wait until the night before**.
- Review the **summary study sheets** that you have prepared.
- Review each section to be tested in the chapter. **REDO** homework questions that you found difficult.
- Do **all review** questions assigned. Try **extra homework** questions that were not assigned.
- **Memorize** formulas, definitions, vocabulary, and steps for longer solutions.
- **Study the wording of questions** so that you will understand the instructions on a test.
- Try to **categorize** the types and variety of questions done over the entire chapter.
- **DO NOT CRAM!** Studying for a math test should be easy if you have been keeping up throughout the chapter.

Chapter 1 Functions

1.1 Functions, Domain, and Range

KEY CONCEPTS

- A relation is a function if for each value in the domain there is exactly one value in the range. This table of values models a function.

x	−2	−1	0	1	2
y	5	3	1	−1	−3

- The vertical line test can be used on the graph of a relation to determine if it is a function. If every vertical line passes through at most one point on the graph, then the relation is a function.
- The domain and the range of a function can be found by determining if there are restrictions based on the defining equation. Restrictions on the domain occur because division by zero is undefined and because expressions under a radical sign must be greater than or equal to zero. The range can have restrictions too. For example, a quadratic that opens upward will have a minimum value.
- Set notation is used to write the domain and range for a function. For example, for the function $y = x^2 + 2$:
domain $\{x \in \mathbb{R}\}$ and range $\{y \in \mathbb{R}, y \geq 2\}$

Example

Write the domain and range of each relation, and then determine if the relation is a function.

a) $\{(8, 10), (1, -8), (5, 0), (-5, 6), (-6, -7), (-5, -2), (0, -9), (-9, 5)\}$

b)

x	−6	−4	−2	0	2	4	6	8
y	12	2	−4	−6	−4	2	12	26

c) $y = \frac{1}{x + 2}$

Solution

a) domain $\{-9, -6, -5, 0, 1, 5, 8\}$, range $\{-9, -8, -7, -2, 0, 5, 6, 10\}$
For some elements of the domain there is more than one corresponding element of the range ($x = -5$ goes with $y = -2$ and $y = 6$). This relation is not a function.

b) domain $\{-6, -4, -2, 0, 2, 4, 6, 8\}$, range $\{-6, -4, 2, 12, 26\}$
Each element of the domain corresponds with a unique element of the range. This relation is a function.

c) The denominator cannot be 0, so $x \neq -2$.
domain $\{x \in \mathbb{R}, x \neq -2\}$

Since the numerator is 1, the fraction can never equal 0.
range $\{y \in \mathbb{R}, y \neq 0\}$
For each x-value, there is only one possible y-value. This relation is a function.

A Practise

1. Does each graph represent a function? Explain.

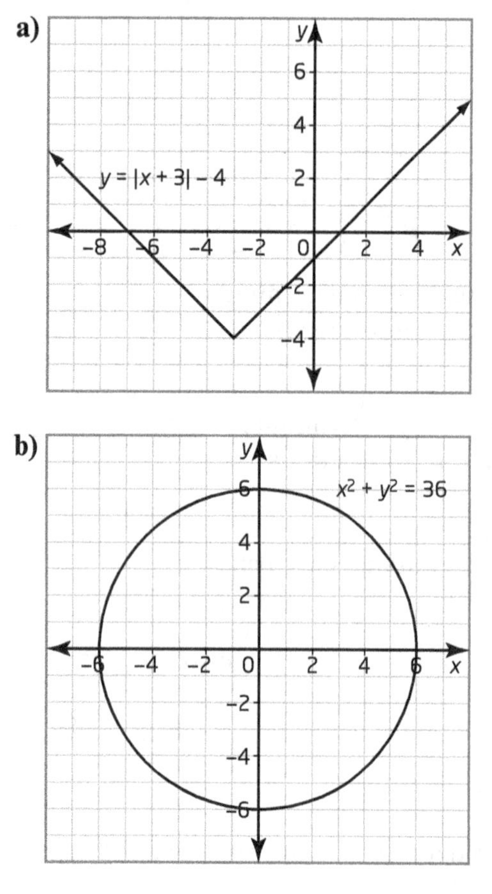

★2. For each relation, determine if the relation is a function, and then sketch a graph of the relation.

a) $y = -3x + 1$

b) $x = y^2 - 2$

c) $y = 3(x + 1)^2 - 5$

3. State the domain and the range of each relation. Is each relation a function? Justify your answer.

a) $\{(2, 4), (3, 6), (4, 8), (5, 10), (6, 12)\}$

b) $\{(-6, 2), (-5, 2), (-4, 2), (-3, 2)\}$

c) $\{(5, -4), (5, -2), (5, 0), (5, 2), (5, 4)\}$

4. The domain and range of some relations are given. Each relation consists of only four points. Determine if each relation is a function. Explain.

a) domain $\{-4, -2\}$, range $\{1, 3, 5, 7\}$

b) domain $\{4, 5, 6, 7\}$, range $\{-1, 3, 7, 11\}$

B Connect and Apply

5. Determine the domain and the range of each relation.

a) $x^2 + y^2 = 49$

b) $y = \dfrac{2}{5 - x}$

6. For each given domain and range, draw two relations on the same axes: one that is a function and one that is not a function.

a) domain $\{x \in \mathbb{R}\}$, range $\{y \in \mathbb{R}\}$

b) domain $\{x \in \mathbb{R}, x \leq 5\}$, range $\{y \in \mathbb{R}, y \geq -6\}$

c) domain $\{x \in \mathbb{R}\}$, range $\{y \in \mathbb{R}, y \leq 3\}$

d) domain $\{x \in \mathbb{R}, x \geq -4\}$, range $\{y \in \mathbb{R}, y \geq 1\}$

7. Hatia has 120 m of fencing. She plans to enclose a large rectangular garden and divide it into three equal parts.

a) Write an area function in terms of x to model the total area of the garden.

b) Determine the domain and the range for the area function.

8. For each function, determine the range for the domain $\{-2, -1, 0, 1, 2\}$.

a) $y = 8$

b) $y = -(x + 3)^2 - 2$

c) $y = \dfrac{8}{x + 5}$

9. State the domain and the range of each relation.

a) $y = x + 2$

b) $y = 0.5(x + 3)^2 - 1$

c) $(y - 1)^2 - 3 = -x$

d) $y = \dfrac{-3}{x + 4}$

10. Describe the graph of a relation that satisfies each set of conditions.

a) There are two entries in the domain and five entries in the range.

b) There are three entries in the domain and three entries in the range.

C Extend

☆**11. a)** State the domain and range of each relation, and then identify if each relation is a function. Justify your answer graphically.

i) $x^2 + y^2 = 16$

ii) $y = \sqrt{16 - x^2}$

iii) $y = -\sqrt{16 - x^2}$

b) Describe how the graphs of ii) and iii) are related to the graph of i).

12. State the domain and the range for each relation. Determine if each relation is a function.

a)

b)

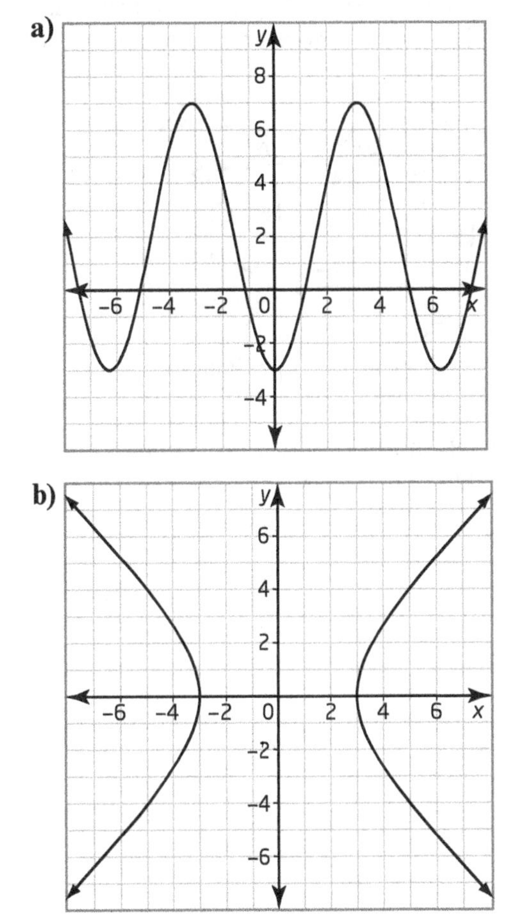

1.2 Functions and Function Notation

KEY CONCEPTS

- In function notation, the symbol $f(x)$ represents the dependent variable. It indicates that the function f is expressed in terms of the independent variable x. For example, $y = 3x^2 - 5$ is written as $f(x) = 3x^2 - 5$.

- Relations and functions given as ordered pairs can be represented using mapping diagrams. This involves using directed arrows from each value in an oval representing the domain to the corresponding value or values in an oval representing the range.

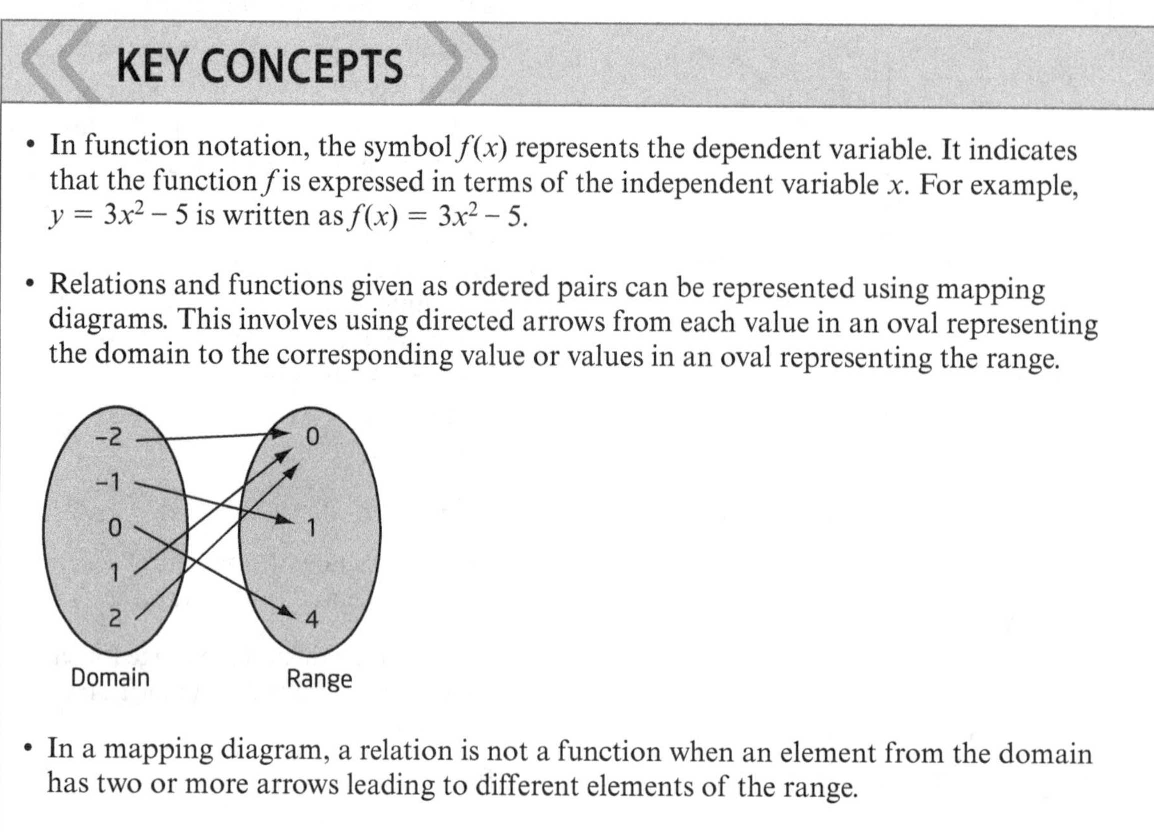

- In a mapping diagram, a relation is not a function when an element from the domain has two or more arrows leading to different elements of the range.

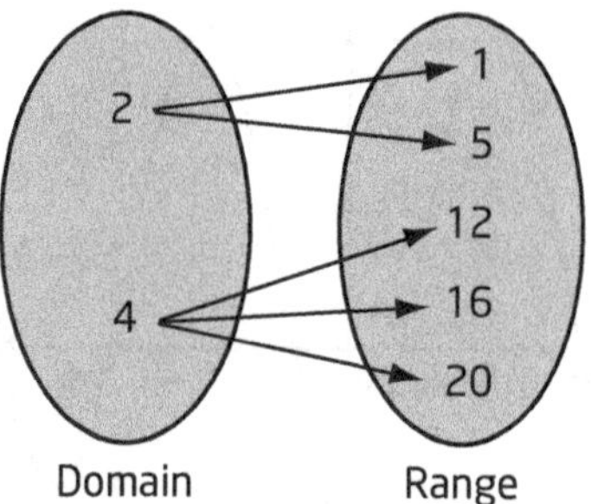

- Mapping notation can replace function notation. For example, $f(x) = 3x^2 - 5$ can be written as $f: x \rightarrow 3x^2 - 5$.

Example

A quadratic function machine uses a function of the form $f(x) = ax^2 + b$. The points (1, 3) and (−2, −3) lie on the function. Determine the values of a and b, and then write the defining equation of the function.

Solution

For (1, 3), $f(1) = 3$.
$a(1)^2 + b = 3$
$a + b = 3$ ①

For (−2, −3), $f(-2) = -3$.
$a(-2)^2 + b = -3$
$4a + b = -3$ ②

$4a + b = -3$ ②
$a + b = 3$ ①
$3a = -6$ ③
$a = -2$

Subtract equation ① from equation ②.

$-2 + b = 3$
$b = 5$

Substitute $a = -2$ in ① to solve for b.

The defining equation is $f(x) = -2x^2 + 5$.

A Practise

1. For each function below,

i) determine $f(-2)$, $f(1)$, and $f\left(\frac{1}{2}\right)$

ii) write the function in mapping notation

a) $f(x) = -\frac{3}{5}x + 2$

b) $f(x) = 6x^2 - 4x + 3$

c) $f(x) = -3(x + 1)^2 - 2$

d) $f(x) = 7$

e) $f(x) = \frac{1}{4x + 1}$

f) $f(x) = \sqrt{3 - 2x}$

2. Find the value of each function at $x = 0$. Sketch the graph of each function.

a) $f(x) = 3x - 1$

b) $k(x) = 5x$

c) $p(x) = -2$

d) $g(x) = 10x^2 + 4x - 1$

e) $h(x) = (5x - 2)(3x + 6)$

f) $q(x) = -\frac{1}{2}(3 - 4x)(x - 5)$

3. Given $f(x) = 4x + 7$, determine the value of x if $f(x) = 15$.

4. A linear function machine uses a function of the form $f(x) = ax + 2$. In each case, suppose the given point is on the function. Find the value of a, and then write the defining equation.

a) (4, −10)

b) (1, 8)

c) (3, 6.5)

d) (−5, 33)

5. Represent each set of data in a mapping diagram.

a) {(−4, 18), (−3, 14), (−2, 10), (−1, 6), (0, 2), (1, −2)}

b) {(−3, 3), (−2, −3), (−1, 3), (−1, −3), (−2, 3), (−3, −3)}

c) {(2, 1), (3, 3), (4, 5), (5, 1), (6, 3), (7, 5)}

d) {(6, −7), (9, −7), (12, −7), (15, −7)}

6. Refer to question 5. Determine if each relation is a function. Justify your answer.

7. Write the ordered pairs associated with each mapping diagram.

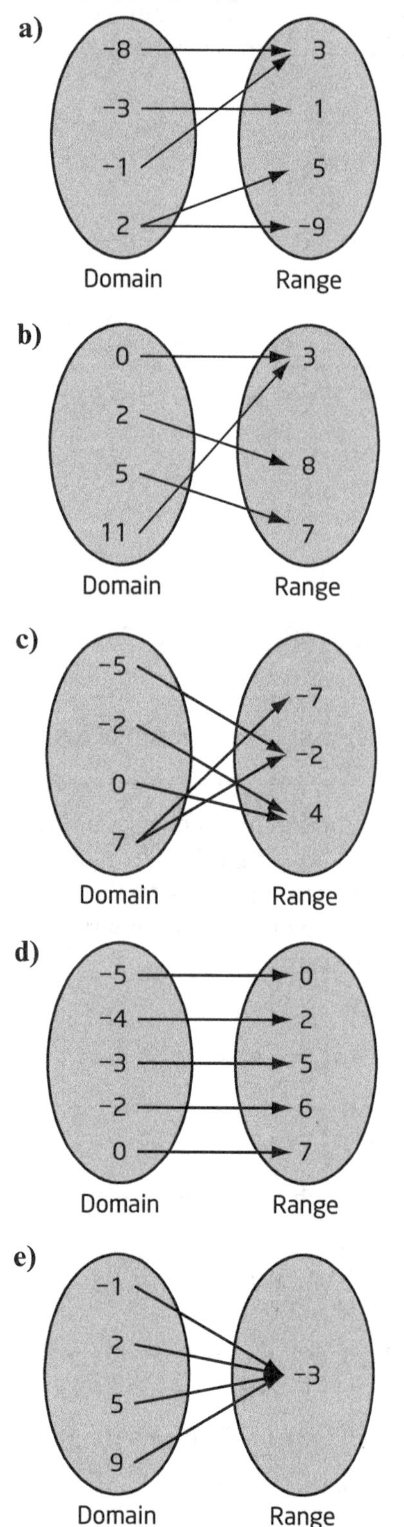

8. Refer to question 7. Determine if each relation is a function. Justify your answer.

9. Write each function in mapping notation.

a) $f(x) = -7x + 1$

b) $g(x) = x^2 + 7x - 5$

c) $h(b) = \sqrt{9b + 9}$

d) $r(k) = \dfrac{1}{5k - 3}$

B Connect and Apply

☆**10.** The period of a pendulum varies on different planets due to the different gravitational forces. On Earth, the period, T, in seconds, of a pendulum is given by the relation $T = 2\sqrt{\ell}$, where ℓ is the length of the pendulum, in metres. On the moon, the relation is $T = 5\sqrt{\ell}$, and on Pluto the relation is $T = 8\sqrt{\ell}$.

a) For each location, determine the period when the length of the pendulum is 1.8 m.

b) For each location, determine the length of the pendulum that results in a period of 3 s.

c) Determine the domain and the range of each relation.

d) Graph each relation on the same set of axes.

e) Is each relation a function? Explain.

f) Write each relation in mapping notation.

11. The population of a town, p, in thousands, t years since 1995, is modelled by the relation $p(t) = \dfrac{240t + 300}{3t + 5}$.

a) What was the population of the town in 1995?

b) Determine the population of the town in each year.

i) 2003

ii) 2008

c) In what year will the population reach 78 750?

d) Is $p(t)$ a function? Justify your answer.

12. Use Technology A quadratic function machine uses a function of the form $f(x) = ax^2 + bx + c$. Given the data $\{(1, 2), (2, 9), (3, 22)\}$, you can use a graphing calculator to determine the equation.

a) Enter the values of the domain in **L1** and the values of the range in **L2**.

b) Plot the data.

c) Run quadratic regression and record the resulting equation.

d) Use this function to determine the range values for the domain values $x = -4$, $x = 0$, and $x = 6$.

13. Michael needs $500 two years from now. The amount to be invested, A, at an interest rate i is given by the relation $A(i) = \frac{500}{(1 + i)^2}$. Note that i must be expressed as a decimal.

a) Determine the domain and range for this relation.

b) Is this relation a function? Explain.

c) How much money needs to be invested at each interest rate?

i) 4%

ii) 8%

d) At what rate of interest would each amount need to be invested?

i) $350

ii) $400

☆**14.** An object is dropped from a height of 80 m above the surface of a planet. On Earth, the relation $t(h) = \sqrt{\frac{80 - h}{4.9}}$ represents the time, t, in seconds, when the object is at a height of h metres above the ground. On Jupiter, the relation is $t(h) = \sqrt{\frac{80 - h}{12.8}}$.

a) Express each relation using mapping notation.

b) Determine the domain and range of each relation.

c) Is each relation a function? Explain.

d) Determine the times when the object is 10 m above the ground on Earth and on Jupiter.

15. A quadratic function machine uses a function of the form $f(x) = ax^2 + b$. Determine the values of a and b for each pair of points, and then write the defining equation of the function.

a) (1, 1) and (−1, 1)

b) (2, 1) and (−4, −5)

C Extend

16. Consider the relations $f(x) = 2x$, $g(x) = 2^x$, $h(x) = x^2$, $q(x) = \frac{x}{2}$, and $p(x) = \frac{2}{x}$.

a) State the domain and range of each relation.

b) Graph each relation on the same set of axes.

c) Is each relation a function? Justify your answer.

d) Which relations have the same value when $x = 2$? Justify your answer.

e) Which relations are equal for other values of x? Justify your answer.

17. a) Express $g : x \rightarrow \frac{-2}{x + 3}$ and $h : x \rightarrow 4x^2 - 5x$ in function notation.

b) Determine each value.

i) $g(-1) + h(1)$

ii) $4g(1) - h(2)$

iii) $\sqrt{h(-1)}$

iv) $7[g(-5)]^2$

18. A quadratic function of the form $f(x) = ax^2 + bx + c$ satisfies the conditions $f(1) = 4$, $f(-1) = 10$, and $f(2) = 7$. Determine the values of a, b, and c, and state the defining equation.

1.3 Maximum or Minimum of a Quadratic Function

KEY CONCEPTS

- The minimum or maximum value of a quadratic function occurs at the vertex of the parabola.
- The vertex of a quadratic function can be found by
  - graphing
  - completing the square: for $f(x) = a(x - h)^2 + k$, the vertex is (h, k)
  - partial factoring: for $f(x) = ax\left(x + \frac{b}{a}\right) + k$, the x-coordinate of the vertex is $-\frac{b}{2a}$
- The sign of the coefficient a in the quadratic function $f(x) = ax^2 + bx + c$ or $f(x) = a(x - h)^2 + k$ determines whether the vertex is a minimum or a maximum.
  If $a > 0$, then the parabola opens upward and has a minimum.
  If $a < 0$, then the parabola opens downward and has a maximum.

Example

A farmer has 5000 m of fencing to enclose a rectangular field and subdivide it into three equal plots. The enclosed area is to be a maximum. Determine the dimensions of one plot of land, to the nearest metre.

Solution

Let x represent the width of the rectangular field.
Write an expression for the length of the field.

$\frac{5000 - 4x}{2} = 2500 - 2x$

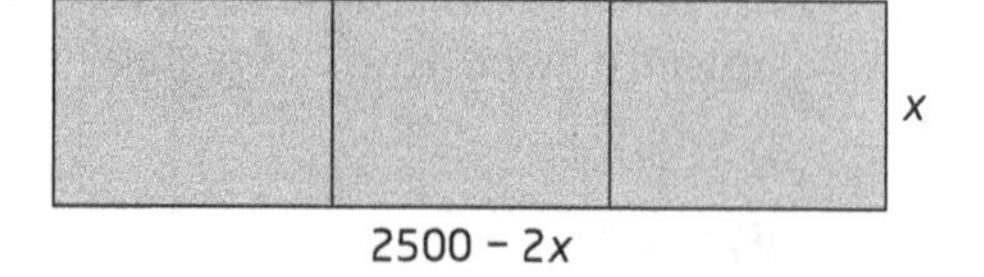

$A(x) = x(2500 - 2x)$

$0 = x(2500 - 2x)$ Use the x-intercepts to find the x-coordinate of the vertex.

$x = 0$ or $2500 - 2x = 0$

$x = 0$ or $x = 1250$

The x-coordinate of the vertex is $x = 625$. This is the width of the field with maximum area.

Length of one plot $= \frac{2500 - 2(625)}{3}$

$\doteq 417$

Length of one plot $= \frac{\text{length of field}}{3}$

The dimensions of each plot of land are approximately 417 m by 625 m.

A Practise

1. Complete the square for each function.

   a) $y = x^2 - 8x$

   b) $f(x) = x^2 + 16x - 4$

   c) $f(x) = x^2 + 5x + 7$

   d) $g(x) = x^2 - x + 2$

   e) $y = x^2 - 8x - 6$

   f) $y = x^2 - 7x - 10$

2. Complete the square to determine the coordinates of the vertex. State if the vertex is a minimum or a maximum.

   a) $f(x) = x^2 + 4x + 1$

   b) $f(x) = -2x^2 + 12x + 7$

   c) $f(x) = -5x^2 - 10x + 3$

   d) $f(x) = 3x^2 - 15x + \frac{59}{4}$

   e) $f(x) = \frac{3}{4}x^2 - 3x + 6$

   f) $f(x) = -\frac{2}{5}x^2 - \frac{4}{5}x - \frac{7}{5}$

3. Use partial factoring to determine the vertex of each function. State if the vertex is a minimum or a maximum.

   a) $f(x) = 4x^2 - 8x + 1$

   b) $f(x) = -3x^2 - 18x - 25$

   c) $f(x) = -\frac{1}{2}x^2 - 4x - 3$

   d) $f(x) = \frac{4}{7}x^2 - \frac{8}{7}x + \frac{25}{7}$

   e) $f(x) = 0.3x^2 - 3.6x + 10.8$

   f) $f(x) = -0.4x^2 + 4x + 1$

4. **Use Technology** Use a graphing calculator to verify your answers to questions 2 and 3.

B Connect and Apply

5. An electronics store sells an average of 52 laptops per month at an average selling price that is $660 more than the cost price. For every $40 increase in the selling price, the store sells two fewer laptops. What amount over the cost price will maximize revenue?

☆6. The student council is organizing a trip to a rock concert. All proceeds from ticket sales will be donated to charity. Tickets to the concert cost $31.25 per person if a minimum of 104 people attend. For every 8 extra people that attend, the price will decrease by $1.25 per person.

   a) How many tickets need to be sold to maximize the donation to charity?

   b) What is the price of each ticket that maximizes the donation?

   c) What is the maximum donation?

7. A ball is kicked into the air. It follows a path given by $h(t) = -4.9t^2 + 8t + 0.4$, where t is the time, in seconds, and $h(t)$ is the height, in metres.

   a) Determine the maximum height of the ball to the nearest tenth of a metre.

   b) When does the ball reach its maximum height?

8. A lifeguard has 40 m of rope to enclose a rectangular swimming area at a small lake. One side of the rectangle is a straight sandy beach. What are the dimensions of the largest swimming area that she can enclose?

☆9. Two numbers have a difference of 8.

   a) What is the maximum product of these numbers?

   b) What are the numbers that produce the maximum product?

10. The sum of two numbers is 26, and the sum of their squares is a minimum.

    a) Determine the numbers.

    b) What is the minimum sum of their squares?

11. Determine the maximum area of a triangle, in square centimetres, if the sum of its base and its height is 15 cm.

12. A ball is thrown upward from the balcony of an apartment building and falls to the ground. The height of the ball, h metres, above the ground after t seconds is modelled by the function $h(t) = -5t^2 + 15t + 55$.

a) Determine the maximum height of the ball.

b) How long does it take the ball to reach its maximum height?

c) How high is the balcony?

13. The parent council is planning the annual spaghetti supper to raise money for new school bleachers. Last year, the tickets sold for $11 each, and 400 people attended. This year the parent council has decided to raise the ticket price. They know that for every $1 increase in price, 20 fewer people will attend the supper.

a) What ticket price would maximize the revenue?

b) What is the maximum revenue?

14. The arch of a bridge is modelled by the function $h(d) = 2 - 0.043d^2 + 2.365d$, where h is the height, in metres, and d is the horizontal distance, in metres, from the origin of the arch.

a) Determine the maximum height of the arch, to the nearest hundredth of a metre.

b) What is the width of the arch at its base?

15. A parabolic arch supporting a bridge over a canal is 10 m wide. The height of the arch 2 m from the edge of the canal is 13 m.

a) Determine an equation to represent the arch, assuming that the edge of the canal is at the origin.

b) Determine the maximum height of the arch, to the nearest tenth of a metre.

16. a) Determine the maximum area of this triangle.

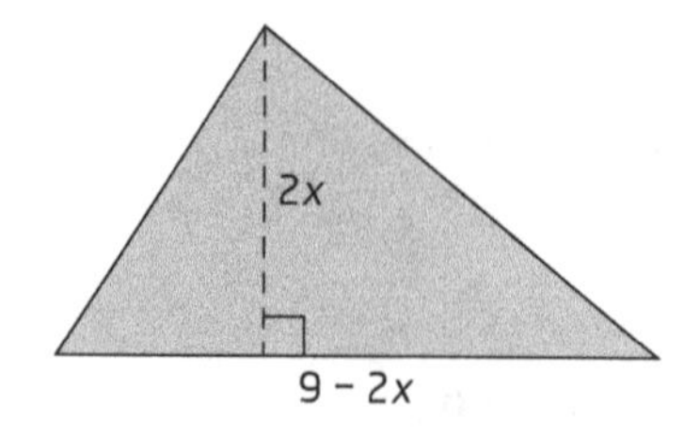

b) What value of x produces the maximum area?

C Extend

17. A ball is thrown vertically upward from an initial height of h_0 metres, with an initial velocity of v m/s, and is affected by the acceleration due to gravity, g. The height function of the ball is given by $h(t) = -\frac{1}{2}gt^2 + vt + h_0$, where $h(t)$ is the height, in metres, and t is the time, in seconds. Write an expression for the maximum height of the ball.

18. In an electrical circuit, the voltage, V volts, as a function of time, t minutes, is modelled by the quadratic function $V(t) = 2t^2 - 9t + 12$.

a) Determine the minimum and maximum voltages during the first 5 min.

b) At what times do the values found in part a) occur?

19. Determine the condition on the value of b so that the minimum value of the quadratic function $f(x) = x^2 + bx + 5$ is an integer.

20. Determine the condition on the value of b so that the maximum value of the quadratic function $f(x) = -4x^2 + bx - 3$ is an integer.

1.4 Skills You Need: Working With Radicals

KEY CONCEPTS

- $\sqrt{a} \times \sqrt{b} = \sqrt{ab}$ for $a \geq 0$ and $b \geq 0$.
- An entire radical can be simplified to a mixed radical in simplest form by removing the largest perfect square from under the radical to form a mixed radical.
  For example, $\sqrt{50} = \sqrt{25 \times 2}$
  $= 5\sqrt{2}$
- Like radicals can be combined through addition and subtraction. For example, $3\sqrt{7} + 2\sqrt{7} = 5\sqrt{7}$.
- Radicals can be multiplied using the distributive property.
  For example, $4\sqrt{2}(5\sqrt{3} - 3) = 20\sqrt{6} - 12\sqrt{2}$ and
  $(\sqrt{2} - 3)(\sqrt{2} + 1) = \sqrt{4} + \sqrt{2} - 3\sqrt{2} - 3$
  $= 2 - 2\sqrt{2} - 3$
  $= -2\sqrt{2} - 1$

Example

Find the length, area, and perimeter of this rectangle. Express your answers in simplified radical form.

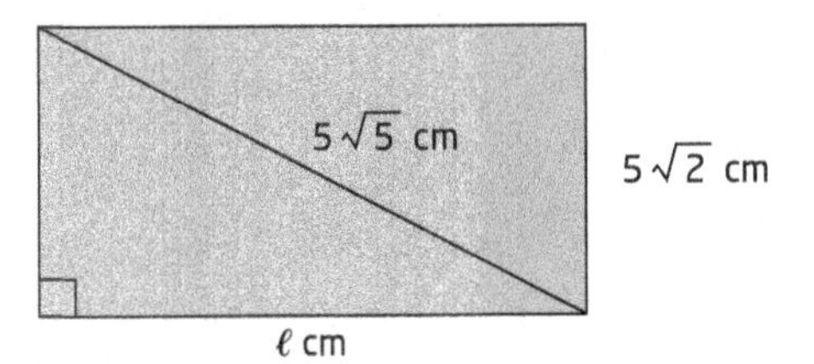

Solution

$$\ell^2 + (5\sqrt{2})^2 = (5\sqrt{5})^2$$
$$\ell^2 = 125 - 50$$
$$\ell^2 = 75$$
$$\ell = 5\sqrt{3}$$

$$A = \ell w$$
$$= (5\sqrt{3})(5\sqrt{2})$$
$$= 25\sqrt{6}$$

$$P = 2\ell + 2w$$
$$= 2(5\sqrt{3}) + 2(5\sqrt{2})$$
$$= 10\sqrt{3} + 10\sqrt{2}$$

The length of the rectangle is $5\sqrt{3}$ cm, the area is $25\sqrt{6}$ cm^2, and the perimeter is $10\sqrt{3} + 10\sqrt{2}$ cm.

A Practise

1. Simplify.
   a) $2(7\sqrt{3})$
   b) $\sqrt{5}(3\sqrt{6})$
   c) $-\sqrt{11}(4\sqrt{3})$
   d) $8\sqrt{3}(-2\sqrt{7})$
   e) $-3\sqrt{3}(5\sqrt{2})$
   f) $-6\sqrt{2}(-\sqrt{11})$
   g) $2\sqrt{5}(-3\sqrt{7})$
   h) $-7\sqrt{6}(7\sqrt{5})$

2. Express each as a mixed radical in simplest form.
   a) $\sqrt{54}$
   b) $\sqrt{98}$
   c) $\sqrt{288}$
   d) $\sqrt{75}$
   e) $\sqrt{72}$
   f) $\sqrt{125}$
   g) $\sqrt{96}$
   h) $\sqrt{126}$
   i) $\sqrt{32}$
   j) $\sqrt{180}$

3. Simplify.
   a) $7\sqrt{2} - 9\sqrt{2} + 15\sqrt{2}$
   b) $-5\sqrt{3} + 11\sqrt{3} - 9\sqrt{3} + 17\sqrt{3}$
   c) $16\sqrt{11} + 3\sqrt{11} - 25\sqrt{11} + 6\sqrt{11} - 2\sqrt{11}$
   d) $9\sqrt{5} + 8\sqrt{6} - 13\sqrt{5} + 19\sqrt{6} + 4\sqrt{6}$

4. Simplify each radical first, and then add or subtract.
   a) $5\sqrt{12} - 2\sqrt{48} - 7\sqrt{75}$
   b) $2\sqrt{8} - 3\sqrt{98} - 2\sqrt{200}$
   c) $\sqrt{20} - 3\sqrt{245} - 2\sqrt{20}$
   d) $-3\sqrt{50} - \sqrt{32} - 5\sqrt{200}$
   e) $-3\sqrt{12} + 5\sqrt{27} - 6\sqrt{48} + 2\sqrt{75}$
   f) $\sqrt{48} - \sqrt{20} - \sqrt{27} - \sqrt{45}$
   g) $2\sqrt{12} + 3\sqrt{50} - 2\sqrt{75} - 6\sqrt{32}$
   h) $4\sqrt{18} - 2\sqrt{63} + \sqrt{175} + 5\sqrt{98}$

5. Simplify.
   a) $\sqrt{5}(\sqrt{50})$
   b) $5\sqrt{3}(-2\sqrt{6})$
   c) $5\sqrt{7}(2\sqrt{14})$
   d) $-6\sqrt{5}(8\sqrt{15})$
   e) $3\sqrt{3}(-7\sqrt{12})$
   f) $4\sqrt{7}(-\sqrt{7})$
   g) $-2\sqrt{15}(5\sqrt{6})$
   h) $9\sqrt{24}(-3\sqrt{3})$

6. Expand. Simplify where possible.
   a) $\sqrt{2}(\sqrt{6} - \sqrt{3})$
   b) $2\sqrt{3}(\sqrt{5} - 2)$
   c) $3\sqrt{5}(2 - \sqrt{2})$
   d) $-2\sqrt{3}(\sqrt{5} + 3\sqrt{7})$
   e) $\sqrt{5}(\sqrt{6} - \sqrt{10})$
   f) $4\sqrt{2}(3\sqrt{11} + 5\sqrt{13})$
   g) $2\sqrt{5}(3\sqrt{2} - 4\sqrt{3})$
   h) $6\sqrt{6}(3\sqrt{2} - 4\sqrt{3})$

7. Expand. Simplify where possible.
   a) $(\sqrt{7} - 6)(\sqrt{7} + 1)$
   b) $(2 + \sqrt{12})(4 - \sqrt{3})$
   c) $(4\sqrt{2} - 5\sqrt{3})(4\sqrt{2} + 5\sqrt{3})$
   d) $(6 - 4\sqrt{2})(2 - 5\sqrt{2})$
   e) $(7 - 3\sqrt{2})^2$
   f) $(3\sqrt{5} - 2\sqrt{3})(3\sqrt{5} + 2\sqrt{3})$

8. Simplify.

a) $\frac{1}{3}\sqrt{27} - \frac{2}{3}\sqrt{108} - \frac{1}{4}\sqrt{72}$

b) $-\frac{3}{4}\sqrt{32} + \frac{3}{7}\sqrt{98} - \frac{4}{5}\sqrt{50}$

B Connect and Apply

☆**9.** Find a simplified expression for the area of each shape.

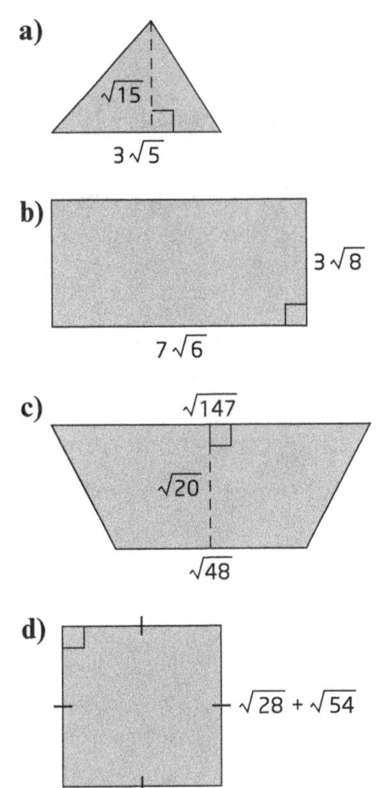

10. Fully simplify $\sqrt{5040}$. Explain your steps.

11. A square has area 756 cm^2. Write an expression in simplified radical form for the length of one side.

☆**12.** A square game board is made up of small squares, each with side length 4 cm. The diagonal of the game board measures $32\sqrt{2}$ cm. How many small squares are on the game board?

☆**13.** Explain why $\sqrt{100 - 64}$ is not equal to $\sqrt{100} - \sqrt{64}$.

C Extend

14. Simplify.

a) $\dfrac{16 + \sqrt{176}}{24}$

b) $\dfrac{35 - 2\sqrt{150}}{40}$

c) $\dfrac{\sqrt{39}}{\sqrt{3}}$

d) $\dfrac{15 + \sqrt{252}}{27}$

e) $\dfrac{-18 + \sqrt{405}}{36}$

15. a) Simplifying a cube root requires the factor to appear three times under the cube root sign. Any factor that does not appear three times is left under the cube root. Simplify each cube root.

i) $\sqrt[3]{320}$

ii) $\sqrt[3]{875}$

iii) $\sqrt[3]{2744}$

b) Explain how you can extend the method of part a) to simplify each radical. Use your method to simplify each fourth root.

i) $\sqrt[4]{240}$

ii) $\sqrt[4]{810}$

iii) $\sqrt[4]{9072}$

16. Simplify.

a) $\sqrt{16m} - \sqrt{9m} + 2\sqrt{25m} + 7\sqrt{4m}$

b) $\sqrt{28ab} + 5\sqrt{c} - 3\sqrt{7ab} + 2\sqrt{36c}$

c) $\sqrt{45a^3b} - \sqrt{12m^2n^3} + 3n\sqrt{48m^2n} + a\sqrt{125ab}$

d) $\sqrt{75ab^3} - \sqrt{c^2d} - b\sqrt{3ab} + 5c\sqrt{4d}$

1.5 Solving Quadratic Equations

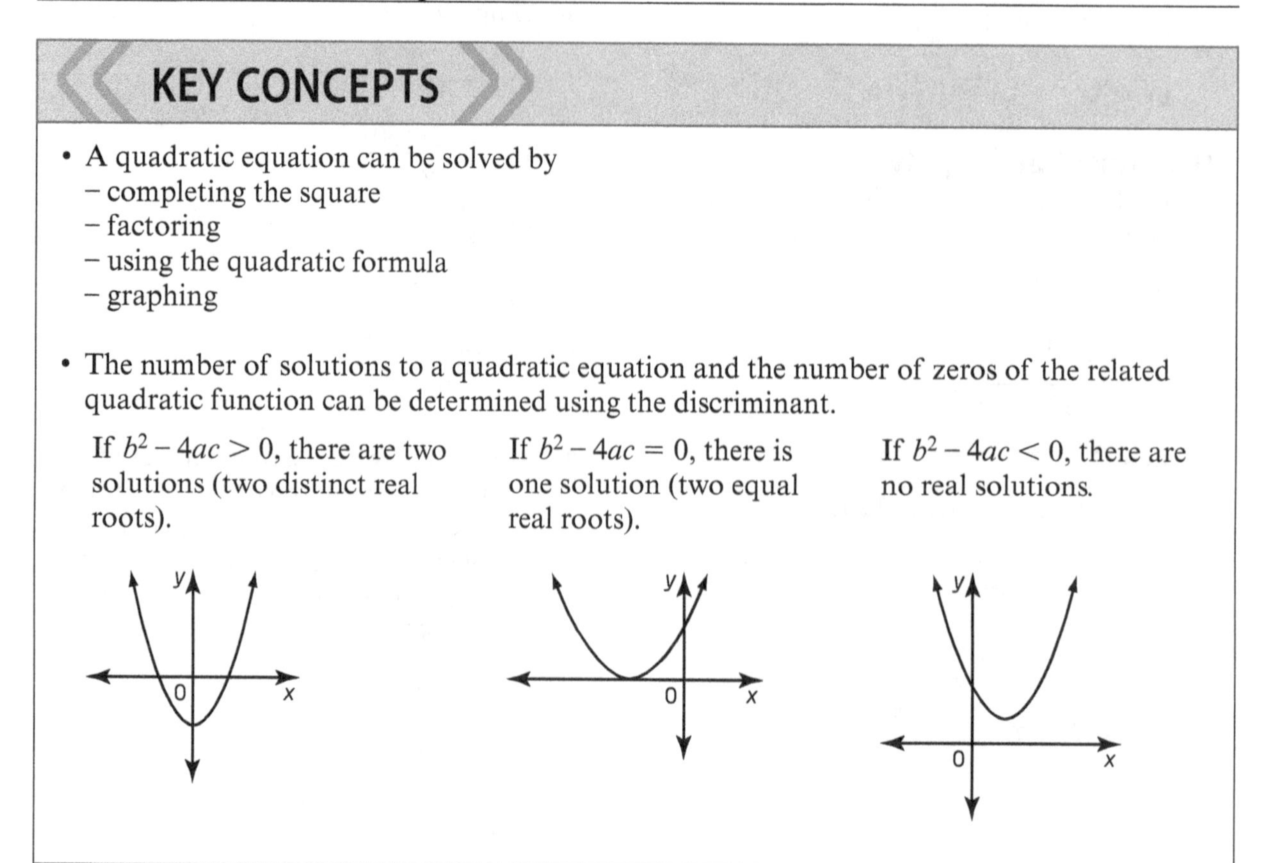

KEY CONCEPTS

- A quadratic equation can be solved by
  - completing the square
  - factoring
  - using the quadratic formula
  - graphing

- The number of solutions to a quadratic equation and the number of zeros of the related quadratic function can be determined using the discriminant.

  If $b^2 - 4ac > 0$, there are two solutions (two distinct real roots).

  If $b^2 - 4ac = 0$, there is one solution (two equal real roots).

  If $b^2 - 4ac < 0$, there are no real solutions.

Example

a) Make a table of values for the function $f(x) = -2x^2 + 5x$ for the domain $\{-2, -1, 0, 1, 2, 3, 4\}$.

b) Graph this quadratic function.

c) On the same set of axes, graph the line $y = -7$.

d) Use your graph to estimate the x-coordinates of the points of intersection of $y = -7$ and $f(x) = -2x^2 + 5x$.

e) Use algebra to determine the coordinates of the points of intersection of $y = -7$ and $f(x) = -2x^2 + 5x$.

Solution

a)

x	$y = f(x)$
−2	−18
−1	−7
0	0
1	3
2	2
3	−3
4	−12

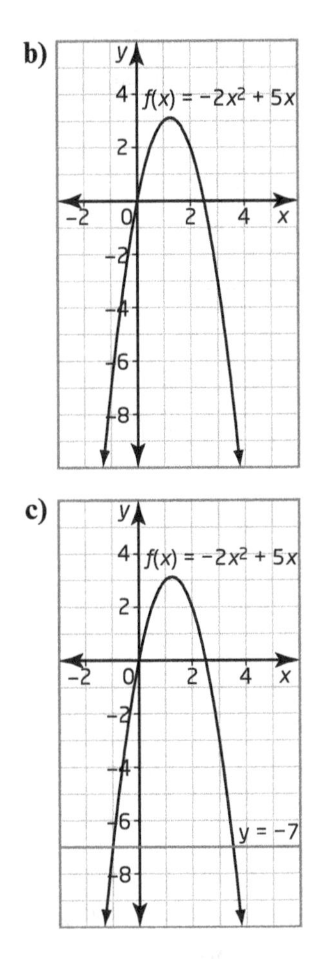

d) The line appears to intersect the parabola at $x = -1$ and $x = 3.5$.

e) To determine the x-coordinates of the points of intersection, substitute $y = -7$ into $f(x) = -2x^2 + 5x$ and solve.

$$-7 = -2x^2 + 5x$$
$$2x^2 - 5x - 7 = 0$$
$$(2x - 7)(x + 1) = 0$$
$$x = \frac{7}{2} \text{ or } x = -1$$

Every point on the line has y-coordinate -7, so the y-coordinates of the points of intersection are -7. The points of intersection are $\left(\frac{7}{2}, -7\right)$ and $(-1, -7)$.

A Practise

1. Solve each quadratic equation by factoring. Check your answers.

   a) $x^2 + x - 6 = 0$

   b) $x^2 + 7x + 12 = 0$

   c) $3x^2 - 75 = 0$

   d) $2x^2 + 12x - 54 = 0$

   e) $3x^2 - 4x - 15 = 0$

   f) $3x^2 + 13x - 10 = 0$

2. Solve each quadratic equation using the quadratic formula. Give exact answers.

   a) $6x^2 - 7x - 3 = 0$

   b) $3x^2 + 6x + 1 = 0$

   c) $2x^2 + 6x + 3 = 0$

   d) $3x^2 + 7x + 3 = 0$

   e) $x^2 + 6x + 4 = 0$

3. **Use Technology** Using a graphing calculator, graph a related function to determine the number of roots for each quadratic equation.

   a) $7x^2 - 2x + 3 = 0$

   b) $-3x^2 + 10x + 8.5 = 0$

   c) $5x^2 + x - 4 = 0$

   d) $\frac{2}{3}x^2 - 4x + 6 = 0$

   e) $\frac{4}{7}x^2 - x + 5 = 0$

   f) $0.8x^2 - 3.20x + 6.2 = 0$

4. Determine the exact values of the x-intercepts of each quadratic function. Use a graphing calculator to check that you have found the correct number of x-intercepts.

   a) $f(x) = 2x^2 + 5x + 1$

   b) $f(x) = x^2 - 6x + 7$

   c) $f(x) = -\frac{1}{2}x^2 + 3x + 6$

   d) $f(x) = \frac{3}{4}x^2 - 5x + 5$

   e) $f(x) = -\frac{5}{8}x^2 + 6x + 2$

5. Use the discriminant to determine the number of roots for each quadratic equation.

   a) $x^2 - 3x + 1 = 0$

   b) $3x^2 - 6x + 3 = 0$

   c) $2x^2 - 5x + 7 = 0$

   d) $-x^2 + 5.5x + 3.25 = 0$

   e) $5x^2 - 10x + 5 = 0$

B Connect and Apply

6. Solve.

   a) $2x^2 - 5x - 12 = 0$

   b) $4x^2 - 81 = 0$

   c) $2x^2 + 5x - 2 = 0$

   d) $\frac{2}{5}x^2 - \frac{3}{5}x = 0$

   e) $0.8x^2 - 2.1x - 3.5 = 0$

   f) $3x^2 - 5x + 2 = 0$

   g) $2x^2 - 10x + 9 = 0$

   h) $4x^2 - x - 3 = 0$

7. Determine the value(s) of k for which the quadratic equation $x^2 + kx + 4 = 0$ will have each number of roots.

   a) two equal real roots

   b) two distinct real roots

   c) no real roots

8. **a)** Create a table of values for the function $f(x) = -x^2 + 5x + 2$ for the domain $\{-2, -1, 0, 1, 2, 3, 4, 5, 6, 7\}$.

   b) Graph this quadratic function.

   c) On the same set of axes, graph the line $y = 4$.

   d) Use your graph to estimate the x-values of the points of intersection of $y = 4$ and $f(x) = -x^2 + 5x + 2$.

   e) Determine the coordinates of the points of intersection of $f(x) = -x^2 + 5x + 2$ and $y = 4$ algebraically.

9. What value(s) of k, where k is an integer, will allow each quadratic equation to be solved by factoring?

   a) $x^2 + kx + 14 = 0$

   b) $x^2 + kx = 10$

   c) $x^2 - 5x = k$

★**10.** The height of a football can be modelled by the function $h(t) = -4.9t^2 + 21.8t + 1.5$, where t is the time, in seconds, since the ball was thrown, and h is the height of the ball, in metres, above the ground. Determine how long the football will be in the air, to the nearest tenth of a second.

11. The function $d = 0.0067v^2 + 0.15v$ can be used to determine the safe stopping distance, d, in metres, for a car given its speed, v, in kilometres per hour. Determine the speed at which a car can be travelling in order to be able to stop in the given distances.

   a) 24 m

   b) 43 m

   c) 82 m

★**12.** The sum of two numbers is 24 and the sum of their squares is 306. What are the numbers?

13. A flaming arrow is fired upward from the deck of a ship to mark the beginning of an evening of entertainment and celebration. The flaming arrow hits the water. The height, h, in metres, of the arrow above the water t seconds after it is fired can be modelled by the quadratic function $h(t) = -4.9t^2 + 98t + 8$.

   a) Determine the maximum height of the arrow.

   b) How long does it take the arrow to reach its maximum height?

   c) When does the arrow hit the water?

   d) How high is the deck of the ship above the water?

14. The perimeter of a right triangle is 36.0 cm and the length of the hypotenuse is 15.0 cm. Determine the length of the other two sides.

15. Three pieces of a rod measure 20 cm, 41 cm, and 44 cm. If the same amount is cut off from each piece, the remaining lengths can be formed into a right triangle. Determine the length that should be cut off each piece.

16. Find two consecutive whole numbers such that the sum of their squares is 265.

17. A square flower garden is surrounded by a brick walkway that is 1.5 m wide. The area of the walkway is equal to the area of the garden. Determine the dimensions of the flower garden, to the nearest tenth of a metre.

18. The sum of the squares of three consecutive integers is 194. Determine the integers.

19. The outward power, P, in watts, of a 120-V electric generator is given by the relation $P = 120I - 5I^2$, where I is the current, in amperes (A). For what value(s) of I is the outward power 500 W?

C Extend

20. Solve. Give exact answers.

   a) $x^4 - 10x^2 + 9 = 0$

   b) $(2x + 1)^2 + (2x + 3)^2 = 26$

   c) $(x - 1)(x + 1)(x + 3) = x^3$

21. Solve. Give exact answers.

   a) $x - 2 - \frac{x}{x + 1} = 0$

   b) $\frac{4x}{x^2 - 1} - 3 = \frac{2}{x - 1} - \frac{3}{x + 1}$

22. The point (1, 2) is on the graph of the quadratic function $f(x) = ax^2 + bx + 1$. Determine the values of a, such that the graph of $f(x)$ intersects the x-axis at two distinct points.

1.6 Determine a Quadratic Equation Given Its Roots

KEY CONCEPTS

- The zeros can be used to find the equation of a family of quadratic functions with the same x-intercepts.
- To determine an individual quadratic function, you also need to be given one other point on the function.

Example

Write the equation of a quadratic function whose only x-intercept is -2 and that passes through $(4, -1)$.

Solution

When a quadratic function has only one x-intercept, then the vertex is on the x-axis.

The vertex of this function is $(-2, 0)$.
The vertex form of the equation is $y = a(x + 2)^2$.

Substitute the point $(4, -1)$ to determine the value of a.

$-1 = a(4 + 2)^2$

$-1 = 36a$

$a = -\frac{1}{36}$

The equation of the quadratic function is $y = -\frac{1}{36}(x + 2)^2$.

Check by graphing the function.

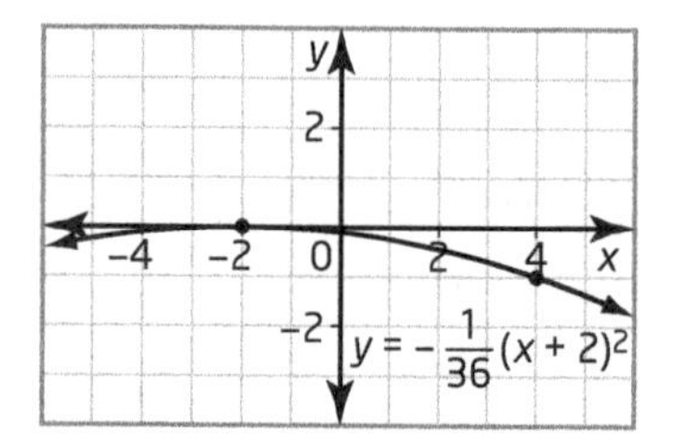

A Practise

1. Determine an equation, in factored form, for a family of quadratic functions with the given roots. Draw a sketch to illustrate each family.

   a) $x = 1$ and $x = -4$

   b) $x = -3$ and $x = -6$

   c) $x = 5$ and $x = -2$

2. Refer to your answers to question 1. Express each equation in standard form.

3. Write the equation for a quadratic function that has the given x-intercepts and that passes through the given point. Express each equation in factored form.

   a) x-intercepts: -3 and 4, point: $(1, -24)$

   b) x-intercepts: -2 and 5, point: $(-1, 3)$

   c) x-intercepts: 0 and $\frac{2}{3}$, point: $(2, -32)$

4. Refer to your answers to question 3. Express each equation in standard form.

5. Write the equation for a quadratic function that has the given zeros and contains the given point. Express each equation in standard form.

   a) zeros: $2 \pm \sqrt{5}$, contains $(1, -12)$

   b) zeros: $-3 \pm \sqrt{6}$, contains $(-1, 4)$

   c) zeros: $4 \pm \sqrt{2}$, contains $(2, 6)$

   d) zeros: $-1 \pm \sqrt{7}$, contains $(-2, 3)$

6. Write the equation for the quadratic function that has the given zeros and contains the given point. Express each function in vertex form.

   a) zeros: 5 and -1, contains $(3, -24)$

   b) zeros: 3 and -4, contains $(2, 12)$

   c) zeros: 1 and -3, contains $(-2, -6)$

   d) zeros: 2 and -6, contains $(1, 21)$

B Connect and Apply

7. A football is kicked off the ground. After travelling a horizontal distance of 24 m, it just passes over a tree that is 3 m tall before hitting the ground 28 m from where it was kicked.

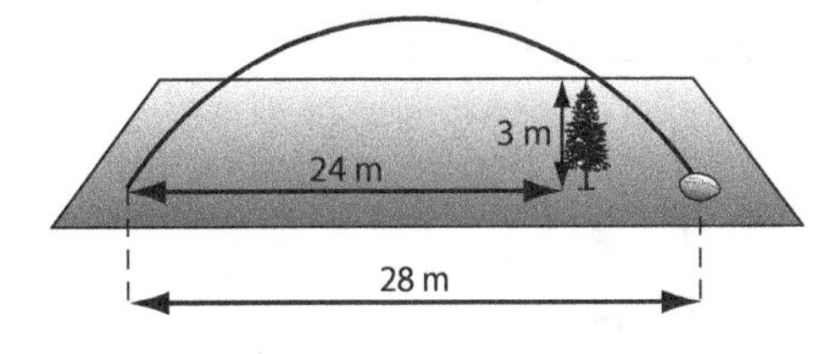

   a) Consider the ground to be the x-axis and assume the vertex lies on the y-axis. Determine the equation of the quadratic function that models the path of the ball.

   b) Determine the maximum height of the football.

   c) How far has the football travelled horizontally when it reaches its maximum height?

   d) Suppose the football is kicked from a starting point at the origin. Develop a new equation of the quadratic function that represents the football.

   e) Describe the similarities and differences between the functions found in parts a) and d).

   f) Use Technology Use a graphing calculator and compare the solutions.

8. Find the quadratic function that has only one x-intercept and passes through the given point.

   a) x-intercept of 0, and through the point $(4, -3)$

   b) x-intercept of 3, and through the point $(-2, 5)$

   c) x-intercept of -6, and through the point $(-3, -9)$

   d) x-intercept of 4, and through the point $(1, -6)$

   e) x-intercept of -1, and through the point $(0, 5)$

9. Write an equation in standard form for each quadratic function.

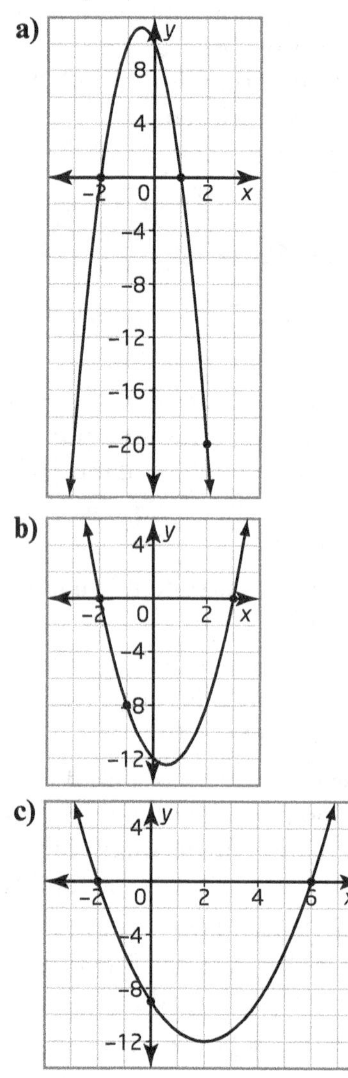

10. **Use Technology** For each function in question 9, use a graphing calculator to verify your solution by plotting the three points and the quadratic function. Explain how you can use this method to check that your solution is correct.

11. If the function $f(x) = ax^2 + 6x + c$ has no x-intercepts, what is the mathematical relationship between a and c?

☆12. The arch of a domed sports arena is in the shape of a parabola. The arch spans a width of 32 m from one side of the arena to the other. The height of the arch is 18 m at a horizontal distance of 8 m from each end of the arch.

a) Sketch the quadratic function so that the vertex of the parabola is on the y-axis and the width is along the x-axis.

b) Use this information to determine the equation that models the arch.

c) Find the maximum height of the arch.

☆13. Consider the domed sports arena described in question 12. Suppose that instead of having the vertex on the y-axis, the parabola was positioned with one end of the arch at the origin of the grid.

a) Determine the equation, in factored form and in standard form, of the quadratic function for this orientation.

b) Find the maximum height of the arch and compare the result to the height calculated in question 12.

C Extend

14. Suppose two points are given. Is it always possible to find the equation of a parabola that passes through one of the points and has the other point as its vertex? Explain.

15. **a)** A family of cubic functions with zeros 2, −1, and 4 is represented by the equation $f(x) = a(x-2)(x+1)(x-4)$. Determine the equation of the member of the family that passes through the point (3, 8). Express your answer in factored form and in expanded form.

b) Write the equation, in factored form, for a family of cubic functions with zeros $\frac{1}{2}$, 3, and −2.

c) Determine the equation, in expanded form, of the member of the family in part b) that passes through the point (−1, −8).

1.7 Solve Linear-Quadratic Systems

KEY CONCEPTS

- A linear function and a quadratic function may
  - intersect at two points (the line is a secant)
  - intersect at one point (the line is a tangent line)
  - never intersect
- The discriminant can be used to determine which of the above situations occurs.
- The quadratic formula can be used to determine the x-values of actual points of intersection.

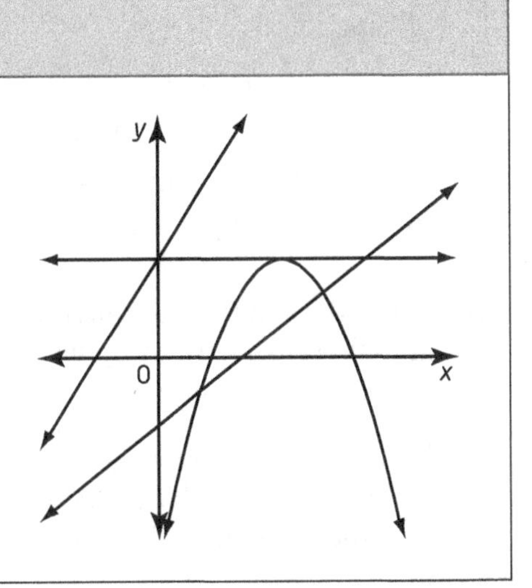

Example

Consider the parabola $y = -x^2 + 6x + k$ and the line $y = 4x - 3$. Determine the value of k in each case.

a) The line intersects the parabola at two points.
b) The line intersects the parabola at one point.
c) The line does not intersect the parabola.

Solution

At the point(s) of intersection, the y-values are equal. Set the expressions equal and simplify.

$-x^2 + 6x + k = 4x - 3$
$-x^2 + 2x + k + 3 = 0$

Use the discriminant; $a = -1$, $b = 2$, $c = k + 3$.

$$\begin{aligned} b^2 - 4ac &= 2^2 - 4(-1)(k + 3) \\ &= 4 + 4k + 12 \\ &= 16 + 4k \end{aligned}$$

a) Two points of intersection occur when the discriminant is positive.

$$\begin{aligned} 16 + 4k &> 0 \\ 4k &> -16 \\ k &> -4 \end{aligned}$$

b) One point of intersection occurs when the discriminant is zero.

$$\begin{aligned} 16 + 4k &= 0 \\ k &= -4 \end{aligned}$$

c) There are no points of intersection when the discriminant is negative.

$$\begin{aligned} 16 + 4k &< 0 \\ k &< -4 \end{aligned}$$

A Practise

1. Determine algebraically the coordinates of the point(s) of intersection of each pair of functions.

   a) $y = x^2 + 4x + 3$ and $y = 5x + 9$

   b) $y = 6x^2 - 4x - 25$ and $y = 3x - 5$

   c) $y = 2x^2 - x - 1$ and $y = -\frac{3}{2}x + \frac{1}{2}$

   d) $y = -x^2 - 4x + 6$ and $y = x - 8$

2. Verify the solutions to question 1 using a graphing calculator or by substituting into the original equations.

3. Determine the number of points of intersection of each quadratic function with the given linear function.

   a) $y = 3x^2 - x + 1$ and $y = 4x - 5$

   b) $y = 3x^2 - 4x - 1$ and $y = -3x + 1$

   c) $y = x^2 - 6x + 11$ and $y = -2x + 7$

   d) $y = -\frac{3}{4}x^2 + 5x - 3$ and $y = 3x - 2$

4. **Use Technology** Verify your responses to question 3 using a graphing calculator.

5. Given the equation of a parabola and the slope of a line that is tangent to the parabola, determine the y-intercept of the tangent line.

   a) $f(x) = 2x^2 + 2x - 5$, tangent line has slope 1

   b) $f(x) = -x^2 + 4x - 6$, tangent line has slope -2

   c) $f(x) = -\frac{1}{2}x^2 + x - 3$, tangent line has slope -3

   d) $f(x) = -3x^2 + x - 4$, tangent line has slope 13

6. Verify your solutions to question 5 using a graphing calculator or by substituting into the original equations.

B Connect and Apply

7. The path of an underground stream can be modelled by the function $f(x) = 3x^2 - 2x - 28$. Two new houses are being built that require wells to be dug. On the site plan, these houses and their wells lie on a line defined by the equation $y = -5x + 32$. Determine the coordinates of the locations of the two new wells.

☆8. The path of an asteroid is in the shape of a parabolic arch modelled by the function $f(x) = -8x^2 + 720x + 56\,800$. For the period of time that it is in the same area, a space probe is moving along a straight path on the same plane as the asteroid according to the linear equation $y = -960x + 145\,000$. Determine if the paths of the asteroid and the space probe will intersect. Show your work.

9. **Use Technology** Check your solutions to questions 7 and 8 using a graphing calculator.

10. Consider the parabola $y = -2x^2 + 13x + k$ and the line $y = 7x + 3$. Determine the value of k in each case.

    a) The line intersects the parabola at two points.

    b) The line intersects the parabola at one point.

    c) The line does not intersect the parabola.

☆11. Consider the parabola $y = kx^2 + 3x + 10$ and the line $y = -5x + 3$. Determine the value of k in each case.

    a) The line intersects the parabola at two points.

    b) The line intersects the parabola at one point.

    c) The line does not intersect the parabola.

12. A section of a roller coaster has a parabolic shape that can be modelled by the equation $f(x) = -0.017x^2 + 0.2x + 6$. There is a support beam that can be modelled by the equation $y = 0.07x - 1$. Determine the points of intersection of the section of the roller coaster and the support beam, to one decimal place.

13. The line $x = 3$ intersects the quadratic function $y = -x^2 + 16$ at (3, 7). Explain why the line $x = 3$ is not considered a tangent line to the quadratic function.

14. Andrea's boss asked her to determine the safety zone needed for a fireworks display. She must determine where the safety fence needs to be placed on a hill. The fireworks are to be launched from a platform at the base of the hill. Using the top of the launch platform as the origin and having taken some measurements, Andrea developed these equations:
Cross section of the hill: $y = 4x - 18$
Path of the fireworks: $y = -x^2 + 11x$

a) Graph both equations on the same set of axes.

b) Calculate the coordinates of the point where the line of the hill and the path of the fireworks will intersect.

15. The UV index on a sunny day can be modelled by the function $f(x) = -0.15(x - 12.5)^2 + 8.6$, where x represents the time of day on a 24-h clock and $f(x)$ represents the UV index. Between what hours was the UV index more than 8?

16. A movie stunt man jumps from the CN Tower and falls freely for several seconds before releasing his parachute. His height, h, in metres, above the ground t seconds after jumping is modelled by $h(t) = -4.9t^2 + t + 350$ before he releases his parachute and by $h(t) = -4t + 141$ after he releases his parachute.

a) How long after jumping does he release his parachute?

b) What is his height above the ground when he releases his parachute?

17. A rectangular field has a perimeter of 500 m and an area of 14 400 m^2. Determine the dimensions of the field.

C Extend

18. Determine the equation of the line that passes through the points of intersection of the parabolas $y = x^2 - x - 18$ and $y = -x^2 + 3x - 2$.

19. In how many ways can two parabolas intersect? Support your answer with examples using equations and sketches.

20. You have used substitution to determine the points where a line intersects a quadratic function. This technique can be extended to other curves, such as circles and ellipses. Estimate the points of intersection of the line and the curve in each graph. Verify your answers algebraically.

a)

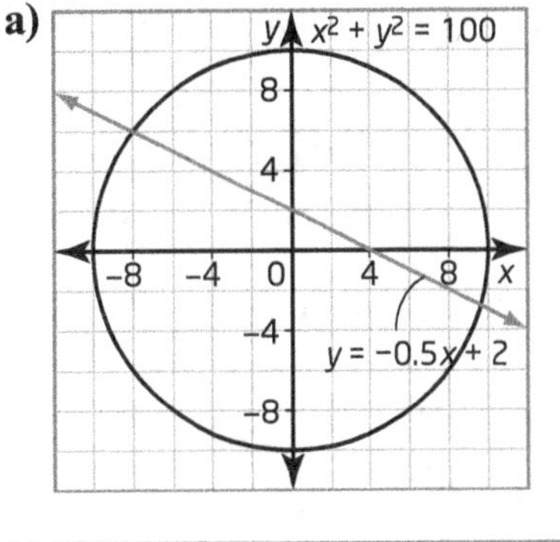

b)

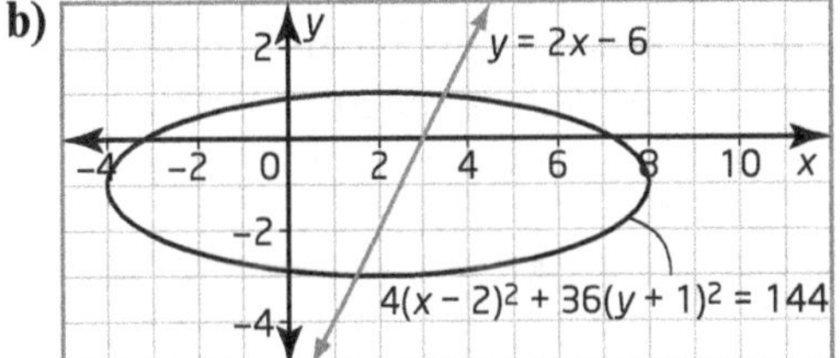

21. Show that the graphs of $2x + 5y = 11$ and $x^2 + y^2 = 4$ do not intersect.

Chapter 1 Review

1.1 Functions, Domain, and Range

1. Does each graph represent a function? Justify your answer.

a)

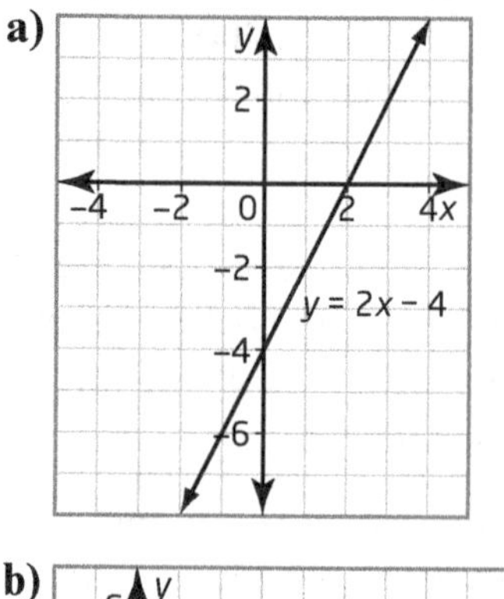

b)

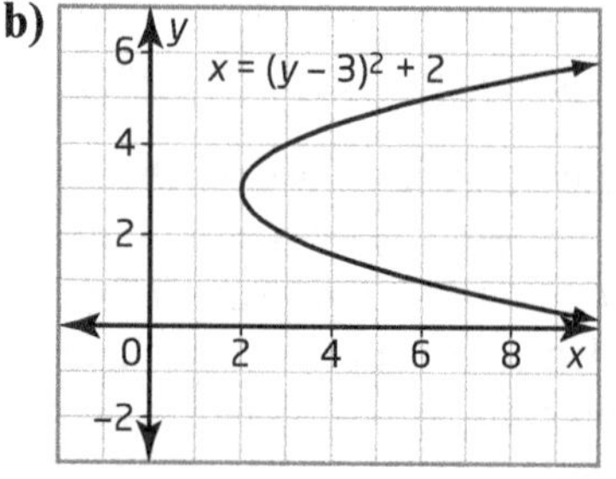

2. The domain and range of some relations are given. Each relation consists of only four points. Is each relation a function? Explain.

a) domain {0, 1, 2, 3}, range {9}

b) domain {−5}, range {8, 9, 10, 11}

3. Determine the domain and the range of each function.

a) $y = -(x - 3)^2 + 2$

b) $y = \sqrt{4 - 3x}$

4. For the given domain and range, draw one relation that is a function and one that is not. Use the same set of axes.
domain $\{x \in \mathbb{R}, x \geq -4\}$,
range $\{y \in \mathbb{R}, y \geq 1\}$

5. Determine the range of each function for the domain {−2, −1, 0, 1, 2}.

a) $y = 4x + 3$

b) $y = 2x^2 - 7$

1.2 Functions and Function Notation

6. Find $f(3)$ for each function. Sketch a graph of each function.

a) $f(x) = 7x - 5$

b) $f(x) = -1$

c) $f(x) = 4x^2 - 12x + 9$

d) $f(x) = 2(x - 3)(x + 1)$

7. Display each set of data in a mapping diagram. State whether each relation is a function. Justify your answer.

a) {(−7, 8), (−5, 7), (−3, 6), (−1, 3), (1, 1), (3, 6)}

b) {(2, 1), (3, 2), (4, 3), (3, 4), (2, 3), (1, 2)}

8. Consider this rectangular swimming pool.

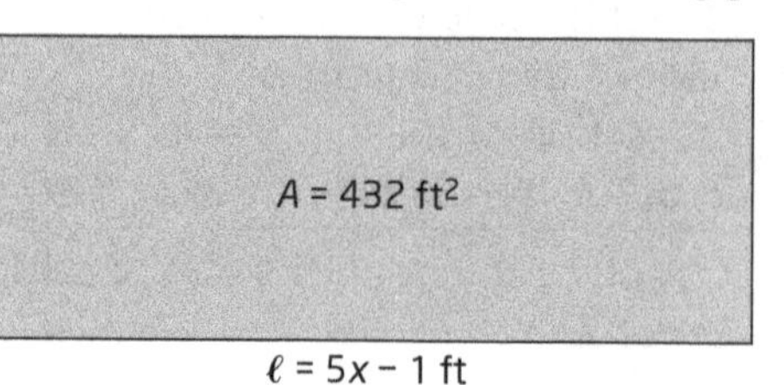

a) What does the expression $\frac{432}{5x - 1}$ represent in this situation?

b) State the domain and range for the expression in part a).

c) Does the expression in part a) represent a function? Justify your answer.

d) Determine the width of the pool when the length is 24 ft.

1.3 Maximum or Minimum of a Quadratic Function

9. Determine the vertex of each quadratic function by completing the square. State if the vertex is a minimum or a maximum.

a) $f(x) = -3x^2 - 18x + 2$

b) $f(x) = -4x^2 + 12x + 7$

c) $f(x) = \frac{1}{4}x^2 + 3x + 10$

10. Use partial factoring to determine the vertex of each function. State if the vertex is a minimum or a maximum.

a) $f(x) = 6x^2 - 6x - \frac{3}{2}$

b) $f(x) = \frac{2}{3}x^2 + x + \frac{19}{8}$

11. The monthly profit, $P(x)$, of a sportswear company, in thousands of dollars, is represented by the quadratic function $P(x) = -3x^2 + 18x - 2$, where x is the amount spent on advertising, in thousands of dollars.

a) Determine the company's maximum monthly profit.

b) Determine the amount spent on advertising to achieve the maximum profit.

1.4 Skills You Need: Working With Radicals

12. Express as a mixed radical in simplest form.

a) $\sqrt{147}$

b) $\sqrt{60}$

13. Simplify.

a) $-3\sqrt{7} + 6\sqrt{3} - 8\sqrt{3} + 9\sqrt{7} - 4\sqrt{7}$

b) $7\sqrt{24} + 3\sqrt{28} + 9\sqrt{54} + 6\sqrt{175}$

c) $2\sqrt{112} - 3\sqrt{18} - 2\sqrt{175} - \sqrt{98}$

d) $2\sqrt{6}(3\sqrt{6} - 5\sqrt{8})$

e) $8\sqrt{6}(3\sqrt{2} - 4\sqrt{3} - 2\sqrt{6})$

f) $(2\sqrt{5} - 3\sqrt{2})(\sqrt{5} + 2\sqrt{2})$

g) $\frac{1}{2}\sqrt{180} - \frac{6}{7}\sqrt{245} + \frac{2}{3}\sqrt{405}$

14. Find the area of this square.

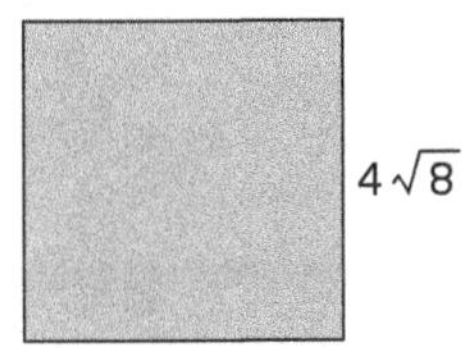

1.5 Solving Quadratic Equations

15. Solve $18x^2 - 3x - 1 = 0$ by factoring.

16. Use the quadratic formula to solve $2x^2 - 6x + 1 = 0$. Give exact answers.

17. Use the discriminant to determine the number of roots for $1.8x^2 - 2x - 1 = 0$.

18. A farmer enclosed a rectangular field with 400 m of fencing. The area of the field is 9000 m^2. Determine the dimensions of the field.

1.6 Determine a Quadratic Equation Given Its Roots

19. Write the equation for each quadratic function given the x-intercepts and the coordinates of a point on the parabola. Express the function in standard form.

a) x-intercepts: $\frac{5}{2}$ and $-\frac{3}{4}$, point: (0, 45)

b) x-intercepts: $5 \pm \sqrt{3}$, point: (4, 2)

20. A small rocket is launched. It reaches a maximum height of 120 m and lands 10 m from the launching pad. Assume the rocket follows a parabolic path. Write the equation that describes its height, h metres, as a function of its horizontal distance, x metres, from the launching pad.

21. Write the equation of a quadratic function with only one x-intercept, at -1, that passes through the point (0, 5).

1.7 Solve Linear-Quadratic Systems

22. Determine algebraically the coordinates of the point(s) of intersection of $y = -2x^2 + x - 2$ and $y = 4x - 7$.

23. Determine the number of points of intersection of $y = x^2 - x + 5$ and $y = 5x - 4$.

24. Determine the y-intercept of a line that has slope 7, and that is tangent to $f(x) = 4x^2 - x + 1$.

25. A parachutist jumps from an airplane and immediately opens her parachute. Her altitude in metres, after t seconds, is modelled by the equation $y = -11t + 500$. A second parachutist jumps 5 s later and freefalls for a few seconds. His altitude during this time is modelled by the equation $y = -4.9(t - 4)^2 + 500$. When does he catch up to the first parachutist?

Chapter 1 Math Contest

1. The graph of $y = -x^2 - 5x + 36$ intersects the x-axis at two points, A and B. The length of line segment AB is

A 9

B 13

C 5

D 36

2. If $f(x) = x^2 + 5x + 3k$ and $f(k) = -16$, $f(2)$ equals

A −4

B −16

C −2

D 2

3. The minimum distance between the parabolas $y = -5x^2 - 8$ and $y = 7x^2 + 6$ is

A 14

B 12

C 8

D 6

4. A quadratic function of the form $f(x) = ax^2 + bx + c$ has roots $x = \frac{-3 \pm \sqrt{31}}{2}$. The graph of the function passes through the point (1, −3). What is the equation of the function?

A $f(x) = 2x^2 - 6x + 11$

B $f(x) = 2x^2 + 6x - 11$

C $f(x) = 3x^2 - 2\sqrt{5}x - 4$

D $f(x) = 2x^2 + 2\sqrt{5}x - 3$

5. The sum, S, and product, P, of the roots of the function $f(x) = -3x^2 + 24x + 477$ are

A $S = 24, P = 477$

B $S = 24, P = 1437$

C $S = 8, P = -159$

D $S = -8, P = 159$

6. If $x^y = 4$, then the value of $x^{3y} - x^{2y}$ is

A 48

B 64

C 4

D 12

7. If $M = 5^x + 5^{-x}$ and $N = 5^x - 5^{-x}$, then the value of $M^2 - N^2$ is

A $2(5^{2x})$

B $2(5^{-2x})$

C 4

D 0

8. In the given diagram, XY = XZ = 15 and YZ = 18. The value of sin Z is

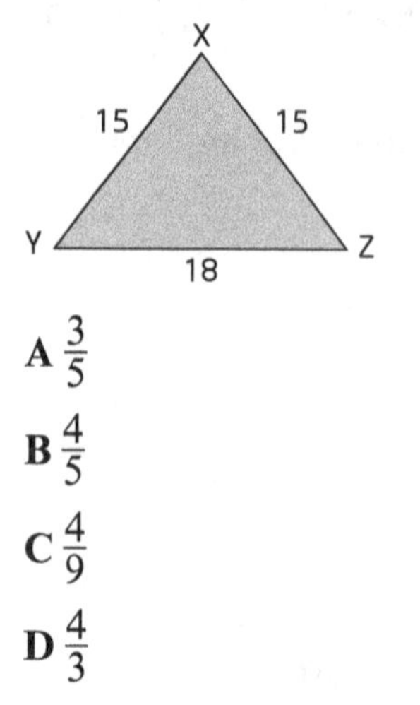

A $\frac{3}{5}$

B $\frac{4}{5}$

C $\frac{4}{9}$

D $\frac{4}{3}$

9. The minimum value of $y = (x - a)^2 + (x - b)^2$ occurs when

A $x = a + b$

B $x = \frac{a - b}{2}$

C $x = a - b$

D $x = \frac{a + b}{2}$

10. A range of values for which $\sin x < \cos x$ is

A $0° \leq x \leq 45°$

B $45° < x \leq 90°$

C $0° \leq x < 45°$

D $45° < x < 90°$

Chapter 2 Transformation of Functions

2.1 Functions and Equivalent Algebraic Expressions

KEY CONCEPTS

- To determine if two expressions are equivalent, simplify both to see if they are algebraically the same.
- Checking several points may suggest that two expressions are equivalent, but it does not prove that they are.
- Rational expressions must be checked for restrictions by determining where the denominator is zero. These restrictions must be stated when the expression is simplified.
- Graphs can suggest whether two functions or expressions are equivalent.

Example

A shipping company designed a scalable box to accommodate different-sized items. The dimensions of the box are $\ell = 3x + 1$, $w = x - 1$, and $h = x + 1$, where x is in metres.

a) Write two equivalent expressions for the volume of the box as a function of x.
b) Write two equivalent expressions for the surface area of the box as a function of x.
c) Determine the domain of the volume and surface area functions.

Solution

a)
$$\begin{aligned} V &= \ell wh \\ V(x) &= (3x + 1)(x - 1)(x + 1) \\ &= (3x + 1)(x^2 - 1) \\ &= 3x^3 + x^2 - 3x - 1 \end{aligned}$$

Two expressions for the volume of the box are $V(x) = (3x + 1)(x - 1)(x + 1)$ and $V(x) = 3x^3 + x^2 - 3x - 1$.

b)
$$\begin{aligned} SA(x) &= 2\ell h + 2\ell w + 2hw \\ &= 2(3x + 1)(x + 1) + 2(3x + 1)(x - 1) + 2(x - 1)(x + 1) \\ &= 2(3x^2 + 4x + 1) + 2(3x^2 - 2x - 1) + 2(x^2 - 1) \\ &= 6x^2 + 8x + 2 + 6x^2 - 4x - 2 + 2x^2 - 2 \\ &= 14x^2 + 4x - 2 \end{aligned}$$

Two expressions for the surface area of the box are $SA(x) = 2(3x + 1)(x + 1) + 2(3x + 1)(x - 1) + 2(x - 1)(x + 1)$ and $SA(x) = 14x^2 + 4x - 2$.

c) None of the dimensions, nor the volume or the surface area, can be negative. The domain for both the volume and the surface area is $\{x \in \mathbb{R}, x > 1\}$.

A Practise

1. **Use Technology** Use a graphing calculator to graph the functions in each pair. Do the functions appear to be equivalent?

   a) $f(x) = 2(x - 4)^2 - (x + 2)(x - 1)$,
   $g(x) = 2x^2 - 17x + 34$

   b) $h(x) = -3(x^2 + 4x - 1) + (2x - 5)^2$,
   $k(x) = x^2 - 32x + 28$

   c) $f(x) = 6(x^2 + 3x - 1) - (4x + 2)(-2x + 3)$,
   $g(x) = 14x^2 - 34x + 10$

   d) $s(x) = (x + 1)^2 - 4(2 - x)(x + 3)$,
   $t(x) = -(x + 3)(x - 4) + 2(x + 3)^2$

   e) $f(x) = (x - 2)(3x + 1)(x + 4)$,
   $g(x) = 3x^3 + 5x^2 - 5x - 8$

   f) $p(x) = (x^2 + 2x - 3)(x^2 - x + 1)$,
   $q(x) = x^4 + x^3 - 4x^2 + 5x - 3$

2. Refer to question 1. For those pairs of functions that appear to be equivalent, show algebraically that they are. Otherwise, show that they are not equivalent by substituting a value for x.

3. State any restrictions for each function.

   a)

   b)

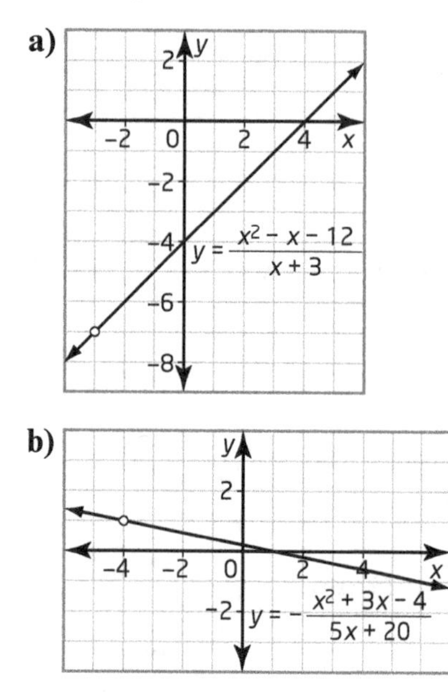

4. State any restrictions for each function.

   a)

   b)

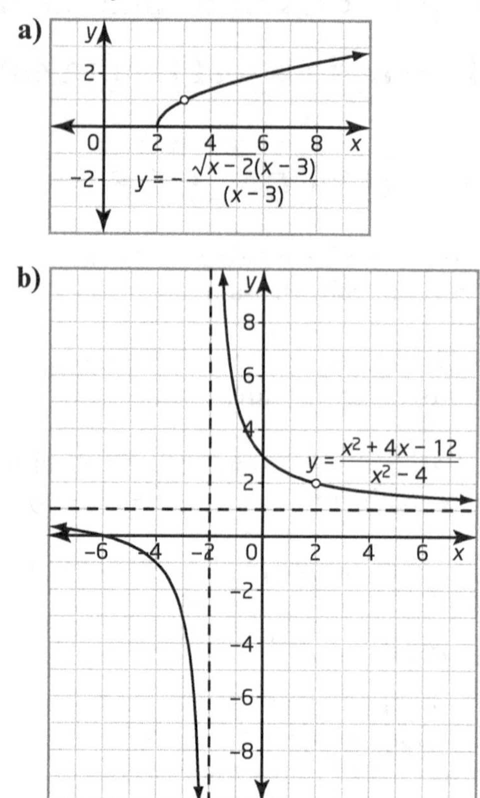

5. Determine if $g(x)$ is the simplified version of $f(x)$. If so, state the restrictions needed. If not, determine the proper simplified version, and then state the restrictions.

   a) $f(x) = \dfrac{x^2 + 12x + 35}{x + 5}$,
   $g(x) = x + 7$

   b) $f(x) = \dfrac{x^2 - 36}{x^2 - 3x - 18}$,
   $g(x) = x + 6$

   c) $f(x) = \dfrac{x^2 + 6x + 5}{x + 5}$,
   $g(x) = 6x$

   d) $f(x) = \dfrac{2x^2 + 5x - 3}{3x^2 + 10x + 3}$,
   $g(x) = \dfrac{2x - 1}{3x + 1}$

6. Simplify each expression. State all restrictions on x.

a) $\dfrac{x-7}{x^2-4x-21}$

b) $\dfrac{(x+3)^2(8-2x)}{4x^2-4x-48}$

c) $\dfrac{2x^2+7x-15}{2x^2+3x-9}$

d) $\dfrac{x^2-5x-36}{x^2-4x-45}$

e) $\dfrac{x^2-2x}{x^2-x-2}$

f) $\dfrac{6x^2-7x+2}{6x^2+2x-4}$

g) $\dfrac{4x^2+4x+1}{4x^2-1}$

h) $\dfrac{2x^3-28x^2-102x}{18x-2x^3}$

B Connect and Apply

7. Evaluate each expression for x-values $-4, -2, 0, 3$, and 10.

a) $(x-4)(x+8)-(x-9)(x+7)$

b) $\dfrac{3x^3+27x^2+60x}{x^2+6x+8}$

c) $\dfrac{x^3-16x}{2x^3-16x^2+32x}$

d) $(x+3)^2+2x(1-x)$

☆8. A circle with diameter 8 cm is removed from a larger circle with radius r cm.

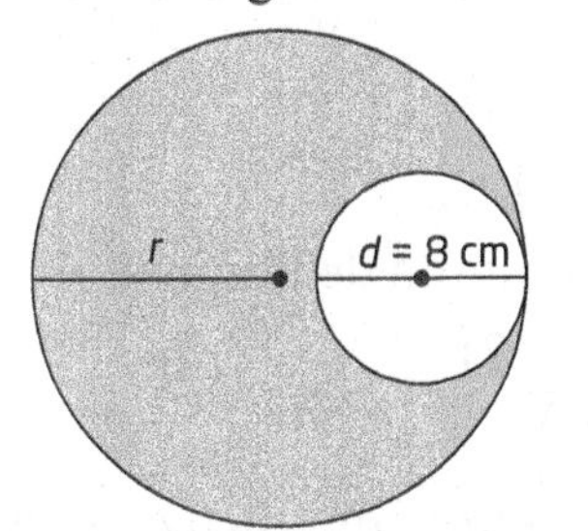

a) Express the area of the shaded region as a function of r.

b) Express the area of the shaded region in factored form.

c) State the domain and range of the area function.

9. A dairy product company has designed a scalable cylindrical container to accommodate the storage of several different-sized products.

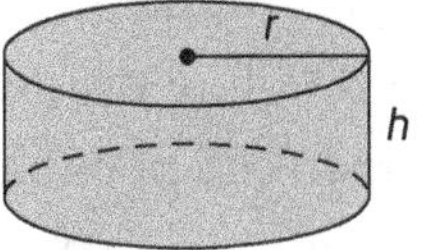

The dimensions are $r = 2x + 1$ and $h = x - 2$, where x is in metres.

a) Write two equivalent expressions for the volume of the cylinder as a function of x.

b) Write two equivalent expressions for the surface area of the cylinder as a function of x.

c) Determine the volume and surface area for $x = 2.5$ m.

d) Determine the domain of the volume and surface area functions.

10. A company that makes modular furniture has designed a scalable box to accommodate several different sizes of items. The dimensions are given by $L = 3x + 2$, $W = 2x - 0.5$, and $H = x + 1$, where x is in metres.

a) Express the volume of the box as a function of x.

b) Express the surface area of the box as a functions of x.

c) Determine the volume and surface area for x-values of 1.25 m, 2 m, and 2.5 m.

C Extend

☆11. Determine if $f(x)$ and $g(x)$ are equivalent. Justify your answer.

$f(x) = x^2 + \left[\frac{1}{2}(x-1)(x+1)\right]^2$,

$g(x) = \left[\frac{1}{2}(x^2+1)\right]^2$

12. Without using technology, describe the graph of $f(x) = \dfrac{(3x+2)(2x^2-7x-4)}{3x^2-10x-8}$. Justify your answer.

2.2 Skills You Need: Operations With Rational Expressions

KEY CONCEPTS

- When multiplying or dividing rational expressions, follow these steps:
  - Factor any polynomials, if possible.
  - When dividing by a rational expression, multiply by the reciprocal of the rational expression.
  - Divide by any common factors.
  - Determine any restrictions.
- When adding or subtracting rational expressions, follow these steps:
  - Factor the denominators.
  - Determine the least common multiple of the denominators.
  - Rewrite the expressions with a common denominator.
  - Add or subtract the numerators.
  - Simplify and state the restrictions.

Example

Simplify and state any restrictions.

a) $\frac{x^2-8x+15}{x-5} \div \frac{x^2+x-12}{6x-18} \times \frac{3x+12}{2x-10}$

b) $\frac{2x-6}{x^2-5x+6} - \frac{3x-12}{x^2-x-12}$

Solution

a) $\frac{x^2-8x+15}{x-5} \div \frac{x^2+x-12}{6x-18} \times \frac{3x+12}{2x-10}$

Change the division to multiplication.

$= \frac{x^2-8x+15}{x-5} \times \frac{6x-18}{x^2+x-12} \times \frac{3x+12}{2x-10}$

Factor, determine the restrictions, and then simplify.

$= \frac{(x-5)(x-3)}{(x-5)} \times \frac{6(x-3)}{(x-3)(x+4)} \times \frac{3(x+4)}{2(x-5)}$

$= \frac{\cancel{(x-5)}(x-3)}{\cancel{(x-5)}} \times \frac{\overset{3}{\cancel{6}}\cancel{(x-3)}}{\cancel{(x-3)}\cancel{(x+4)}} \times \frac{3\cancel{(x+4)}}{\cancel{2}(x-5)}$

$= (x-3) \times 3 \times \frac{3}{(x-5)}$

$= \frac{9(x-3)}{(x-5)}; x \neq -4, 3, 5$

b) $\frac{2x-6}{x^2-5x+6} - \frac{3x-12}{x^2-x-12}$

Factor and determine the restrictions.

$= \frac{2(x-3)}{(x-3)(x-2)} - \frac{3(x-4)}{(x-4)(x+3)}$

Simplify.

$= \frac{2}{(x-2)} - \frac{3}{(x+3)}$

Rewrite with a common denominator.

$= \frac{2(x+3)-3(x-2)}{(x-2)(x+3)}$

Expand the numerator, and then simplify.

$= \frac{2x+6-3x+6}{(x-2)(x+3)}$

$= \frac{-x+12}{(x-2)(x+3)}; x \neq -3, 2, 3, 4$

A Practise

1. Simplify and state any restrictions.

a) $\frac{16y}{18x} \times \frac{72y}{4x}$

b) $\frac{36x^4}{5x^2} \times \frac{80x^3}{12x}$

c) $\frac{24b^5}{6b} \times \frac{48b^2}{16b^3}$

d) $\frac{3x}{32y} \div \frac{27x^2}{96y}$

e) $\frac{44a^3b}{15b} \div \frac{11a^2}{60b}$

f) $\frac{27p^3q}{18r^2} \div \frac{3p^2q}{36r^4}$

2. Simplify and state any restrictions.

a) $\frac{12}{x-6} \times \frac{x-6}{3}$

b) $\frac{x+2}{x} \times \frac{9x}{x+2}$

c) $\frac{x-8}{x+2} \times \frac{x+2}{x-6}$

d) $\frac{7x^2}{6x^2+3x} \times \frac{12x+6}{2x+8}$

e) $\frac{4x-20}{x^2+6x} \times \frac{3x^2}{3x-15}$

f) $\frac{x^2+12x+32}{x+8} \times \frac{x+1}{x^2+7x+12}$

g) $\frac{x^2+3x+2}{x^2-1} \times \frac{x-1}{x^2-2x-8}$

h) $\frac{x^2-2x-8}{x+2} \times \frac{x-3}{x^2+2x-24}$

3. Simplify and state any restrictions.

a) $\frac{x+1}{x} \div \frac{x+1}{2x}$

b) $\frac{x}{x-3} \div \frac{1}{x-3}$

c) $\frac{x+12}{x+10} \div \frac{x+12}{x-5}$

d) $\frac{x^2+15x}{4x+24} \div \frac{3x}{3x+18}$

e) $\frac{6x}{8x-72} \div \frac{9x}{2x-18}$

f) $\frac{x^2+15x+26}{6x^2} \div \frac{x^2-3x-10}{30x^3}$

g) $\frac{x^2-7x+10}{x^2-4} \div \frac{x^2-4x-5}{3x+6}$

h) $\frac{2x^2-5x-12}{x^2+x-20} \div \frac{2x^2+5x+3}{x^2+8x+7}$

4. Simplify and state any restrictions.

a) $\frac{x+2}{6} + \frac{x-2}{4}$

b) $\frac{x+9}{3} - \frac{3x-4}{7}$

c) $\frac{5}{7x} - \frac{3}{4x}$

d) $\frac{4}{ab} + \frac{9}{2b}$

e) $\frac{11}{12ab^2} - \frac{7}{16a^2}$

f) $\frac{1+a}{2a} + \frac{a-1}{5a}$

g) $\frac{2}{x-3} - \frac{5}{x+3}$

h) $\frac{7}{x+4} + \frac{11}{x-5}$

i) $\frac{x+9}{x-2} - \frac{x-4}{x+5}$

5. Simplify and state any restrictions.

a) $\frac{4x}{x^2-9x+18} + \frac{2x-1}{x-6}$

b) $\frac{x-7}{x^2-2x-15} - \frac{3x}{x-5}$

c) $\frac{2x}{x-2} - \frac{3}{x^2-4}$

d) $\frac{3x}{x-1} - \frac{2x}{x^2+x-2}$

e) $\frac{x+3}{x^2+11x+24} - \frac{2x+10}{x^2+11x+30}$

f) $\frac{x-4}{x^2-8x+16} + \frac{3x+21}{x^2+12x+35}$

g) $\frac{3x+9}{x^2+5x+6} - \frac{2x-2}{x^2+x-2}$

h) $\frac{4x^2-20x}{x^2+2x-35} + \frac{3x-6}{x^2-12x+20}$

☆6. David competed in a 40-km dirt bike race. For the first half of the race he rode his bike at an average speed 8 km/h faster than in the second half.

a) Let x represent David's speed in the first half. Determine a simplified expression in terms of x for the total time he took to complete the race.

b) If David rode his bike at an average speed of 35 km/h in the first half, how long did it take him to finish the race?

B Connect and Apply

7. In each expression, factor −1 from one of the denominators to identify the common denominator. Then simplify the expression and state the restrictions.

a) $\frac{1}{x-5} - \frac{1}{5-x}$

b) $\frac{2x+1}{x-4} + \frac{x-3}{4-x}$

c) $\frac{a+1}{5-2a} - \frac{a-4}{2a-5}$

d) $\frac{2b+5}{2b-3} + \frac{9+b}{3-2b}$

e) $\frac{x+2}{x-2} - \frac{4x}{2-x}$

f) $\frac{3x+2}{3-4x} + \frac{2x+1}{-3+4x}$

g) $\frac{6b-5}{2+b} + \frac{b+3}{-2-b}$

h) $\frac{3c+7}{1-5c} + \frac{-8}{5c-1}$

☆**8.** Anna wants to make an open-topped box using a rectangular piece of cardboard with dimensions 120 cm by 100 cm. She plans to cut a square of side length x from each corner.

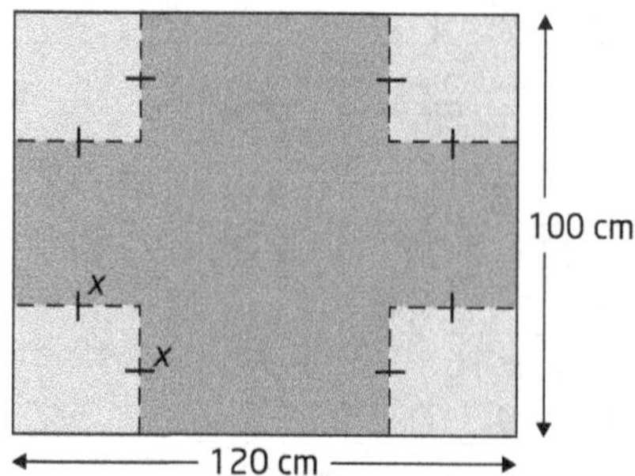

a) Write an expression for the volume of the box as a function of x.

b) Write an expression for the surface area of the open-topped box as a function of x.

c) State the domain for this situation.

d) Write a simplified expression for the ratio of the volume of the box to the surface area.

e) Refer to your answer to part d). What are the restrictions on x?

9. Consider a cylinder with height $h = 3x - 4$ and radius $r = 2x + 3$.

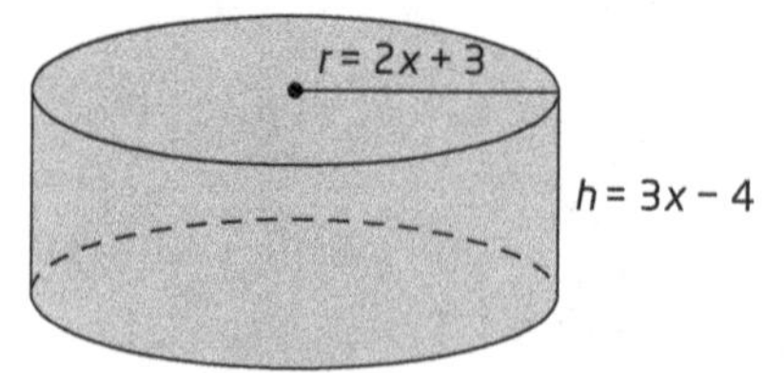

a) Determine the ratio of the volume of the cylinder to its surface area.

b) Determine any restrictions on x for your answer to part a).

10. Use Technology

a) Use graphing technology to graph $f(x) = \frac{1}{x+4} + \frac{1}{x-4}$.

b) Rewrite the function using a common denominator. Then, graph the rewritten function.

c) Compare the graphs. Identify how the restrictions affect the graph.

C Extend

11. Simplify the expression and state any restrictions.

$$\frac{x^2-16}{x^2-x-12} \times \frac{2x^2+6x}{3x^2+9x-12} + \frac{3x^2+7x+4}{2x^2-x-3} \div \frac{-3x^2-x+4}{14x^2-21x}$$

12. If $a = \frac{1}{x}$ and $b = \frac{1}{y}$, write each expression in terms of x and y, in simplified form.

a) $\frac{a+b}{a-b}$

b) $\frac{a}{a-b} - \frac{b}{a+b}$

13. If $x = \frac{a+1}{a+2}$, write each expression in terms of a, in simplified form.

a) $x^2 - 1$

b) $\frac{x+1}{x+2}$

2.3 Horizontal and Vertical Translations of Functions

KEY CONCEPTS

- Translations are transformations that cause functions to shift from one place to another without changing shape.
- The graph of $g(x) = f(x) + c$ is a vertical translation of the graph of $f(x)$ by c units. If $c > 0$, the graph moves up c units. If $c < 0$, the graph moves down c units.
- The graph of $g(x) = f(x - d)$ is a horizontal translation of the graph of $f(x)$ by d units. If $d > 0$, the graph moves to the right d units. If $d < 0$, the graph moves to the left d units.
- A sketch of the graph of any transformed function can be created by transforming the related base function.
- In general, the domain and range of a function of the form $g(x) = f(x - d) + c$ can be determined by adding the d-value and the c-value to restrictions on the domain and range, respectively, of the base function.

Example

Each graph represents a transformation of a base function, $f(x) = x$, $f(x) = x^2$, $f(x) = \sqrt{x}$, or $f(x) = \frac{1}{x}$. State the base function and the equation of the transformed function.

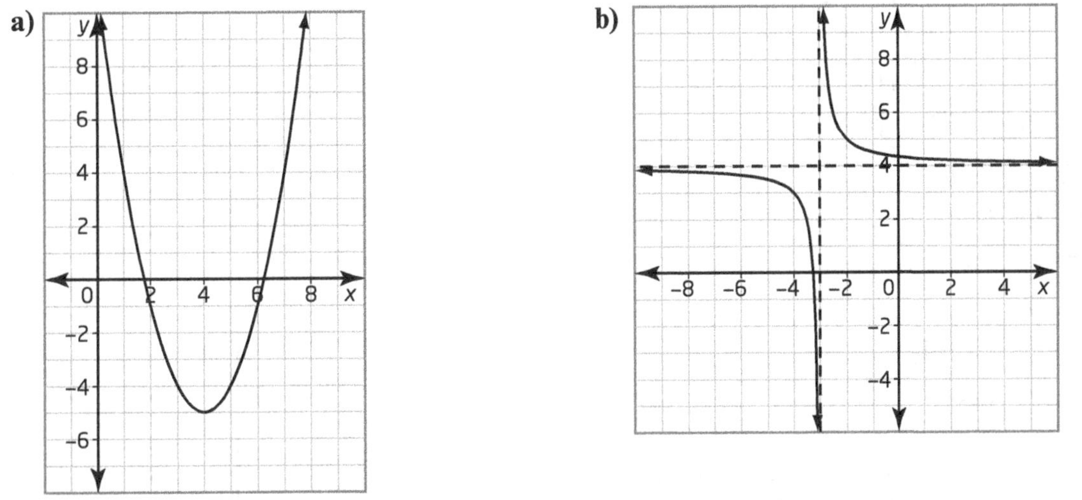

Solution

a) The base function is $f(x) = x^2$. The vertex of the graph is $(4, -5)$, so $f(x) = x^2$ has been translated 4 units right and 5 units down; $d = 4$ and $c = -5$.
The equation of the transformed function is $g(x) = (x - 4)^2 - 5$.

b) The base function is $f(x) = \frac{1}{x}$, which has asymptotes at $x = 0$ and $y = 0$. The asymptotes of the graph are $x = -3$ and $y = 4$, so $f(x) = \frac{1}{x}$ has been translated 3 units left and 4 units up; $d = -3$ and $c = 4$.
The equation of the transformed function is $g(x) = \frac{1}{x + 3} + 4$.

A Practise

1. **a)** Copy and complete the table of values.

x	$f(x) = \sqrt{x}$	$r(x) = f(x) - 4$	$s(x) = f(x + 5)$
0			
1			
4			
9			

   b) Use the points to graph each function on the same set of axes.

   c) Explain how the points of the translated functions relate to the actual transformation.

2. Given the graph of $f(x)$, sketch a graph of each function by determining the image points A′, B′, C′, D′, E′, F′, and G′.

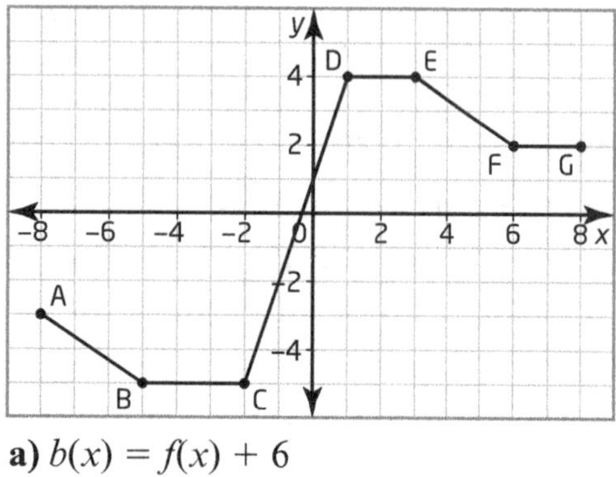

   a) $b(x) = f(x) + 6$

   b) $g(x) = f(x) - 4$

   c) $h(x) = f(x - 3)$

   d) $m(x) = f(x + 1)$

   e) $n(x) = f(x - 1) + 9$

   f) $r(x) = f(x + 2) - 7$

3. For each function $g(x)$, identify the base function as one of $f(x) = x$, $f(x) = x^2$, $f(x) = \sqrt{x}$, or $f(x) = \frac{1}{x}$, and describe the transformation in the form $y = f(x - d) + c$ and in words. Then sketch a graph of $g(x)$ and state the domain and range of each function.

   a) $g(x) = x - 7$

   b) $g(x) = x^2 + 3$

   c) $g(x) = \sqrt{x} + 9$

   d) $g(x) = (x - 5)^2$

   e) $g(x) = \frac{1}{x} + 2$

   f) $g(x) = \sqrt{x + 3}$

   g) $g(x) = \frac{1}{x - 8}$

4. Use words and function notation to describe the transformation that can be applied to each graph of $f(x)$ to obtain the graph of $g(x)$. State the domain and range of $f(x)$ and $g(x)$.

   a)

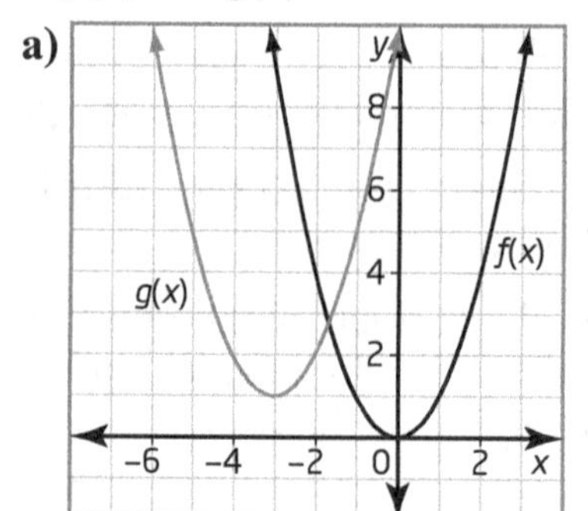

   b)

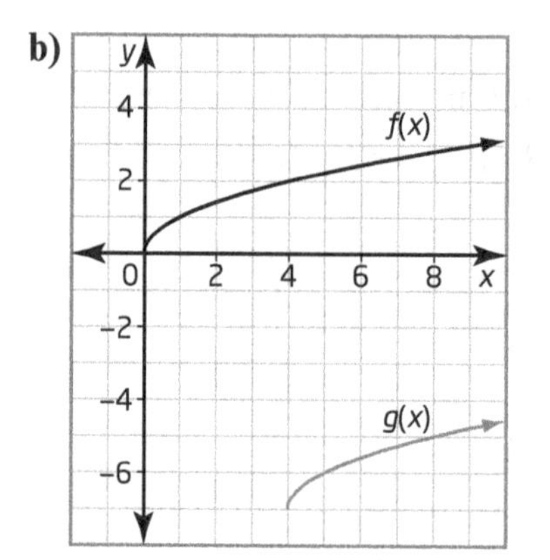

   c)

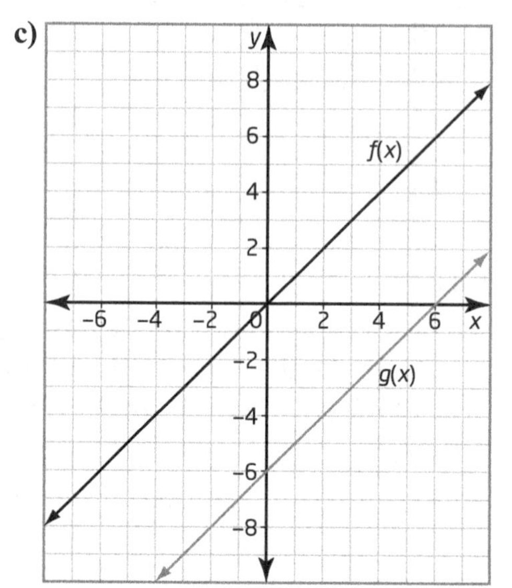

5. Use words and function notation to describe the transformation that can be applied to each graph of $f(x)$ to obtain the graph of $g(x)$. State the domain and range of $f(x)$ and $g(x)$.

a) 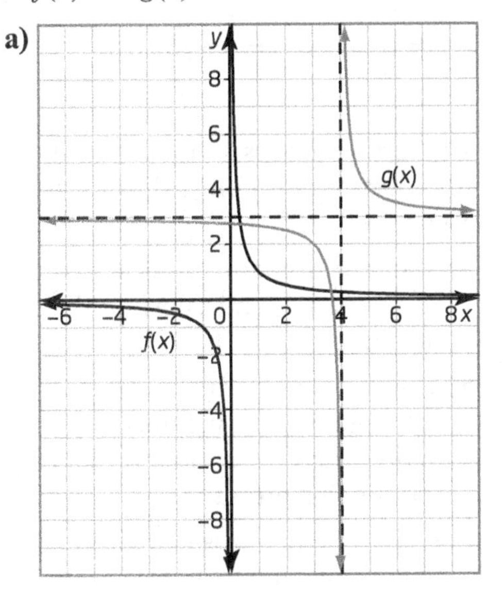

b) 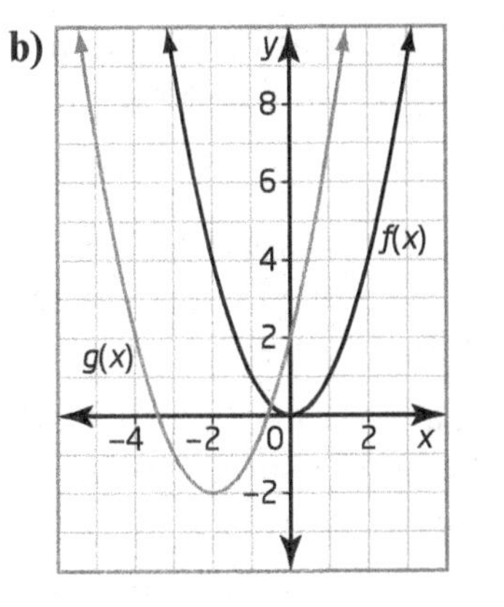

c) 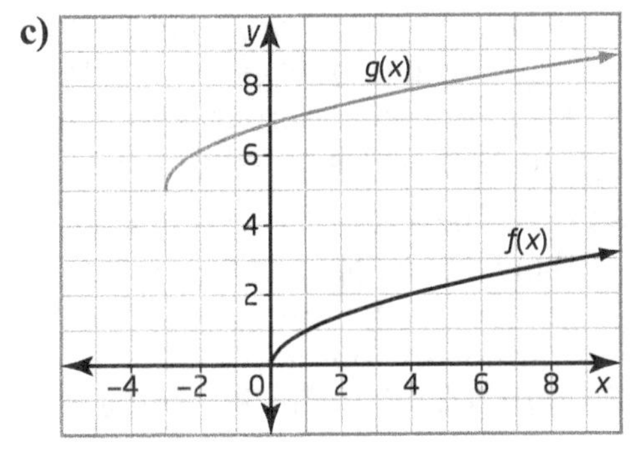

B Connect and Apply

6. Use the base function $f(x) = x$. Write the equation for each transformed function.

   a) $b(x) = f(x + 2)$

   b) $h(x) = f(x) - 5$

   c) $m(x) = f(x) + 9$

   d) $n(x) = f(x - 3) - 7$

   e) $r(x) = f(x + 4) + 6$

   f) $s(x) = f(x + 2) - 8$

   g) $t(x) = f(x - 5) + 1$

7. Repeat question 6 using the base function $f(x) = x^2$.

8. Repeat question 6 using the base function $f(x) = \sqrt{x}$.

9. Repeat question 6 using the base function $f(x) = \frac{1}{x}$.

☆**10.** Is each statement true or false? Support your answer with an example or a graph.

   a) When transforming a function using translations, a horizontal translation must be applied before a vertical translation.

   b) The function $y = x - 2$ could be a vertical translation of $y = x$ two units downward or a horizontal translation of $y = x$ two units to the right.

☆**11.** Which of these transformations are equivalent to horizontally shifting $f(x) = x$ five units left? Justify your answer by writing the transformed equation.

   a) vertical translation of 5 units up

   b) vertical translation of 5 units down

   c) vertical translation of 3 units up and horizontal translation of 2 units right

   d) horizontal translation of 3 units left and vertical translation of 2 units up

   e) vertical translation of 1 unit up and horizontal translation of 4 units right

12. Each graph represents a transformation of one of the base functions $f(x) = x$, $f(x) = x^2$, $f(x) = \sqrt{x}$, or $f(x) = \frac{1}{x}$. State the base function and the equation of the transformed function.

a)

b)

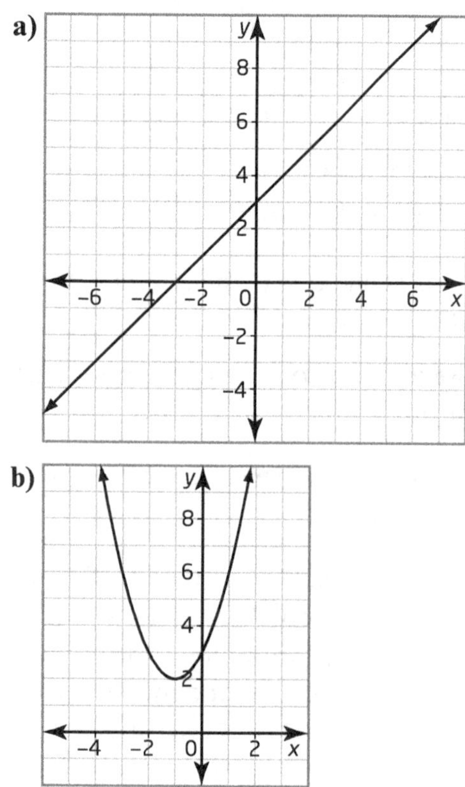

c)

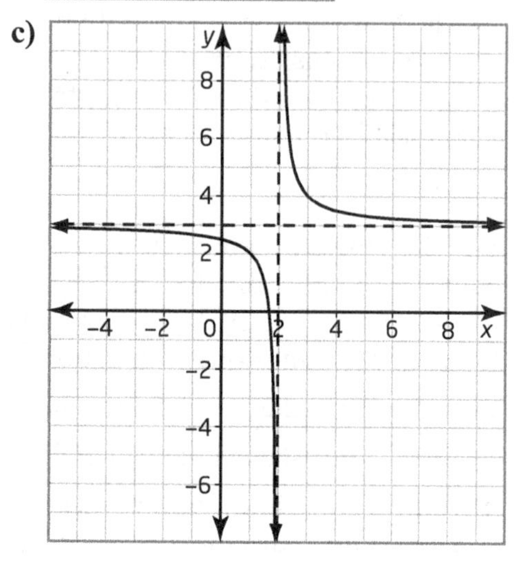

d)

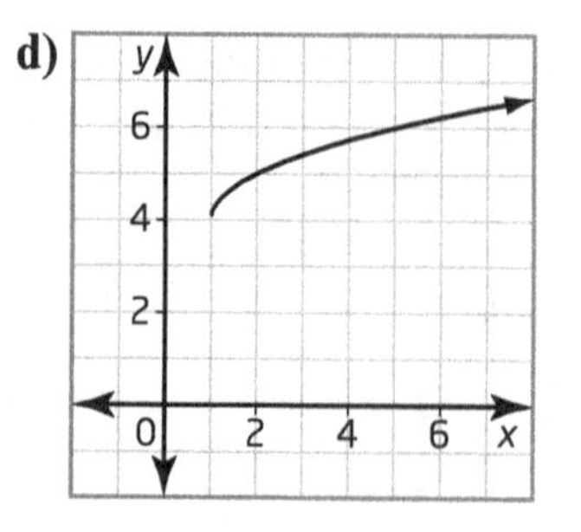

13. The cost, in dollars, to produce x units of a product can be modelled by the function $c(x) = \sqrt{x} + 400$.

a) State the domain and range of the cost function and interpret their meanings.

b) The first 8 units of this product are sold, but are not included in the cost. Write a new function representing the cost of this product.

c) What type of transformation does the change in part b) represent?

d) How does the transformation in part b) affect the domain and range?

C Extend

14. a) State the transformed function $g(x) = f(x + 6) + 5$ for each of the base functions $f(x) = x$, $f(x) = x^2$, $f(x) = \sqrt{x}$, and $f(x) = \frac{1}{x}$. Use words to describe how each base function is transformed.

b) Transform the resulting function $g(x)$ in part a) by applying another transformation, $h(x) = g(x - 4) - 3$. Use words to describe how each function $g(x)$ is transformed.

c) Describe a transformation $p(x)$ that can be applied to $f(x)$ that gives the same result as the two transformations applied in parts a) and b). Justify your answer.

2.4 Reflections of Functions

KEY CONCEPTS

Reflection	Numerical Representation	Graphical Representation	Algebraic Representation
$y = f(-x)$	A point (x, y) becomes $(-x, y)$.	The graph is reflected in the y-axis. 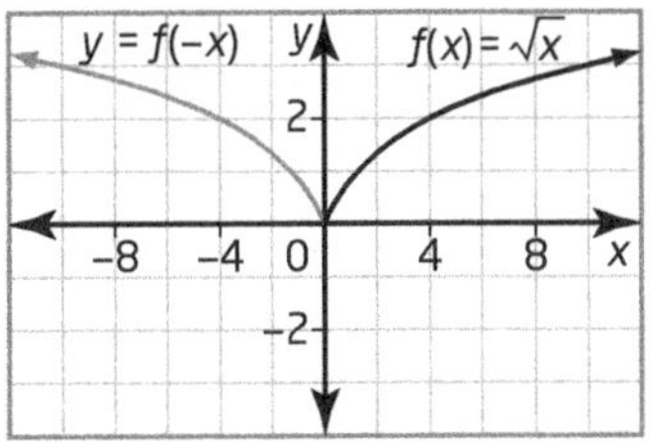	Replace x with $-x$ in the expression.
$y = -f(x)$	A point (x, y) becomes $(x, -y)$.	The graph is reflected in the x-axis. 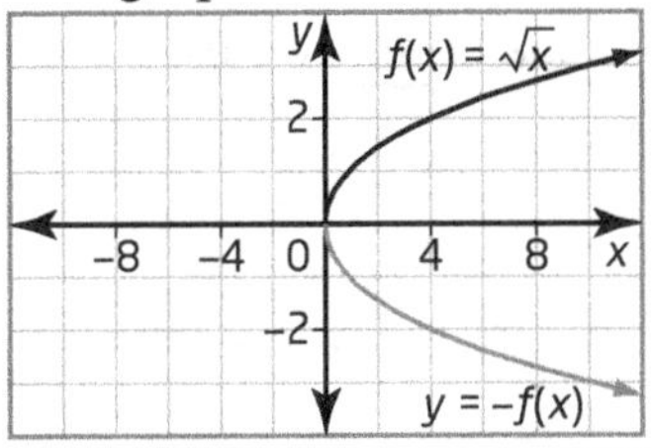	Multiply the entire expression by -1.
$y = -f(-x)$	A point (x, y) becomes $(-x, -y)$.	The graph is reflected in one axis and then the other. 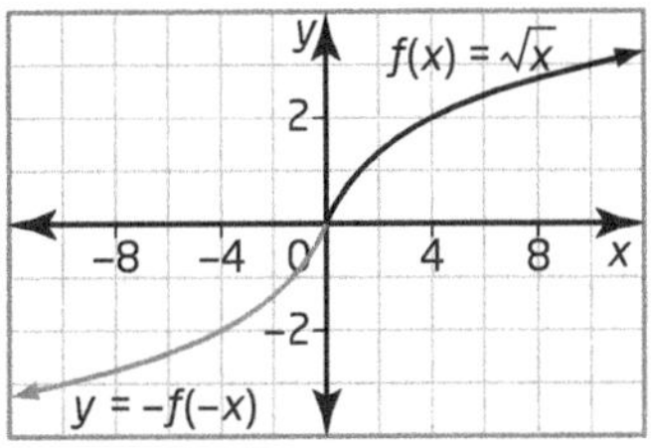	First replace x with $-x$ in the expression and then multiply the entire expression by -1.

Example

Use algebra to determine if $g(x)$ is a reflection of $f(x)$. Check by graphing.

a) $f(x) = x^2 - 5$ $\quad g(x) = -x^2 + 5$

b) $f(x) = \sqrt{x + 8}$ $\quad g(x) = \sqrt{8 - x}$

c) $f(x) = \dfrac{1}{x - 1} + 3$ $\quad g(x) = \dfrac{1}{x - 1} - 3$

Solution

$g(x)$ is a reflection of $f(x)$ if one of these conditions is true:

i) $g(x) = -f(x)$

ii) $g(x) = f(-x)$

iii) $g(x) = -f(-x)$

a) $f(x) = x^2 - 5$

Check condition i).

$$-f(x) = -(x^2 - 5)$$
$$= -x^2 + 5$$
$$= g(x)$$

Since $g(x) = -f(x)$, $g(x)$ is a reflection of $f(x)$ in the x-axis.

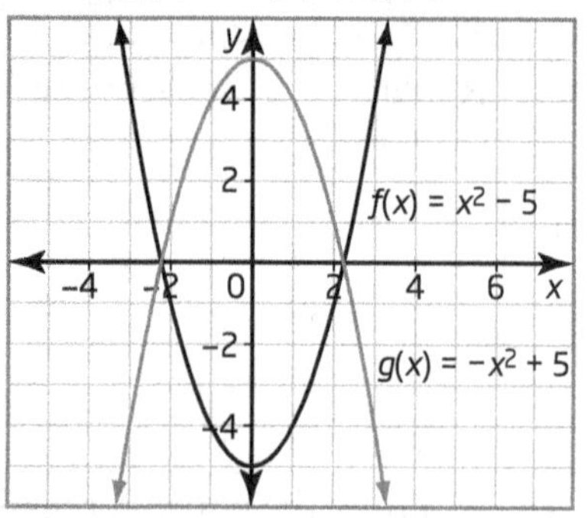

b) $f(x) = \sqrt{x + 8}$

Check condition i).

$$-f(x) = -\sqrt{x + 8}$$
$$\neq g(x)$$

Check condition ii).

$$f(-x) = \sqrt{-x + 8}$$
$$= \sqrt{8 - x}$$
$$= g(x)$$

Since $g(x) = f(-x)$, $g(x)$ is a reflection of $f(x)$ in the y-axis.

g(x) = √(8 − x)
f(x) = √(x + 8)

c) $f(x) = \dfrac{1}{x - 1} + 3$

Check condition i).

$$-f(x) = \frac{-1}{x - 1} - 3$$
$$= \frac{1}{1 - x} - 3$$
$$\neq g(x)$$

Check condition ii).

$$f(-x) = \frac{1}{-x - 1} + 3$$
$$= \frac{-1}{x + 1} + 3$$
$$\neq g(x)$$

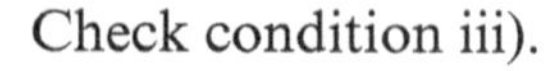
Check condition iii).

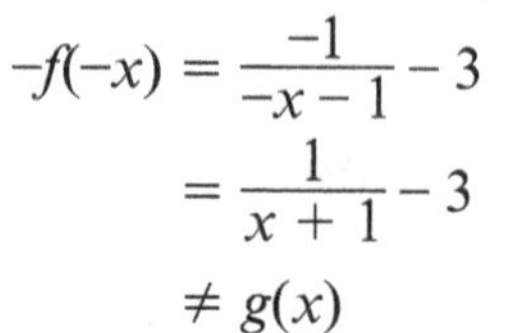
$$-f(-x) = \frac{-1}{-x - 1} - 3$$
$$= \frac{1}{x + 1} - 3$$
$$\neq g(x)$$

Since $g(x)$ is not equivalent to $f(-x)$, $-f(x)$, or $-f(-x)$, $g(x)$ is not a reflection of $f(x)$. Note that $g(x)$ is a vertical translation of $f(x)$ 6 units down.

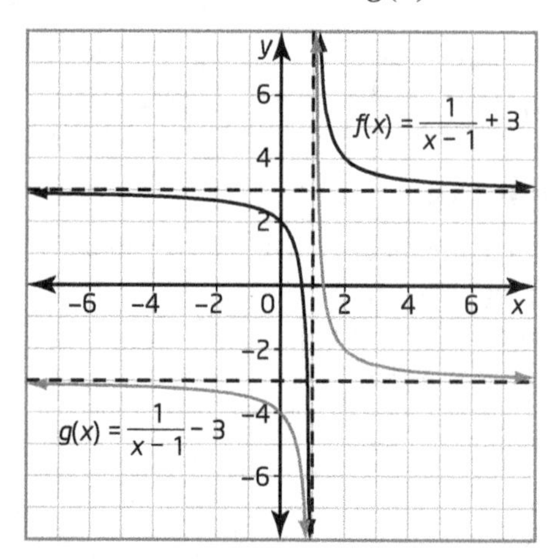

A Practise

1. Copy each graph of $f(x)$. Sketch $g(x)$, which is the reflection of $f(x)$ in the y-axis. State the domain and range of each function.

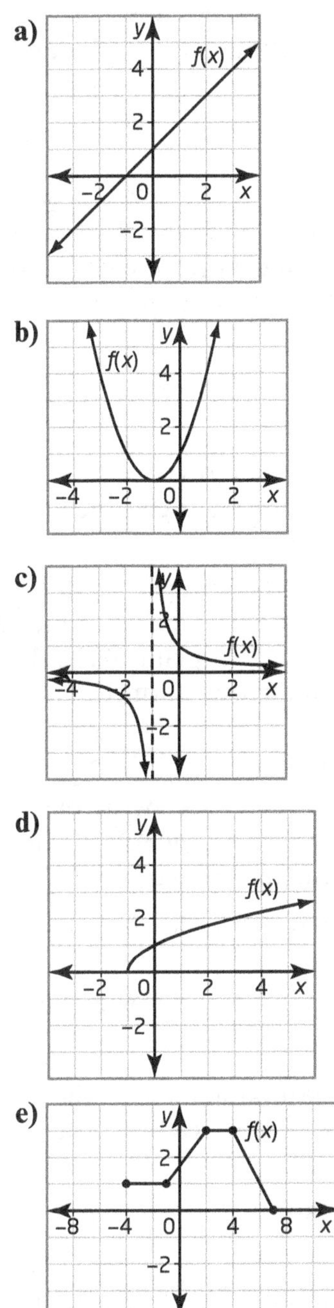

2. For each function in question 1, sketch $h(x)$, which is the reflection of $f(x)$ in the x-axis. State the domain and range of each function.

3. For each function $f(x)$ in question 1, sketch a graph of $k(x) = -f(-x)$. State the domain and range of each function.

4. For each function $f(x)$, determine the equation for $g(x)$.

   a) $f(x) = \sqrt{x - 21} + 9$ $\quad g(x) = -f(x)$

   b) $f(x) = (x + 8)^2 - 17$ $\quad g(x) = f(-x)$

   c) $f(x) = (x - 1)^2 + 11$ $\quad g(x) = -f(-x)$

   ☆ **d)** $f(x) = \dfrac{1}{x - 6} + 5$ $\quad g(x) = -f(-x)$

   e) $f(x) = -\sqrt{x + 4} + 19$ $\quad g(x) = f(-x)$

   f) $f(x) = \dfrac{1}{x - 8} + 3$ $\quad g(x) = -f(x)$

   g) $f(x) = x + 18$ $\quad g(x) = -f(-x)$

5. For each graph, describe the reflection that transforms $f(x)$ into $g(x)$.

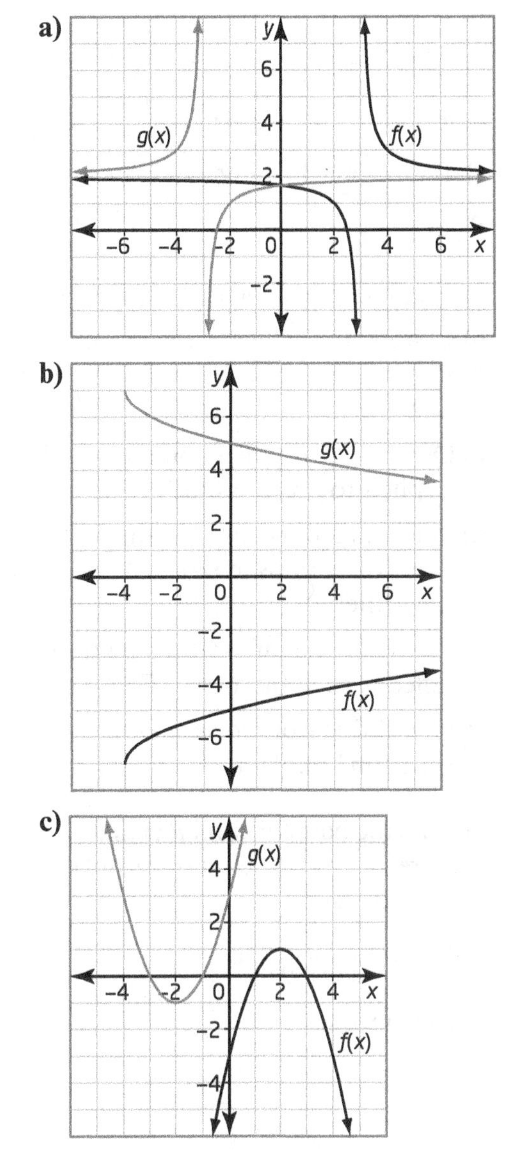

B Connect and Apply

6. **Use Technology** Use graphing technology to graph the function $f(x) = (x + 3)^2 - 1$.

   a) Determine the invariant point(s), if any, when $f(x)$ is reflected in

   i) the x-axis

   ii) the y-axis

   iii) the x-axis and the y-axis

   b) Write the equation of a quadratic function that has an invariant point for all the reflections in part a). Justify your answer.

7. Determine algebraically whether $g(x)$ is a reflection of $f(x)$. Check by graphing.

   a) $f(x) = x^2 + 2$ $\quad g(x) = -x^2 + 2$

   b) $f(x) = \sqrt{x}$ $\quad g(x) = -\sqrt{x}$

   c) $f(x) = \frac{1}{x + 3}$ $\quad g(x) = \frac{1}{3 - x}$

   d) $f(x) = (x - 6)^2 + 2$ $\quad g(x) = -(x + 6)^2 - 2$

   e) $f(x) = \sqrt{x + 12} - 7$ $\quad g(x) = -\sqrt{x + 12} - 7$

   f) $f(x) = \frac{1}{x} - 9$ $\quad g(x) = -\frac{1}{x} - 9$

☆8. **a)** Graph the function $f(x) = (x + 3)^2 - 2$.

   b) Graph $g(x)$, which is the reflection of $f(x)$ in the y-axis. Write the equation of $g(x)$.

   c) Determine a translation that can be applied to $f(x)$ to obtain $g(x)$.

   d) Verify algebraically that the transformations in parts b) and c) are the same.

   e) Predict if the same would be true for reflections in the x-axis. Explain.

   f) Would this work for any other type of function? Explain.

9. **a)** State the base function $f(x)$ that corresponds to each transformed function, $g(x)$.

   i) $g(x) = \frac{1}{x - 9} + 4$

   ii) $g(x) = \sqrt{x + 5} - 7$

   b) Describe the transformations that are applied to the base function to obtain each function in part a).

   c) For each function in part a) write the equations for
   $k(x)$: a reflection in the x-axis,
   $p(x)$: a reflection in the y-axis, and
   $q(x)$: a reflection in the x-axis and in the y-axis.

C Extend

10. **a)** Sketch a graph of $f(x) = \sqrt{x}$ reflected in each given line. Write the equation of the transformed function, $g(x)$.

   i) $x = -1$

   ii) $x = -2$

   iii) $x = -3$

   b) In each case, describe two transformations that give the same result as $g(x)$.

   c) Will the results from part b) be true when $f(x) = \sqrt{x}$ is reflected in the line $x = a, \{a \in \mathbb{R}\}$? Explain. Write the corresponding transformed function.

11. **Use Technology**

   a) Given $f(x) = \sqrt{16 - x^2}$, write the equations of $f(-x)$, $-f(x)$, and $-f(-x)$. Which functions are equivalent?

   b) Graph each function. Determine any invariant points.

   c) State the domain and range of each function.

12. **a)** Identify the invariant points when the circle $x^2 + y^2 = 36$ is reflected in

   i) the x-axis

   ii) the y-axis

   iii) the x-axis and the y-axis

   b) Will the results in part a) be true for all circles? Explain.

2.5 Stretches of Functions

KEY CONCEPTS

- Stretches and compressions are transformations that cause functions to change shape.
- The graph of $g(x) = af(x)$, $a > 0$, is a vertical stretch or a vertical compression of the graph of $f(x)$ by a factor of a. If $a > 1$, the graph is vertically stretched by a factor of a. If $0 < a < 1$, the graph is vertically compressed by a factor of a.
- The graph of $g(x) = f(kx)$, $k > 0$, is a horizontal stretch or a horizontal compression of the graph of $f(x)$ by a factor of $\frac{1}{k}$. If $k > 1$, the graph is horizontally compressed by a factor of $\frac{1}{k}$. If $0 < k < 1$, the graph is horizontally stretched by a factor of $\frac{1}{k}$.

Example

In each case, write the equation of the transformed function, $g(x)$, that results from applying the given transformation(s) to the base function $f(x)$. Sketch $f(x)$ and $g(x)$ on the same set of axes.

a) $f(x) = \frac{1}{x}$ is stretched horizontally by a factor of 4

b) $f(x) = \sqrt{x}$ is compressed vertically by a factor of $\frac{1}{5}$

Solution

a) The parameter that corresponds to a horizontal stretch by a factor of 4 is $k = \frac{1}{4}$.

$$g(x) = f\left(\frac{1}{4}x\right)$$
$$= \frac{1}{\left(\frac{1}{4}x\right)}$$
$$= \frac{4}{x}$$

The transformed function is $g(x) = \frac{4}{x}$.

b) The parameter that corresponds to a vertical compression by a factor of $\frac{1}{5}$ is $a = \frac{1}{5}$.

$$g(x) = \frac{1}{5}f(x)$$
$$= \frac{1}{5}\sqrt{x}$$

The transformed function is $g(x) = \frac{1}{5}\sqrt{x}$.

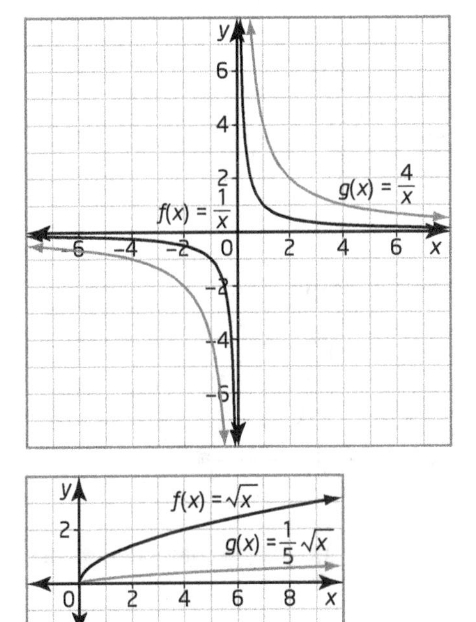

A Practise

1. a) Copy and complete the table of values.

x	$f(x) = x^2$	$g(x) = \frac{3}{4}f(x)$	$h(x) = f\left(\frac{3}{4}x\right)$
−4			
−2			
0			
2			
4			

b) Sketch a graph of the functions on the same set of axes.

c) Explain how the points on the graphs of $g(x)$ and $h(x)$ relate to the transformation.

2. Given each graph of $f(x)$, graph and label $g(x)$.

a) $g(x) = 2f(x)$

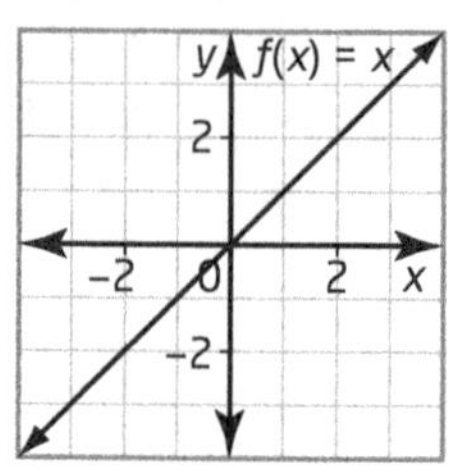

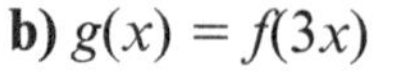

b) $g(x) = f(3x)$

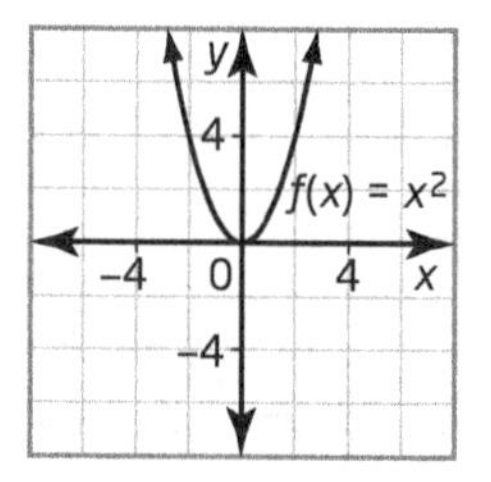

c) $g(x) = f(4x)$

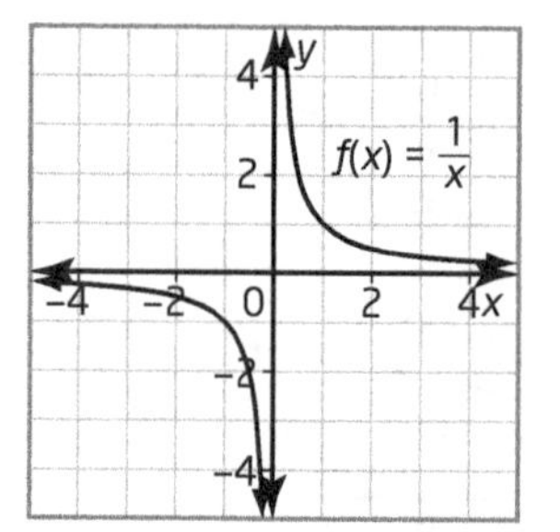

d) $g(x) = f\left(\frac{x}{4}\right)$

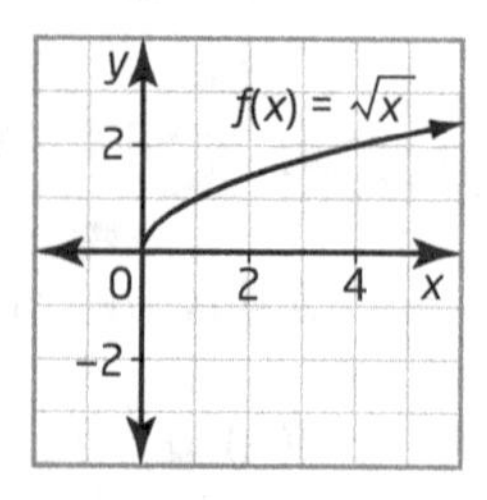

3. For each function $g(x)$, identify the value of a or k and describe how the graph of $g(x)$ can be obtained from the graph of $f(x)$.

a) $g(x) = 8f(x)$

b) $g(x) = f(6x)$

c) $g(x) = \frac{2}{3}f(x)$

d) $g(x) = f\left(\frac{1}{9}x\right)$

4. For each function $g(x)$, describe the transformation from a base function of $f(x) = x$, $f(x) = x^2$, $f(x) = \sqrt{x}$, or $f(x) = \frac{1}{x}$. Then sketch a graph of $f(x)$ and $g(x)$ on the same axes.

a) $g(x) = 12x$

b) $g(x) = (4x)^2$

c) $g(x) = \sqrt{\frac{x}{6}}$

d) $g(x) = \frac{7}{x}$

e) $g(x) = \sqrt{25x}$

f) $g(x) = \frac{x}{8}$

B Connect and Apply

5. In each case, write the equation of the transformed function $g(x)$ that results from applying the given transformation to the base function $f(x)$. Sketch $f(x)$ and $g(x)$ on the same set of axes.

a) $f(x) = x^2$ is stretched vertically by a factor of 2

b) $f(x) = \sqrt{x}$ is compressed horizontally by a factor of $\frac{2}{3}$

c) $f(x) = \frac{1}{x}$ is stretched horizontally by a factor of 2

☆**6.** Acceleration due to gravity, a, varies from planet to planet. The distance of the object from the drop location after t seconds is given by $d(t) = \frac{a}{2}t^2$. The table shows the estimated acceleration due to gravity for different planets.

Planet	Acceleration Due to Gravity (m/s^2)
Earth	9.8
Neptune	11.4
Mercury	3.6

a) State the base function, $f(t)$, for $d(t)$.

b) Describe the transformation that is applied to $f(t)$ to obtain $d(t)$.

c) Write the equation that represents the distance of an object from the drop location on each planet.

d) Compare the domain and range of each function in part c). What do you notice?

7. Describe the transformation applied to the graph of $f(x)$ to obtain the graph of $g(x)$. Write the equation for $g(x)$.

a)

b)

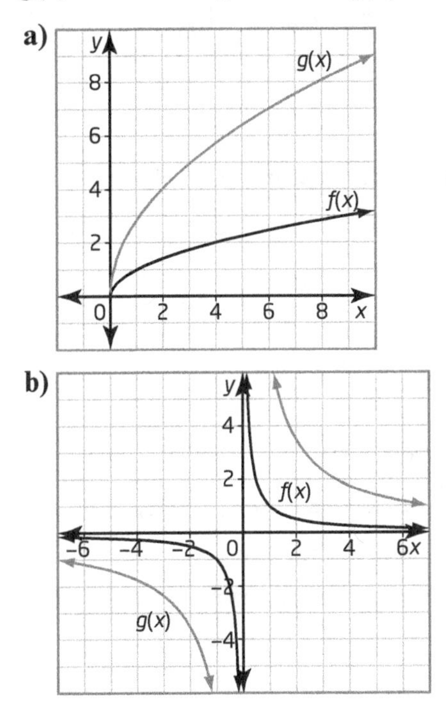

8. Consider the graph of $f(x) = \sqrt{25 - x^2}$.

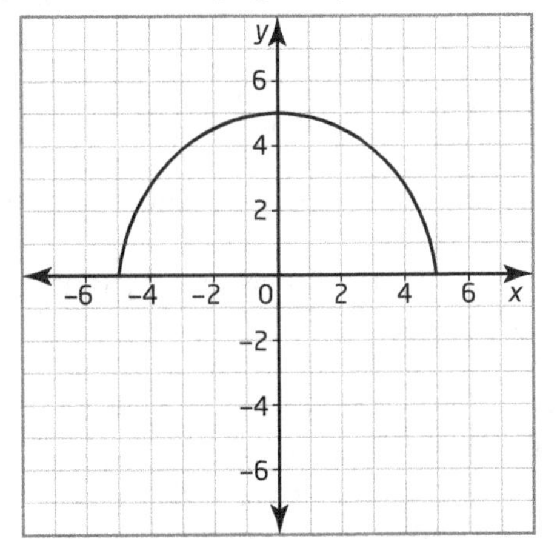

Use transformations to sketch each graph of $g(x)$. Write the equation of $g(x)$ and state the domain and range.

a) $g(x) = 2f(x)$

b) $g(x) = f(2x)$

c) $g(x) = \frac{1}{2}f(x)$

d) $g(x) = f\left(\frac{1}{2}x\right)$

C Extend

9. a) Use Technology Use technology to graph $f(x) = x^4 - x^2$.

b) If $g(x) = 2f(x)$ and $h(x) = g(2x)$, determine the equations for $g(x)$ and $h(x)$.

c) Without using technology, describe and sketch a graph of $g(x)$ and $h(x)$.

d) Is there a single transformation that will transform $f(x)$ into $h(x)$? Explain.

☆**10.** Describe how the graph of $f(x) = -0.4x^2 + 18$ can be transformed into the graph of $g(x) = -10x^2 + 18$.

2.6 Combinations of Transformations

KEY CONCEPTS

- Stretches, compressions, and reflections can be performed in any order before translations.
- Ensure that the function is written in the form $y = af[k(x - d)] + c$ to identify specific transformations.
- The parameters a, k, d, and c in the function $y = af[k(x - d)] + c$ correspond to the following transformations:
  a corresponds to a vertical stretch or compression and, if $a < 0$, a reflection in the x-axis.
  k corresponds to a horizontal stretch or compression and, if $k < 0$, a reflection in the y-axis.
  d corresponds to a horizontal translation to the right or left.
  c corresponds to a vertical translation up or down.

Example

Transformations are applied to each function $f(x)$. Identify the parameters a, k, d, and c that correspond to the transformations, and then write the equation of the transformed function, $g(x)$.

a) The graph of $f(x) = \sqrt{x}$ is reflected in the y-axis, stretched horizontally by a factor of 3, and then translated 5 units left and 7 units down.

b) The graph of $f(x) = \frac{1}{x}$ is reflected in the x-axis, compressed horizontally by a factor of $\frac{1}{4}$, and then translated 6 units right and 2 units up.

Solution

a) Since the graph of $f(x) = \sqrt{x}$ is reflected in the y-axis and stretched horizontally by a factor of 3, then $k = -\frac{1}{3}$. A translation of 5 units left indicates that $d = -5$. A translation of 7 units down indicates that $c = -7$.

$$g(x) = f\left[-\frac{1}{3}(x + 5)\right] - 7$$
$$= \sqrt{-\frac{1}{3}x + 5} - 7$$

b) Since the graph of $f(x) = \frac{1}{x}$ is reflected in the x-axis, then $a = -1$.

A horizontal compression by a factor of $\frac{1}{4}$ indicates that $k = 4$. A translation of 6 units right indicates that $d = 6$. A translation of 2 units up indicates that $c = 2$.

$$g(x) = -f[4(x - 6)] + 2$$
$$= -\frac{1}{4(x - 6)} + 2$$

A Practise

1. Compare each transformed equation to $y = af[k(x - d)] + c$ to determine the values of a, k, d, and c. Then describe, in the appropriate order, the transformations that must be applied to a base function $f(x)$ to obtain the transformed function.

   a) $g(x) = 3f(x - 5)$

   b) $g(x) = \frac{1}{4}f(x) + 4$

   c) $g(x) = f(x + 6) + 2$

   d) $g(x) = f\left(\frac{1}{3}x\right) + 7$

   e) $g(x) = f(2x) - 8$

   f) $g(x) = 5f(x) - 3$

2. Repeat question 1 for each transformed function $g(x)$.

   a) $g(x) = 4f(3x) - 2$

   b) $g(x) = -5f(x) + 6$

   c) $g(x) = \frac{1}{3}f(x - 8) + 1$

   d) $g(x) = f(-2x) + 6$

   e) $g(x) = -f\left(\frac{1}{4}x\right) - 1$

   f) $g(x) = \frac{2}{5}f(5x) - 7$

3. Describe, in the appropriate order, the transformations that must be applied to the base function $f(x)$ to obtain the transformed function. Then write the corresponding equation and transform the graph of $f(x)$ to sketch a graph of $g(x)$.

   a) $f(x) = \sqrt{x}$

   $g(x) = 2f(4x)$

   b) $f(x) = \frac{1}{x}$

   $g(x) = -3f(x - 1) + 7$

   c) $f(x) = x^2$

   $g(x) = f\left[\frac{1}{2}(x + 1)\right]$

   d) $f(x) = x$

   $g(x) = -4f(x) - 6$

4. Repeat question 3 for $f(x)$ and the transformed function $g(x)$.

   a) $f(x) = x$

   $g(x) = -\frac{1}{3}f[3(x + 2)] - 4$

   b) $f(x) = x^2$

   $g(x) = -4f[2(x - 1)] + 6$

   c) $f(x) = \sqrt{x}$

   $g(x) = \frac{1}{3}f[2(x + 5)] + 4$

   d) $f(x) = \frac{1}{x}$

   $g(x) = 5f[-(x - 1)] + 2$

5. For each function, identify the base function as one of $f(x) = x$, $f(x) = x^2$, $f(x) = \sqrt{x}$, or $f(x) = \frac{1}{x}$. Sketch the graphs of the base function and the transformed function, and state the domain and range of the functions.

   a) $b(x) = 7x - 2$

   b) $e(x) = 4x^2 - 3$

   c) $h(x) = (3x + 18)^2$

   d) $p(x) = 4\sqrt{x - 3}$

   e) $m(x) = \frac{2}{x + 9}$

   f) $r(x) = \frac{3}{4 - x} + 6$

B Connect and Apply

6. Given the graph of the function $f(x)$, sketch each graph of $g(x)$.

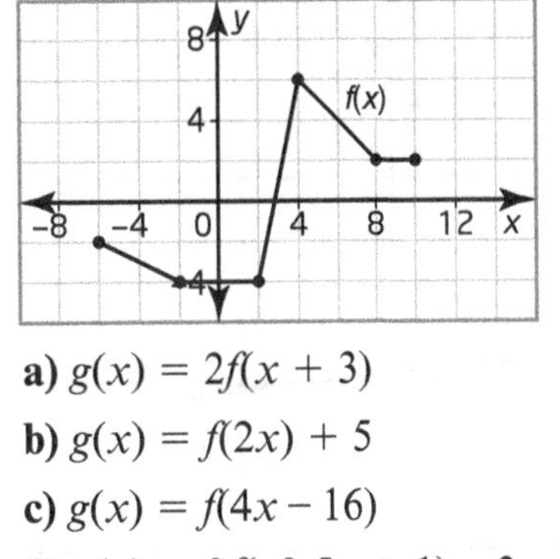

   a) $g(x) = 2f(x + 3)$

   b) $g(x) = f(2x) + 5$

   c) $g(x) = f(4x - 16)$

   d) $g(x) = 3f(-0.5x + 1) - 3$

7. Match each equation with its graph below. Justify your choice.

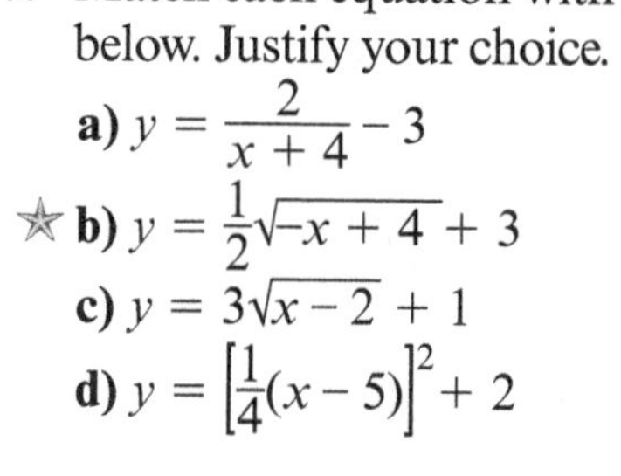

a) $y = \frac{2}{x + 4} - 3$

☆ **b)** $y = \frac{1}{2}\sqrt{-x + 4} + 3$

c) $y = 3\sqrt{x - 2} + 1$

d) $y = \left[\frac{1}{4}(x - 5)\right]^2 + 2$

i)

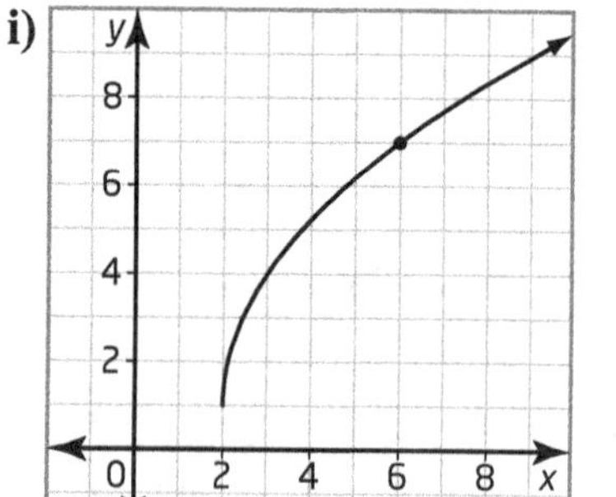

ii)

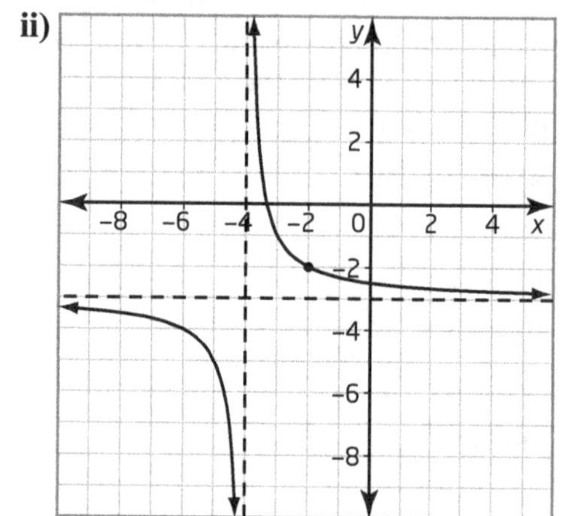

iii)

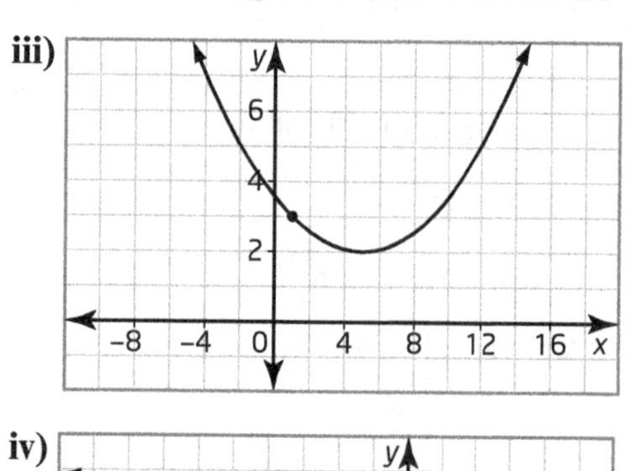

iv)

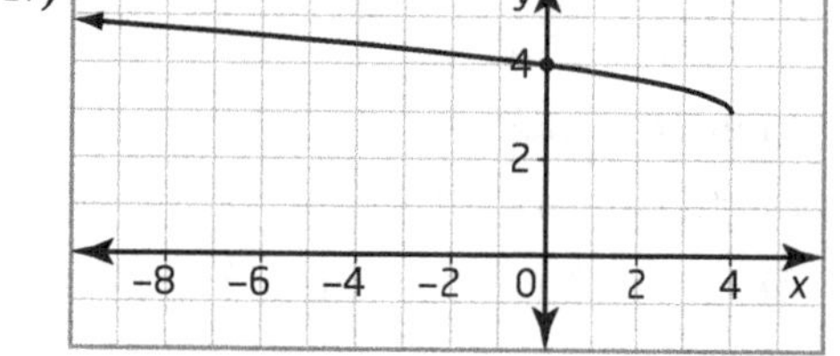

8. Match each equation with its graph below. Justify your choice.

a) $y = -\frac{2}{x + 3} + 1$

b) $y = 2\sqrt{-x + 4} - 1$

c) $y = \frac{4}{-x + 2} + 1$

d) $y = \frac{1}{2}\sqrt{x + 5} - \frac{5}{2}$

i)

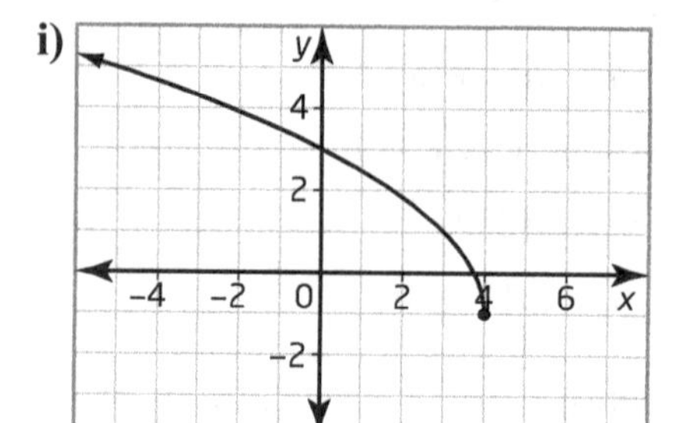

ii)

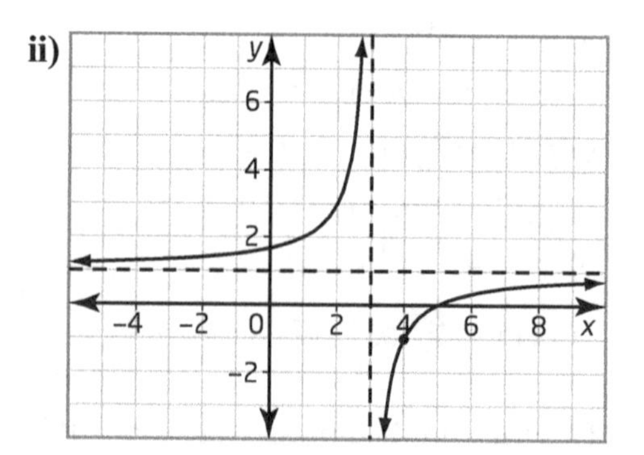

iii)

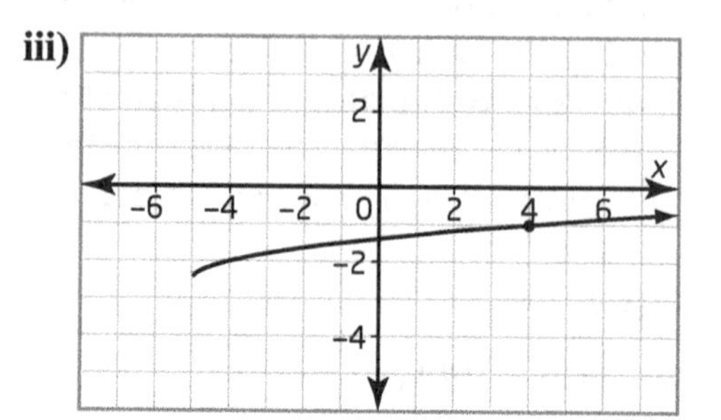

iv)

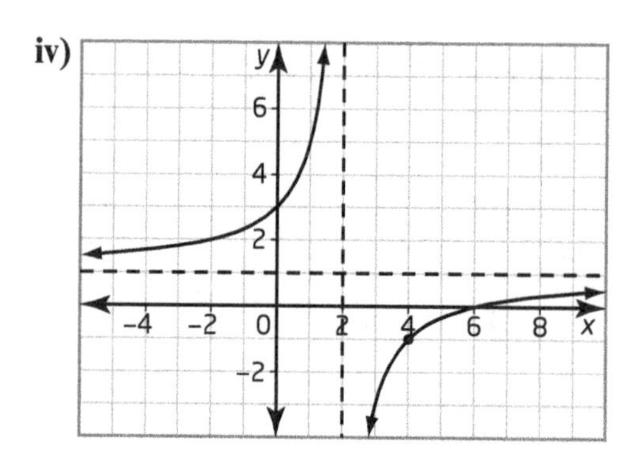

★9. Andrew and David are planning a canoe trip. They want to compare how the travel time for each portion of the trip will vary according to the speed at which they travel. For the first part of the trip, they will travel 24 km across a calm lake. For the second part of the trip, they will travel 18 km up a river whose current flows at 4 km/h. For the last part of the trip, they will travel 36 km down a river that flows at 3 km/h. They used the relationship $t = \frac{d}{s}$, where t is time in hours, d is distance in kilometres, and s is speed in kilometres per hour, to establish that at a speed of s km/h, the time it will take to travel along the lake is $t_1 = \frac{24}{s}$, the time to travel up the river is $t_2 = \frac{18}{s-4}$, and the time taken to travel down the river is $t_3 = \frac{36}{s+3}$.

a) Identify the base function $f(s)$ for this situation.

b) Describe the transformations that must be applied to $f(s)$ to obtain each time function.

c) Graph each function on the same set of axes.

d) How long will each part of the trip take if they paddle their canoe at a constant speed of 6 km/h?

10. The value, in thousands of dollars, of a certain new boat can be modelled by the equation $V(t) = \frac{24}{t+6}$, where t is the time, in years.

a) Sketch a graph of this relation. State the domain and range for thissituation.

b) What was the initial value of the boat?

c) What is the projected value of the boat after each time?

i) 1 year
ii) 3 years
iii) 7 years

C Extend

11. Given each graph of a base function $f(x)$, sketch the graph of $g(x) = 2f(0.5x - 1.5) + 4$.

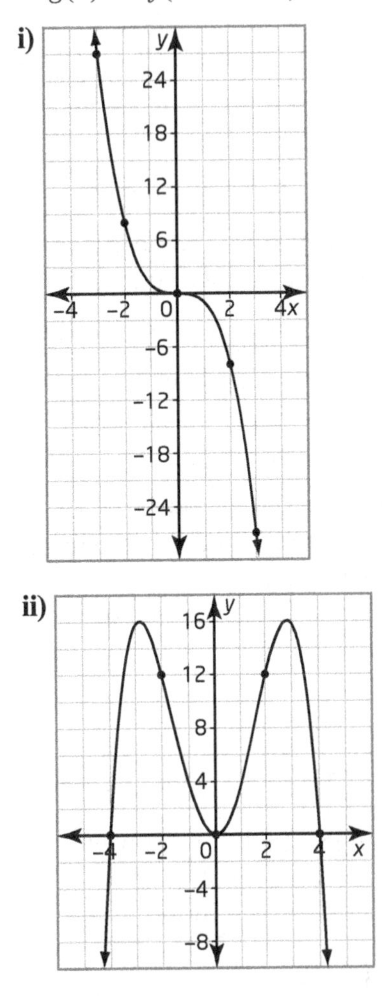

12. a) Given the base function $f(x) = x^4$, use a table of values or a graphing calculator to sketch a graph of $y = f(x)$.

b) Sketch a graph and determine an equation for each transformed function.

i) $g(x) = 4f(-x + 5)$

ii) $h(x) = -f\left(\frac{1}{4}x - 1\right) + 3$

13. The equation of a circle, with centre at the origin and radius r, is given by $x^2 + y^2 = r^2$. Describe the transformations needed to graph each circle, and sketch the circles.

a) $(x - 3)^2 + (y - 5)^2 = 16$
b) $(x + 2)^2 + (y - 7)^2 = 4$

2.7 Inverse of a Function

KEY CONCEPTS

- The inverse of a function $f(x)$ is denoted by $f^{-1}(x)$.
- The inverse of a function can be found by interchanging the x- and y-coordinates of the function.
- The graph of $f^{-1}(x)$ is the graph of $f(x)$ reflected in the line $y = x$.
- The inverse of a function can be found by interchanging x and y in the equation of the function and then solving the new equation for y.
- For algebraic inverses of quadratic functions, the functions must be in vertex form.
- The inverse of a function is not necessarily a function.

Example

Consider the function $f(x) = x^2 + 4x + 1$.

a) Determine the equation of the inverse, $f^{-1}(x)$, of $f(x)$.

b) Graph $f(x)$ and $f^{-1}(x)$ on the same set of axes.

c) Determine if $f^{-1}(x)$ is a function.

Solution

a) $y = x^2 + 4x + 1$

$y = (x^2 + 4x + 4) + 1 - 4$

$y = (x + 2)^2 - 3$

Interchange x and y and solve for y.

$$x = (y + 2)^2 - 3$$
$$x + 3 = (y + 2)^2$$
$$\pm\sqrt{x + 3} = y + 2$$
$$\pm\sqrt{x + 3} - 2 = y$$
$$f^{-1}(x) = \pm\sqrt{x + 3} - 2$$

b)

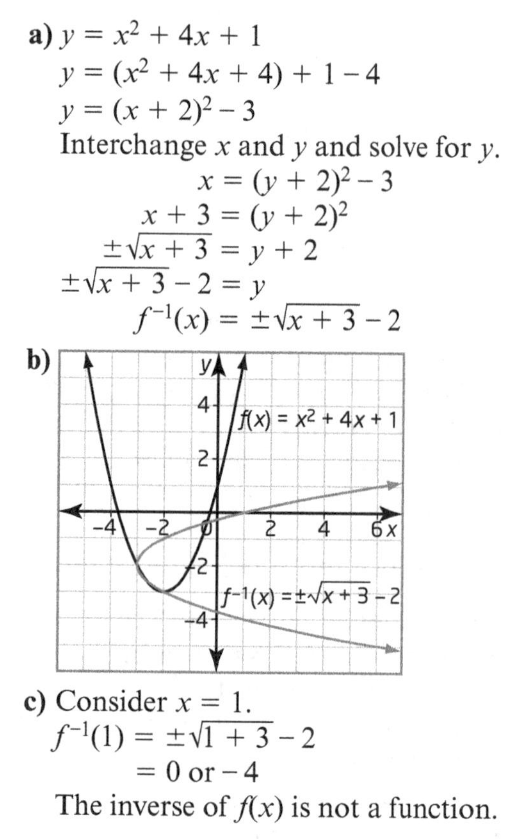

c) Consider $x = 1$.

$f^{-1}(1) = \pm\sqrt{1 + 3} - 2$

$= 0 \text{ or } -4$

The inverse of $f(x)$ is not a function.

A Practise

1. Write the inverse of each function. Then state the domain and range of the function and of its inverse.

   a) $\{(2, 6), (3, 1), (4, -1), (5, 2)\}$

   b) $\{(-3, 7), (-2, 5), (-1, -2), (0, -6)\}$

   c)

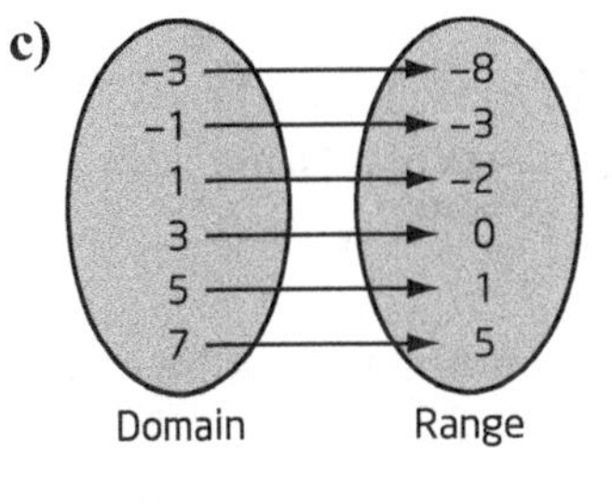

   d)

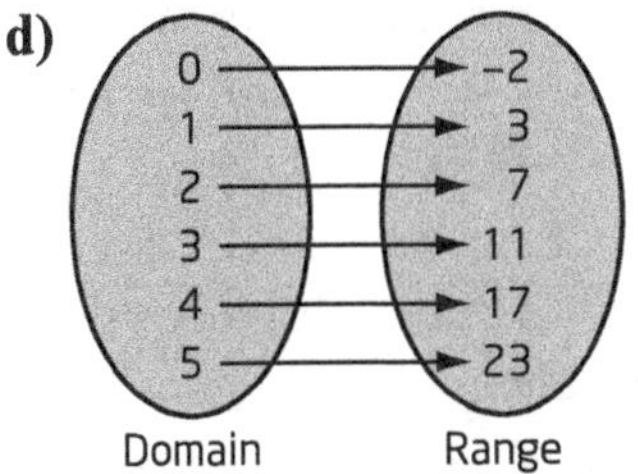

2. Copy each function. Then sketch the inverse of the function, and state the domain and range of the function and of its inverse.

   a) **b)**

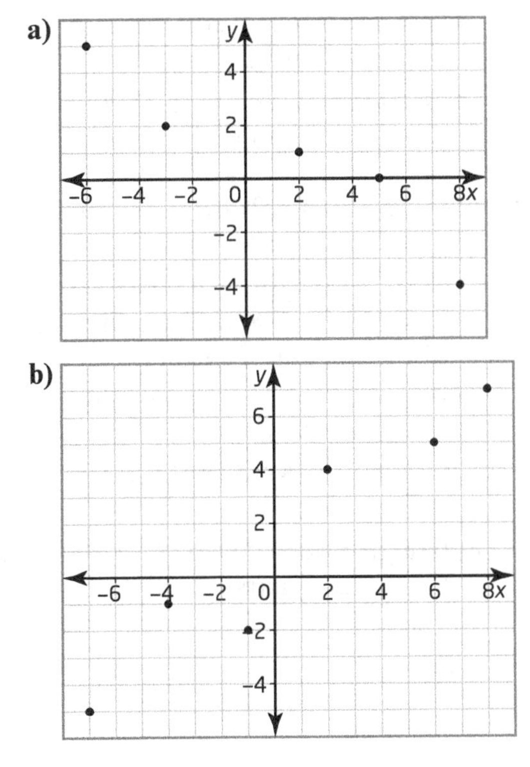

3. Copy each graph of $f(x)$ and then sketch the graph of the inverse of $f(x)$ by reflecting in the line $y = x$. State whether or not the inverse is a function.

   a) **b)** **c)**

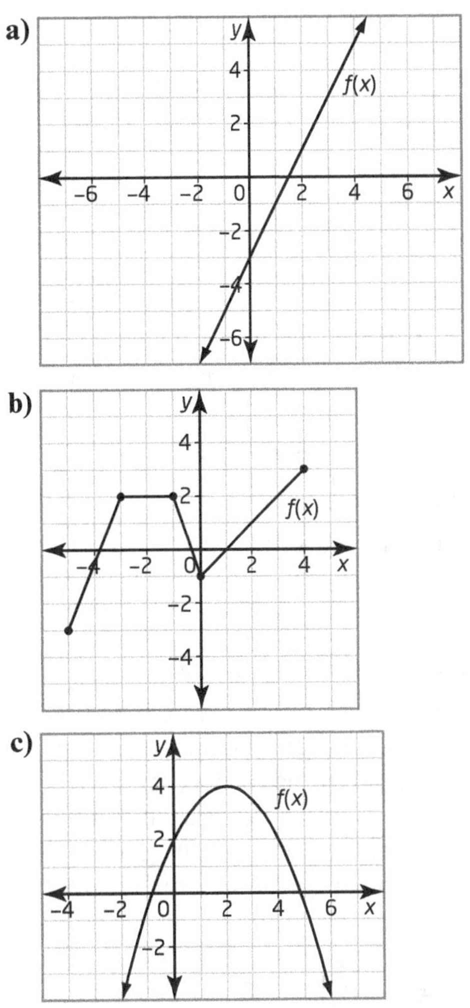

4. Determine an equation for the inverse of each function.

   a) $f(x) = 5x$

   b) $f(x) = 4x - 3$

   c) $f(x) = -x + 7$

   d) $f(x) = \dfrac{-2x + 1}{3}$

5. Determine an equation for the inverse of each function.

   a) $f(x) = x^2 + 5$

   b) $f(x) = 7x^2$

   c) $f(x) = (x + 3)^2$

   d) $f(x) = \frac{1}{3}x^2 - 4$

6. For each quadratic function, complete the square and then determine the equation of the inverse.

   a) $f(x) = x^2 - 4x + 3$

   b) $f(x) = -x^2 + 14x - 39$

   c) $f(x) = 2x^2 + 16x + 30$

   d) $f(x) = -3x^2 - 24x - 100$

7. For each function $f(x)$,

   i) determine $f^{-1}(x)$

   ii) graph $f(x)$ and its inverse, with or without technology

   iii) determine if the inverse of $f(x)$ is a function

   a) $f(x) = -4x + 5$

   b) $f(x) = \frac{1}{2}x - 6$

   c) $f(x) = (x - 3)^2 + 8$

   d) $f(x) = -x^2 + 16x - 61$

B Connect and Apply

8. The relationship between the surface area of a sphere and its radius can be modelled by the function $S(r) = 4\pi r^2$, where S represents the surface area and r represents the radius. The graphs of this function and its inverse are shown.

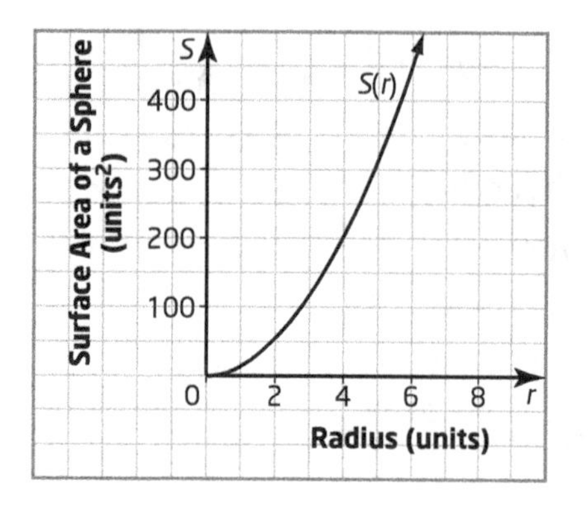

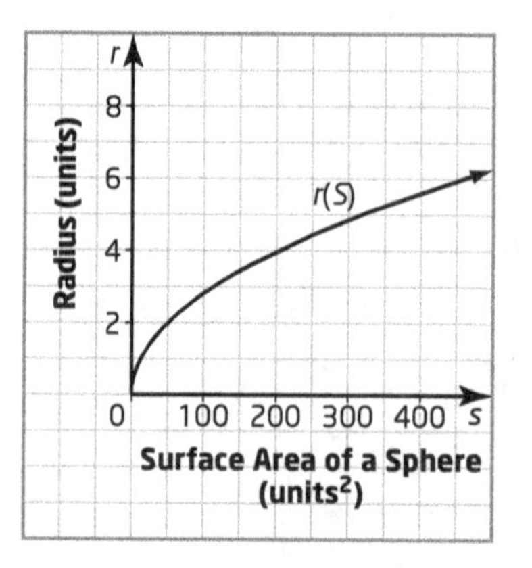

   a) State the domain and range of the function $S(r)$.

   b) Determine an equation for the inverse of the function. State its domain and range.

☆9. Aubrey works at an appliance warehouse. She earns \$450 a week, plus a commission of 8% of her sales.

   a) Write a function that represents Aubrey's total weekly earnings as a function of her sales.

   b) Find the inverse of the function from part a).

   c) What does the inverse represent for this situation?

   d) One week Aubrey earned \$1025. Calculate her sales for that week.

10. At one point in 2008 the Canadian dollar was worth US\$0.89.

   a) Write a function that expresses the value of the U.S. dollar, u, in terms of the Canadian dollar, c.

   b) Find the inverse of the equation in part a). Round to the nearest hundredth. What does the inverse represent?

   c) Use the inverse to convert US\$250 to Canadian dollars.

★**11.** If an object is dropped from a height of 100 m, its approximate height, $h(t)$ metres, above the ground t seconds after being dropped is modelled by the function $h(t) = 100 - 4.9t^2$.

a) Graph the function. State the domain and range for this situation.

b) Determine the inverse of $h(t)$. State its domain and range.

c) Explain what this inverse represents in terms of the context of the question.

d) How long does it take for the object to hit the ground?

12. Determine whether $f(x)$ and $g(x)$ shown in each graph are inverses of each other. Explain your reasoning.

a)

b)

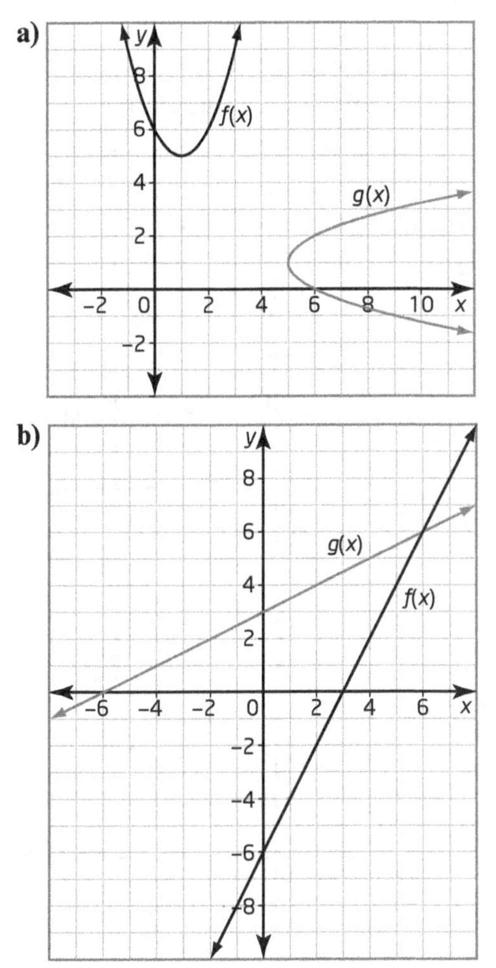

c)

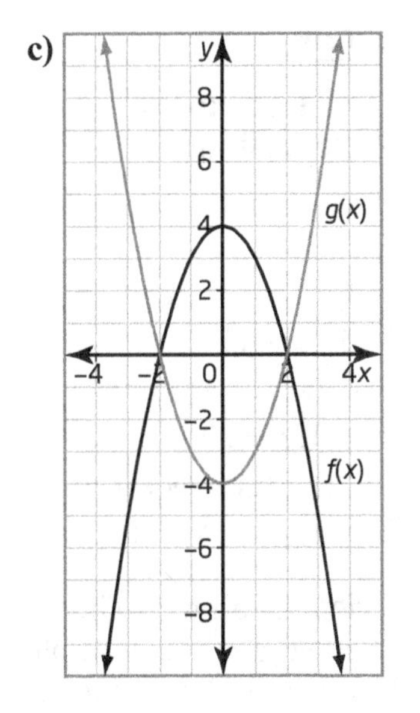

C Extend

13. a) Determine the inverse of the function $f(x) = \sqrt{2x - 5}$.

b) State the domain and range of the function and its inverse.

c) Sketch a graph of the function and its inverse.

14. a) Determine the inverse of the function $f(x) = \frac{2}{3x - 1}$.

b) State the domain and range of the function and its inverse.

15. The relationship between the measure of an interior angle, a, in degrees, of a polygon and its number of sides, n, can be modelled by the function $a(n) = 180 - \frac{360}{n}$.

a) Determine the inverse of the function.

b) State the domain and range of the function and its inverse.

c) Sketch a graph of the function and its inverse.

Chapter 2 Review

2.1 Functions and Equivalent Algebraic Expressions

1. Determine if the functions in each pair are equivalent.

   a) $f(x) = -4(x^2 + x - 2) + (2x - 3)^2$,
   $g(x) = x^2 - 16x + 17$

   b) $f(x) = 5(x^2 + 2x - 3) - (2x + 5)(-x + 1)$,
   $g(x) = 7x^2 + 13x - 20$

   c) $f(x) = (x + 5)^2 - 2(3 - x)(x + 1)$,
   $g(x) = -2(-x^2 + 4x - 8) + (x + 4)^2 - 6$

2. State the restrictions on $f(x)$. Then determine whether $g(x)$ is the simplified version of $f(x)$. If not, determine the proper simplified version.

   a) $f(x) = \dfrac{8x^2 + 10x - 3}{4x^2 - x}$ $\quad g(x) = \dfrac{2x + 3}{x}$

   b) $f(x) = \dfrac{8x^2 - 12x - 8}{4x^2 - 8x}$ $\quad g(x) = 2x + 1$

3. Simplify each expression and state any restrictions on x.

   a) $\dfrac{x + 8}{x^2 + 10x + 16}$

   b) $\dfrac{8x^2 - 6x - 9}{4x^2 + 27x + 18}$

2.2 Skills You Need: Operations With Rational Expressions

4. Simplify and state any restrictions.

   a) $\dfrac{64a^2b}{21ab^2} \times \dfrac{63a^3b^3}{8a^2b}$

   b) $\dfrac{54a^3b^2}{81c^2} \div \dfrac{108a^2b}{45c}$

   c) $\dfrac{3x - 4}{x + 9} \times \dfrac{2x + 18}{3x - 4}$

   d) $\dfrac{x^2 - 5x - 24}{x^2 - 2x - 15} \times \dfrac{x - 5}{x + 4}$

   e) $\dfrac{x - 4}{x - 3} \div \dfrac{4 - x}{2x - 6}$

   f) $\dfrac{x^2 + 11x + 24}{x^2 + 2x - 3} \div \dfrac{x - 8}{x - 1}$

5. Simplify and state any restrictions.

   a) $\dfrac{2}{3x} + \dfrac{3}{5x}$

   b) $\dfrac{2 - a}{6ab} + \dfrac{7 + b}{12b^2}$

   c) $\dfrac{x + 10}{x - 1} + \dfrac{x - 3}{x + 2}$

   d) $\dfrac{8x - 3}{x^2 - 7x + 12} - \dfrac{2x + 1}{x - 4}$

   e) $\dfrac{4x + 1}{x + 3} + \dfrac{x - 6}{x^2 - 9}$

   f) $\dfrac{5x + 25}{x^2 + 7x + 10} - \dfrac{10x - 20}{x^2 - 4}$

2.3 Horizontal and Vertical Translations of Functions

6. Use the base function $f(x) = x$. Write the equation for each transformed function.

   a) $s(x) = f(x + 2) - 8$

   b) $t(x) = f(x - 5) + 1$

7. Repeat question 6 for each base function.

   i) $f(x) = x^2$ **ii)** $f(x) = \sqrt{x}$ **iii)** $f(x) = \dfrac{1}{x}$

8. Each graph represents a transformation of one of the base functions $f(x) = x$, $f(x) = x^2$, $f(x) = \sqrt{x}$, or $f(x) = \dfrac{1}{x}$. State the base function and the equation of the transformed function.

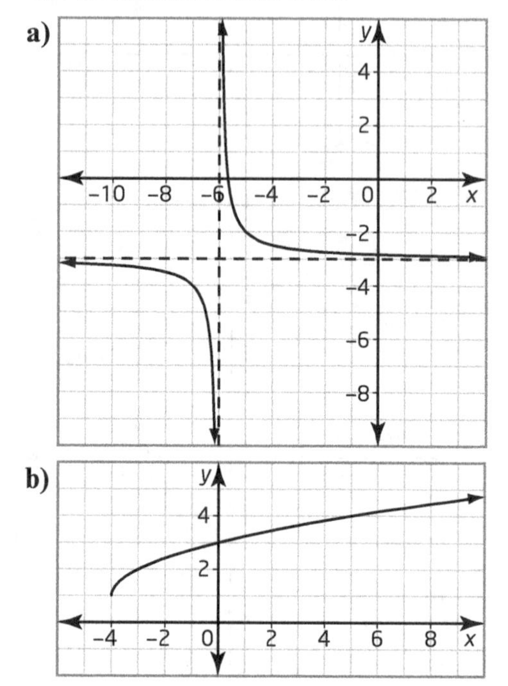

2.4 Reflections of Functions

9. Determine if $g(x)$ is a reflection of $f(x)$. Justify your answer.

a) $f(x) = \sqrt{x - 13} + 6$ $\quad g(x) = -\sqrt{13 - x} - 6$

b) $f(x) = x^2 - 2$ $\quad g(x) = x^2 - 2$

c) $f(x) = \sqrt{x + 7}$ $\quad g(x) = \sqrt{x - 7}$

d) $f(x) = \frac{1}{x + 15} - 8$ $\quad g(x) = \frac{-1}{x + 15} + 8$

10. For each function $f(x)$, determine the equation for $g(x)$.

a) $f(x) = \sqrt{x - 1} + 8$ $\quad g(x) = -f(x)$

b) $f(x) = (x - 3)^2 + 10$ $\quad g(x) = -f(-x)$

c) $f(x) = \frac{1}{x + 7} - 2$ $\quad g(x) = -f(-x)$

2.5 Stretches of Functions

11. For each function $g(x)$, identify the value of a or k and describe how the graph of $g(x)$ can be obtained from the graph of $f(x)$.

a) $g(x) = 9f(x)$

b) $g(x) = f(3x)$

c) $g(x) = \frac{2}{5}f(x)$

d) $g(x) = f\left(\frac{1}{7}x\right)$

12. For each function $g(x)$, describe the transformation from a base function of $f(x) = x$, $f(x) = x^2$, $f(x) = \sqrt{x}$, or $f(x) = \frac{1}{x}$. Then transform the graph of $f(x)$ to sketch a graph of $g(x)$.

a) $g(x) = 13x$

b) $g(x) = (5x)^2$

c) $g(x) = \sqrt{\frac{x}{3}}$

d) $g(x) = \frac{6}{x}$

2.6 Combinations of Transformations

13. Compare the transformed equation to $y = af[k(x - d)] + c$ to determine the values of the parameters a, k, d, and c. Then describe, in the appropriate order, the transformations that must be applied to a base function $f(x)$ to obtain the transformed function.

a) $g(x) = 7f(x - 1)$

b) $g(x) = \frac{1}{5}f(x) - 3$

c) $g(x) = f(x + 9) + 8$

d) $g(x) = f\left(\frac{1}{2}x\right) + 10$

14. Given each base function $f(x)$, write the equation of the transformed function $g(x)$. Then transform the graph of $f(x)$ to sketch a graph of $g(x)$.

a) $f(x) = \sqrt{x}$ $\quad g(x) = 3f(2x)$

b) $f(x) = \frac{1}{x}$ $\quad g(x) = f(x - 4) + 9$

c) $f(x) = x^2$ $\quad g(x) = f\left[\frac{1}{4}(x + 5)\right]$

d) $f(x) = x$ $\quad g(x) = -2f(x - 7)$

2.7 Inverse of a Function

15. Copy each graph of $f(x)$. Then sketch the inverse of each function, and state the domain and range of the function and of its inverse.

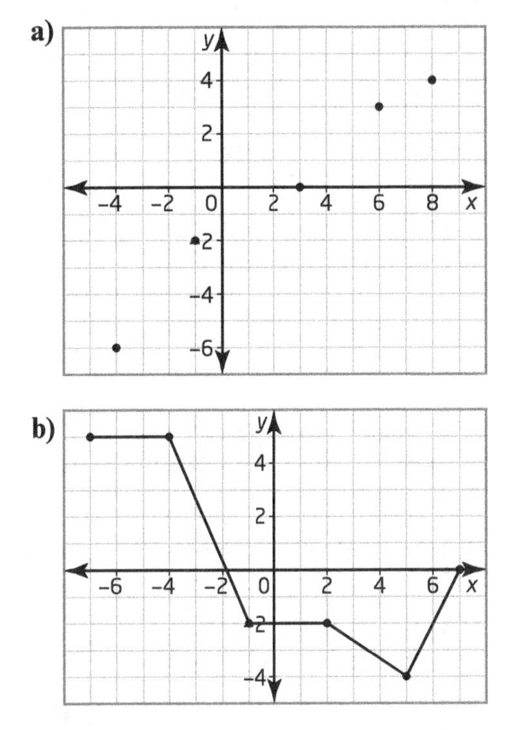

16. Determine an equation for the inverse of each function.

a) $f(x) = -2x + 7$

b) $f(x) = \frac{5x - 3}{4}$

c) $f(x) = (x - 3)^2 + 1$

d) $f(x) = -\frac{1}{4}x^2 + 9$

Chapter 2 Math Contest

1. The roots of $8x^2 - 6x = 9$ are x_1 and x_2. What is the value of $(x_1 + 1)(x_2 + 2)$?

A $\frac{3}{2}$ **B** $\frac{5}{8}$ **C** $\frac{7}{8}$ **D** $-\frac{3}{4}$

2. What is the greatest possible integer value for k such that the equation $(1 - 5k)x^2 + 6x - 2 = 0$ has two distinct real roots?

A −2 **B** 0 **C** 1 **D** − 1

3. Given $f(x) = 2^{5x-3}$, what is the product of $f(x)$ and $f(2 - x)$?

A 1024 **B** 16 **C** 256 **D** 8

4. Determine the value of x such that $3^x - 3^{x-2} = \frac{24}{729}$.

A $x = 8$

B $x = 3$

C $x = -4$

D $x = -3$

5. Determine the integer values of x and y so that $3^{x+1} + 3^x = 4^{y+2} - 7(4^y)$.

A $x = 0, y = 0$

B $x = 1, y = 2$

C $x = 2, y = 1$

D $x = -1, y = -2$

6. Consider the function $y = ax^r$. What is the value of r so that $y = 6$ when $x = 4$, and $y = 24$ when $x = 64$?

A $\frac{1}{2}$ **B** $\frac{1}{4}$ **C** 4 **D** 2

7. If $\cos A = \frac{4}{5}$ such that $\pi < A < 2\pi$, what is the value of tan A?

A $\frac{4}{3}$ **B** $-\frac{4}{3}$ **C** $\frac{3}{4}$ **D** $-\frac{3}{4}$

8. Consider △ABC, with vertices A(2, 2), B(0, 0), and C(4, −2). What is the measure of ∠C to the nearest degree?

A 37° **B** 48° **C** 53° **D** 65°

9. In the diagram, O is the centre of the circle, ∠OAB = 25°, and ∠OCB = 48°. Determine the measure of ∠ABC.

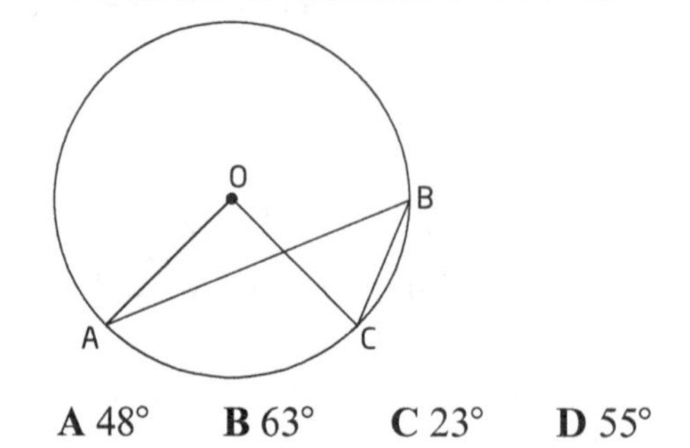

A 48° **B** 63° **C** 23° **D** 55°

10. Determine the sum of four natural numbers a, b, c, and d if $a^3 + b^3 = 1729$ and $c^3 + d^3 = 1729$.

A 24 **B** 32 **C** 28 **D** 36

11. What is the ones digit for the value 8^{1001}?

12. If $x = a + b$ and $y = a - b$,

express $\left(\frac{3x - 21y}{6x + 12y}\right)^2 \div \frac{x^2 - 49y^2}{2x^2 + 8xy + 8y^2}$

in terms of a and b, in simplified form.

13. Determine the least number that can be expressed as the sum of two perfect squares in two different ways. Justify your answer.

14. Determine the value of $(1 + 3 + 5 + \cdots + 49) - (2 + 4 + 6 + \cdots + 50)$.

15. How many rectangles are in this diagram?

Chapter 3 Exponential Functions

3.1 The Nature of Exponential Growth

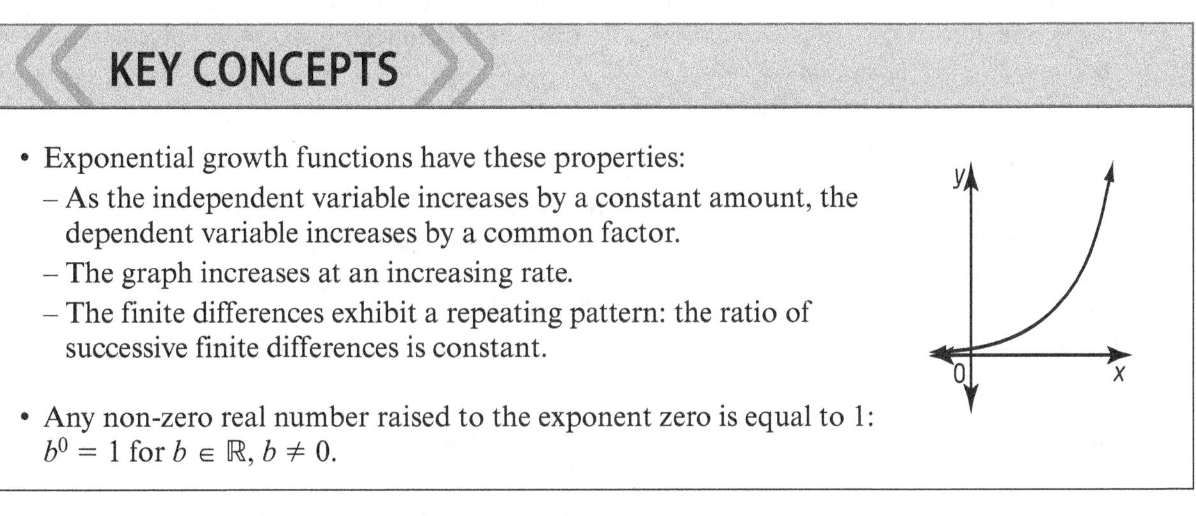

KEY CONCEPTS

- Exponential growth functions have these properties:
  - As the independent variable increases by a constant amount, the dependent variable increases by a common factor.
  - The graph increases at an increasing rate.
  - The finite differences exhibit a repeating pattern: the ratio of successive finite differences is constant.
- Any non-zero real number raised to the exponent zero is equal to 1: $b^0 = 1$ for $b \in \mathbb{R}, b \neq 0$.

Example

A flu virus is spreading among the students at Mathematica High School. Initially, on day 0, three students become ill. Each of these students passes the virus to two other students who become ill on day 1. Each of these six students passes the virus to two more students who fall ill on day 2, and so on. Assume that no one can become sick from the virus more than once.

a) How many students become ill
  i) on day 3?
  ii) on day 5?

b) Write the equation that represents this situation.

c) If the student population at Mathematica High School is 1852, how long will it take for the virus to spread throughout the entire school?

Solution

a) Three students become ill on day 0. Because each of these three students passes the virus to two other students, six students become ill on day 1. Each of these six then passes the virus to two more students, so that 12 students become ill on day 2, and so on.
Organize the information in a table. From the table, it can be seen that
  i) 24 students fall ill on day 3
  ii) 96 students fall ill on day 5

Day	Number of Students Falling Ill
0	3
1	6
2	12
3	24
4	48
5	96

b) The equation relating the number of students, s, who become ill on any day, n, is $s(n) = 3 \times 2^n$.

c) Because the number of students falling ill doubles each day, the virus will have spread throughout the entire school population on the day that the number of students becoming sick is one half of the total population. Use this number in the equation to solve for n.

$1852 = 3 \times 2^n$ Divide each side by 3.

$617.67 = 2^n$ Use trial and error to solve for n.

For $n = 9$, $2^9 = 512$.

For $n = 10$, $2^{10} = 1024$.

Since 617.67 is between 512 and 1024, n is between 9 and 10.

Try $n = 9.5$. $2^{9.5} \doteq 724$, which is higher than 617.67. So n is less than 9.5.

Try $n = 9.3$, $2^{9.3} \doteq 630$, which is a bit high.

Try $n = 9.27$, $2^{9.27} \doteq 617.37$, which is very close to 617.33.

Therefore, it will take approximately 9.27 days for the virus to spread throughout the entire school.

A Practise

1. An ant colony has an initial population of 25. The number of ants triples every day.

a) Copy and complete the table.

Day	Population	First Differences	Second Differences
0	25		
1	75		
2			
3			
4			
5			

b) Is the relationship between the ant population and the number of days an exponential relation? Explain how you can tell.

c) Examine the finite differences. Describe how the first differences and second differences are related.

d) Will the pattern of first and second differences observed in part c) continue with the third and fourth differences? Write down your conjecture.

e) Calculate the third and fourth differences. Was your conjecture in part d) correct? Explain.

2. Consider these three functions:

$y = 5x$ $\quad y = x^5$ $\quad y = 5^x$

a) How do the equations differ? How do the graphs of these functions differ?

b) Describe the domain and range of each function.

3. What is the value of 11^0? Use patterns and numerical reasoning to justify your answer.

4. a) Rewrite the expression $\frac{a^5}{a^5}$ by expanding both powers.

b) Divide out common factors in the numerator and denominator. What is the simplified value of this expression?

c) Write the expression $\frac{a^5}{a^5}$ as a single power by applying the quotient law.

d) Write a statement that explains how the results of parts b) and c) are related.

5. An insect colony has an initial population of 15. The number of insects quadruples every day.

   a) Which function models this exponential growth?

      A $p(n) = 15 \times 4n$
      B $p(n) = 15 \times 4^n$
      C $p(n) = 60 \times 4^n$

   b) For the correct model, explain what each part of the equation means.

6. Evaluate.

   a) 12^0
   b) $(-7)^0$
   c) $\left(\frac{5}{9}\right)^0$
   d) m^0
   e) $(2x)^0$
   f) -7^0

B Connect and Apply

☆7. Identify each function as linear, quadratic, exponential, or none of these. Justify your choice.

   a) $f(x) = 8^x$
   b) $f(x) = 11 - 9x$
   c) $f(x) = \sqrt{x}$
   d) $f(x) = x^2 - 3x + 1$

8. Identify the type of function that each table of values represents. Justify your answer.

a)

x	y
−4	16
−3	8
−2	4
−1	2
0	1
1	0.5
2	0.25

b)

x	y
−4	13
−3	10
−2	7
−1	4
0	1
1	−2
2	−5

c)

x	y
−4	−18
−3	−11
−2	−6
−1	−3
0	−2
1	−3
2	−6

d)

x	y
−4	625
−3	125
−2	25
−1	5
0	1
1	0.2
2	0.04

e)

x	y
−4	2.2
−3	0.8
−2	−0.2
−1	−0.8
0	−1
1	−0.8
2	−0.2

9. a) Use linking cubes, colour tiles, or the tools of your choice to design a growing pattern that can be described by $t(n) = 4^n$, where n is the term number and t is the total number of items in that term.

b) Draw diagrams to illustrate the first 4 terms in your pattern, where $t(0)$ is the first term.

c) How many items would you need to build

i) the 6th term?

ii) the 12th term?

d) Suppose that you have 1000 items in total to use when constructing a model of this pattern. What is the greatest number of terms you can build at the same time?

e) Suppose that you have 5000 items in total. What is the greatest number of terms you can build at the same time?

f) How does your answer to part e) differ from your answer to part d)? Explain this result.

☆**10.** A bacterial colony has an initial population of 32. The population doubles every half-hour.

a) Write an equation that relates the population, p, to time, t, measured in 30-min intervals.

b) Sketch a graph of this relationship for 2 h.

c) Use the graph to determine the approximate population after 1 h. Verify your answer using the equation. Which tool do you prefer to use? Explain why.

d) Determine the approximate population after 3.5 h. Which tool do you prefer to use for this, the equation or the graph? Explain why.

11. Adam deposits $200 into a savings account that pays interest at 4.5% per year, compounded annually. After each compounding period, interest earned is added to the principal (the initial deposit amount) and that sum is used to calculate interest in the following period. The amount, A, in dollars, in the account can be determined using the formula $A = P(1 + i)^n$, where P is the principal, i is the annual interest rate (expressed as a decimal), and n is the number of compounding periods.

a) Write an equation that represents the amount in the account after n years.

b) Copy and complete the following table. Round values to two decimal places.

Number of Compounding Periods (years)	Amount ($)
0	200
1	209
2	
3	
4	
5	
6	

$A(1) = 200(1 + 0.045)^1$
$= 200(1.045)^1$
$= 209$

c) Calculate the first and second differences. Is the function linear, quadratic, or neither? Explain.

d) Use the finite differences to determine what type of function this represents.

e) How does the equation confirm your result in part d)?

f) If interest is paid only at the end of each compounding period, do the points between the values in the table have meaning? Explain why or why not.

12. Refer to the formula in question 11 for calculating compound interest. Cassie deposits an inheritance of $1500 into an account that earns interest of 3.5% per year, compounded annually. How much is in the account at the end of

 a) 3 years?

 b) 8 years?

13. A rural community has an emergency telephone notification plan. Phone calls are set up in equal time intervals. Initially, in interval 0, four residents know about an emergency. In the next interval, each of them calls five other residents. In the following interval, each of those residents calls five other residents, and so on for the following intervals. No resident is called more than once.

 a) How many residents will be called
 i) in the 3rd interval?
 ii) in the 5th interval?

 b) Write an equation to represent this situation.

 c) If 23 698 people live in the community, how long will it take for everyone to receive a call?

 d) Is this an example of exponential growth? Explain your reasoning.

14. Justin deposits $700 into an account that earns interest of 5.5% per year, compounded annually.

 a) How long will it take for Justin's investment to double in value? Explain how you solved this.

 b) How much longer would it take if the account paid simple interest, at the same rate? Simple interest does not get added to the principal after each compounding period. Use the formula $I = Prt$, where I is the interest, in dollars, P is the principal, in dollars, r is interest rate (as a decimal), and t is the time, in years.

C Extend

15. Suppose you win a lottery and are given a choice of either of two prizes. Which prize would you select? Justify your answer.
 Prize A: 1 cent in the first week, 2 cents in the second week, 4 cents in the third week, and so on, for 26 weeks
 Prize B: $10 000 per week for 26 weeks

16. Bacteria A has an initial population of 100 and doubles every day. Bacteria B has an initial population of 2 and quadruples daily.

 a) After how long will the population of Bacteria B exceed the population of Bacteria A? What will the populations be at this point?

 b) How much sooner would Bacteria B's population overtake Bacteria A's population if the doubling period for Bacteria A were twice as long?

17. The amount of a drug that remains in the human body often follows an exponential model. Suppose that a new drug follows the model $M = M_0(0.82)^{\frac{h}{4}}$, where M represents the mass of drug remaining in the body, M_0 represents the mass of the dose taken, in milligrams, and h is the time, in hours, since the dose was taken.

 a) A standard dose is 200 mg. Sketch a graph showing the mass remaining in the body up to 48 h.

 b) Use your graph to estimate the half-life of the drug in the body. This is the time it takes for the mass of the dosage to decrease to half of its starting value.

 c) Check your estimate in part b) using the equation.

 d) **Use Technology** Once the mass remaining drops to less than 1 mg, the standard test can no longer detect the drug. How long will it take before the drug is no longer detectable? Use a graphing calculator.

3.2 Exponential Decay: Connecting to Negative Exponents

KEY CONCEPTS

- Exponential decay functions have the following properties:
  - As the independent variable increases by a constant amount, the dependent variable decreases by a common factor.
  - The graph decreases at a decreasing rate.
  - They have a repeating exponential pattern of finite differences: the ratio of successive finite differences is constant.

- A power involving a negative exponent can be expressed using a positive exponent:
  $b^{-n} = \frac{1}{b^n}$ for $b \in \mathbb{R}$, $b \neq 0$, and $n \in \mathbb{N}$.

- The exponent rules hold for powers involving negative exponents.

- Rational expressions raised to a negative exponent can be simplified:
  $\left(\frac{a}{b}\right)^{-n} = \left(\frac{b}{a}\right)^n$ for $a, b \in \mathbb{R}$, $a, b \neq 0$, and $n \in \mathbb{N}$.

Example

What amount of money will grow to \$2000 in 5 years if it is invested in an account that pays interest at the rate 5.5% per annum, compounded annually? The amount, A, in dollars, in an account earning interest, compounded annually, with a single deposit can be calculated using the formula $A = P(1 + i)^n$, where P is the principal, i is the annual interest rate (expressed as a decimal), and n is the number of years the principal has been earning interest.

Solution

Substitute $n = 5$, $A = 2000$, and $i = 0.055$ in the formula $A = P(1 + i)^n$. Solve for P.

$$A = P(1 + i)^n$$
$$2000 = P(1 + 0.055)^5$$
$$2000 = P(1.055)^5$$
Divide each side by $(1.055)^5$.
$$\frac{2000}{(1.055)^5} = P$$
$$P \doteq 1530.27$$

Therefore, \$1530.27 is the required amount.

A Practise

1. Write each as a power with a positive exponent.

   a) 7^{-1} b) 10^{-2}

   c) a^{-4} d) $(mn)^{-1}$

   e) -4^{-1} f) $(2b)^{-1}$

2. Write each as a power with a negative exponent.

   a) $\frac{1}{a^3}$ b) $\frac{2}{x^5}$

   c) $-\frac{1}{x^9}$ d) $\frac{2}{5b^6}$

3. Evaluate. Express as a fraction in simplest terms.

   a) 5^{-2}

   b) 3^{-4}

   c) 10^{-3}

   d) $(-4)^{-2}$

   e) -4^{-2}

   f) $(-4)^{-3}$

   g) $3^{-3} + 9^{-2}$

   h) $4^{-2} - 2^{-3} - 6^{-1}$

4. Apply the exponent rules to evaluate. Do not use decimals.

   a) $(5^{-2})^{-1}$

   b) $(2^{-3})^3$

   c) $\frac{9}{9^{-2}}$

   d) $6^{-4} \div 6^{-2}$

   e) $3^2 \times 3^{-4} \times 63 \times 6^0$

   f) $\frac{4^2\,(4^6)}{4^5}$

5. Simplify. Express your answers using only positive exponents.

   a) $a^{-4} \times a^8$

   b) $(4v^{-5})(-3v^{-2})$

   c) $a^6 \div a^{-4}$

   d) $\frac{12m^{-5}}{4m^{-3}}$

6. Evaluate. Do not use decimals.

   a) $\left(\frac{1}{6}\right)^{-1}$

   b) $\left(\frac{4}{7}\right)^{-2}$

   c) $\left(\frac{3}{4}\right)^{-3}$

   d) $-\left(\frac{5}{3}\right)^{-4}$

7. Simplify.

   a) $\left(\frac{1}{xy}\right)^{-3}$

   b) $\left(\frac{1}{11b}\right)^{-2}$

   c) $\left(\frac{a^3}{b^2}\right)^{-4}$

   d) $\left(\frac{5m^2}{2n^4}\right)^{-3}$

B Connect and Apply

☆8. Polonium-210 is a radioactive isotope that has a half-life of 20 days. Suppose you start with a 40-mg sample.

   a) Create a table of values that gives the amount of polonium-210 remaining at the end of five intervals of 20 days each.

   b) Write an equation, in the form $f(x) = ab^x$, that relates the amount of polonium-210 remaining and time. Identify what each variable in the equation represents and give the appropriate unit for each variable.

   c) Sketch a graph of the relation. Describe the shape of the curve.

   d) How much polonium-210 will remain after 10 weeks?

   e) How long will it take for the amount of polonium-210 to decay to 8% of its initial mass? Describe the tools and strategies you used to solve this.

   f) Write two different functions to model the same situation. Explain why the two functions are equivalent.

9. Daniel is very excited about his new motorcycle! Although the motorcycle costs \$13 500, its resale value will depreciate (decline) by 20% of its current value every year. The equation relating the motorcycle's depreciated value, v, in dollars, to the time, t, in years, since the purchase is $v(t) = 13\,500(0.8^t)$.

   a) Explain the significance of each part of this equation.

   b) How much will Daniel's motorcycle be worth in
   i) 1 year?
   ii) 6 years?

   c) Explain why this is an example of exponential decay.

   d) How long will it take for Daniel's motorcycle to depreciate to 50% of its original cost?

10. The amount, A, in dollars, of an investment can be determined using the formula $A = P(1 + i)^n$, where P is the principal, i is the annual interest rate (expressed as a decimal), and n is the number of compounding periods. What amount of money will grow to \$3500 in 4 years if it is invested in an account that pays interest of 6.5% per annum compounded annually?

★11. The formula $P = A(1 + i)^{-n}$ allows you to calculate the principal (the initial amount invested), P, in an account that has been accumulating annually compounded interest, where A is the current amount in the account, i is the annual interest rate (expressed as a decimal), and n is the number of years that the principal has been earning interest.
Five years ago, Denise deposited an amount into an account that pays 7.5% per year, compounded annually. Today the account balance is \$4200.

   a) What was the amount of Denise's initial deposit?

   b) How much was in the account 2 years ago?

   c) How much will be in the account 2 years from now? What is the total interest earned up to this point?

C Extend

12. In 1947, an investor bought Van Gogh's painting *Irises* for \$84 000. Forty years later, the same investor sold the artwork for \$49 million. If the initial investment had been deposited in a savings account paying interest compounded annually, what would be the annual interest rate for the amount to grow to \$49 million? Round your answer to one decimal place.

13. A cup of coffee contains approximately 100 mg of caffeine. When you drink the coffee, the caffeine is absorbed into the bloodstream and eventually metabolized. The half-life of caffeine in the bloodstream is approximately 5 h.

   a) Write an equation that expresses the amount of caffeine, c, in milligrams, in the bloodstream t hours after drinking a cup of coffee.

   b) How many hours does it take for the amount of caffeine in the bloodstream to be reduced to
   i) 10 mg?
   ii) 1 mg?

14. A pot of water on a stove is brought to a boil and then removed from the heating element. Every 5 min thereafter, the difference between the temperature of the water and the room temperature (20 °C) is reduced by 50%.

   a) Write an equation to express the water temperature, T, in degrees Celsius, as a function of time, t, in minutes, since the pot of water was removed from the heating element.

   b) How many minutes does it take for the temperature of the water to fall to 30 °C?

3.3 Rational Exponents

KEY CONCEPTS

- A power involving a rational exponent with numerator 1 and denominator n can be interpreted as the nth root of the base:
  For $b \in \mathbb{R}$ and $n \in \mathbb{N}$, $b^{\frac{1}{n}} = \sqrt[n]{b}$. If n is even, b must be greater than or equal to 0.

- You can evaluate a power involving a rational exponent with numerator m and denominator n by taking the nth root of the base raised to the exponent m:
  For $b \in \mathbb{R}$, $b^{\frac{m}{n}} = \left(\sqrt[n]{b}\right)^m$ for $m \in \mathbb{Z}$, $n \in \mathbb{N}$. If n is even, b must be greater than or equal to 0.

- The exponent rules hold for powers involving rational exponents.

Example

Express each radical as a power with a rational exponent.

a) $\left(\sqrt[4]{16}\right)^3$

b) $\left(\sqrt[6]{729}\right)^3$

c) $\left(\sqrt[3]{-343}\right)^2$

Solution

First write each radical using a rational exponent. Then apply the power of a power law of exponents.

a) $\left(\sqrt[4]{16}\right)^3 = \left(16^{\frac{1}{4}}\right)^3$
$= 16^{\frac{3}{4}}$

b) $\left(\sqrt[6]{729}\right)^3 = \left(729^{\frac{1}{6}}\right)^3$
$= 729^{\frac{3}{6}}$
$= 729^{\frac{1}{2}}$

c) $\left(\sqrt[3]{-343}\right)^2 = \left((-343)^{\frac{1}{3}}\right)^2$
$= (-343)^{\frac{2}{3}}$

A Practise

1. Evaluate each cube root.

a) $\sqrt[3]{216}$

b) $(-1331)^{\frac{1}{3}}$

c) $\sqrt[3]{\frac{125}{343}}$

d) $\left(\frac{64}{729}\right)^{\frac{1}{3}}$

2. Evaluate each root.

a) $625^{\frac{1}{4}}$

b) $\sqrt[4]{\frac{1296}{81}}$

c) $729^{\frac{1}{6}}$

d) $\sqrt[5]{-1024}$

☆**3.** Express each power as a radical, and then evaluate.

a) $32^{\frac{3}{5}}$

b) $(-64)^{\frac{2}{3}}$

c) $64^{\frac{5}{6}}$

d) $6561^{\frac{5}{8}}$

☆**4.** Evaluate.

a) $1728^{-\frac{1}{3}}$

b) $36^{-\frac{3}{2}}$

c) $\left(-\frac{8}{125}\right)^{-\frac{5}{3}}$

d) $\left(\frac{1024}{243}\right)^{-\frac{3}{5}}$

☆**5.** Write as a single power, and then evaluate.

a) $8^{\frac{1}{3}} \times 8^{\frac{2}{3}}$

b) $16^{\frac{1}{4}} \div 16^{\frac{1}{2}} \times 16^{\frac{3}{4}}$

c) $64^{\frac{1}{3}} \times 64^{\frac{1}{6}} \div 64^{\frac{2}{3}}$

d) $3^{\frac{2}{3}} \times 27^{\frac{4}{9}}$

6. Simplify. Express your answers using only positive exponents.

a) $x^{\frac{1}{3}} \times x^{\frac{1}{3}}$

b) $\left(a^{\frac{1}{2}}\right)\left(a^{\frac{2}{3}}\right)$

c) $\dfrac{a^3 b^{\frac{1}{2}}}{a^{\frac{1}{3}} b^2}$

d) $\left(z^{\frac{2}{3}}\right)^{\frac{4}{5}}$

7. Simplify. Express your answers using only positive exponents.

a) $b^{\frac{4}{5}} \div b^{\frac{2}{3}}$

b) $\dfrac{a^{-\frac{3}{4}}}{a^{\frac{1}{3}}}$

c) $\left(w^{-\frac{6}{11}}\right)^{-\frac{2}{3}}$

d) $(16a)^{\frac{3}{4}}(265a)^{-\frac{1}{4}}$

8. The volume of a sphere can be expressed in terms of its surface area using the formula $V(S) = 3^{-1}(4\pi)^{-\frac{1}{2}} S^{\frac{3}{2}}$, where $V(S)$ is the volume of a sphere with surface area S. Determine the volume of an exercise ball whose surface area is 676 cm^2. Round your answer to one decimal place.

B Connect and Apply

9. a) Write a formula that expresses the circumference, C, of a circle in terms of its area, A.

b) Express your formula in part a) in an equivalent way.

c) Use your formula from part a) to determine the circumference of each circle with the given area. Round answers to one decimal place.

i) 314 cm^2

ii) 928 cm^2

iii) 1475 cm^2

d) Verify your answers in part c) using the equivalent formula from part b).

10. Yeast cells are microscopic plants that ferment sugars and starches. Yeast is used to make bread because the gases produced by the fermentation process make dough rise. The cells duplicate themselves about every half-hour, so the doubling period is 0.5 h. If the initial number of yeast cells is N_0, then the formula for the number of cells, N, after t hours is given by $N = N_0\left(2^{\frac{t}{0.5}}\right)$.

a) Determine the number of yeast cells after 1.5 hours if the initial number of cells is 50.

b) If the initial number of cells is 25, how long will it take for there to be 1000 cells?

c) Compare the formula $N = N_0(2^{2t})$ with the formula above. Are they equivalent? Explain.

d) Use the formula in part c) to verify your answer to part b).

11. Refer to question 10. Some cells double at rates different from that for yeast. In general, if an initial number of cells, N_0, has a doubling period d, then the number of cells, N, after time, t, is given by the formula $N = N_0\left(2^{\frac{t}{d}}\right)$. Note that t and d must be expressed in the same unit of time. Suppose that a bacterial strain doubles in number every 3 min and that there are 1000 bacteria initially.

   a) Write the formula that corresponds with this situation.

   b) How many bacteria will there be after 0.25 h?

   c) When will there be 60 000 bacteria?

12. The formulas $h = 241m^{-\frac{1}{4}}$ and $r = \frac{107}{2}m^{-\frac{1}{4}}$ give the heartbeat frequency, h, in beats per minute, and respiratory frequency, r, in breaths per minute, for a resting animal with mass m, in kilograms.

   a) Determine the heartbeat frequency for each animal.
   i) elephant: 11 450 kg
   ii) cow: 980 kg
   iii) cat: 5.3 kg

   b) Determine the respiratory frequency for each animal in part a).

   c) Use the formula $B = \frac{1}{100}m^{\frac{2}{3}}$ to determine the brain mass, B, for each animal in part a).

   d) Describe the relationships between the size of the animal and
   i) the heartbeat frequency
   ii) the respiratory frequency
   iii) the brain mass

   e) Determine the heartbeat frequency, respiratory frequency, and brain mass for your pet or an animal of your choice.

C Extend

13. Determine the inverse for each function. Then evaluate the inverse at the given x-value.

   a) $f(x) = x^{\frac{3}{2}}$, $x = 64$
   b) $f(x) = x^{\frac{4}{5}} - 2$, $x = 79$
   c) $f(x) = \sqrt[3]{x^4 - 4}$, $x = 1728$

14. Simplify. Express your answers using positive exponents.

   a) $x^{-\frac{1}{2}} \times x^{\frac{4}{5}} \div x^{-\frac{2}{3}}$
   b) $\dfrac{\sqrt[4]{x^3} \times \sqrt[3]{x^5}}{\sqrt[3]{x^6} \times \sqrt{x^7}}$
   c) $\dfrac{\sqrt[4]{81m^8}}{\sqrt[3]{343m^{12}}} \div \dfrac{\sqrt[5]{32m^{10}}}{\sqrt{36m^6}}$
   d) $\dfrac{\sqrt[3]{64b^{3-6x}}}{\sqrt[4]{1296b^{12x+24}}} \times \dfrac{\sqrt[5]{243b^{10-5x}}}{\sqrt{144b^{6x-4}}}$
   e) $\dfrac{\left(a^{-\frac{x}{4}}\right)^{-\frac{1}{2}}\left(b^{-\frac{x}{3}}\right)^2}{\left(a^{-\frac{x}{2}}\right)\left(b^{\frac{2x}{3}}\right)^{-1}}$

15. In favourable breeding conditions, the population of a swarm of desert locusts can multiply 10-fold in 20 days.

   a) Write an equation that represents the population, P, of a swarm of locusts with initial population P_0, at any time t, in days.

   b) Use your answer from part a) to compare the population of a swarm of locusts after 30 days with its population after 20 days. How many times greater is the population after 30 days?

16. **a)** Is $(a + b)^{\frac{1}{2}} = a^{\frac{1}{2}} + b^{\frac{1}{2}}$, where a and b are positive integers? Justify your answer.

   b) In general, is $(a + b)^{\frac{1}{n}} = a^{\frac{1}{n}} + b^{\frac{1}{n}}$, where a, b, and n are positive integers? Justify your answer.

3.4 Properties of Exponential Functions

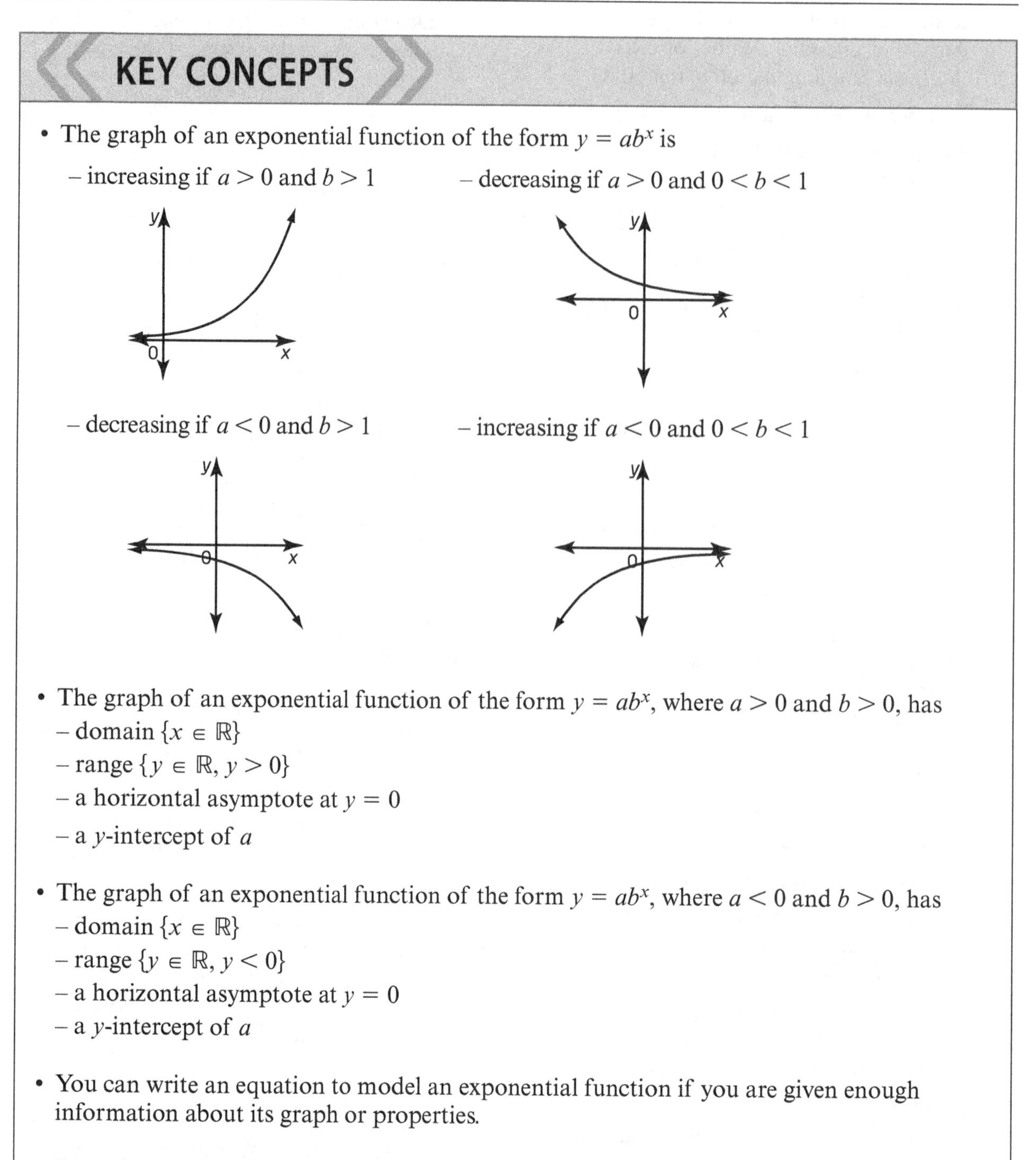

KEY CONCEPTS

- The graph of an exponential function of the form $y = ab^x$ is
  - increasing if $a > 0$ and $b > 1$
  - decreasing if $a > 0$ and $0 < b < 1$
  - decreasing if $a < 0$ and $b > 1$
  - increasing if $a < 0$ and $0 < b < 1$

- The graph of an exponential function of the form $y = ab^x$, where $a > 0$ and $b > 0$, has
  - domain $\{x \in \mathbb{R}\}$
  - range $\{y \in \mathbb{R}, y > 0\}$
  - a horizontal asymptote at $y = 0$
  - a y-intercept of a

- The graph of an exponential function of the form $y = ab^x$, where $a < 0$ and $b > 0$, has
  - domain $\{x \in \mathbb{R}\}$
  - range $\{y \in \mathbb{R}, y < 0\}$
  - a horizontal asymptote at $y = 0$
  - a y-intercept of a

- You can write an equation to model an exponential function if you are given enough information about its graph or properties.

- Sometimes it makes sense to restrict the domain of an exponential model based on the situation it represents.

Example

A radioactive substance decays exponentially. The percent, P, of the substance that remains after t years is represented by the function $P(t) = 100\left(\frac{6}{5}\right)^{-t}$.

a) Express the function using a positive exponent.

b) Which part of the equation from part a) indicates that the function represents exponential decay? Explain.

c) Graph the function. How does the graph support your answer to part b)?

d) State the domain and range of the function.

e) What does the horizontal asymptote indicate for this situation?

f) Determine the percent of the substance that remains after 12 years by using

i) the graph

ii) the equation

Solution

a) To express the function using a positive exponent, take the reciprocal of the fraction $\frac{6}{5}$.

$P(t) = 100\left(\frac{5}{6}\right)^{t}$

b) The common ratio $\frac{5}{6}$ is a proper fraction (value is between 0 and 1) that when multiplied by 100 will make the value smaller.

c)

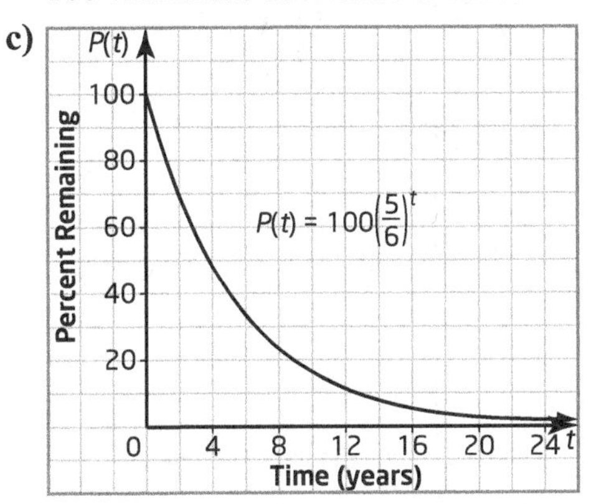

The graph falls from left to right, which means that as time passes the percent of radioactive substance remaining is decreasing.

d) domain $\{t \in \mathbb{R}, t \geq 0\}$; range $\{P \in \mathbb{R}, 0 \leq P < 100\}$

e) The horizontal asymptote indicates that as time passes the percent remaining of the substance decreases, becoming closer to 0 but never actually falling to 0. This means that there is always some amount of the radioactive substance that remains.

f) i) From the graph, it can be estimated that at 12 years approximately 11% of the initial amount of the substance remains.

ii) Substitute $t = 12$ in the equation and solve for P.

$$P(12) = 100\left(\frac{6}{5}\right)^{-12}$$
$$\doteq 11.2$$

Therefore, approximately 11.2% of the substance remains.

A Practise

1. Match each graph with its corresponding equation.

a)

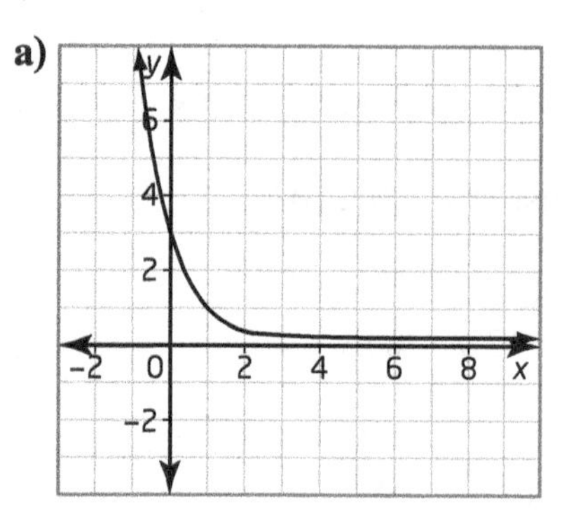

b)

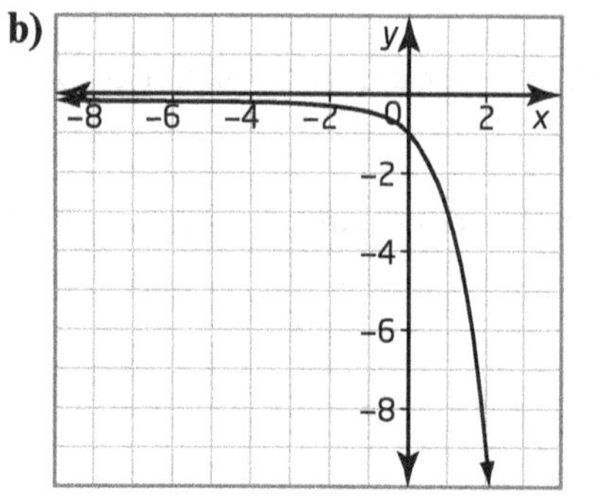

c)

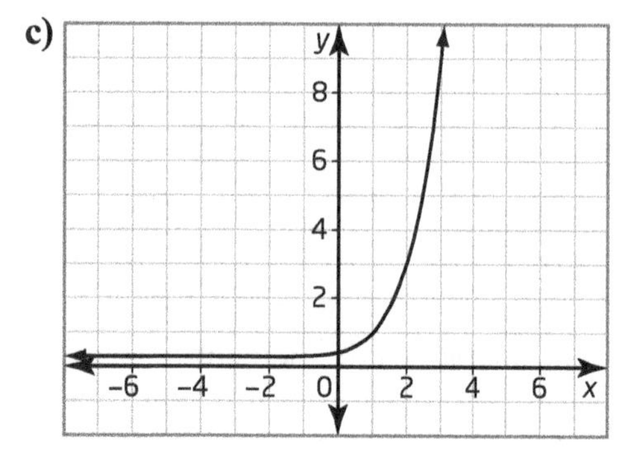

d)

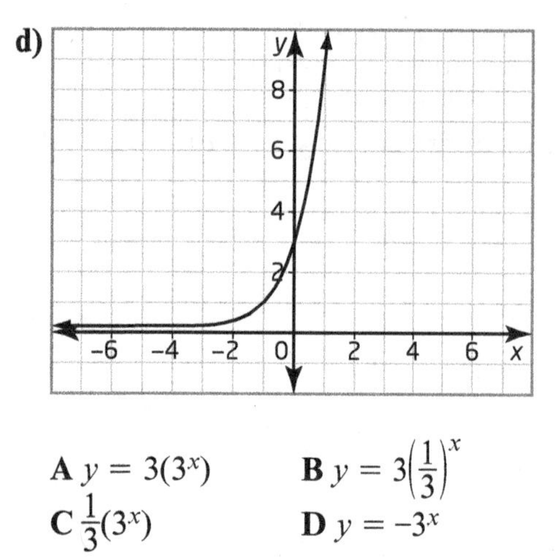

A $y = 3(3^x)$ **B** $y = 3\left(\frac{1}{3}\right)^x$

C $\frac{1}{3}(3^x)$ **D** $y = -3^x$

2. Match each equation with its corresponding graph. Justify your choice.

a)

b)

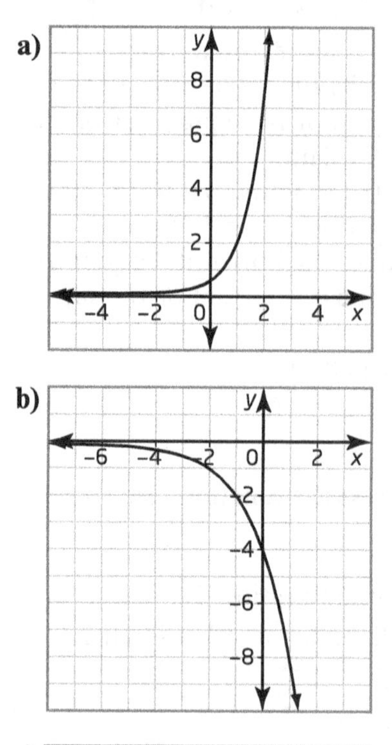

c)

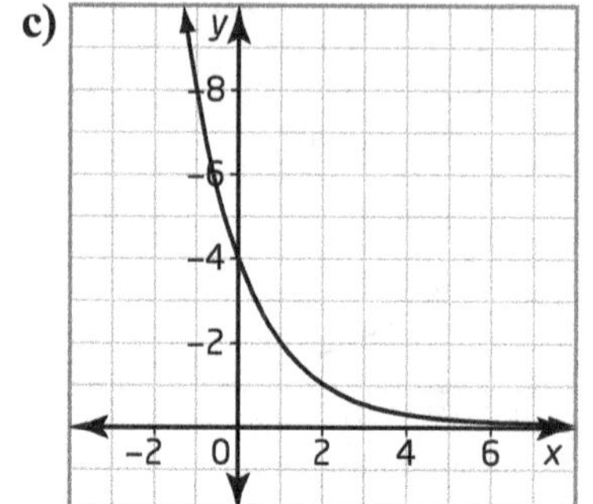

d)

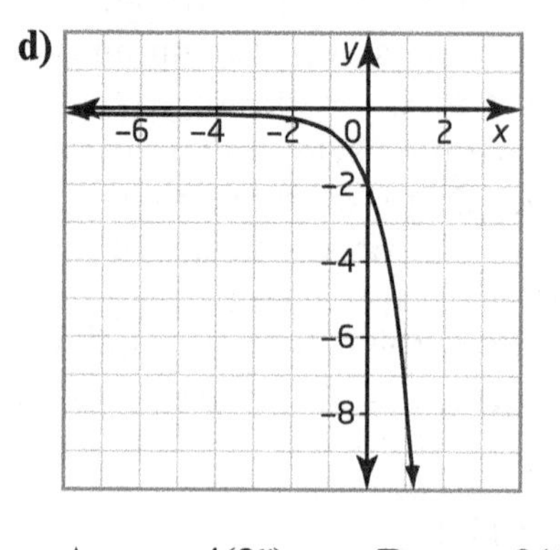

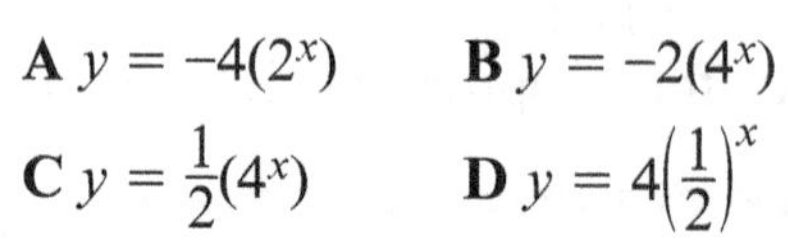

A $y = -4(2^x)$ **B** $y = -2(4^x)$

C $y = \frac{1}{2}(4^x)$ **D** $y = 4\left(\frac{1}{2}\right)^x$

3. a) Sketch the graph of an exponential function that satisfies all of these conditions:
- domain $\{\mathbb{R}\}$
- range $\{y \in \mathbb{R}, y > 0\}$
- y-intercept is 2
- function is increasing

b) Is this the only possible curve? Explain.

4. a) Sketch the graph of an exponential function that satisfies all of these conditions:
- domain $\{\mathbb{R}\}$
- range $\{y \in \mathbb{R}, y < 0\}$
- y-intercept is -3
- function is decreasing

b) Is this the only possible curve? Explain.

5. Write an exponential equation to match the graph.

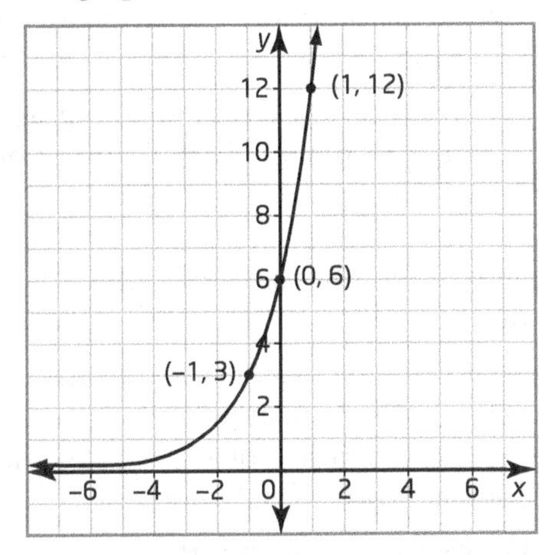

6. Write an exponential equation to match the graph.

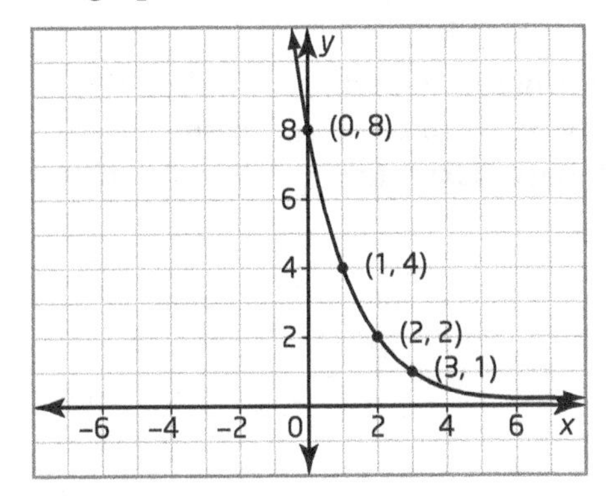

7. A radioactive sample, with an initial mass of 32 mg, has a half-life of 4 days.

a) Which of the following equations models this exponential decay?

A $A = 32\left(2^{\frac{t}{4}}\right)$

B $A = 32\left(\frac{1}{2}\right)^{4t}$

C $A = 32\left(\frac{1}{2}\right)^{\frac{t}{4}}$

D $A = 2\left(25^{\frac{t}{4}}\right)$

b) What is the amount of radioactive material remaining after 1 week?

B Connect and Apply

☆**8.** Graph each function and identify the
i) domain
ii) range
iii) x- and y-intercepts, if they exist
iv) intervals of increase/decrease
v) asymptote

a) $f(x) = \left(\frac{1}{4}\right)^x$

b) $y = 3 \times 2.5^x$

c) $y = -\left(\frac{1}{5}\right)^x$

☆**9. a)** Graph each function, with or without graphing technology.

i) $f(x) = 3^x$

ii) $g(x) = \frac{3}{x}$

b) In what way are the graphs
i) alike?
ii) different?

c) Compare the asymptotes of these functions. What do you observe?

10. a) Graph each function, with or without graphing technology.

i) $f(x) = \left(\frac{1}{3}\right)^x$

ii) $g(x) = \frac{3}{x}$

b) In what way are the graphs
i) alike?
ii) different?

c) Compare the asymptotes of these functions. What do you observe?

11. a) Predict how the graphs of the following functions are related.

i) $f(x) = 4^{-x}$

ii) $g(x) = \left(\frac{1}{4}\right)^x$

b) **Use Technology** Graph both functions using graphing technology and check your prediction from part a).

c) Use algebraic reasoning to explain this relationship.

12. A radioactive substance decays exponentially. The percent, P, of the substance that remains after t years is represented by the function $P(t) = 100(2.3)^{-t}$.

a) Express the function using a positive exponent and no decimal.

b) Which part of the equation from part a) indicates that the function represents exponential decay? Explain.

c) Graph the function. How does the graph support your answer in part b)?

d) State the domain and range of the function.

e) What does the horizontal asymptote indicate for this situation?

f) Determine the percent of the substance that remains after 4 years by using

i) the graph

ii) the equation

13. The percent, P, of surface light present under water is expressed as a function of depth, d, in metres, by the equation $P = 100(0.975)^d$.

a) Graph the function.

b) At what depth is only 50% of the surface light present?

14. The formula $V(S) = \frac{(4\pi)^{-\frac{1}{2}}}{3} \times S^{\frac{3}{2}}$ relates the volume, V, and surface area, S, of a sphere.

a) Find the volume, to the nearest cubic metre, of a spherical tank with surface area 250 m^2.

b) Rewrite the above formula to express S in terms of V.

c) Use your formula from part b) to find the surface area, to the nearest square metre, of a spherical tank with volume 150 m^3.

C Extend

15. In a laboratory, 320 mg of iodine-131 is stored for 40 days. At the end of this period only 10 mg of the element remain.

a) Determine the half-life of iodine-131.

b) State two different equations to model this situation.

c) Graph the function. State the domain and range.

d) After how many days did 60 mg of iodine-131 remain? Explain how you found this answer.

16. Suppose a cone has a fixed height of 25 m.

a) Write an equation, using rational exponents where appropriate, to express the radius of the base of the cone in terms of its volume.

b) How should you limit the domain of this function so that the mathematical model fits the situation?

c) What impact does doubling the volume have on the radius of the base? Explain.

3.5 Transformations of Exponential Functions

KEY CONCEPTS

- Exponential functions can be transformed in the same way as other functions.

- The graph of $y = ab^{k(x-d)} + c$ can be found by performing the following transformations on the graph of the base $y = b^x$:

Horizontal and Vertical Translations

– If $d > 0$, translate right d units; if $d < 0$, translate left.

– If $c > 0$, translate up c units; if $c < 0$, translate down.

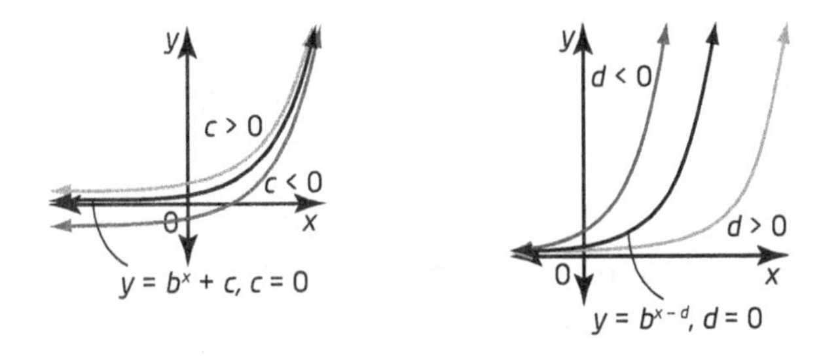

Vertical Stretches, Compressions, and Reflections

– If $a > 1$, stretch vertically by a factor of a.

– If $0 < a < 1$, compress vertically by a factor of a.

– If $a < 0$, reflect in the x-axis and stretch or compress.

y = abˣ, a = 1

a > 1

0 < a < 1

a < −1

−1 < a < 0

a = −1

Horizontal Stretches, Compressions, and Reflections

– If $k > 1$, compress horizontally by a factor of $\frac{1}{k}$.

– If $0 < k < 1$, stretch horizontally by a factor of $\frac{1}{k}$.

– If $k < 0$, reflect in the y-axis and stretch or compress.

k = −1

y = bᵏˣ, k = 1

−1 < k < 0

0 < k < 1

k < −1

k > 1

- Some exponential functions can easily be written using different bases. For example, $y = 2^{4x}$ is equivalent to $y = 16^x$.

Example

a) Write two equivalent equations for $y = -\left(\frac{1}{9}\right)^{3x} + 1$.

b) For each of the three equations, state the base function and the parameters. Then describe the corresponding transformations.

Solution

a) $y = -\left(\frac{1}{9}\right)^{3x} + 1$

Express $\frac{1}{9}$ as 9^{-1} or as 3^{-2}. Two equivalent equations are

i) $y = -(9^{-1})^{3x} + 1$
$= -9^{-3x} + 1$

ii) $y = -(3^{-2})^{2x} + 1$
$= -3^{-6x} + 1$

b) i) For the function $y = -\left(\frac{1}{9}\right)^{3x} + 1$, the base function is $y = \left(\frac{1}{9}\right)^{x}$ and the parameters are $a = -1$, $k = 3$, $d = 0$, $c = 1$.

- Since $a = -1$, the graph of $y = \left(\frac{1}{9}\right)^{x}$ is reflected in the x-axis.
- Since $k = 3$, the graph is compressed horizontally by a factor of $\frac{1}{3}$.
- Since $c = 1$, the graph is then translated up 1 unit.

ii) For the function $y = -(9^{-1})^{3x} + 1$, the base function is $y = 9^{x}$ and the parameters are $a = -1$, $k = -3$, $d = 0$, $c = 1$.

- Since $a = -1$, the graph of $y = 9^{x}$ is reflected in the x-axis.
- Since $k = -3$, the graph of $y = 9^{x}$ is reflected in the y-axis and compressed horizontally by a factor of $\frac{1}{3}$.
- Since $c = 1$, the graph is then shifted up 1 unit.

iii) For the function $y = -(3^{-2})^{2x} + 1$, the base function is $y = 3^{x}$ and the parameters are $a = 1$, $k = -6$, $d = 0$, $c = 1$.

- Since $a = -1$, the graph of $y = 3^{x}$ is reflected in the x-axis.
- Since $k = -6$, the graph of $y = 3^{x}$ is reflected in the y-axis, compressed horizontally by a factor of $\frac{1}{6}$.
- Since $c = 1$, the graph is then translated up 1 unit.

A Practise

1. Complete the second column of the table by describing the transformation associated with the parameter described in the first column.

The Roles of the Parameters a, k, d, and c in Exponential Functions of the Form $y = ab^{k(x-d)} + c$ $(b > 0, b \neq 1)$	
Role of c	**Transformation on Graph of $y = b^x$**
$c > 0$	
$c < 0$	
Role of d	
$d > 0$	
$d < 0$	
Role of a	
$a > 1$	
$0 < a < 1$	
$-1 < a < 0$	
$a < -1$	
Role of k	
$k > 1$	
$0 < k < 1$	
$-1 < k < 0$	
$k < -1$	
Domain and Range of $y = ab^{k(x-d)} + c$	
The domain is always _______.	i) When the graph is below its horizontal asymptote the range is _______. ii) When the graph is above its horizontal asymptote the range is _______.

2. Describe the transformation that maps the function $y = 5^x$ onto each function.

   a) $y = 5^x + 3$
   b) $y = 5^{x-2}$
   c) $y = 5^{x+1}$
   d) $y = 5^{x-4} - 6$

3. Sketch a graph of each function in question 2. Use the graph of $y = 5^x$ as the base.

4. Describe one or more transformations that map the function $y = 7^x$ onto each function.

   a) $y = \left(\frac{1}{3}\right)7^x$
   b) $y = 7^{2x}$
   c) $y = -7^x$
   d) $y = 7^{-\frac{1}{3}x}$

5. Sketch a graph of each function in question 4. Use the graph of $y = 7^x$ as the base. Be sure to choose an appropriate scale for your axes.

6. Write an equation for the function that results from each transformation applied to the base $y = 11^x$.

   a) reflection in the y-axis
   b) stretch vertically by a factor of 4
   c) stretch horizontally by a factor of 3
   d) reflect in the x-axis and compress horizontally by a factor of $\frac{1}{5}$

B Connect and Apply

☆7. The graph of $y = 4^x$ is transformed to obtain the graph of $y = -3[4^{2(x+1)}] + 5$.

   a) State the parameters. Describe the corresponding transformations and use these to complete the table. Then use the points to graph $y = -3[4^{2(x+1)}] + 5$.

$y = 4^x$	$y = 4^{2x}$	$y = -3[4^{2x}]$	$y = -3[4^{2(x+1)}] + 5$
(−1, 0.25)			
(0, 1)			
(1, 4)			
(2, 16)			
(3, 64)			

   b) State the domain, range, and equation of the horizontal asymptote for this function.

8. Sketch a graph of $y = \left(-\frac{1}{5}\right)5^{x+4} - 2$ by using $y = 5^x$ as the base and applying transformations.

☆9. a) Describe the transformations that must be applied to the graph of $f(x) = 3^x$ to obtain the transformed function $y = -f(4x) - 7$. Then write the corresponding equation.

b) State the domain, range, and equation of the horizontal asymptote.

10. a) Write the equation of the function that represents $f(x) = 2^x$ after it is reflected in the x-axis, stretched horizontally by a factor of 5, reflected in the y-axis, and then translated down 3 units and right 1 unit.

b) State the domain and range, and the equation of its horizontal asymptote.

11. The temperature, in degrees Celsius, of a cooling metal bar is given by the function $T = 18 + 100(0.5)^{0.3t}$, where t is the time, in minutes.

a) Sketch a graph of this relation.

b) What is the asymptote of this function? What does it represent?

c) How long will it take for the temperature to be within 0.1 °C of the value of the asymptote?

12. a) Rewrite the function $y = \left(\frac{1}{16}\right)^x$ in three different ways, using a different base in each case.

b) State the base function for each equation and describe how the base function is transformed.

13. a) Write an equation for a function whose asymptote is $y = -5$, with a y-intercept of 3.

b) Is the function you produced in part a) the only possible answer? Use transformations to help explain your answer.

C Extend

14. A 250-g sample of one type of radioactive substance has a half-life of 138 days. A 175-g sample of another type of radioactive substance has a half-life of 16 days.

a) For each substance, write an equation that represents the amount A, in grams, of the radioactive sample that remains after t days.

b) What is the base function for each equation?

c) Describe the transformations that must be applied to the base function to obtain each equation.

d) Use a negative exponent to write an equivalent equation for each of the equations in part a).

i) What is the base function?

ii) Which transformations that must be applied to this base function are the same as those in part c)?

iii) Which new transformation is required?

e) For each substance, determine the mass that remains after 20 weeks.

f) How long does it take for each sample to decay to 10% of its original amount?

15. Refer to question 14. Suppose there is an initial amount of A_0 grams of a radioactive substance that has a half-life of h days.

a) Write a general equation to represent the amount A, in grams, that remains after t days.

b) Describe the role of A_0 and h in the equation in terms of transformations.

c) Rewrite the equation in part a) so that it includes a reflection in the y-axis.

3.6 Making Connections: Tools and Strategies for Applying Exponential Models

KEY CONCEPTS

- You can use a variety of tools to construct algebraic and graphical models, including
  - a graphing calculator
  - dynamic statistics software such as *Fathom*™
  - a spreadsheet
- Various types of regression (e.g., linear, quadratic, exponential) can be used to model a relationship. The best choice will effectively describe the trend between and beyond the known data values.
- Exponential functions are useful in modelling situations involving continuous growth or decay/depreciation.

Example

In 1940, the population of the town of Mathville was 3000. Since then, the population has doubled every 6 years.

a) Copy and complete the table.

Year	6-Year Interval	Population
1940	0	
1946	1	
1952	2	
1958	3	
1964	4	
1970	5	
1976	6	
1982	7	
1988	8	
1994	9	
2000	10	

b) Graph the data.

c) Use your graph to estimate the population in 1991.

d) Use your graph to estimate when the population will reach 5 million.

e) Write an equation to model this situation, where P represents the population of Mathville, in thousands, and t represents the time, in 6-year intervals, since 1940.

Solution

a)

Year	6-Year Interval	Population
1940	0	3 000
1946	1	6 000
1952	2	12 000
1958	3	24 000
1964	4	48 000
1970	5	96 000
1976	6	192 000
1982	7	384 000
1988	8	768 000
1994	9	1 536 000
2000	10	3 072 000

b) Graph the data using an appropriate scale for each axis. In this solution, each square represents one 6-year interval on the horizontal axis and a population of 300 000 on the vertical axis.

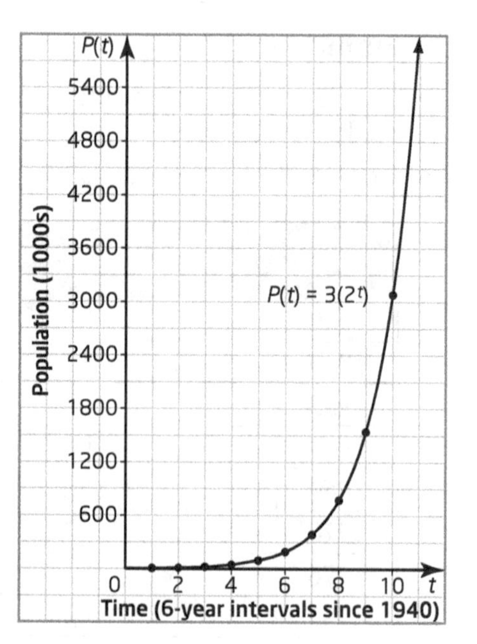

c) 1991 is in the middle of the 6-year interval from 1988 to 1994. This point is at 8.5 along the horizontal axis. For this point, the corresponding value on the vertical axis is about 1 100 000, which is the estimated population in 1991.

d) To determine when the population will reach 5 million, find that value on the vertical axis and then find its corresponding value on the horizontal axis.

The horizontal value is approximately 10 and $\frac{2}{3}$ intervals.

This corresponds to $(10 \times 6) + \left(\frac{2}{3} \times 6\right)$,

or 64 years since 1940. Therefore, the population of Mathville reached 5 000 000 in 2004.

e) Since the population is doubling, the equation will be of the form $P = P_0(2^t)$, where P_0 is the initial population, in thousands, and 2 represents the doubling.

The initial population is $P_0 = 3$ (in thousands), so the equation that models this situation is $P(t) = 3(2^t)$.

A Practise

1. For each exponential scatter plot, select the corresponding equation of its curve of best fit.

Graph A

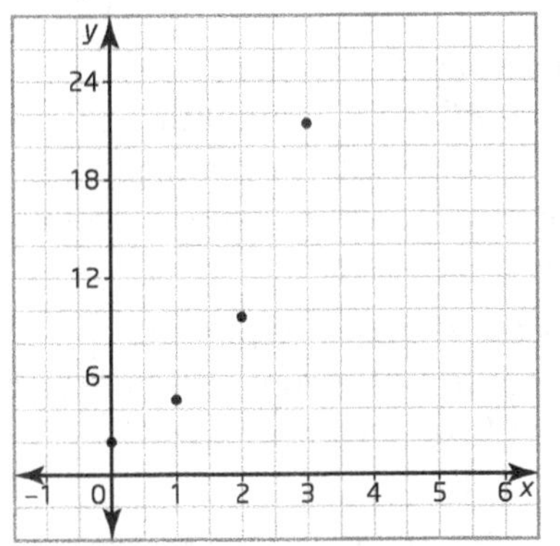

Graph B

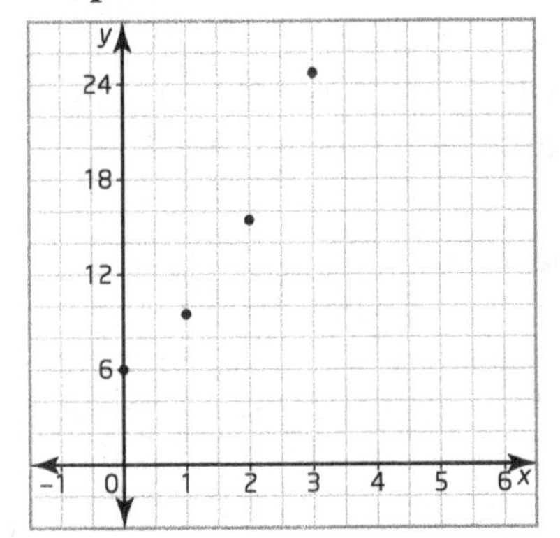

Graph C

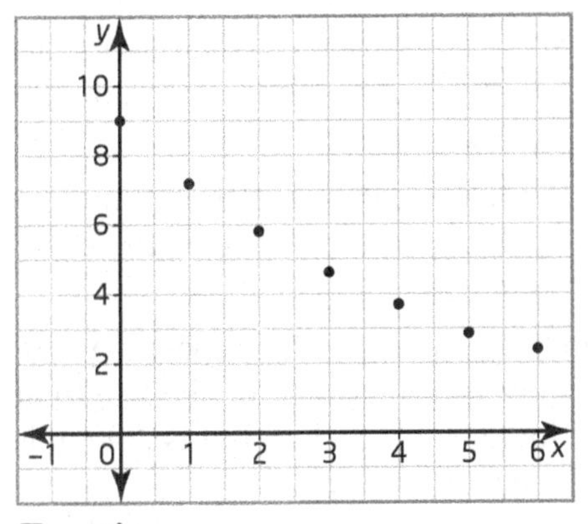

Equations

$y = 20 \times 0.85^x$
$y = 6 \times 1.6^x$
$y = 2 \times 0.7^x$
$y = 2 \times 2.2^x$
$y = 9 \times 0.8^x$
$y = 9 \times 1.2^x$

2. Pick one of the unmatched equations from question 1. Sketch a scatter plot that the equation could fit.

3. Toni has invested some money in a mutual fund. The scatter plot shows the value of her investment after the first few years.

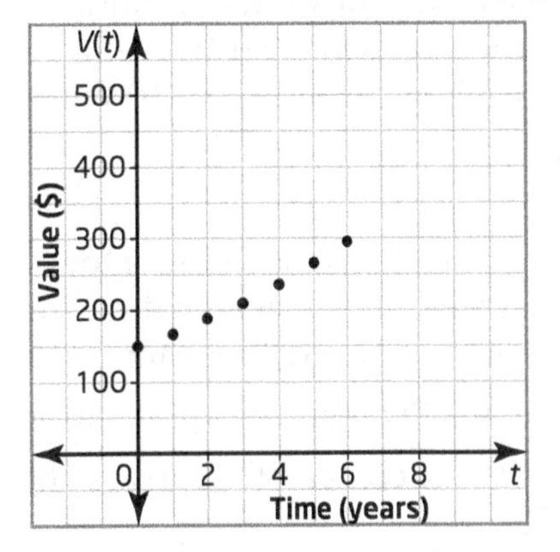

a) Do the data appear to have an exponential trend? Explain your reasoning.

b) Estimate values of a and b to develop an exponential model for the data of the form $V(n) = a \times b^n$. Explain how you arrived at your estimated values.

c) Use the tool of your choice to find an exponential model of these data.

d) Use the exponential model you produced in part c) to predict the value of Toni's investment after 12 years.

e) Approximately how long it will take for Toni's investment to grow to $1000?

4. A fully charged cell phone battery loses 2% of its charge every day.

a) Determine an equation that models the percent charge, C, that remains in the battery after t days.

b) Determine the percent charge remaining in the battery after
i) 25 days
ii) 50 days
iii) 75 days
iv) 100 days

c) Determine the half-life of the battery.

B Connect and Apply

☆5. *Best Electronics* has had constant growth since 1995. Its profits are modelled by the equation $P(t) = 7.4(1.59)^t$, where P is the yearly profit, in thousands of dollars, and t is the number of years since 1995.

a) Make a table of values to show annual profits for year 0 (1995) and each of the following 10 years. Approximate values to one decimal place.

b) Graph the data in the table. Does this represent exponential decay or exponential growth? Explain.

c) What was the company's profit in 1995?

d) Predict the company's yearly profit in 2015.

e) According to the model, when does the yearly profit reach $500 000 000?

6. Air pressure decreases as altitude increases. The following table gives the air pressure, $p(a)$, measured in kilopascals (kPa), at an altitude of a km above sea level.

Altitude (km)	Pressure (kPa)
0	100.0
4	70.0
8	49.0
12	34.3
16	24.0
20	16.8
24	11.8

a) Construct a scatter plot and the curve of best fit for the data.

b) Determine the equation of the exponential function that best represents the data.

c) Determine the air pressure at the summit of each mountain.
i) Mount Logan, altitude 6050 m
ii) Mount Everest, altitude 8848 m

d) What altitude corresponds to an air pressure of 20 kPa?

7. Coffee, tea, cola, and chocolate contain caffeine. When you consume caffeine, the percent, P, of caffeine remaining in your body over time is represented by the function $P = 100(0.87)^t$, where t is the elapsed time, in hours.

a) Make a table of values for the percent of caffeine remaining for a 24-hour period, in 2-h intervals. Approximate values to one decimal place.

b) Does the function represent exponential growth or exponential decay? Justify your answer graphically.

c) Determine the percent of caffeine remaining in your body after
i) 1 h **ii)** 9 h **iii)** 15 h

d) How long will it take for the percent of caffeine to drop by 50%?

C Extend

8. In a steel mill, red-hot slabs of steel are pressed many times between heavy rollers. The width of the slab remains the same on every pass; however, the length increases by 20% and the thickness decreases by 17%. Consider a slab that is p metres long and q metres thick.

a) Write an equation to represent the length, l, in metres, of the slab after n passes.

b) Write an equation to represent the thickness, t, in metres, of the slab after n passes.

c) Use your results from parts a) and b) to write equations for the length and thickness of a slab that is 2.00 m long and 0.50 m thick.

d) How many passes are needed until the length is at least 20 m? How thick is the slab at this point?

e) How many passes are needed until the thickness is about 1 mm? How long is the slab at this point?

Chapter 3 Review

3.1 The Nature of Exponential Growth

1. A bacteria colony that has an initial population of 85 triples every hour.

   a) Which function models this exponential growth?

   A $p(n) = 85 \times 3^n$

   B $p(n) = 85 \times 2^n$

   C $p(n) = 85 \times 3^n$

   b) For the correct model, explain what each part of the equation means.

2. Evaluate.

   a) 11^0

   b) $(-4)^0$

   c) $\left(\frac{2x}{7}\right)^0$

   d) -2^0

3. **a)** Identify each function as linear, quadratic, or neither. Justify your choice.

   i) $f(x) = 7^x$

   ii) $f(x) = 3x + \sqrt{6}$

   iii) $f(x) = 1 - x^2$

   b) Without calculating the finite differences, describe the relationship between the finite differences and each type of function.

3.2 Exponential Decay: Connecting to Negative Exponents

4. Write each as a power with a positive exponent.

   a) x^{-3}

   b) $3b^{-2}$

5. Write each as a power with a negative exponent.

   a) $\frac{1}{w^4}$

   b) $\frac{-3}{b^8}$

6. Evaluate.

   a) 6^{-3}

   b) $5^{-2} + 5^{-3}$

   c) $(12^{-4})(12^3)$

   d) $\frac{(8^3)(8^{-4})}{8^{-2}}$

   e) $\left(\frac{6}{5}\right)^{-3}$

   f) $\left(-\frac{8}{7}\right)^{-2}$

7. Simplify. Express your answers using only positive exponents.

   a) $(3b^{-5})^{-2}$

   b) $(-2a^2b^{-2})^{-3}$

   c) $(3x^4)^9 \div (3^5x^6)^3$

   d) $\left(\frac{2c^4}{3d^2}\right)^{-5}$

   e) $\left(\frac{6^3\,a^5}{5^5\,b^9}\right)^7 \times \left(\frac{5^{11}\,b^2}{6^6\,a^3}\right)^3$

3.3 Rational Exponents

8. Evaluate.

   a) $\left(-\frac{27}{64}\right)^{-\frac{2}{3}}$

   b) $\left(\frac{16}{81}\right)^{-\frac{7}{4}}$

   c) $27^{\frac{1}{3}} + 16^{\frac{3}{4}} - 32^{\frac{4}{5}}$

   d) $\sqrt[5]{243^2}$

9. Express each radical as a power with a rational exponent.

   a) $(\sqrt[5]{-3125})^4$

   b) $(\sqrt[5]{32})^3$

10. Express each power as a radical. Then evaluate.

    a) $(-32)^{\frac{4}{5}}$

    b) $343^{-\frac{2}{3}}$

    c) $(-125)^{\frac{2}{3}}$

11. Express as a single power and then evaluate.

a) $16^{\frac{5}{4}} \times 16^{\frac{1}{2}} \div 16^{\frac{9}{4}}$

b) $81^{\frac{1}{2}} \div 81^{\frac{3}{4}} \times 81^{\frac{7}{4}}$

c) $256^{\frac{1}{4}} \times 256^{\frac{3}{8}} \div 256^{\frac{1}{2}}$

12. Simplify. Express your answers using only positive exponents.

a) $\frac{s^{\frac{3}{4}}}{s^{\frac{1}{3}}}$

b) $\left(m^{\frac{3}{7}}n^{\frac{4}{5}}\right)^{\frac{2}{3}}$

c) $\left(k^{\frac{3}{7}}\right)^{-\frac{1}{2}}$

d) $6v^{\frac{1}{2}}\left(32v^{-\frac{1}{3}}\right)^{-\frac{6}{5}}$

13. The area, A, of an equilateral triangle with side length s is given by $A = \frac{\sqrt{3}}{4s^{-2}}$.

a) Rearrange the formula to express the side length s in terms of the area A.

b) Use your answer in part a) to determine the length of the sides when the area is 12.6 m^2.

3.4 Properties of Exponential Functions

14. Graph each function and identify the

i) domain

ii) range

iii) x- and y-intercepts, if they exist

iv) intervals of increase/decrease

v) asymptote

a) $f(x) = \left(\frac{1}{6}\right)^x$

b) $y = 4 \times 3.5^x$

c) $y = -\left(\frac{1}{4}\right)^x$

15. A radioactive sample, with an initial mass of 28 mg, has a half-life of 5 days.

a) Write an equation to represent the amount, A, of radioactive sample that remains after t days.

b) Explain why this situation represents exponential decay.

c) Without graphing, describe the shape of the graph of this function. State the domain and range.

d) What is the amount of radioactive sample remaining after 2 weeks?

3.5 Transformations of Exponential Functions

16. Sketch a graph of $y = 4^{-1.5x + 3}$, by using $y = 4^x$ as the base and applying transformations.

17. a) Describe the transformations that must be applied to the graph of $f(x) = 0.5^x$ to obtain the transformed function $y = 2f\left[\frac{1}{3}(x - 5)\right]$. Then write the corresponding equation.

b) State the domain, range, and equation of the horizontal asymptote.

18. a) Write the equation of the function that represents $f(x) = \left(\frac{1}{4}\right)^x$ after it is compressed horizontally by a factor of $\frac{1}{2}$, compressed vertically by a factor of $\frac{1}{3}$, reflected in the x-axis, and shifted 4 units to the left and 6 units up.

b) State the domain, range, and equation of the horizontal asymptote.

3.6 Making Connections: Tools and Strategies for Applying Exponential Models

19. The population of Canada in 1981 was approximately 24 million. The population since then has increased approximately 1.4% per year.

a) Make a table of values by determining the population every 2 years for 20 years, since 1981.

b) Determine an equation that models the data in part a).

c) What was the population of Canada in 2000? Round your answer to the nearest hundred thousand.

d) Predict the population in 2012, to the nearest hundred thousand.

e) According to the model, when will Canada's population reach 40 million?

Chapter 3 Math Contest

1. Given that $\frac{a^9c^3}{b} = 8$ and $\frac{b^7c^3}{a^3} = 18$, one possible value of $(abc)^3$ is

   A 4 **B** 6
   C 144 **D** 12

2. If $f(x) = 4^{3-2x}$, then the value of $[f(2 + x)][f(2 - x)]$ is

   A 16 **B** $\frac{1}{16}$
   C 4 **D** $\frac{1}{4}$

3. The y-intercept of the function $y = 8\left(\frac{1}{4}\right)^{3x+2} - 1$ is

   A −1 **B** 8
   C − 1 **D** $-\frac{1}{2}$

4. Consider the following system of equations.
   $x_1 + x_2 = 6$
   $x_2 + x_3 = 7$
   $x_1 + x_3 = 8$
   What is the value of $x_1 + x_2 + x_3$?

   A 21 **B** 7.5
   C 7 **D** 10.5

5. A new operation $a \otimes b$ is defined as $a \otimes b = (b - 1)^{a+2}$. The value of $[(-3) \otimes 4] \otimes 9$ is

   A 128 **B** $\frac{1}{128}$
   C 512 **D** $\frac{1}{512}$

6. Without using a calculator, determine the value of $\frac{36^{\frac{4}{7}}}{\sqrt[7]{6}}$.

7. Find all the solutions to $3^x - 2x - 1 = 0$.

8. A number is between 25 and 35. When this number is added to its cube, the result is 29 822. When the same number is subtracted from its cube the result is

   A 29 672 **B** 29 758
   C 29 772 **D** 29 760

9. Consider the function $y = 18\left(\frac{1}{3}\right)^x - 2$. If the x-intercept is a and the y-intercept is b, determine the value of $6a - b$.

   A 4 **B** 12
   C −4 **D** 8

10. If $f(x) = (-2)^x$ and $f(x + 2) - f(x + 3) + f(x + 5) = kf(x)$, what is the value of k?

11. If $3^y = 5$, then the value of $3^{4y} - 11(3^{2y})$ is

    A 350 **B** $\sqrt[4]{5} - 11\sqrt{5}$
    C $-10\sqrt[4]{5}$ **D** 550

12. Consider three circles such that the radius of the first circle is r, the radius of the second circle is $4r$, and the radius of the third circle is $8r$. What is the ratio of the area of the circles, in order from smallest to largest?

    A 1:4:8 **B** 1:2:4
    C 1:2:2 **D** 1:16:64

13. What is the range of the function $y = -5\left(\frac{1}{3}\right)^x + 2$?

Chapter 4 Trigonometry

4.1 Special Angles

KEY CONCEPTS

- Using a unit circle is one way to find the trigonometric ratios for angles greater than 90°.
- Any point on a unit circle can be joined to the origin to form the terminal arm of an angle. The angle θ is measured starting from the initial arm along the positive x-axis, proceeding counterclockwise to the terminal arm.

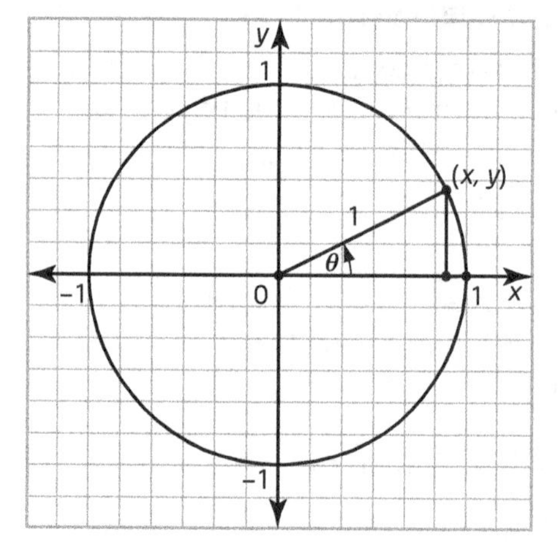

The coordinates of the point (x, y) on a unit circle are related to θ such that $x = \cos\theta$ and $y = \sin\theta$.

- $\tan\theta = \frac{y}{x}$
- Exact trigonometric ratios for special angles can be determined using special triangles.

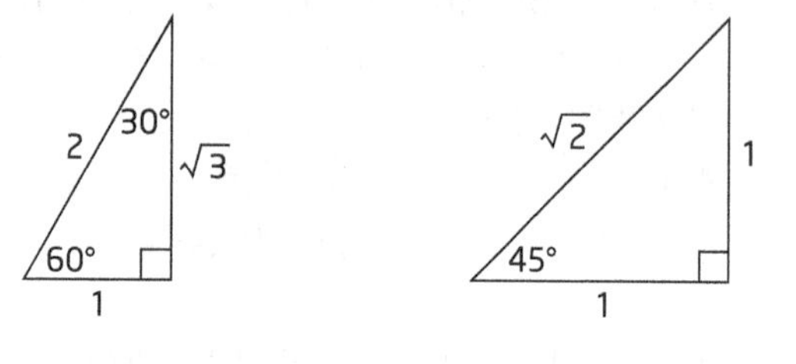

- The exact trigonometric ratios for 45° are $\sin 45° = \frac{1}{\sqrt{2}}$, $\cos 45° = \frac{1}{\sqrt{2}}$, and $\tan 45° = 1$.

Example

A ladder that is 2.5 m long is placed against a vertical wall so that the top of the ladder makes an angle of 30° with the wall.

a) Draw a diagram to represent this situation.

b) How far up the wall is the top of the ladder? Give an exact answer.

Solution

a)

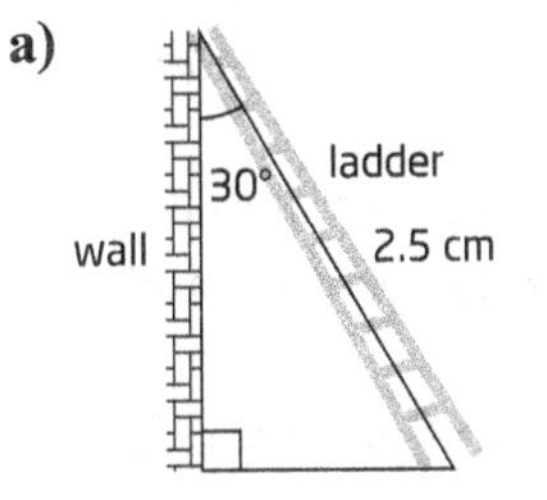

b) Let h represent the height, in metres, from the top of the ladder to the ground. We know the length of the hypotenuse and we want to find the length of the side adjacent to 30°. Use the cosine ratio.

$\cos 30° = \frac{h}{2.5}$

Substitute $\cos 30° = \frac{\sqrt{3}}{2}$.

$\frac{\sqrt{3}}{2} = \frac{h}{2.5}$

Solve for h.

$h = \frac{2.5\sqrt{3}}{2}$

$= 1.25\sqrt{3}$

Substitute $1.25 = \frac{5}{4}$.

$h = \frac{5\sqrt{3}}{4}$

The top of the ladder is $\frac{5\sqrt{3}}{4}$ m up the wall.

A Practise

1. Complete the table. Use exact values only.

θ	$\sin \theta$	$\cos \theta$	$\tan \theta$
0°			
30°			
45°			
60°			
90°			
180°			
270°			
360°			

2. **Use Technology** Use a calculator to complete the table. Express answers to four decimal places.

θ	$\sin \theta$	$\cos \theta$	$\tan \theta$
0°			
30°			
45°			
60°			
90°			
180°			
270°			
360°			

3. **a)** What reference angle on the unit circle should you use to find the trigonometric ratios for 225°?

   b) State two other angles that have the same reference angle on the unit circle.

   c) Use a unit circle to find exact values for the three trigonometric ratios for 225°.

   d) State the exact values for the three trigonometric ratios for the angles in part b).

4. **a)** What reference angle on the unit circle would you use to find the trigonometric ratios for 150°?

   b) State two other angles that have the same reference angle on the unit circle.

   c) Use a unit circle to find exact values for the three trigonometric ratios for 150°.

   d) State the exact values for the three trigonometric ratios for the angles in part b).

5. **a)** What reference angle on the unit circle would you use to find the trigonometric ratios for 300°?

   b) State two other angles that have the same reference angle on the unit circle.

   c) Use a unit circle to find exact values for the three trigonometric ratios for 300°.

   d) State the exact values for the three trigonometric ratios for the angles in part b).

6. Use a unit circle to find the primary trigonometric ratios for 70°. Measure any side lengths needed. Compare your answers to those generated by a calculator.

7. Use a unit circle to find the primary trigonometric ratios for 220°. Measure any side lengths needed. Compare your answers to those generated by a calculator.

B Connect and Apply

☆8. **a)** Describe the CAST rule.

   b) Use the CAST rule to identify the two quadrants where each trigonometric ratio is positive and the two quadrants where each ratio is negative. Copy and complete the table to organize your results.

Trigonometric Ratio	Positive Quadrants	Negative Quadrants
Sine		
Cosine		
Tangent		

9. A ladder that is 3 m long is placed against a vertical wall so that the top of the ladder makes an angle of 60° with the wall.

   a) Draw a diagram to represent this situation.

   b) Find an exact expression for the distance between the bottom of the ladder and the wall.

   c) How far up the wall is the top of the ladder?

10. A sports car is 14 km south of an intersection. A van is 14 km west of the same intersection.

   a) Use trigonometry to find an exact expression for the distance between the two vehicles.

   b) Describe an alternate method that can be used to solve this problem. Check your answer using that method.

☆**11.** A hydro pole is stabilized at its top by two guy wires of equal length, each of which makes an angle of 60° with the ground. The wires are secured to the ground at points that are 10 m apart and on opposite sides of the pole.

   a) Draw a diagram to represent this situation.

   b) How tall is the hydro pole? Express your answer using exact values.

   c) What is the length of each wire? Express your answer using exact values.

12. A floor tile in the shape of a regular hexagon has side lengths of 8 cm. Determine the area of the tile.

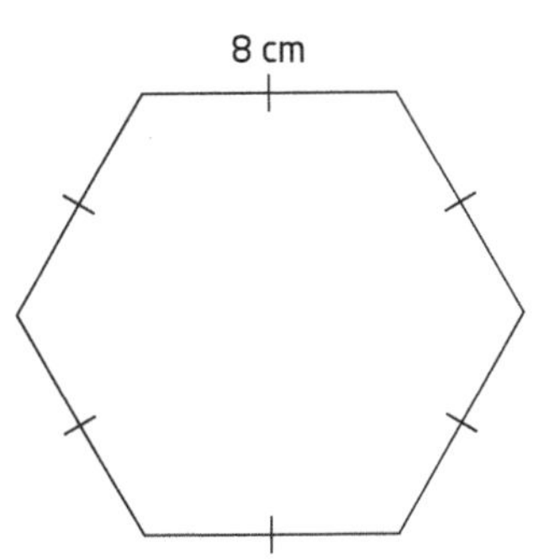

13. Determine the exact value of each expression.

   a) $\cos 45° \times \sin 225° + \cos 210°$

   b) $\tan 330° \times \cos 240° - 2 \cos 270°$

   c) $\tan 60° \times 3 \sin 90° - \sin 315°$

14. Prove that $(\sin 30°)^2 + (\cos 30°)^2 = (\sin 315°)^2 + (\cos 315°)^2$.

C Extend

15. Determine all the possible measures of θ, where $0° \leq \theta \leq 360°$, that satisfy each equation.

   a) $\sin \theta = \frac{\sqrt{3}}{2}$

   b) $(\cos \theta)^2 = \frac{1}{2}$

   c) $\sqrt{3} \tan \theta + 1 = 0$

16. The angle of elevation from point A on the ground to the top of a water tower is 30°. From point B, which is 10 m closer to the tower than point A, the angle of elevation is 45°. Determine the height of the water tower.

17. Each trigonometric ratio has a reciprocal ratio. The reciprocal of the tangent ratio is the cotangent ratio.

   $\cot \theta = \frac{1}{\tan \theta}$

   a) Show that the formula for the area, A, of a regular polygon with n sides in terms of its side length, s, is $A = \frac{ns^2}{4} \cot\left(\frac{180°}{n}\right)$.

   b) Use the trigonometric ratios of special triangles and the formula in part a) to derive a formula for the area of each regular polygon.

      i) square

      ii) hexagon

      iii) equilateral triangle

4.2 Co-terminal and Related Angles

KEY CONCEPTS

- The primary trigonometric ratios for the angle θ in standard position that has a point (x, y) on its terminal arm can be calculated as $\sin \theta = \frac{y}{r}$, $\cos \theta = \frac{x}{r}$, and $\tan \theta = \frac{y}{x}$, where $r = \sqrt{x^2 + y^2}$.

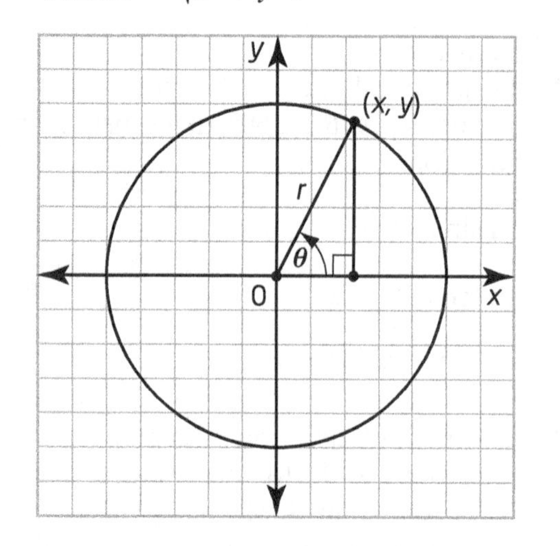

- Exactly two angles between 0° and 360° have the same sine ratio.
- Exactly two angles between 0° and 360° have the same cosine ratio.
- Exactly two angles between 0° and 360° have the same tangent ratio.
- Pairs of related angles can be found using the coordinates of the endpoints of their terminal arms. Use a reference angle in the first quadrant.
- Co-terminal angles are angles with the same terminal arm. They can be positive or negative.

Example

Solve the equation $\sin \theta = -\frac{15}{17}$ for $0° \leq \theta \leq 360°$.

Solution

Note that the sign of $\sin \theta = -\frac{15}{17}$ is negative. From the CAST rule we know that the sine function is negative in the third and fourth quadrants, so there are two angles that satisfy this equation.

Use a calculator to determine the smallest positive angle such that $\sin \theta = \frac{15}{17}$.

$\sin^{-1}\left(\frac{15}{17}\right) = 62°$

In the third quadrant, the angle is $180° + 62° = 242°$.

In the fourth quadrant, the angle is $360° - 62° = 298°$.

Therefore, the two solutions to $\sin \theta = -\frac{15}{17}$ are $\theta = 242°$ and $\theta = 298°$.

A Practise

Unless specified otherwise, all angles are between 0° and 360°.

1. The coordinates of a point on the terminal arm of an angle θ are shown. Determine the exact trigonometric ratios of θ.

a) A(3, 4)

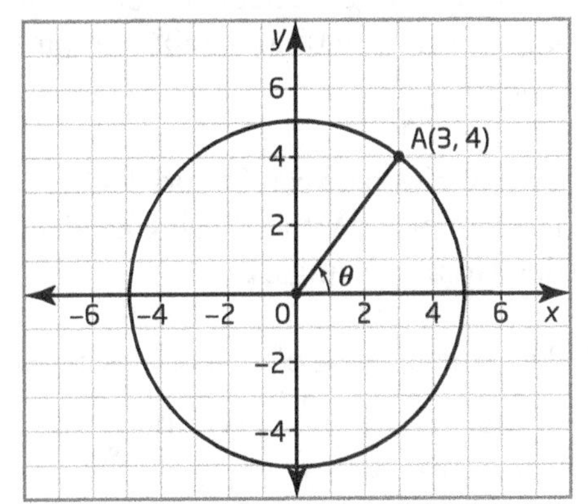

b) C(−7, −2)

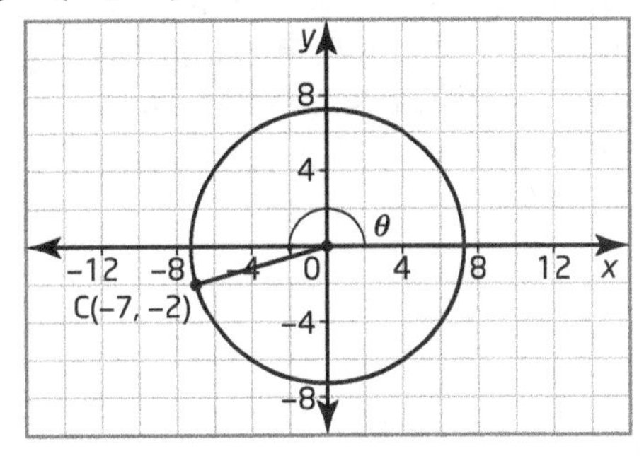

c) B(−6, 3)

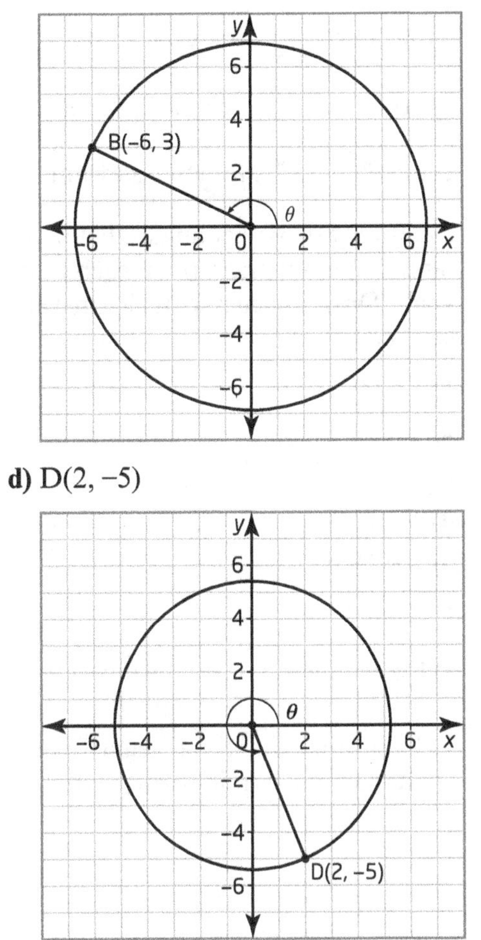

d) D(2, −5)

2. The coordinates of a point on the terminal arm of an angle θ are given. Determine the exact trigonometric ratios of θ.

   a) G(−3, 5)

   b) H(−15, 8)

   c) I(−3, −4)

   d) J(−5, 12)

   e) K(7, 3)

   f) L(1, −9)

3. One of the primary trigonometric ratios of an angle is given, as well as the quadrant in which the terminal arm lies. Find the other two primary trigonometric ratios.

   a) $\cos A = -\frac{8}{17}$, second quadrant

   b) $\sin B = -\frac{4}{5}$, third quadrant

   c) $\tan C = -\frac{12}{5}$, fourth quadrant

   d) $\sin D = \frac{7}{\sqrt{85}}$, first quadrant

   e) $\cos E = -\frac{3}{13}$, second quadrant

   f) $\tan F = -\frac{8}{13}$, fourth quadrant

4. Determine two other angles that have the same trigonometric ratio as each given angle. Draw a sketch with all three angles labelled.

   a) sin 60°

   b) cos 210°

   c) tan 315°

   d) sin 140°

   e) cos 285°

   f) tan 190°

☆**5.** **a)** Determine any three positive angles that are co-terminal with 205°.

   b) Determine any three negative angles that are co-terminal with 310°.

6. Which pairs of angles are co-terminal? Justify your answer.

   a) 40° and 280°

   b) 80° and 440°

   c) 110° and 830°

   d) 170° and 510°

   e) 50° and −310°

   f) 200° and −520°

   g) 100° and −200°

   h) 320° and 680°

7. Determine the exact primary trigonometric ratios of each angle. You may wish to use the unit circle to help you.

   a) $\angle A = -30°$

   b) $\angle B = -240°$

   c) $\angle C = -180°$

   d) $\angle D = 405°$

   e) $\angle E = 750°$

   f) $\angle F = 570°$

B Connect and Apply

☆**8.** Without using a calculator, determine two angles between 0° and 360° that have a sine of $-\frac{1}{\sqrt{2}}$.

9. Two angles between 0° and 360° have a tangent of 1. Without using a calculator, determine the angles.

10. The sine of each of two angles between 0° and 360° is $-\frac{\sqrt{3}}{2}$. Without using a calculator, determine the angles.

11. Three angles between 0° and 360° have a tangent that is 0. What are the angles? Which other trigonometric ratio is 0 for these angles?

12. The point P(5, −7) is on the terminal arm of ∠A.

a) Determine the primary trigonometric ratios for ∠A and ∠B such that ∠B has the same sine as ∠A.

b) Use a calculator and a diagram to determine the measures of ∠A and ∠B, to the nearest degree.

13. The point Q(−6, −1) is on the terminal arm of ∠C.

a) Determine the primary trigonometric ratios for ∠C and ∠D such that ∠D has the same cosine as ∠C.

b) Use a calculator and a diagram to determine the measures of ∠C and ∠D, to the nearest degree.

14. The point R(−2, 3) is on the terminal arm of ∠E.

a) Determine the primary trigonometric ratios for ∠E and ∠F such that ∠F has the same tangent as ∠E.

b) Use a calculator and a diagram to determine the measures of ∠E and ∠F, to the nearest degree.

15. Solve each equation for $0° \leq \theta \leq 360°$.

a) $\sin \theta = -\frac{3}{4}$

b) $\cos \theta = \frac{2}{3}$

c) $\tan \theta = -\frac{5}{7}$

16. Determine the area of the sector of the circle shown.

a)

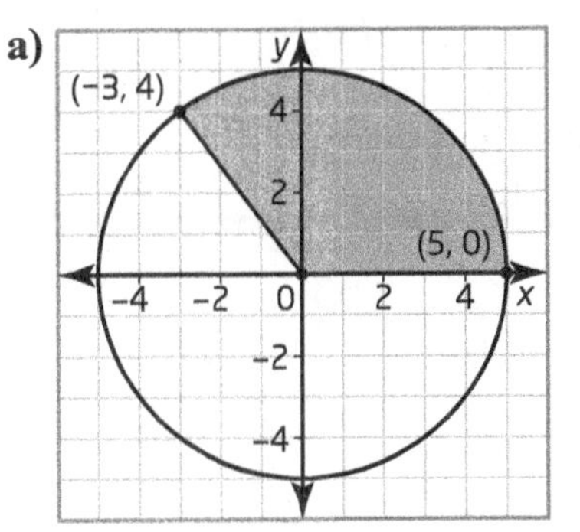

b)

c)

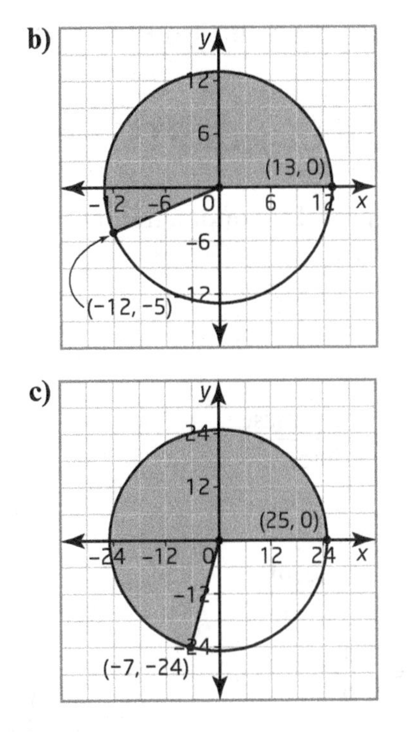

C Extend

17. An angle θ is in standard position on a coordinate grid. The terminal arm of θ is in the second quadrant on the line with equation $3y + 2x = 0$. Determine the measure of angle θ.

18. △ABO has vertices A(−3, 0), B(−3, −7), and O(0, 0). A circle, of radius 1 unit and centre O(0, 0), intersects OB at point P. Point C has coordinates C(1, 0), and ∠COP = θ.

a) Determine the coordinates of P.

b) Use the results of part a) to determine $\sin \theta$ and $\cos \theta$.

c) Compare the values of $\sin \theta$ and $\cos \theta$ with those you would obtain by using the lengths of the sides of △ABO. What do you notice?

4.3 Reciprocal Trigonometric Ratios

KEY CONCEPTS

- The reciprocal trigonometric ratios are defined as follows:

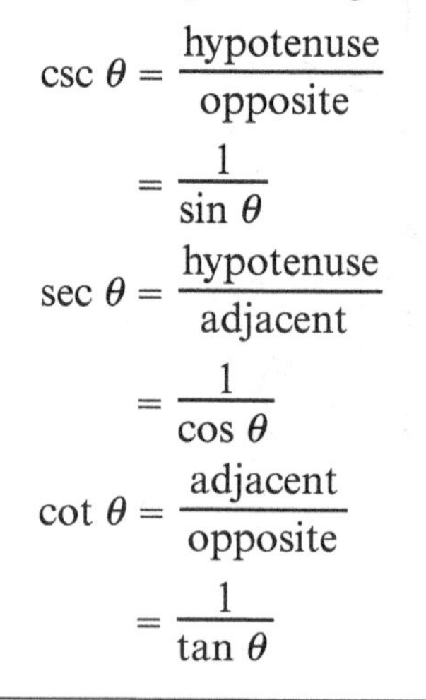

$$\csc\theta = \frac{\text{hypotenuse}}{\text{opposite}} = \frac{1}{\sin\theta}$$

$$\sec\theta = \frac{\text{hypotenuse}}{\text{adjacent}} = \frac{1}{\cos\theta}$$

$$\cot\theta = \frac{\text{adjacent}}{\text{opposite}} = \frac{1}{\tan\theta}$$

Example

A kite on a string is flying at a height of 15.3 m above the ground. The angle between the kite and the ground is 53°. Use a reciprocal trigonometric ratio to determine the length of the string, to the nearest centimetre.

Solution

Draw a diagram to represent this situation.

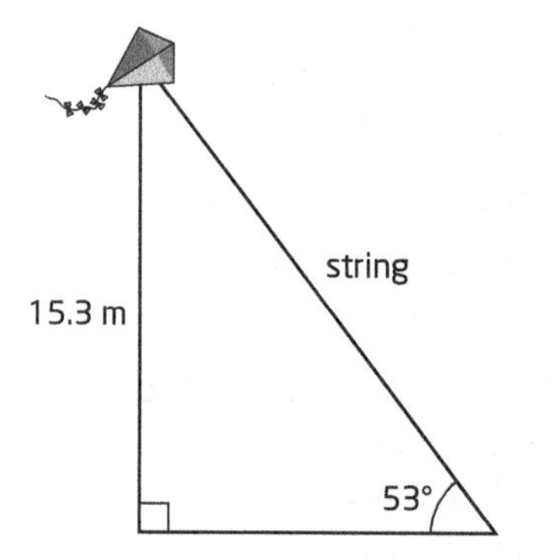

Let s represent the length of the string, in metres. Since we know the side opposite the angle and we need to find the hypotenuse, use the cosecant ratio.

$$\csc 53° = \frac{s}{15.3}$$
$$s = 15.3 \csc 53°$$
$$\doteq 19.2$$

The string is 19.2 m long.

A Practise

1. Given ΔABC, determine the six trigonometric ratios for $\angle C$.

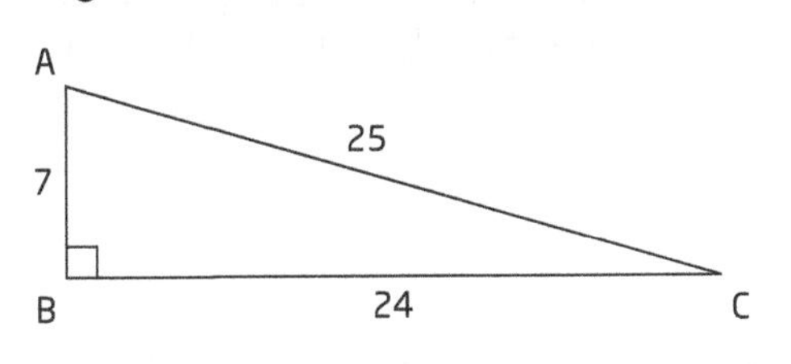

2. Repeat question 1 for $\angle A$.

3. State the reciprocal trigonometric ratio that corresponds to each primary trigonometric ratio.

a) $\sin\theta = \frac{3}{5}$

b) $\cos\theta = \frac{1}{\sqrt{2}}$

c) $\tan\theta = \frac{7}{3}$

d) $\cos\theta = -\frac{6}{\sqrt{61}}$

e) $\tan\theta = -5$

f) $\sin\theta = -\frac{12}{13}$

g) $\cos\theta = 0$

h) $\sin\theta = 1$

4. State the primary trigonometric ratio that corresponds to each reciprocal trigonometric ratio.

a) $\sec\theta = \frac{8}{3}$

b) $\csc\theta = \frac{5}{4}$

c) $\cot\theta = -\frac{1}{\sqrt{3}}$

d) $\sec\theta = -\frac{17}{15}$

e) $\csc\theta = \sqrt{2}$

f) $\cot\theta = -\frac{9}{4}$

g) $\sec\theta = -1$

h) $\csc\theta =$ undefined

5. Use a calculator to determine the six trigonometric ratios of each angle, to three decimal places.

a) 40°

b) 36°

c) 88°

d) 110°

e) 237°

f) 319°

g) 95°

h) 67°

i) 124°

6. Use a calculator to find each value of θ, to the nearest degree, where $0° \leq \theta \leq 90°$.

a) $\csc\theta = 1.624$

b) $\cot\theta = 0.675$

c) $\sec\theta = 1.058$

d) $\cot\theta = 0.554$

e) $\sec\theta = 1.325$

f) $\csc\theta = 1.305$

g) $\cot\theta = 3.732$

h) $\sec\theta = 3.628$

7. Determine exact expressions for the six trigonometric ratios for 210°. Hint: Draw a diagram of the angle in standard position. Then, use special triangles to determine exact values.

8. Determine exact expressions for the six trigonometric ratios for 225°.

9. Determine exact expressions for the six trigonometric ratios for 90°.

10. Determine two angles between 0° and 360° that have a cosecant of $-\frac{2}{\sqrt{3}}$. Use the unit circle to help you. Do not use a calculator.

11. Find the measure, to the nearest degree, of an angle in the first quadrant that satisfies each ratio.

a) $\sin A = \frac{6}{11}$

b) $\cos B = \frac{4}{5}$

c) $\tan C = \frac{13}{5}$

d) $\csc D = \frac{10}{7}$

e) $\sec E = \frac{8}{5}$

f) $\cot F = \frac{14}{9}$

g) $\sec G = 3$

h) $\csc H = \frac{7}{4}$

12. Determine two angles between 0° and 360° that have a cotangent of 1. Use the unit circle to help you. Do not use a calculator.

13. Each point lies on the terminal arm of an angle in standard position. Determine exact expressions for the six trigonometric ratios for the angle.

a) P(−3, 4)

b) Q(−12, −5)

c) R(−8, 15)

d) S(6, 2)

e) T(2, −3)

f) U(−7, −12)

g) V(1, 5)

h) W(6, 11)

i) X(−5, 5)

j) Y(8, −3)

B Connect and Apply

14. Determine the three reciprocal trigonometric ratios for each triangle. Then, use one of the ratios to find the measure of angle θ, to the nearest degree.

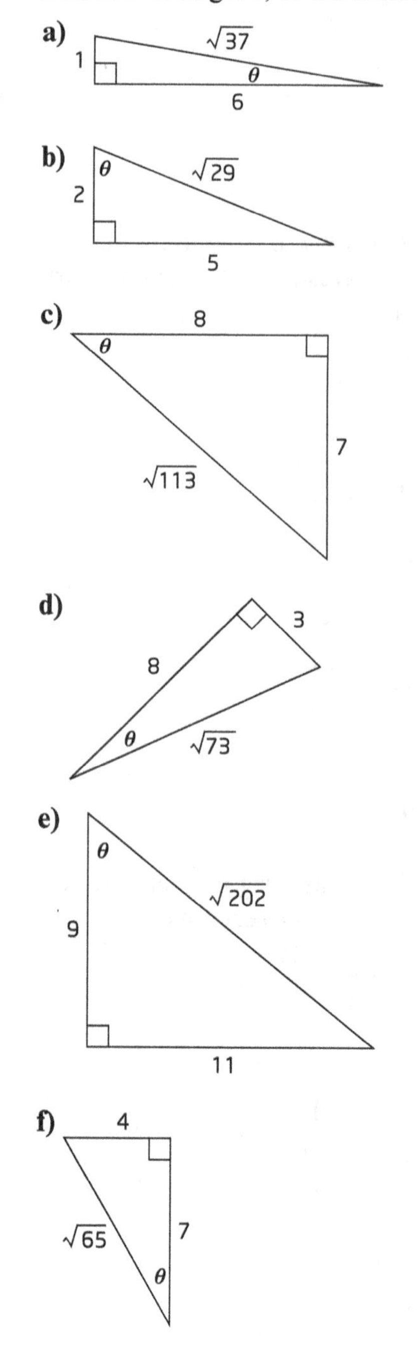

★ **15.** Determine two angles between 0° and 360° that have a cosecant of −3.5. Round answers to the nearest degree.

16. Determine two angles between 0° and 360° that have a secant of −6.3.

17. Determine two angles between 0° and 360° that have a cotangent of 4.

18. Find the value of the other five trigonometric ratios for angle θ if $\tan \theta = -\frac{24}{7}$ and the terminal arm lies in the fourth quadrant.

19. Find the value of the other five trigonometric ratios for angle θ if $\csc \theta = \frac{5}{4}$ and the terminal arm lies in the second quadrant.

20. Find the value of the other five trigonometric ratios for angle θ if $\cos \theta = -\frac{1}{3}$ and the terminal arm lies in the third quadrant.

21. Find the value of the other five trigonometric ratios for angle θ if $\sec \theta = \frac{7}{4}$ and the terminal arm lies in the first quadrant.

22. A guy wire supporting a telephone pole is secured to the ground at a point 16.7 m from the base of the pole. The wire makes an angle of 48° with the ground.

a) Use a reciprocal trigonometric ratio to write an equation that can be used to determine the length of the wire.

b) Use your equation in part a) to find the length of the wire, to the nearest centimetre.

23. A wheelchair ramp to the front porch of a house is to be built so that it has an angle of inclination of 14.5° and a height of 1.3 m.

a) Use a reciprocal trigonometric ratio to write an equation that can be used to determine the length of the ramp.

b) Use your equation in part a) to find the length of the ramp, to the nearest centimetre.

24. Determine the value of each expression if $\cos A = \frac{5}{14}$ and $\sin B = \frac{4}{13}$.

a) $\frac{\cos A \tan A}{\csc A}$

b) $\frac{\sin B \sec B}{\cot B}$

c) $\frac{\sin A \cot A}{\sec A}$

d) $\frac{\cos B \csc B}{\tan B}$

C Extend

★ **25. a)** Use expressions for the primary trigonometric ratios in terms of x, y, and r to show that $\sin^2 \theta + \cos^2 \theta = 1$, regardless of the value of θ. This equation is known as the Pythagorean identity. Why is this name appropriate?

b) Write an equivalent equation in terms of the reciprocal trigonometric ratios.

26. Consider an angle θ in the third quadrant such that $\sec \theta = -\frac{a}{b}$. Determine expressions in terms of a and b for the other five trigonometric ratios for θ. State any restrictions on a and b.

27. Given that $\cot \theta = \frac{2x}{x + 1}$, $x \neq -1$, and θ is in the first quadrant, determine the other two reciprocal trigonometric ratios.

4.4 Problems in Two Dimensions

KEY CONCEPTS

- Primary trigonometric ratios are used to solve triangles that contain a right angle.
- The sine law is used to solve oblique triangles when two angles and a side are given. In the case when two sides and an opposite angle are given, there may be two possible solutions, one solution, or no solution. This is known as the ambiguous case.
- The cosine law is used to solve oblique triangles when two sides and a contained angle or three sides and no angles are given.

Example

Given $\triangle ABC$ with known side lengths a and b and known angle A, state the conditions for no solution, one solution, and two solutions for the length of the third side, c.

Solution

Case 1: $a \geq b$

In this case, $CB \geq CA$. Therefore, only one triangle can be constructed.

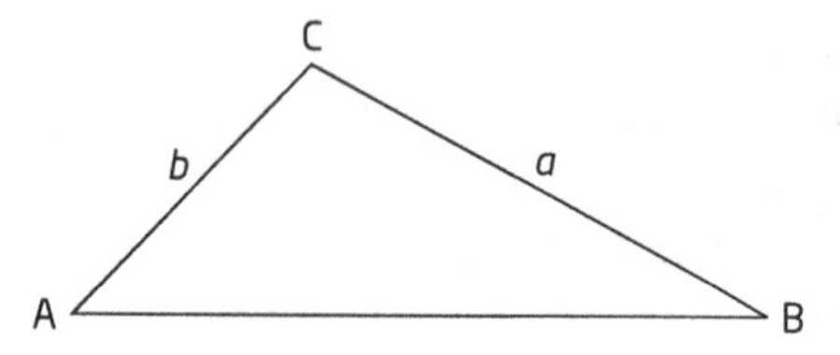

Case 2: $a < b$

In this case, there are three possibilities.

i) If $a < b \sin A$, then no triangle can be drawn.

ii) If $a = b \sin A$, then there is one right triangle and one solution.

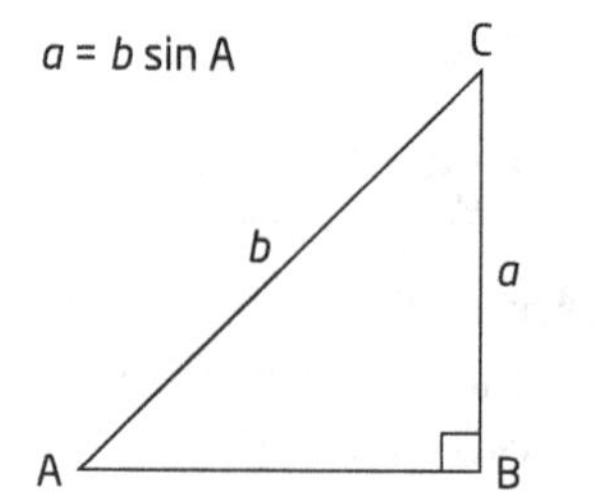

iii) If $a > b \sin A$, then there are two possible triangles. This is the ambiguous case.

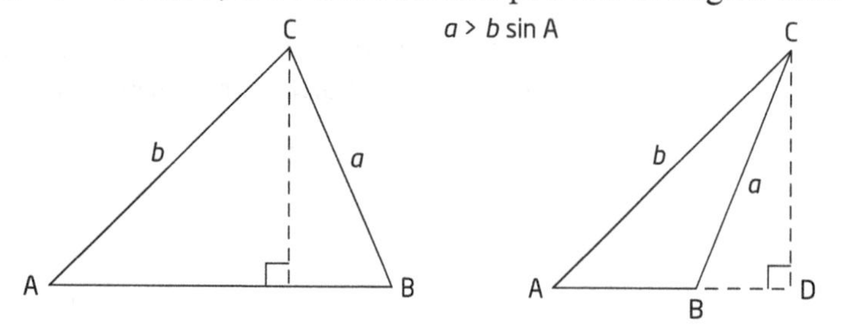

A Practise

1. For each triangle, select the most appropriate method among primary trigonometric ratios, the sine law, and the cosine law. Justify your choice.

   a) In $\triangle ABC$, $\angle C = 90°$, $\angle B = 28°$, and $c = 12$ cm. Determine a.

   b) In $\triangle PQR$, $\angle P = 51°$, $\angle R = 39°$, and $p = 9$ m. Determine r.

   c) In $\triangle ABC$, $a = 10$ cm, $b = 7$ cm, and $c = 8$ cm. Determine $\angle B$.

   d) In $\triangle DEF$, $\angle D = 130°$, $e = 10$ cm, and $f = 8$ cm. Determine d.

   e) In $\triangle XYZ$, $\angle X = 90°$, $y = 15.6$ km, and $z = 12.3$ km. Determine $\angle Y$.

2. Determine the indicated quantity for each triangle in question 1. Round each answer to one decimal place.

3. The shadow of a tree that is 18.5 m tall measures 10.2 m in length. Determine the angle of elevation of the sun.

4. Solve each triangle by finding all unknown values.

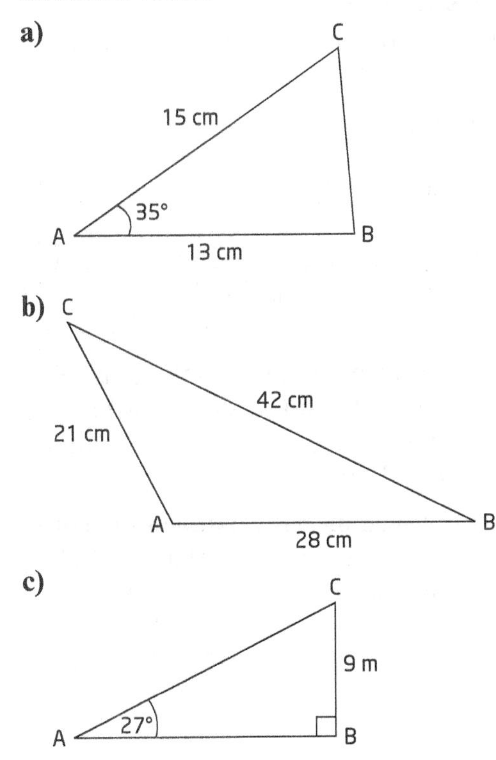

5. A roof truss spans a width of 8.2 m. One piece of the truss is 6.8 m long and set at an angle of 35°, as shown. How long is the third piece of the truss?

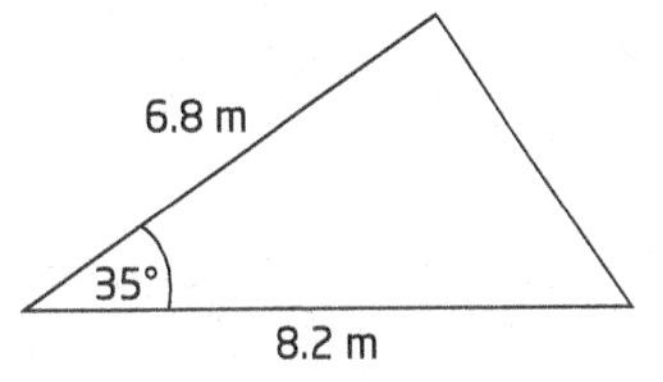

6. A radar station at point A is tracking two ships. Ship B is 4.5 km away in a direction 42° east of north. Ship C is 3.3 km away in a direction 58° west of north. How far apart are the two ships, to the nearest tenth of a kilometre?

7. A tunnel is to be built through a hill to connect the towns of Mathville and Trigville with a straight road. A straight road between Mathville and Functionville is 2 km long. A straight road from Trigville to Functionville is 5 km long. The angle between the two roads is 63°.

   a) Determine the length of the road between Mathville and Trigville, to the nearest tenth of a kilometre.

   b) Determine the angle between the road connecting Functionville and Mathville and the road from Mathville to Trigville.

8. For each of the following, draw possible diagrams that match the given measurements. Then, calculate the length of the unknown side.

   a) In $\triangle ABC$, $c = 9$ cm, $b = 11$ cm, and $\angle B = 48°$.

   b) In $\triangle ABC$, $a = 5.9$ m, $b = 7.8$ m, and $\angle A = 36°$.

9. For each triangle, two sides and a non-included angle are given. Determine two possible measures for $\angle C$ and for the length of side b.

   a) In $\triangle ABC$, $a = 2.4$ cm, $c = 3.2$ cm, and $\angle A = 28°$.

   b) In $\triangle DEF$, $d = 3$ cm, $e = 5$ cm, and $\angle D = 30°$.

B Connect and Apply

☆**10.** In ΔABC, $a = 1.2$ cm, $b = 2.7$ cm, and $\angle A = 32°$.

a) Calculate $b \sin A$.

b) How many solutions occur for ΔABC?

11. In ΔABC, $a = 2.4$ cm, $b = 4.8$ cm, and $\angle A = 30°$.

a) Calculate $b \sin A$.

b) How many solutions occur for ΔABC?

12. In ΔABC, $a = 6.1$ cm, $b = 8.1$ cm, and $\angle A = 32°$.

a) Calculate $b \sin A$.

b) How many solutions occur for ΔABC?

13. Two forest fire stations, A and B, are 20 km apart. A ranger at station A sees a fire at point C, 15 km away. The angle between the line AB and the line AC to the fire is 21°. How far, to the nearest tenth of a kilometre, is station B from the fire?

14. Two ships, S and T, are 120 km apart when they pick up a distress call from a yacht. Ship T estimates that the yacht is 70 km away and that the angle between the line from T to S and the line from S to the yacht is 28°. What are two possible distances, to the nearest tenth of a kilometre, from ship S to the yacht?

15. A pedestrian bridge is built over a river. The angle of depression from one end of the bridge to a large rock beside the river is 37°. The distance from that end of the bridge to the rock is 112 m, while the distance from the rock to the other end of the bridge is 75 m. Determine the length of the bridge.

16. Two small islands, Aqua and Belli, are 32.0 km apart. How far is each island from a lighthouse, at point L, on the main shore if $\angle A = 68°$ and $\angle B = 42°$?

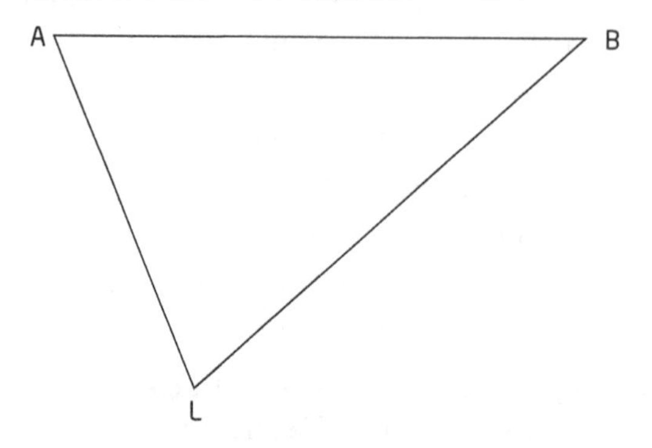

17. Kettletown is 27.0 km from Teatown and 32.0 km from Coffeetown. The angle from Kettletown to Coffeetown to Teatown is 29°. Determine two possible distances between Teatown and Coffeetown.

18. A parallelogram has vertices A(4, 4), B(9, 1), C(0, −5), and D(−3, −2). Determine the length of each diagonal.

19. Solve ΔABC, given BC = 6.0 cm, AC = 4.0 cm, and $\angle B = 30°$.

C Extend

20. In ΔABC, AC = 2, AB = 3, and BC = 4. Prove each statement.

a) $\sin B = \frac{1}{2} \sin A$

b) $\sin C = \frac{3}{4} \sin A$

☆**21. a)** Determine the possible range of values for side a so that ΔABC has two solutions if $\angle A = 40°$ and $b = 50.0$.

b) Determine the possible range of values for side a so that ΔABC has no solution if $\angle A = 56°$ and $b = 125.7$.

c) Determine the possible range of values for side a so that ΔABC has exactly one solution if $\angle A = 57°$ and $b = 73.7$.

4.5 Problems in Three Dimensions

KEY CONCEPTS

- Three-dimensional problems involving triangles can be solved using one or more of the following: the Pythagorean theorem, the six trigonometric ratios, the sine law, and the cosine law.
- The method chosen to solve a triangle depends on the known information.

Example

Two stunt pilots are flying to an air show to join an aerial formation at noon. At 9:30 a.m., the first pilot passes over a navigational beacon, A, at a speed of 200 km/h and sets a course 40° east of north to go directly to the formation point for a noon arrival. At 10:00 a.m., the second pilot reaches another beacon, B, located 150 km northwest of beacon A.

a) Determine the speed and direction that the second pilot must fly from beacon B in order to reach the formation point at noon.

b) As seen from an airfield due east of the formation point, the angle of elevation of the aircraft is 10°. If both aircraft are at an altitude of 1500 m, how far is the airfield from beacon B? Round your answer to the nearest kilometre.

Solution

Draw a diagram to represent this situation. In the illustration, A represents the location of the first navigational beacon, B is the location of the second beacon, C is the ground point directly below the aerial formation area, and D is the airfield.

The first pilot is flying at 200 km/h so that in 2.5 h (from 9:30 a.m. to noon) the pilot travels a distance of 500 km.

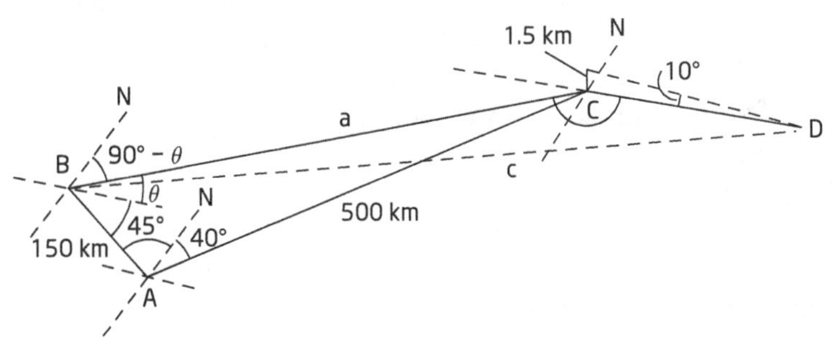

a) From the diagram, $\angle A = 85°$ and the angle $90° - \theta$ represents the direction of flight of the second aircraft.

Since the length of two sides and the measure of the contained angle are known, use the cosine law to solve for a.

$$a^2 = 150^2 + 500^2 - 2(150)(500)\cos 85°$$
$$\doteq 259\,426.64$$
$$a \doteq 509.3$$

The second pilot must fly a distance of 509.3 km in 2 h, so the plane must travel at a speed of approximately 255 km/h.

To find the measure of angle θ, first use the sine law to determine $\angle$B.

$$\frac{\sin B}{500} = \frac{\sin 85^\circ}{509.3}$$
$$\sin B \doteq 0.978\ 00$$
$$\angle B \doteq 78^\circ$$

$$\theta = 78^\circ - 45^\circ$$
$$= 33^\circ$$

The direction that the second aircraft must head is 90° – 33°, or 57° east of north.

Therefore, in order to join the aerial formation at noon, the second pilot must fly from beacon B at a speed of 255 km/h in a direction 57° east of north.

b) From the diagram, CD represents the distance from the formation point to the airfield and is the base of a right triangle having a vertical distance of 1.5 km (the altitude of the aircraft). Use the primary trigonometric ratios to calculate the length of CD.

$$\tan 10^\circ = \frac{\text{opposite}}{\text{adjacent}}$$
$$\tan 10^\circ = \frac{1.5}{CD}$$
$$CD = \frac{1.5}{\tan 10^\circ}$$
$$CD \doteq 8.506$$

Therefore, the airfield is approximately 8.5 km east of the formation point.
As illustrated on the diagram, DB is the distance from the airfield to the second beacon. The line is one side of ΔBCD. $\angle$C equals 90° + (90 – θ)°, or 147°. The angle is contained by sides BC and CD, the lengths of which are known. Therefore, use the cosine law in ΔBCD to determine the distance, c, from the airfield to the second beacon:

$$c^2 = (509.3)^2 + (8.5)^2 - 2(509.3)(8.5) \cos 147^\circ$$
$$c^2 = 259\ 386.49 + 72.25 - (8658.1) \cos 147^\circ$$
$$c^2 \doteq 266\ 720.03$$
$$c \doteq 516.45$$

The airfield is approximately 516 km from the second beacon.

A Practise

1. The bases on a baseball diamond are 27.4 m apart. The pitcher pitches, and the batter hits a fly ball straight up 18 m. What is the maximum angle of elevation of the ball, to the nearest degree, as seen by the pitcher if he is standing at the centre of the diamond?

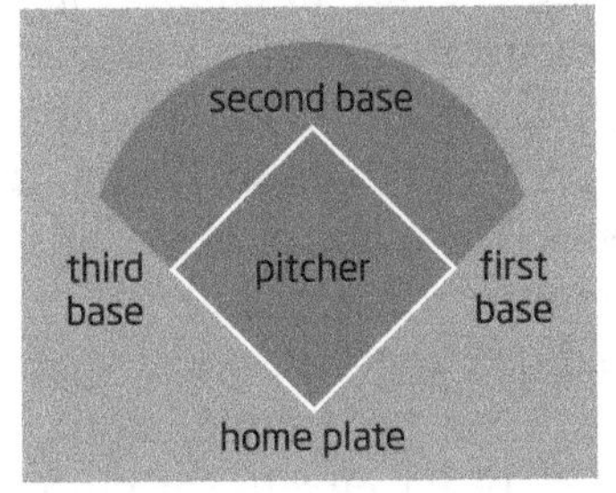

2. A pyramid has a square base of side length 10.5 m. The slant height of the pyramid is 19.5 m.
   a) Determine the height of the pyramid, to the nearest tenth of a metre.
   b) Determine the angle θ between one face and the base, to the nearest tenth of a degree.

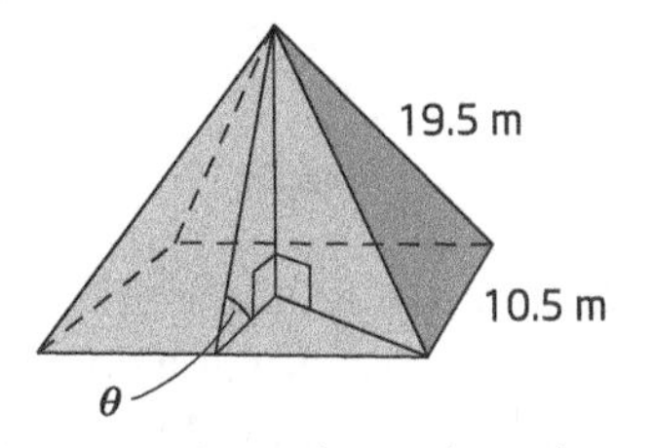

3. A square-based tent has the cross-sectional shape shown. The side wall goes up at an angle of elevation of 55° for 2.8 m, then continues at an angle of elevation of 32° for another 2.1 m to the peak.

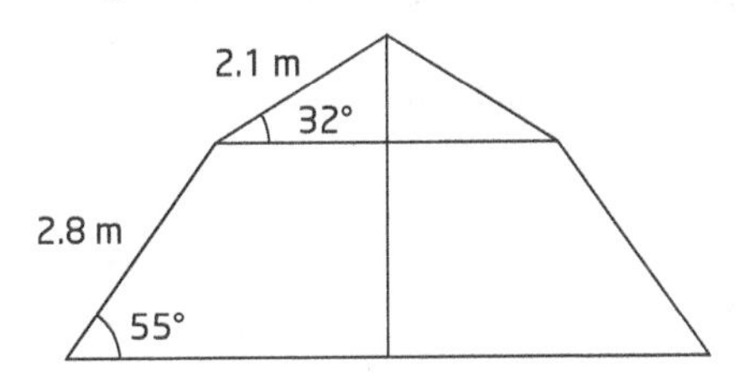

   a) Determine the height of the tent.
   b) Determine the side length of the base.
   c) Determine the length of one of the diagonals of the base.

4. A gift box for a perfume bottle is in the shape of a pyramid with a rectangular base. The dimensions of the base are 10 cm by 7 cm and the length of each side edge is 16 cm. Determine the height of the pyramid.

B Connect and Apply

5. Beni and Alessio watch a rocket as it is launched. Beni is 0.8 km closer to the launching pad than Alessio. When the rocket disappears from view, its angle of elevation for Beni is 36.5° and for Alessio is 31.9°. Determine the altitude of the rocket, to the nearest tenth of a kilometre, at the time it disappears from view.

6. A rectangular prism has length 10 cm, width 8 cm, and height 5 cm.

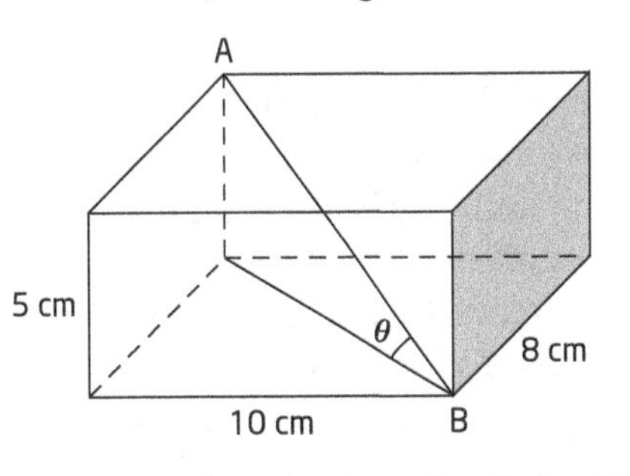

   a) Determine the length of the diagonal AB.
   b) Determine the measure of angle θ.

☆7. Angela is a surveyor. To find the height, h, of an inaccessible cliff, she takes measurements at point A some distance from the cliff and at a second point, C, which is along the base of the cliff and 400 m from point A. Angela determines the angle of elevation from point C to the top of the cliff is 18°. She finds that the angle from point B, which is at the base of the cliff directly below the top, to C to A is 35°, and that the angle from B to A to C is 27°.
   a) Draw a diagram to represent this situation.
   b) What is the height of the cliff, to the nearest metre?

8. Annette and Devon want to determine how high their model rocket can fly. The rocket is launched from point B and reaches an altitude, h. Annette is standing at point A and measures the angle of elevation to the tip of the rocket at its highest point (D) to be 41°. Devon is standing at point C, 300 m from Annette, and measures the angle of elevation to be 30°. If ∠BAC is 42.6° and ∠BCA is 25.2°, what altitude does the rocket reach, to the nearest metre?

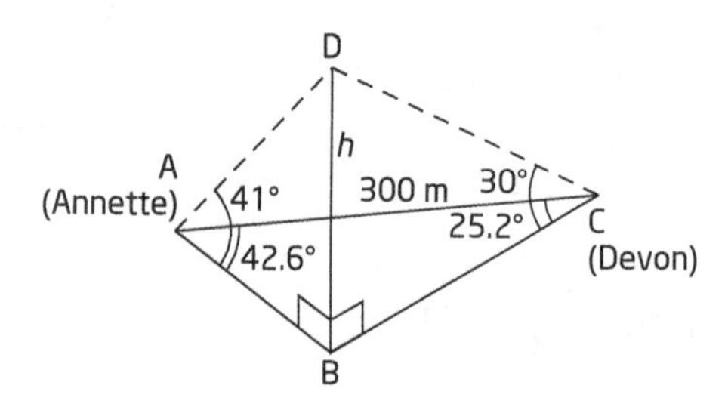

★**9.** Kamira is flying in a hot-air balloon and notices a barn directly below the balloon and a farmhouse located at an angle of depression of 28°. After the balloon rises vertically a further 58 m, the angle of depression to the farmhouse is 42°.

a) How high is the balloon before it rises?

b) How far is the barn from the farmhouse?

10. To determine the height, h, of a tree in Algonquin Park, a conservation officer records measurements in a diagram. Determine the height of the tree.

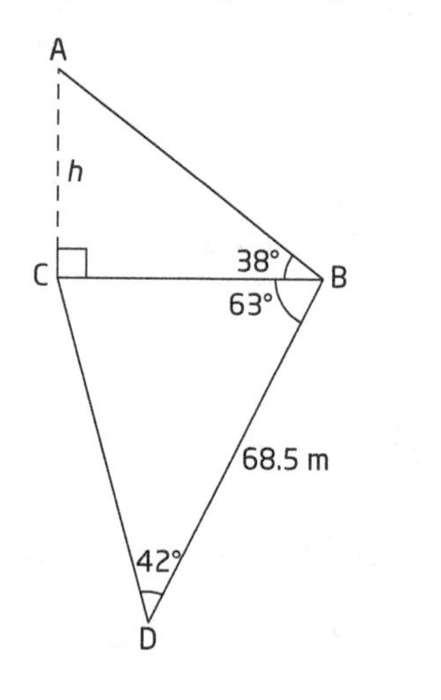

11. A hydro tower located on the side of a hill casts a 55-m-long shadow down the hill when the angle of elevation of the sun is 48.3°. Determine the height of the tower if the angle of inclination of the hill is 21.4°.

C Extend

12. Maria is flying in a hot-air balloon at a height of 64 m. Her friends, Leah, Gina, and Annette, are on the ground at different points so that the balloon is between them. The angle of elevation from each girl to the balloon is 71°. The angle formed between the lines of sight from Gina to Leah and from Gina to Annette is 82°. Determine the distance between Leah and Annette.

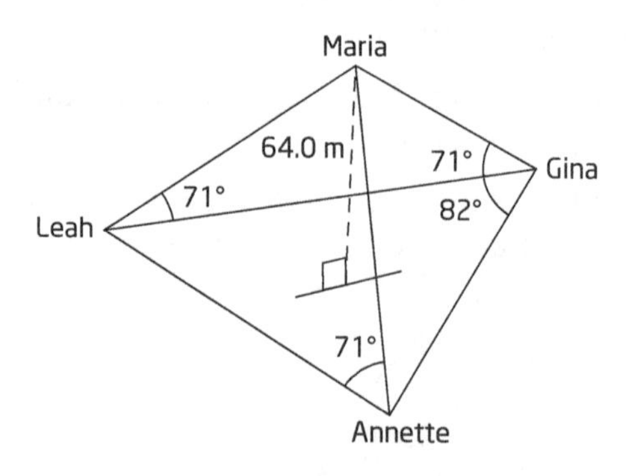

13. A jet is flying in a straight line at an average speed of 850 km/h at a constant altitude above level ground. At a certain time, the jet's location is due south of an island such that the angle of elevation from the island to the jet is 59°. Ten seconds later, the jet is due west of the island at an angle of elevation of 51°. Determine the altitude of the jet.

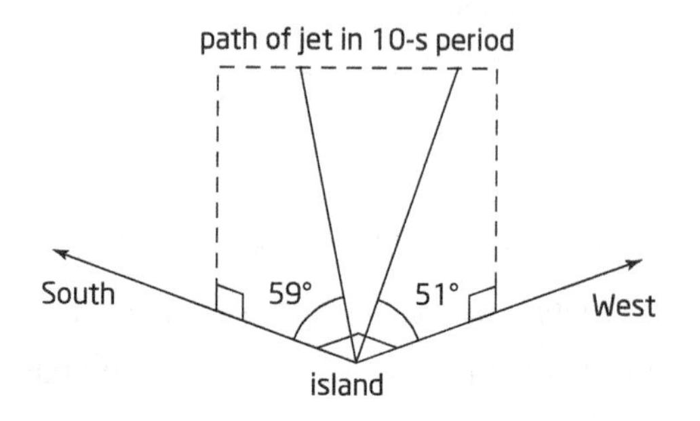

4.6 Trigonometric Identities

KEY CONCEPTS

- A trigonometric identity is a relation among trigonometric ratios that is true for all angles for which both sides are defined.
- The basic identities are the Pythagorean identity, the quotient identity, and the reciprocal identities:
- **Pythagorean Identity** $\sin^2 \theta + \cos^2 \theta = 1$
- **Quotient Identity** $\frac{\sin \theta}{\cos \theta} = \tan \theta$
- **Reciprocal Identities** $\csc \theta = \frac{1}{\sin \theta}$

  $\sec \theta = \frac{1}{\cos \theta}$

  $\cot \theta = \frac{1}{\tan \theta}$
- The basic identities can be used to prove more complex identities.
- Identities can be used to simplify solutions to problems that result in trigonometric expressions.

Example

Prove that $\sin^4 \theta + 2\cos^2 \theta - \cos^4 \theta = 1$ for all θ.

Proof

$$
\begin{aligned}
\text{L.S.} &= \sin^4 \theta + 2\cos^2 \theta - \cos^4 \theta \\
&= \sin^4 \theta - \cos^4 \theta + 2\cos^2 \theta && \text{Rearrange the terms.} \\
&= (\sin^2 \theta - \cos^2 \theta)(\sin^2 \theta + \cos^2 \theta) + 2\cos^2 \theta && \text{Factor using difference of squares.} \\
&= (\sin^2 \theta - \cos^2 \theta)(1) + 2\cos^2 \theta && \text{Substitute } \sin^2 \theta + \cos^2 \theta = 1 \\
&= \sin^2 \theta - \cos^2 \theta + 2\cos^2 \theta \\
&= \sin^2 \theta + \cos^2 \theta \\
&= 1 \\
&= \text{R.S.}
\end{aligned}
$$

Therefore, L.S. = R.S., and the statement is true for all θ.

A Practise

1. Using the Pythagorean identities, state an equivalent expression for each.

   a) $\sin^2 \theta$

   b) $\tan^2 \theta$

   c) $\sec^2 \theta$

   d) $1 - \sin^2 \theta$

   e) $1 - \csc^2 \theta$

   f) $\cot^2 \theta - \csc^2 \theta$

   g) $-\dfrac{1}{\csc^2 \theta}$

   h) $\dfrac{\cos^2 \theta}{\sin^2 \theta}$

2. Express each expression in a simpler form.

   a) $\cos \theta \sec \theta$

   b) $\tan \theta \cos \theta$

   c) $\tan \theta + \cot \theta$

   d) $\sqrt{1 - \cos^2 \theta}$

   e) $\tan^2 \theta - \sec^2 \theta$

   f) $\dfrac{\cos \theta}{1 + \sin \theta} + \dfrac{\cos \theta}{1 - \sin \theta}$

3. Factor to simplify each expression.

   a) $\sin^4 \theta + \sin^2 \theta \cos^2 \theta$

   b) $(\sec \theta)^2 (\sin \theta)^2 + (\sin \theta)^2$

   c) $4 \cos^2 \theta + 8 \cos \theta \sin \theta + 4 \sin^2 \theta$

   d) $\sin^4 \theta - \cos^4 \theta$

4. Use the definitions of the primary trigonometric ratios in terms of x, y, and r to prove each identity.

   a) $\tan \theta \cos \theta = \sin \theta$

   b) $\cot \theta \sec \theta = \csc \theta$

   c) $\dfrac{1 + \cot^2 \theta}{\csc^2 \theta} = 1$

5. Prove that $\cos \theta \cot \theta = \dfrac{1}{\sin \theta} - \sin \theta$.

6. Explain how technology may be used to verify an identity.

B Connect and Apply

7. Prove that $\dfrac{\cos^2 \theta}{1 - \sin \theta} = 1 + \sin \theta$.

★8. Prove that $\dfrac{1 + \cot \theta}{\csc \theta} = \sin \theta + \cos \theta$.

9. Prove that $\dfrac{\tan^2 \theta}{1 + \tan^2 \theta} = \sin^2 \theta$.

★10. Refer to the Example at the beginning of this section. Use an alternate method to prove the given statement.

11. Prove each identity.

    a) $\dfrac{\cos \theta \sin \theta}{\cot \theta} = 1 - \cos^2 \theta$

    b) $\dfrac{\sin^2 \theta}{1 - \cos \theta} = 1 + \cos \theta$

    c) $\dfrac{1 + \sec \theta}{\sec \theta - 1} = \dfrac{1 + \cos \theta}{1 - \cos \theta}$

    d) $\dfrac{1 + \sin \theta}{1 - \sin \theta} = \dfrac{\csc \theta - 1}{\csc \theta + 1}$

12. Simplify $\sin^2 \theta + \dfrac{1 + \cot^2 \theta}{1 + \tan^2 \theta} + \cos^2 \theta$.

13. Prove that $2 \sin (-\theta) - \cot \theta \sin \theta \cos \theta = (\sin \theta - 1)^2 - 2$.

14. **a)** Start with an identity that has already been proved. Make substitutions and rearrange terms until the identity is no longer recognizable.

    b) Trade the new identity you have written with that of a classmate. Use a different method to prove the identity written by your classmate.

15. Explain why the identity $\dfrac{\cos \theta}{1 + \sin \theta} + \dfrac{\cos \theta}{1 - \sin \theta} = \dfrac{2}{\cos \theta}$ is not true for $\theta = 90°$ and $\theta = 270°$.

16. Prove that $\dfrac{1 + \sin \theta + \cos \theta}{1 - \sin \theta + \cos \theta} = \dfrac{1 + \sin \theta}{\cos \theta}$.

17. Prove that
$$\frac{1}{1 + \sin\theta} + \frac{1}{1 - \sin\theta} = \frac{2}{\cos^2\theta}.$$

18. Prove that
$$\frac{7\sin\theta + 5\cos\theta}{\cos\theta\sin\theta} = 7\sec\theta + 5\csc\theta.$$

19. Prove that $(\csc\theta - \cot\theta)^2 = \frac{1 - \cos\theta}{1 + \cos\theta}$.

20. Prove that $\sec^2\theta + \csc^2\theta = \frac{\csc^2\theta}{\cos^2\theta}$.

21. Prove that $\sec\theta - \frac{\sin\theta}{\cot\theta} = \frac{1}{\sec\theta}$.

22. Prove that $\tan^2\theta\cos^2\theta = 1 - \frac{\sin^2\theta}{\tan^2\theta}$.

23. Prove that $\frac{\tan\theta - \sin\theta}{\sin^3\theta} = \frac{\sec\theta}{1 + \cos\theta}$.

24. Prove that $\frac{1 + \sin\theta}{\tan\theta} = \cos\theta + \cot\theta$.

25. Prove that $(\tan\theta + \cot\theta)^2$
$= \sec^2\theta + \frac{1}{\sin^2\theta}$.

26. **Use Technology** For each equation, use a graphing calculator to graph each side to determine if the equation appears to be an identity.

a) $\frac{1}{\sin^2\theta} + \frac{1}{\cos^2\theta} = 1$

b) $\cos\theta\,(\cos\theta - \sec\theta) = -\sin^2\theta$

c) $2\sin\theta + (1 - \sin\theta)^2 = 2 - \cos^2\theta$

d) $\frac{\sin^3\theta - \cos^3\theta}{\sin\theta - \cos\theta} = \sin^2\theta + \cos^2\theta$

27. Refer to your results in question 26.

a) Prove each of the statements that you found is an identity.

b) For those statements that are not identities, provide an example to show why.

28. Prove that
$$(\sin\theta + \cos\theta)^2 = \frac{2 + \sec\theta\csc\theta}{\sec\theta\csc\theta}.$$

29. Prove that
$$\frac{\cot\theta}{\csc\theta - 1} + \frac{\cot\theta}{\csc\theta + 1} = 2\sec\theta.$$

30. Prove that
$$\frac{\tan\theta + \cos\theta}{\sin\theta} = \frac{1}{\cos\theta} + \frac{\cos\theta}{\sin\theta}.$$

31. Prove that
$$\frac{\cos^2\theta - \sin^2\theta}{\cos^2\theta + \sin\theta\cos\theta} = \frac{\cot\theta - 1}{\cot\theta}.$$

32. Prove that $\tan\theta\sin\theta + \cos\theta - \sec\theta + 1$
$= \sec^2\theta\cos^2\theta$.

33. Prove that $\frac{1 - \tan^2\theta}{\tan\theta - \tan^2\theta} = 1 + \frac{1}{\tan\theta}$.

34. **a)** Prove that $\tan^2\theta(1 + \cot^2\theta) = \sec^2\theta$.

b) Create an identity similar to the identity in part a) and prove it.

35. **a)** Prove each identity.

i) $(1 - \cos^2\theta)(1 + \tan^2\theta) = \tan^2\theta$

ii) $(1 - \sin^2\theta)(1 + \cot^2\theta) = \cot^2\theta$

b) For each identity in part a), create a similar identity and prove it.

C Extend

36. Prove that $\sin^2\theta - \cos^2\theta = \frac{2 - \sec^2\theta}{-\sec^2\theta}$.

37. Prove that
$$\frac{\csc\theta}{1 - \csc\theta} + \frac{\csc\theta}{\csc\theta + 1} = -\frac{2\sin\theta}{\cos^2\theta}.$$

38. Prove that $\sec^2\theta - \frac{\tan\theta}{\cos\theta} = \frac{1}{1 + \sin\theta}$.

39. Prove that $\frac{\tan^3\theta}{1 + \tan^2\theta} + \frac{\cot^3\theta}{1 + \cot^2\theta}$
$= \frac{1 - 2\sin^2\theta\cos^2\theta}{\sin\theta\cos\theta}$.

40. Simplify $\frac{1}{4\sin^2\theta\cos^2\theta} - \frac{(1 - \tan^2\theta)^2}{4\tan^2\theta}$.

Chapter 4 Review

4.1 Special Angles

1. For each angle, use exact values to show that $\sin^2 x + \cos^2 x = 1$.

   a) $x = 60°$ **b)** $x = 150°$ **c)** $x = 225°$

2. Determine the exact value of each expression.

   a) $\sin 45° \times \tan 30° \times \cos 120°$

   b) $\sin 240° + \tan 225° - \cos 330°$

   c) $\sin 270° \times \tan 300° - \cos 180°$

3. A guy wire is fastened 6 m from the base of a flagpole and makes an angle θ with the ground. For each given angle θ, determine

   i) the length of the wire

   ii) how far up the pole the wire is fastened

   a) 45° **b)** 30° **c)** 60°

4. A tiling company develops a floor tile in the shape of a regular hexagon that has an area of 30 cm^2. Determine the exact length of the six equal sides of the tile.

4.2 Co-terminal and Related Angles

5. The coordinates of a point on the terminal arm of an angle θ are shown. Determine the exact trigonometric ratios for θ.

   a) E(−5, 12)

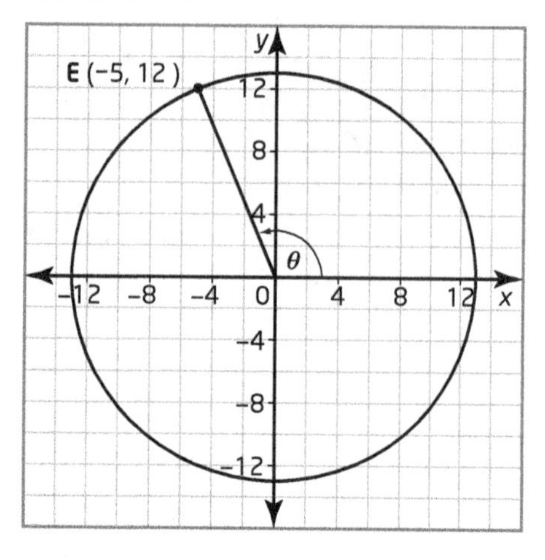

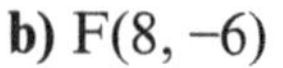
b) F(8, −6)

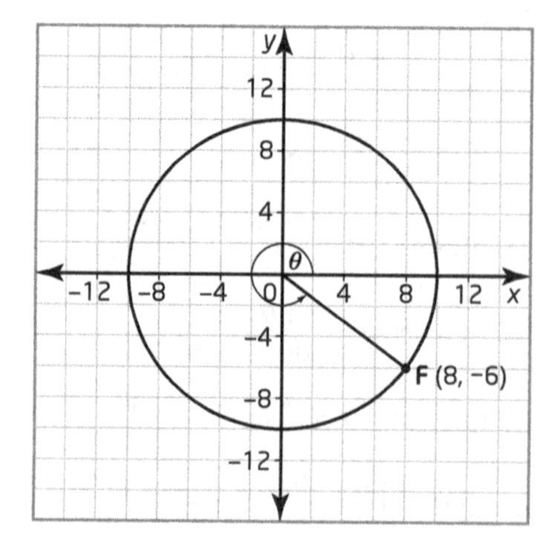

6. One of the primary trigonometric ratios for an angle is given, as well as the quadrant in which the terminal arm lies. Find the other two primary trigonometric ratios.

   a) $\sin G = -\frac{5}{11}$, third quadrant

   b) $\cos E = \frac{4}{7}$, first quadrant

7. Solve each equation for $0° \leq \theta \leq 360°$.

   a) $\sin \theta = \frac{5}{8}$

   b) $\cos \theta = -0.35$

   c) $\tan \theta = \frac{4}{9}$

4.3 Reciprocal Trigonometric Ratios

8. Determine exact expressions for the six trigonometric ratios for 120°.

9. Each point lies on the terminal arm of an angle in standard position. Determine exact expressions for the six trigonometric ratios for each angle.

   a) T(24, −7)

   b) U(−5, −3)

   c) V(4, −9)

   d) W(1, 3)

4.4 Problems in Two Dimensions

10. For each triangle, determine the number of solutions then solve the triangle if possible.

a) In ΔABC, $\angle$A = 71°, a = 12.2 m, and b = 11.4 m.

b) In ΔABC, $\angle$A = 55°, a = 7.1 cm, and b = 9.6 cm.

c) In ΔABC, $\angle$A = 44°, a = 9.3 mm, and b = 12.3 mm.

d) In ΔDEF, $\angle$D = 42°, d = 8.5 km, and f = 7.3 km.

e) In ΔDEF, $\angle$E = 38°, d = 16.6 mm, and e = 13.4 mm.

f) In ΔDEF, $\angle$D = 47°, d = 8.1 m, and f = 12.2 m.

11. A marathon swimmer starts at Island A, swims 9.2 km to Island B, then 8.6 km to Island C. The angle formed by a line from Island B to Island A and a line from Island C to Island A is 52°. How far does the swimmer have to swim to return directly to Island A?

12. A solar-heated house is 10 m wide. The south side of the roof, containing the solar collectors, rises for 8 m at an angle of elevation of 60°.

a) Determine the length of the north side of the roof.

b) At what angle of elevation does the north side of the roof rise?

4.5 Problems in Three Dimensions

13. The pilot of a hot-air balloon, flying above a bridge, measures the angles of depression to each end of the bridge to be 54° and 71°. The direct distance from the balloon to the nearer end of the bridge is 270 m. Determine the length of the bridge.

14. Two roads intersect at an angle of 34°. Car A leaves the intersection on one of the roads and travels at 80 km/h. At the same time, Car B leaves the intersection on the other road and travels at 100 km/h. Two hours later a reporter in a traffic helicopter, which is above and between the two cars, notes that the angle of depression to the slower car is 20° and that the helicopter is 1 km from that vehicle. How far is the faster car from the helicopter?

15. The port of Math Harbour is located 200 km from Trig Town Inlet in a direction 50° east of north. A yacht leaves Trig Town Inlet at 8:00 a.m. and sails in a direction 15° west of north at a speed of 15 km/h. At the same time, a fishing boat leaves Math Harbour on a course 80° west of south at a speed of 20 km/h. Determine the distance, to the nearest kilometre, between the yacht and the fishing boat at 1:00 p.m.

4.6 Trigonometric Identities

16. State an equivalent expression for each.

a) $\cos^2 \theta$

b) $\csc^2 \theta$

c) $\cot^2 \theta$

d) $\sec^2 \theta - 1$

e) $\sec^2 \theta - \tan^2 \theta$

f) $\dfrac{1}{\sec^2 \theta}$

17. Prove each identity.

a) $\sec^2 \theta + \csc^2 \theta = (\tan \theta + \cot \theta)^2$

b) $\dfrac{\sin \theta + \cos \theta \cot \theta}{\cot \theta} = \sec \theta$

c) $\sin^2 \theta = \cos \theta (\sec \theta - \cos \theta)^2$

d) $\dfrac{1}{1 + \cos \theta} = \csc^2 \theta - \dfrac{\cot \theta}{\sin \theta}$

e) $\dfrac{1 + \csc \theta}{\cot \theta} - \sec \theta = \tan \theta$

Chapter 4 Math Contest

1. In $\triangle ABC$, $\angle B = 60°$ and $\angle C = 90°$. The bisector of $\angle B$ meets AC at D. Determine the ratio AD:DC.

2. An equilateral triangle is inscribed in a circle. Determine the exact ratio of the area of the triangle to the area of the circle.

3. The perpendicular bisectors of the sides of an equilateral triangle, with side lengths 20 cm, intersect at the centroid. How far is the centroid from each side?

4. Which is the perimeter of an equilateral triangle with height $5\sqrt{3}$ cm?

A $30\sqrt{3}$ cm　　**B** $10\sqrt{3}$ cm

C $10 + 5\sqrt{3}$　　**D** 30 cm

5. An equilateral triangle with side length 12 cm is divided into three triangles of equal area by two line segments of length x passing through a vertex. Which is the exact length of x?

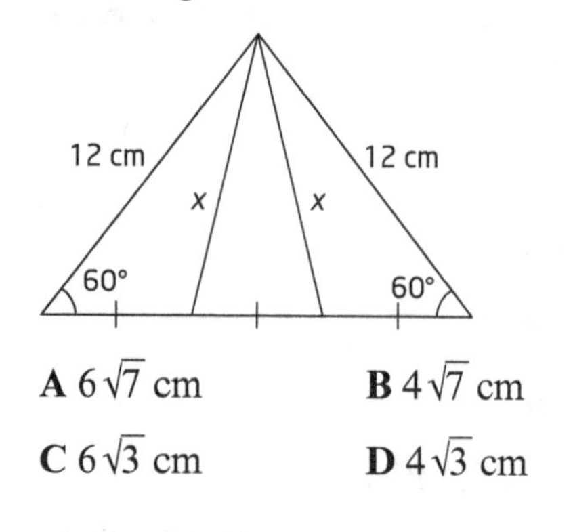

A $6\sqrt{7}$ cm　　**B** $4\sqrt{7}$ cm

C $6\sqrt{3}$ cm　　**D** $4\sqrt{3}$ cm

6. The length of one diagonal of a rhombus is equal to the length of one of its sides, x. Which is the length of the other diagonal in terms of the length of its sides?

A $x\sqrt{2}$　　**B** $\sqrt{2x}$

C $x\sqrt{3}$　　**D** $\sqrt{3x}$

7. In $\triangle ABC$, $\angle A = x$, $\angle B = 3x$, and $\angle C = 4x$. Which is the value of the expression $4 \sin 4x + 2 \cos^2 2x + 6 \tan 6x$?

A 1　　**B** -1

C $-\frac{1}{2}$　　**D** $\frac{1}{2}$

8. If P, Q, and R are the angles of a triangle such that $\cos P = 0$ and $\cos R = \frac{1}{2}$, then the value of $\sin Q + \cos Q$ is

A $\frac{1 + \sqrt{3}}{2}$　　**B** 0

C $\frac{\sqrt{2}}{2}$　　**D** $\sqrt{2}$

9. Determine the degree measure of the two equal angles in an isosceles triangle whose side lengths are 4 cm, 4 cm, and $(\sqrt{24} - \sqrt{8})$ cm.

A 45°　　**B** 75°

C 55°　　**D** 65°

10. Given $\frac{\tan \theta}{\cos \theta} = \frac{3}{8}$, where $0° < \theta < 180°$, which is the exact value of $\sin \theta$?

A 3　　**B** $\frac{8}{3}$

C $\frac{1}{8}$　　**D** $\frac{1}{3}$

11. When simplified, the expression $1 - \frac{\sin^2 \theta}{1 + \cot \theta} - \frac{\cos^2 \theta}{1 + \tan \theta}$ is equivalent to

A $\sin^2 \theta - \cos^2 \theta$

B 1

C $\sin \theta \cos \theta$

D $\frac{\sin \theta + \cos \theta}{1 + \sec \theta}$

Chapter 5 Trigonometric Functions

5.1 Modelling Periodic Behaviour

KEY CONCEPTS

- A pattern that repeats itself regularly is periodic.
- A periodic pattern can be modelled using a periodic function.
- One repetition of a periodic pattern is called a cycle.
- The horizontal length of a cycle on a graph is called the period. The period may be in units of time or other units of measurement.
- A function is periodic if there is a positive number, p, such that $f(x + p) = f(x)$ for every x in the domain of $f(x)$. The least value of p that works is the period of the function.
- $f(x + np) = f(x)$, where p is the period and n is any integer.
- The amplitude of a periodic function is half the difference between the maximum value and the minimum value in a cycle.

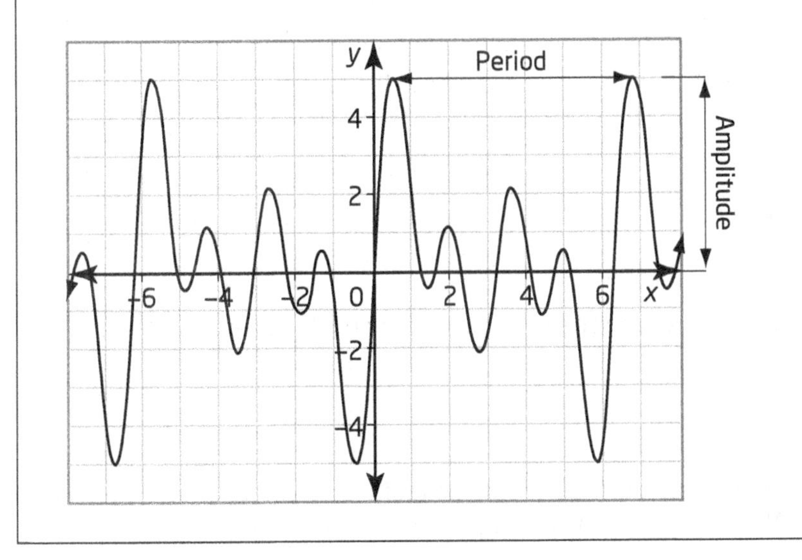

Example

David is on a competitive swim team. As part of his daily practice at the community pool, he is required to swim the breaststroke for 10 consecutive laps of the pool. The pool is 200 m long, and he swims from the shallow end to the deep end at a constant speed of 50 m/min.

a) Graph David's distance, in metres, from his starting point in the shallow end, versus time, for 10 laps of the pool.

b) Determine the period and amplitude of the function.

c) State the domain and range.

Solution

a) Recall that speed = distance ÷ time. So, time = distance ÷ speed.

$$\text{time} = 200 \div 50$$
$$= 4$$

It takes David 4 min to swim 200 m.

So, after 4 min he is 200 m away from his starting point. After another 4 min, or 8 min after starting, he is back at his starting point. Then, three points on the graph of distance versus time are (0, 0), (4, 200), and (8, 0). These points are joined with a straight line because David swims at constant speed of 50 km/h. The pattern continues until David has completed 10 laps of the pool.

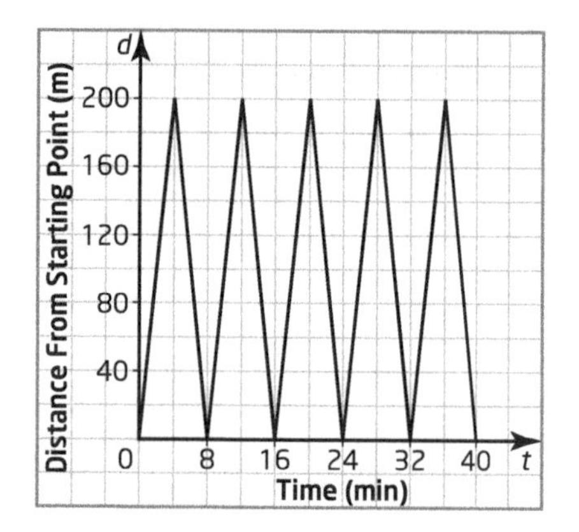

b) The period of the function is 8 min, because the pattern repeats itself in 8-min intervals.

$$\text{Amplitude} = \frac{200 - 0}{2}$$
$$= 100$$

The amplitude is 100 m.

c) Let t represent the time, in minutes, and let d represent the distance from the starting point, in metres. The domain is $\{t \in \mathbb{R}, 0 \leq t \leq 40\}$. The range is $\{d \in \mathbb{R}, 0 \leq d \leq 200\}$.

A Practise

1. Classify each graph as periodic or not periodic. Justify your answers.

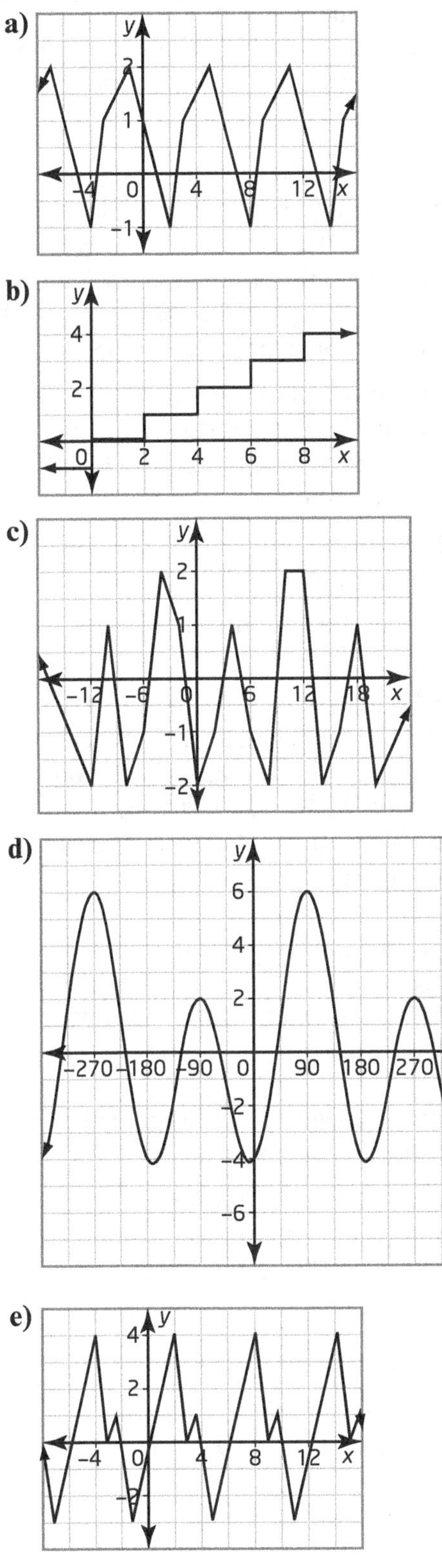

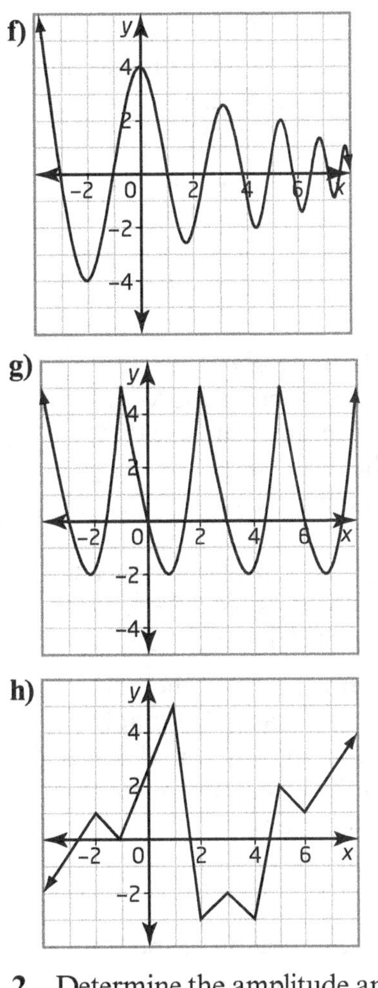

2. Determine the amplitude and period for any graph in question 1 that is periodic.

3. Sketch four cycles of a periodic function with an amplitude of 5 and a period of 2.

4. Sketch five cycles of a periodic function with an amplitude of 3 and a period of 4.

5. Do your graphs in questions 3 and 4 match those of your classmates? Explain why or why not.

6. A periodic function $f(x)$ has a period of 7. The values of $f(-2)$, $f(0)$, and $f(3)$ are −4, 6, and 2, respectively. Predict the value of each of the following. If a prediction is not possible, explain why.

   a) $f(70)$

   b) $f(26)$

   c) $f(-32)$

   d) $f(80)$

7. **a)** Sketch the graph of a periodic function, $f(x)$, with a maximum value of 6, a minimum of -2, and a period of 4.

   b) Select a value a for x, and determine $f(a)$.

   c) Determine two other values, b and c, such that $f(a) = f(b) = f(c)$.

B Connect and Apply

★8. Sunita draws a periodic function so that $f(3) = f(9)$. Can you conclude that the period of the function is 6? Justify your answer, including a diagram.

★9. A search light on a rocky point on a lake flashes 2 s on, and 1 s off. After 2 flashes, the light stays off for an extra 2 s.

   a) Let a 2 represent "on" and a 0 represent "off." Sketch a graph with time on the horizontal axis to represent the flashing of the light. Include two cycles.

   b) Explain why this pattern may be considered periodic.

   c) What is the period of the pattern?

   d) What is the amplitude?

10. Which of the following values do you expect to follow a periodic pattern? Justify your answer for each case.

   a) a basketball that is thrown and bounces 6 times on the ground

   b) the intensity of a signal emitted by a rotating radar antenna in a submarine

   c) Sandria's height above the ground as she skips rope

11. **Use Technology** The cycle of ocean tides represents periodic behaviour and can be modelled with a periodic function. Each day, at various locations around the world, the height of the tide above the mean low-water level is recorded. Use the Internet to find data that represents the time and height of low tide and high tide for a particular ocean location that you may have visited or would like to visit. Graph your data and explain why they represent a periodic function.

12. Anoop is on the school track team. Each day he practises by running back and forth on a straight track that is 800 m long. The beginning of the track is 25 m from the back entrance of the school. He runs at a constant speed of 8 km/h.

   a) Graph Anoop's distance, in metres, from the back entrance of the school, versus time, for 6 lengths of the track.

   b) Determine the period and amplitude of the pattern.

   c) State the domain and range.

C Extend

13. Describe the relationship between the period and the domain of a periodic function whose number of cycles is a whole number. Use an example to support your answer.

14. Describe the relationship between the range and the amplitude of a periodic function. Use an example to support your answer.

15. Is the following piecewise function periodic? Justify your answer.

$$f(x) = \begin{cases} x - 5, & 0 \le x < 10 \\ x - 15, & 10 \le x < 20 \\ x - 25, & 20 \le x < 30 \end{cases}$$

5.2 The Sine Function and the Cosine Function

KEY CONCEPTS

- The sine and cosine ratios, along with the unit circle, can be used to construct sine and cosine functions.
- Both the sine and cosine functions have a wave-like appearance, with a period of 360°.

Properties	$y = \sin x$	$y = \cos x$
sketch of graph	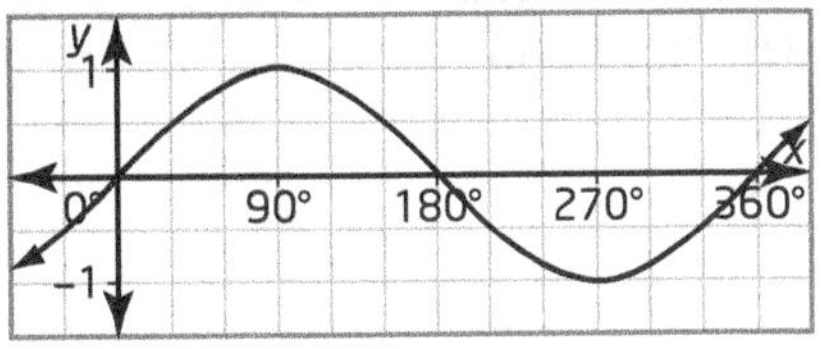	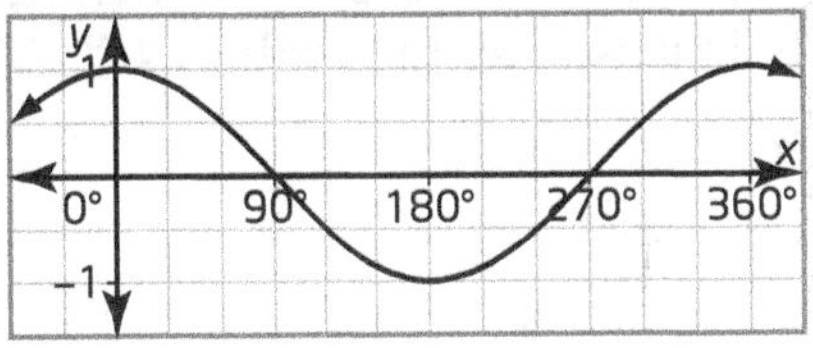
maximum value	1	1
minimum value	−1	−1
amplitude	1	1
domain	$\{x \in \mathbb{R}\}$	$\{x \in \mathbb{R}\}$
range	$\{y \in \mathbb{R}, -1 \leq y \leq 1\}$	$\{y \in \mathbb{R}, -1 \leq y \leq 1\}$
x-intercepts	0°, 180°, and 360° over one cycle	90° and 270° over one cycle
y-intercept	0	1
intervals of increase (over one cycle)	$\{x \in \mathbb{R}, 0° \leq x \leq 90°, 270° \leq x \leq 360°\}$	$\{x \in \mathbb{R}, 180° \leq x \leq 360°\}$
intervals of decrease (over one cycle)	$\{x \in \mathbb{R}, 90° \leq x \leq 270°\}$	$\{x \in \mathbb{R}, 0° \leq x \leq 180°\}$

Example

Consider the function $y = \sin x - \cos x$.

a) Predict the y-intercept of the function.

b) Predict the x-intercepts from 0° to 720°. Justify your answer.

c) Use a graph or a graphing calculator to verify your answers to parts a) and b).

Solution

a) The y-intercept of the function $y = \sin x$ is 0, and the y-intercept of the function $y = \cos x$ is 1. So, the y-intercept of $y = \sin x - \cos x$ is $0 - 1$, or -1.

b) The x-intercepts occur when $y = 0$.
Solve $\sin x - \cos x = 0$, that is, where $\sin x = \cos x$.
This is true for x-values 45°, 225°, 405°, and 585°.

c)

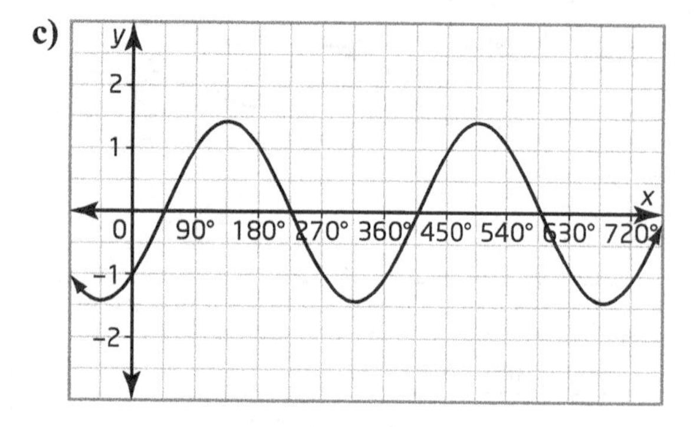

From the graph, the y-intercept is −1 and the x-intercepts are 45°, 225°, 405°, and 585°.

B Connect and Apply

☆**1.** You are in a car of a Ferris wheel. The wheel has a radius of 10 m and turns counterclockwise. Let the origin be at the centre of the wheel. Begin each sketch in parts a) and b) when the radius from the centre of the wheel to your car is along the positive x-axis.

a) Sketch a graph of your horizontal displacement versus the angle through which you turn for one rotation of the wheel. Which function models the horizontal displacement? Justify your choice.

b) Sketch a graph of your vertical displacement versus the angle through which you turn for one rotation of the wheel. Which function models the vertical displacement? Justify your choice.

2. Refer to question 1. Suppose each sketch in parts a) and b) begins when the radius from the centre of the wheel to your car is along the negative y-axis. Sketch a graph of your horizontal displacement versus the angle through which you turn for one rotation of the wheel. Which function models the horizontal displacement? Justify your choice.

3. The hour hand on a clock has a length of 14 cm. Let the origin be at the centre of the clock.

   a) Sketch a graph of the vertical position of the tip of the hour hand versus the angle through which the hand turns for a time period of 48 h, assuming the hour hand starts at 9.

   b) Sketch a graph of the horizontal position of the tip of the hour hand versus the angle through which the hand turns for a time period of 48 h, assuming the hour hand starts at 3.

   c) How many cycles appear in the graph of part a)?

   d) How many cycles will appear in the graph of part a) if you use the minute hand rather than the hour hand? Explain your prediction.

C Extend

4. a) Predict what the graph of $y = -\sin x$ looks like. Use a table of values or technology to draw a sketch of the graph. Is your prediction correct?

   b) Sketch the graph of $y = \sin x$ on the same set of axes as the graph of $y = -\sin x$ from part a).

   c) Describe the similarities and differences between graph of $y = -\sin x$ and the graph of $y = \sin x$.

5. Repeat question 4 for the function $y = -\cos x$.

☆6. Consider the function $y = (\sin x)^2$.

   a) Predict the y-intercept of the function. Justify your prediction.

   b) Predict the x-intercepts from 0° to 720°. Justify your predictions.

   c) Predict the maximum value and the minimum value of the function. Justify your predictions.

   d) Predict the range and the amplitude of the function. Justify your predictions.

   e) Use a graph or a graphing calculator to verify your answers to parts a) to d).

   f) Describe the similarities and differences between the graph of $y = (\sin x)^2$ and the graph of $y = \sin x$.

7. Consider the function $y = (\cos x)^2$.

   a) Predict the y-intercept of the function.

   b) Predict the x-intercepts from 0° to 720°.

   c) Predict the maximum value and the minimum value of the function.

   d) Predict the range and the amplitude of the function.

   e) Use a graph or a graphing calculator to verify your answers to parts a) to d).

   f) Describe the similarities and differences between the graph of $y = (\cos x)^2$ and the graph of $y = \cos x$.

8. a) Predict how the graphs of $y = \frac{\sin x}{\cos x}$ and $y = \tan x$ are related. Justify your prediction.

   b) Graph the functions in part a) to verify your predictions.

9. Repeat question 8 for the functions $y = \frac{\cos x}{\sin x}$ and $y = \cot x$.

5.3 Investigate Transformations of Sine and Cosine Functions

KEY CONCEPTS

- The sine function may be transformed by introducing factors a, k, d, and c: $y = a \sin [k(x - d)] + c$
  - a determines the amplitude of the function. The amplitude is $|a|$.
  - k determines the period, p, of the function according to the relation $p = \frac{360°}{|k|}$.
  - d determines the horizontal translation, or phase shift, of the function. If d is positive, the shift is to the right. If d is negative, the shift is to the left.
  - c determines the vertical translation, or vertical shift, of the function. If c is positive, the shift is up. If c is negative, the shift is down.
- The cosine function may be transformed in the same way: $y = a \cos [k(x - d)] + c$. You will work through examples involving the cosine function in the exercises.

Example

a) Write an equation in the form $y = a \sin [k(x - d)] + c$ that models each graph with the following properties.

i) The graph of $y = \sin x$ is reflected in the x-axis, has a phase shift of 20° to the left, and a period of 360°. The range of the graph is $\{y \in \mathbb{R}, 1 \leq y \leq 5\}$.

ii) The maximum value of the graph is 1, the minimum value is −7, the period is 180°, and the phase shift is 0.

b) Write an equation in the form $y = a \sin x + c$ that models each graph.

i)

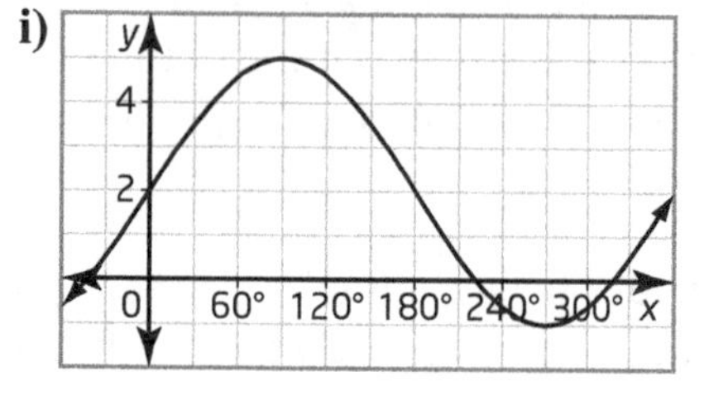

ii)

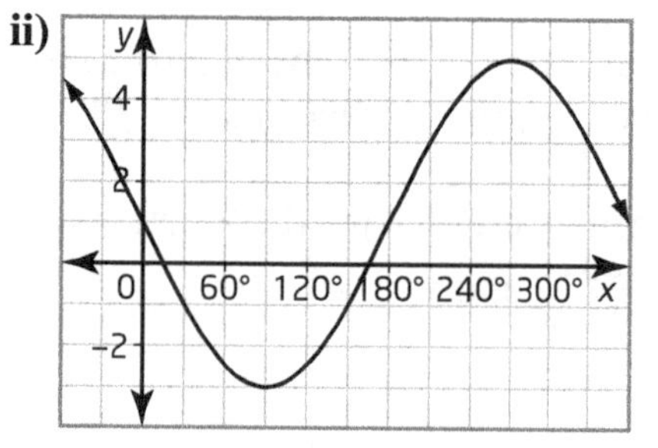

Solution

a) i) The range of the graph is used to find the amplitude and the vertical translation. Since the y-values extend from 1 to 5, the amplitude is $\frac{5-1}{2}$, or 2. Since the graph is reflected in the x-axis, $a = -2$.

The graph of $y = -2 \sin x$ extends from -2 to 2, but this graph extends from 1 to 5. Translate the graph of $y = -2 \sin x$ up 3 units. Therefore, $c = 3$.

The phase shift is 20° to the left, so $d = -20°$.

The period is 360°, so $k = 1$.

An equation that models this graph is $y = -2 \sin (x + 20°) + 3$.

ii) The minimum and maximum values indicate the range of the graph. Use this information to find the amplitude and the vertical shift.

The amplitude is $\frac{1-(-7)}{2}$, or 4. So, $a = 4$.

The graph of $y = 4 \sin x$ extends from -4 to 4. Since the maximum value of the given graph is 1, it must be shifted down 3 units. So, $c = -3$.

Since the period is 180°, then $\frac{360°}{k}$ and $k = 2$.

The phase shift is 0, so $d = 0$.

An equation that models this graph is $y = 4 \sin 2x - 3$.

b) i) The amplitude and vertical shift can be determined by finding the horizontal reference line that cuts the graph in half. This represents the middle or rest position of the graph. It occurs at $y = 2$.

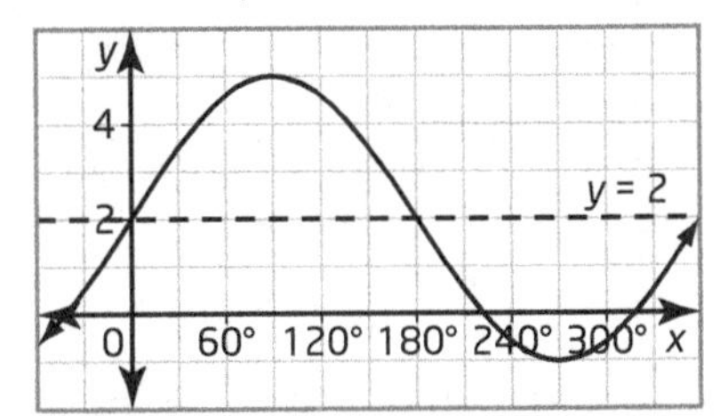

This means that the vertical shift is 2 units up, so $c = 2$.

The maximum value is 3 units above this horizontal line and the minimum value is 3 units below this horizontal line. So, the amplitude of the graph is $a = 3$.

An equation that models this graph is $y = 3 \sin x + 2$.

ii) The horizontal reference line is $y = 1$, as shown.

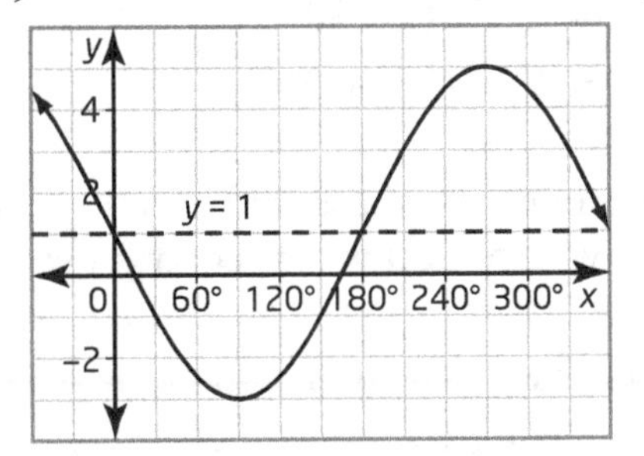

This means that the vertical shift is 1 unit up, so $c = 1$.

The maximum value is 4 units above this horizontal line and the minimum value is 4 units below this horizontal line. So, the amplitude of the graph is 4. Since the graph is reflected in the x-axis, $a = -4$.

An equation that models this graph is $y = -4 \sin x + 1$.

A Practise

1. Sketch one cycle for each function. Include an appropriate scale on each axis. State the vertical stretch or compression and amplitude of the function.

   a) $y = 5 \sin x$

   b) $y = \frac{4}{5} \sin x$

   c) $y = -4 \sin x$

   d) $y = -\frac{4}{3} \sin x$

2. Sketch one cycle for each function. Include an appropriate scale on each axis. State the vertical stretch or compression and the amplitude of the function.

   a) $y = 6 \cos x$

   b) $y = \frac{3}{2} \cos x$

   c) $y = -3 \cos x$

   d) $y = -\frac{1}{2} \cos x$

3. Determine the horizontal stretch or compression and the period of each function.

   a) $y = 3 \sin 2x$

   b) $y = 4 \sin \frac{1}{2}x$

   c) $y = 2 \sin \frac{2}{3}x$

   d) $y = -5 \sin \frac{1}{4}x$

   e) $y = 2 \cos 3x$

   f) $y = -6 \cos 5x$

   g) $y = -\frac{3}{4} \cos \frac{3}{4}x$

   h) $y = \frac{7}{4} \cos \frac{3}{2}x$

★4. Match each graph with its corresponding equation. Give reasons for your choices.

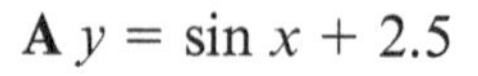

   A $y = \sin x + 2.5$

   B $y = \sin x - 3$

   a)

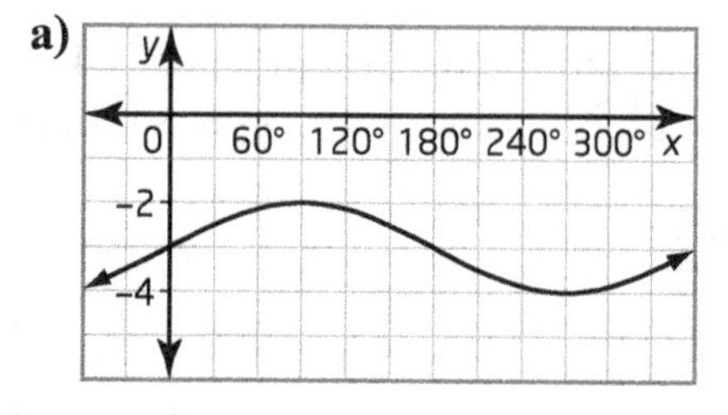

   b)

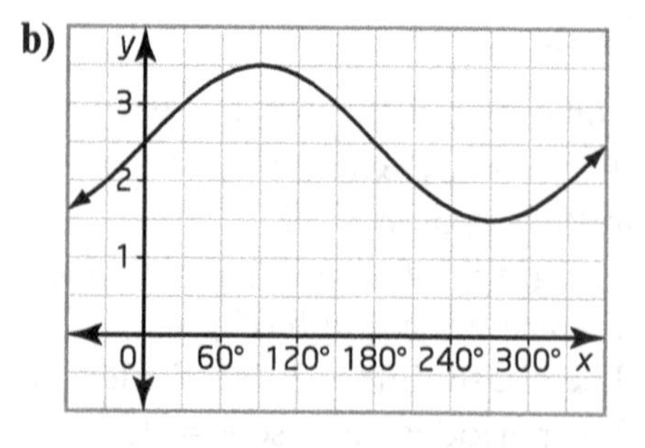

5. Match each graph with its corresponding equation. Give reasons for your choices.

   A $y = \cos (x - 30°)$

   B $y = \cos (x + 60°)$

   a) b)

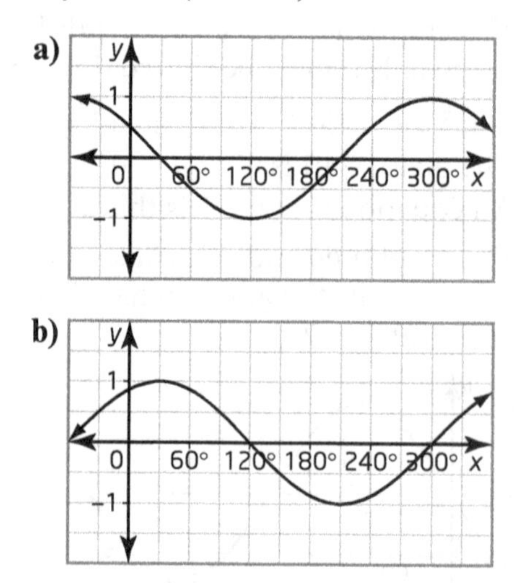

6. Determine the phase shift and the vertical shift with respect to $y = \sin x$ for each function.

   a) $y = \sin (x - 40°) + 2$

   b) $y = 2 \sin (x + 60°) - 3$

   c) $y = -3 \sin (x - 38°) + 5$

   d) $y = 4 \sin [3(x + 30°)] - 6$

7. Determine the phase shift and the vertical shift with respect to $y = \cos x$ for each function.

   a) $y = \cos (x + 70°)$

   b) $y = 7 \cos (x - 82°) + 8$

   c) $y = -5 \cos (x + 100°) - 1$

   d) $y = 10 \cos [3(x - 120°)] + 9$

8. Write two equations, one in the form $y = a \sin kx$ and one in the form $y = a \cos [k(x - d)]$, to match each graph.

a)

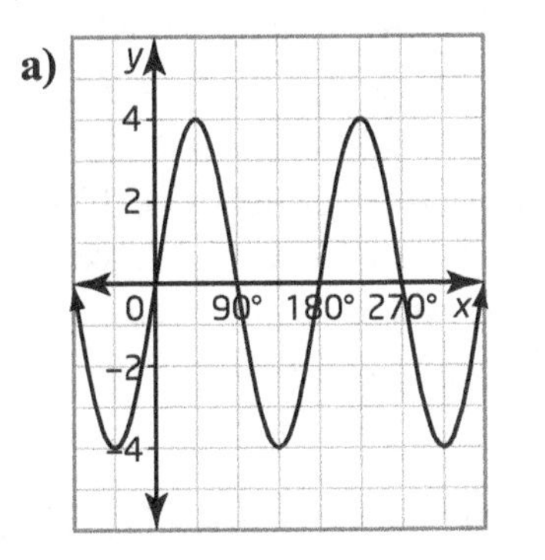

b)

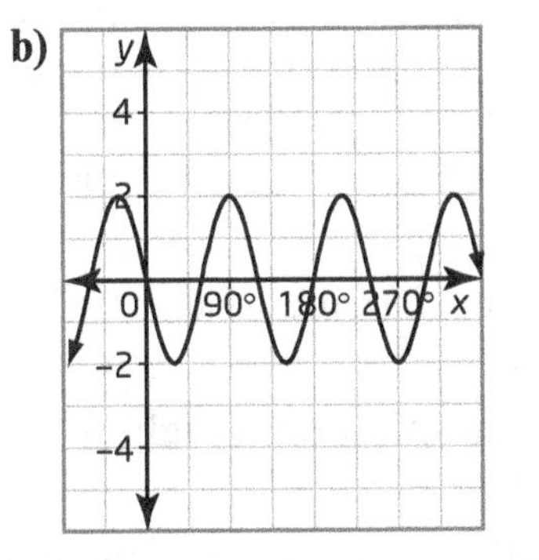

c)

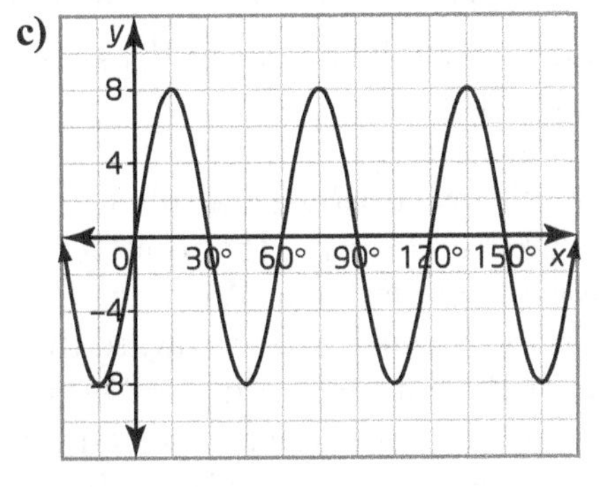

9. Write two equations, one in the form $y = a \cos kx$ and one in the form $y = a \sin [k(x - d)]$, to match each graph.

a)

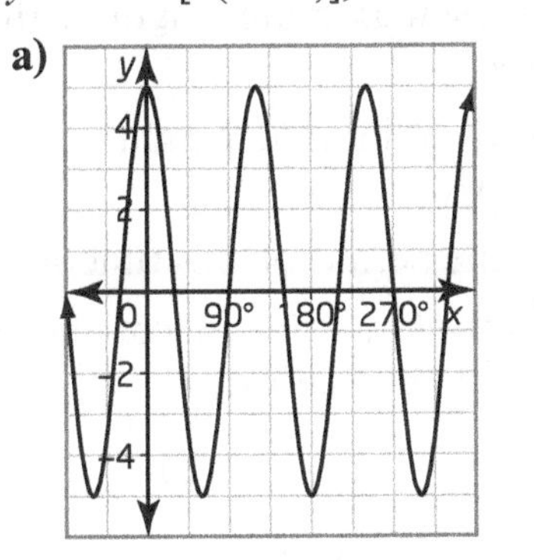

b)

c)

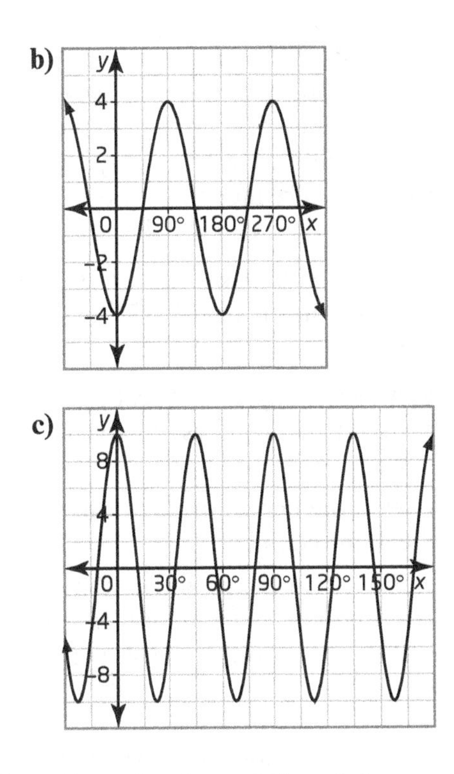

10. a) State the phase shift and the vertical shift of each sinusoidal function.

i) $y = \sin (x + 140°) + 5$

ii) $y = 3 \sin x + 2$

iii) $y = \sin (x + 55°) - 8$

iv) $y = 5 \sin (x - 90°) + 7$

b) Sketch one cycle of the graph of each function. Include an appropriate scale on each axis.

11. a) State the vertical shift and the amplitude of each sinusoidal function.

i) $y = \cos (x - 80°)$

ii) $y = 3 \cos x - 2$

iii) $y = \cos (x + 25°) + 1$

iv) $y = 5 \cos (x - 135°) - 4$

b) Sketch one cycle of the graph of each function. Include an appropriate scale on each axis.

B Connect and Apply

☆ **12.** The vertical position, y, in centimetres, of a point on the rim of the wheel of a stationary spinning bicycle after time, t, in seconds, can be modelled by the equation $y = 30 \sin 540t + 45$.

a) What is the lowest vertical position that the point reaches? Justify your answer.

b) What is the highest vertical position that the point reaches? Justify your answer.

c) What is the period of rotation of the wheel, in seconds?

d) Suppose that the period of the rotation of the wheel doubles. How does the equation change? Justify your answer.

13. What transformations must be applied to the graph of $y = \sin x$ to obtain the graph of each of the following? Justify your answer.

a) $y = \sin (x + 90°) - 2$

b) $y = -\sin (x - 60°) + 4$

☆**14.** Write an equation in the form $y = a \sin (x - d) + c$ for each of the following. Justify your answer.

a) The graph of $y = \sin x$ is shifted 25° to the left and 5 units up.

b) The graph of $y = \sin x$ is reflected in the x-axis, and shifted 42° to the right and 2 units down.

15. Determine the amplitude, the period, the phase shift, and the vertical shift of each function.

a) $y = 3 \sin [2(x - 30°)] + 1$

b) $y = \frac{1}{2} \cos [3x + 360°] - 6$

c) $y = 4 \sin \left[\frac{1}{4}(x + 45°)\right] - 3$

d) $y = 0.6 \cos [1.2(x - 90°)] + 2$

C Extend

16. The siren of an alarm system is set up so that the frequency of the sound fluctuates with time. In a 12-s interval, the maximum frequency of 1100 Hz is heard four times, including at 0 s and 12 s. The minimum frequency of 120 Hz is heard three times. Determine a cosine function that models the frequency, f, in Hertz, of the siren in terms of time, t, in seconds.

17. A performer in a circus spins a lasso in a circle perpendicular to the ground. The height, h, in metres, of the knot above the ground is modelled by the function $h = -1.2 \cos (300t) + 1.5$, where t is the time, in seconds.

a) What is the maximum height of the knot?

b) What is the minimum height of the knot?

c) What is the period of this function?

d) Determine the height of the knot after 20 s.

18. A child's toy consists of a rubber kangaroo on a spring that is attached to a wooden platform. When the toy kangaroo is pulled down toward the base of the platform and then released, it bounces up and down. Its height, h, in centimetres, above the base after t seconds is modelled by the function $h(t) = 10 \sin [360t + 540] + 15$.

a) What is the maximum height of the kangaroo?

b) What is the minimum height of the kangaroo?

c) What is the period of this function?

d) When is the kangaroo 18 cm above the base of the platform?

5.4 Graphing and Modelling with $y = a \sin [k(x - d)] + c$ and $y = a \cos [k(x - d)] + c$

KEY CONCEPTS

- The amplitude, period, phase shift, and vertical shift of sinusoidal functions can be determined when the equations are given in the form $f(x) = a \sin [k(x - d)] + c$ or $f(x) = a \cos [k(x - d)] + c$.
- The domain of a sinusoidal function is $\{x \in \mathbb{R}\}$. The range extends from the minimum value to the maximum value of the function. Any cycle can be used to determine the minimum and the maximum.
- Transformations can be used to adjust the basic sine and cosine functions to match a given amplitude, period, phase shift, and vertical shift.
- The equation of a sinusoidal function can be determined given its properties.
- The equation of a sinusoidal function can be determined given its graph.

Example

a) State the values of the parameters in the transformed function $y = -\frac{4}{5} \sin \left[\frac{2}{3}(x + 60°)\right] + 1$.

b) Describe the transformations that must be applied to the graph of $y = \sin x$ to obtain the graph of $y = -\frac{4}{5} \sin \left[\frac{2}{3}(x + 60°)\right] + 1$.

c) State the period and the range of the transformed function in part a).

Solution

a) Comparing the given equation $y = -\frac{4}{5} \sin \left[\frac{2}{3}(x + 60°)\right] + 1$ to the general equation $y = a \sin [k(x - d)] + c$ gives $a = -\frac{4}{5}$, $k = \frac{2}{3}$, $d = -60°$, and $c = 1$.

b) Since $a = -\frac{4}{5}$ is negative, the graph of $y = \sin x$ is reflected in the x-axis and the amplitude is $\frac{4}{5}$.

Since $k = \frac{2}{3}$, the graph is horizontally stretched by a factor of $\frac{3}{2}$.

Since $d = -60°$ and $c = 1$, the graph is shifted left 60° and up 1 unit.

c) The period is $\frac{360°}{\frac{2}{3}}$, or 540°.

Since the graph is shifted up 1 unit and the amplitude is $\frac{4}{5}$, the range is

$\left\{y \in \mathbb{R}, -\frac{1}{5} \le y \ge \frac{9}{5}\right\}$.

A Practise

1. Determine the amplitude, the period, the phase shift, and the vertical shift of each function with respect to $y = \sin x$.

   a) $y = 2 \sin [3(x - 15°)] + 4$

   b) $y = -5 \sin [12(x + 60°)] - 2$

   c) $y = 6 \sin [18(x + 45°)] + 1$

   d) $y = \frac{2}{3} \sin \left[\frac{3}{5}(x - 30°)\right] + \frac{4}{5}$

2. Determine the amplitude, the period, the phase shift, and the vertical shift of each function with respect to $y = \cos x$.

   a) $y = -\frac{4}{7} \cos [10(x + 16°)] + 9$

   b) $y = 11 \cos [36(x + 75°)] - 3$

   c) $y = 8 \cos [60(x - 12°)] + 7$

   d) $y = -\frac{5}{9} \cos \left[\frac{2}{5}(x - 85°)\right] + \frac{3}{8}$

3. **a)** Describe the transformations that must be applied to the graph of $f(x) = \sin x$ to obtain the graph of $g(x) = 5 \sin 3x - 3$. Apply each transformation, one step at a time, to sketch the graph of $g(x)$.

   b) State the domain and range of $f(x)$ and $g(x)$.

   c) Modify the equation for $g(x)$ to include a phase shift of 45° to the left. Call this function $h(x)$. Apply the phase shift to the graph of $g(x)$ and transform it to $h(x)$.

4. **a)** Transform the graph of $f(x) = \cos x$ to $g(x) = 3 \cos 4x + 1$ by applying transformations to the graph one step at a time.

   b) State the domain and range of $f(x)$ and $g(x)$.

   c) Modify the equation for $g(x)$ to include a phase shift of 45° to the right. Call this function $h(x)$. Apply the phase shift to the graph of $g(x)$ and transform it to $h(x)$.

5. A sinusoidal function has an amplitude of 6 units, a period of 180°, and a maximum at (0, 2).

   a) Represent the function with an equation using a sine function.

   b) Represent the function with an equation using a cosine function.

6. A sinusoidal function has an amplitude of $\frac{3}{4}$ units, a period of 1080°, and a maximum at $\left(0, \frac{11}{4}\right)$.

   a) Represent the function with an equation using a sine function.

   b) Represent the function with an equation using a cosine function.

B Connect and Apply

7. Consider the function $f(x) = 8 \sin [3x + 60°] - 8$.

   a) Determine the amplitude, the period, the phase shift, and the vertical shift of the function with respect to $y = \sin x$.

   b) What are the maximum and minimum values of the function?

   c) Determine the first three x-intercepts to the right of the origin.

   d) Determine the y-intercept of the function.

8. Consider the function $g(x) = 6 \cos [5(x - 60°)]$.

   a) Determine the amplitude, the period, the phase shift, and the vertical shift of the function with respect to $y = \cos x$.

   b) What are the maximum and minimum values of the function?

   c) Determine the first three x-intercepts to the right of the origin.

   d) Determine the y-intercept of the function.

9. **Use Technology** Use a graphing calculator or graphing software to verify your answers to questions 7 and 8.

★10. Write an equation in the form $y = a \sin [k(x - d)] + c$ that represents the graph of $y = \sin x$ after it is reflected in the x-axis, vertically stretched by a factor of 3, horizontally compressed by a factor of $\frac{1}{4}$, shifted 35° to the left, and translated 8 units down.

11. a) Transform the graph of $f(x) = \sin x$ to $g(x) = -3 \sin \left[\frac{1}{4}(x - 50°)\right] + 7$. Show each step in the transformation.

b) State the domain and range of $f(x)$ and $g(x)$.

12. a) Transform the graph of $f(x) = \cos x$ to $g(x) = \frac{3}{4} \cos [6(x + 45°)] - 2$. Show each step in the transformation.

b) State the domain and range of $f(x)$ and $g(x)$.

★13. Represent the graph of $f(x) = 6 \sin [5(x - 60°)]$ with an equation using a cosine function.

14. a) Determine the equation of a sine function that represents the graph shown.

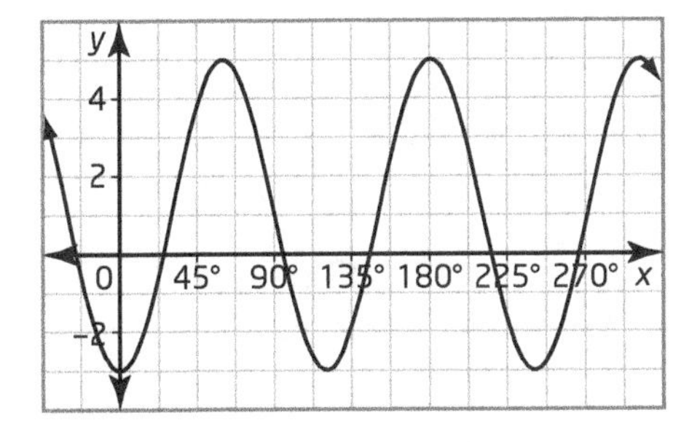

b) Determine the equation of a cosine function that represents the graph.

15. At the end of a dock, high tide of 16 m is recorded at 9:00 a.m. Low tide of 6 m is recorded at 3:00 p.m. A sinusoidal function can model the water depth versus time.

a) Construct a model for the water depth using a cosine function, where time is measured in hours past high tide.

b) Construct a model for the water depth using a sine function, where time is measured in hours past high tide.

c) Construct a model for the water depth using a sine function, where time is measured in hours past low tide.

d) Construct a model for the water depth using a cosine function, where time is measured in hours past low tide.

e) Compare your models. Which is the simplest representation if time is referenced to high tide? low tide? Explain why there is a difference.

C Extend

16. Consider the relation $y = \sqrt{\cos x}$.

a) Sketch the graph of the function $y = \cos x$ over two cycles.

b) Use the graph from part a) to sketch a prediction for the shape of the graph of $y = \sqrt{\cos x}$.

c) Use Technology Use technology to graph $y = \sqrt{\cos x}$ and to check your prediction. Resolve any differences.

d) Predict how the graph of $y = \sqrt{\cos x + 1}$ differs from the graph of $y = \sqrt{\cos x}$.

e) Graph $y = \sqrt{\cos x + 1}$ and compare it to your prediction. Resolve any differences.

17. Consider the function $y = a \sin [k(x - d)] + c$.

a) Write an expression for the maximum value of y. For what values of x does this occur?

b) Write an expression for the minimum value of y. For what values of x does this occur?

18. Repeat question 17 for $y = a \cos [k(x - d)] + c$.

5.5 Data Collecting and Modelling

KEY CONCEPTS

- Data can be collected from physical models using tools such as a motion sensor.
- Data can be downloaded from statistical sources such as Statistics Canada.
- Data can sometimes be modelled using a sinusoidal function.
- Use a graph or a table to build a model to determine the amplitude, phase shift, period, and vertical shift of a sinusoidal function.
- Predictions about the behaviour of an altered model can be made by considering the effect of changing a parameter on the graph of the original equation.
- The graph or equation can be used to determine values.

Example

The table shows the daily high temperature, as recorded every 30 days, for the town of Mathville, for two years beginning January 1, 2007.

Day Number	High Temperature (°C)
0	−1.9
30	0.1
60	5.5
90	13.1
120	20.5
150	25.9
180	27.9
210	26.0
240	20.3
270	13.2
300	5.6
330	0.2
360	−1.9
390	0.1
420	5.5
450	13.1
480	20.5
510	25.9
540	27.9
570	26.0
600	20.3
630	13.2
660	5.6
690	0.2
720	−1.9

a) Draw a graph to represent the data.

b) Does the graph model a periodic function? Explain.

c) Determine the amplitude of the function.

d) Determine the period of the function.

e) Explain how your graph can be used to predict the daily high temperature for another cycle of 360 days.

f) Extend your graph. Predict the daily high for day 840. Will this be the actual daily high temperature for day 840? Explain.

g) Construct a model for the daily high temperature by writing an equation using a sine function.

h) Construct a model for the daily high temperature by writing an equation using a cosine function.

Solution

a)

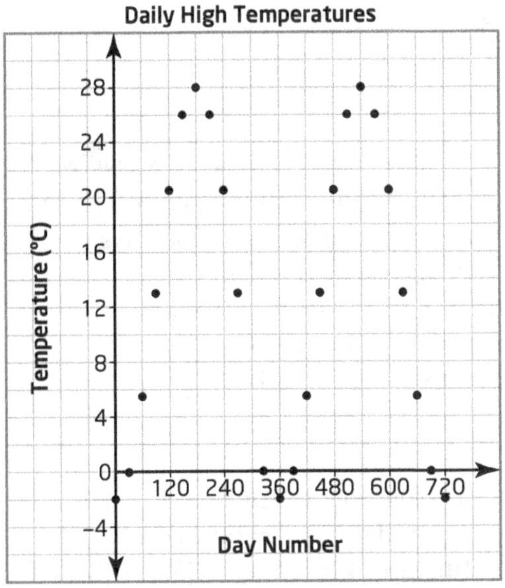

Daily High Temperatures

Temperature (°C): −4, 0, 4, 8, 12, 16, 20, 24, 28

Day Number: 120, 240, 360, 480, 600, 720

b) The graph models a periodic function because the values along the vertical axis are repeated. So, the graph contains a repeating pattern.

c) From the data, the minimum value is −1.9 and the maximum value is 27.9.

The amplitude is $\dfrac{27.9 - (-1.9)}{2}$, or 14.9.

d) The first cycle begins at day 0 and ends at day 360. So, the period is 360 days.

e) The graph can be extended by drawing another cycle for the next 360 days. The values on the graph can then be used to predict the daily high temperature for 30-day periods.

f) From the graph, the predicted daily high temperature for day 840 is approximately 20 °C. There is no guarantee that this will be the actual daily high temperature for day 840, since weather patterns may change.

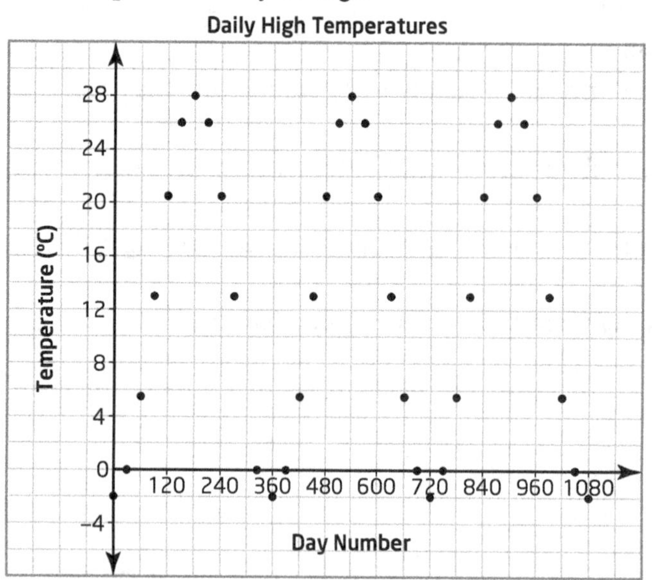

g) Let n represent the day number and T represent the temperature, in degrees Celsius.
Since the amplitude, a, is 14.9 and the maximum is 27. 9, the vertical shift, c, is 13. The sine wave starts at day 90, so the phase shift, d, is 90. From part d), the period is 360 days. So, $k = 1$.
A sine equation that models this function is $T = 14.9 \sin (n - 90) + 13$.

h) The amplitude, the period, and the vertical shift remain the same as in part g). The start of the first cosine wave is at day 180, so the phase shift, d, is 180 to the right.
A cosine equation that models this function is $T = 14.9 \cos (n - 180) + 13$.

A Practise

1. The height, h, in metres, of the tide in a given location on a given day at t hours after midnight is modelled using the sinusoidal function
$h(t) = 4.5 \sin [30(t - 4)] + 6$.
   a) Find the maximum and minimum values for the depth, h, of the water.
   b) What time is high tide? What time is low tide?
   c) What is the depth of the water at 11:00 a.m.?
   d) Find all the times during a 24-h period when the depth of the water is 6 m.

2. The number of tourists, V, visiting a popular city is modelled using the function $V = 3500 \sin [30(t - 8)] + 5600$, where t is the number of months after New Year's Day.
   a) Find the maximum and minimum number of tourists visiting the city over the period of a year.
   b) When is the number of tourists a maximum? When is it a minimum?
   c) How many tourists visit the city on July 30?
   d) When is the number of tourists visiting the city about 3000?

3. A motion sensor is used to gather data on the motion of a pendulum. The table of values is exported to a computer, and graphing software is used to draw the graph shown.

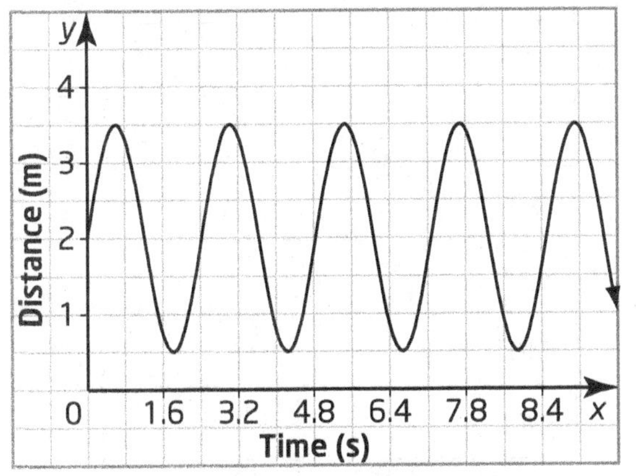

a) Use the graph to estimate the maximum and minimum values. Then, use these values to find the amplitude, a.

b) Sketch a horizontal reference line. Estimate the vertical shift, c.

c) Use the horizontal reference line to estimate the phase shift, d.

d) Use the horizontal reference line to estimate the period. Use the period to find the value of k.

e) Construct a model for the motion by writing an equation using a sine function.

f) Construct a model for the motion by writing an equation using a cosine function.

g) **Use Technology** Use technology to graph your models from parts e) and f). Compare your models to the graph shown. If you see any significant difference, check and adjust your model.

★ 4. A motion sensor is used to gather data on the motion of a child on a swing. The table of values is exported to a computer, and graphing software is used to draw the graph shown.

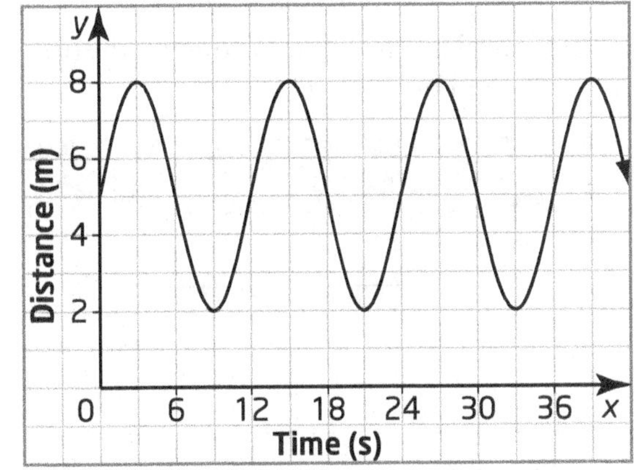

a) Use the graph to estimate the maximum and minimum values. Then, use these values to find the amplitude, a.

b) Sketch a horizontal reference line. Estimate the vertical shift, c.

c) Use the horizontal reference line to estimate the phase shift, d.

d) Use the horizontal reference line to estimate the period. Use the period to find the value of k.

e) Construct a model for the motion by writing an equation using a sine function.

f) Construct a model for the motion by writing an equation using a cosine function.

g) **Use Technology** Use technology to graph your models from parts e) and f). Compare your models to the graph shown. If you see any significant difference, check and adjust your model.

B Connect and Apply

☆**5.** The height above the ground of a rider on a Ferris wheel can be modelled by the sine function $h(x) = 25 \sin (x - 90°) + 27$, where $h(x)$ is the height, in metres, and x is the angle, in degrees, that the radius to the rider makes with the horizontal.

a) Complete the table for one revolution of the Ferris wheel.

x	$h(x) = 25 \sin (x - 90°) + 27$
0°	
30°	
60°	
90°	
120°	
150°	
180°	
210°	
240°	
270°	
300°	
330°	
360°	

b) Predict the values for a second revolution of the Ferris wheel. Explain your reasoning.

x	$h(x) = 25 \sin (x - 90°) + 27$
390°	
420°	
450°	
480°	
510°	
540°	
570°	
600°	
630°	
660°	
690°	
720°	

c) Graph the function for two revolutions.

d) Determine the maximum and minimum heights of the rider.

e) Use the graph to predict the measures of the angle when the height of the rider is 40 m.

f) Use the cosine function to write an equation to model the height of the rider on the Ferris wheel.

6. The period of a pendulum, T, in seconds, is related to the length, l, in metres, according to the relation $T = 2\pi \sqrt{\frac{l}{g}}$, where g is the acceleration due to gravity, about 9.8 m/s^2, near the surface of Earth.

a) If the length is tripled, by what factor does the period increase?

b) If you want a pendulum with double the period of the given pendulum, what must you do to the length?

★7. **a)** The graph shows the time of sunset in Saskatoon over a 720-day period. Determine a sine equation that models the time of sunset. Justify your answer.

b) Determine a cosine equation that models the time of sunset.

c) State the range of the function.

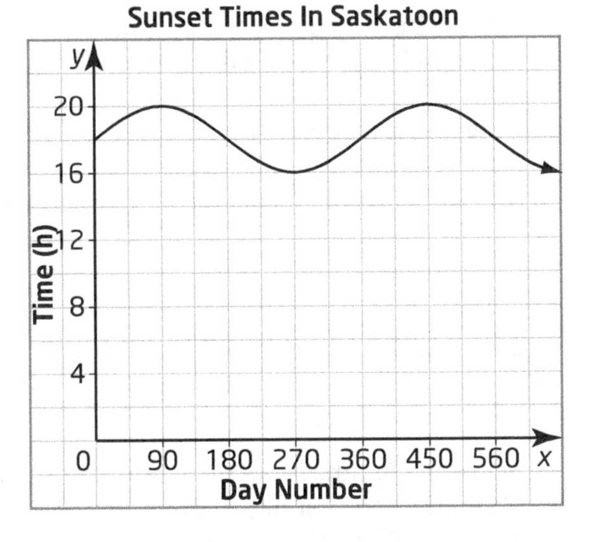

8. The Ferris wheel at a carnival has a diameter of 18 m and descends to 3 m above ground level at its lowest point. Assume that a rider enters a car from a platform that is located 40° around the rim before the car reaches its lowest point.

a) Model the rider's height above ground versus angle using a transformed sine function.

b) Model the rider's height above ground versus angle using a transformed cosine function.

c) Suppose that the platform is moved to 50° around the rim from the lowest position of the car. How will the equations in parts a) and b) change? Write the new equations.

9. Suppose that the axle of the Ferris wheel in question 8 is moved upward 2.5 m, but the platform is left in place at a point 40° before the car reached its lowest point. How do the equations in parts a) and b) of question 8 change? Write the new equations.

10. The movement of a piston in the engine of a certain vehicle can be modelled by the function $y = 45 \sin (9000t) + 18$, where y is the distance, in centimetres, from the crankshaft and t is the time, in seconds.

a) What is the period of the motion?

b) Determine the maximum, the minimum, and the amplitude.

c) When do the maximum and minimum values occur?

d) What is the vertical position of the piston at $t = \frac{1}{20}$ s?

C Extend

11. The diameter of a motorcycle tire is 60 cm. While the motorcycle is being driven, a small sharp stone lodges itself in one of the grooves of the tire. How high above the ground is the stone 1 km after the motorcycle hit the stone?

12. Aubrey is riding on a Ferris wheel at a constant rate of 10 km/h. He boards the Ferris wheel from a platform that is 1.5 m high. The diameter of the wheel is 16 m. Determine an equation, in terms of the cosine function, that models Aubrey's height above the ground given that Aubrey begins at the highest point on the Ferris wheel.

13. a) High-voltage electricity with a maximum of 1100 V is transmitted at a frequency of 260 Hz, or 260 cycles per second. Determine a sinusoidal equation that represents the voltage as a function of time.

b) A transformer station reduces the voltage by half and the frequency by one quarter. Determine a sinusoidal equation for the new voltage.

5.6 Use Sinusoidal Functions to Model Periodic Phenomena Not Involving Angles

KEY CONCEPTS

- Sinusoidal functions can be used to model periodic phenomena that do not involve angles as the independent variable.
- The amplitude, phase shift, period, and vertical shift of the basic sine or cosine function can be adjusted to fit the characteristics of the phenomenon being modelled.
- Technology can be used to quickly draw and analyse the graph modelled by the equation.
- The graph can be used to solve problems related to the phenomenon.

Example

The number of hours of daylight varies throughout the year. The graph shows the amount of daylight in southern Ontario over one year, starting on March 21, the first day of spring, which has 12 h of daylight. December 21 is the "shortest day," and June 21 is the "longest day."

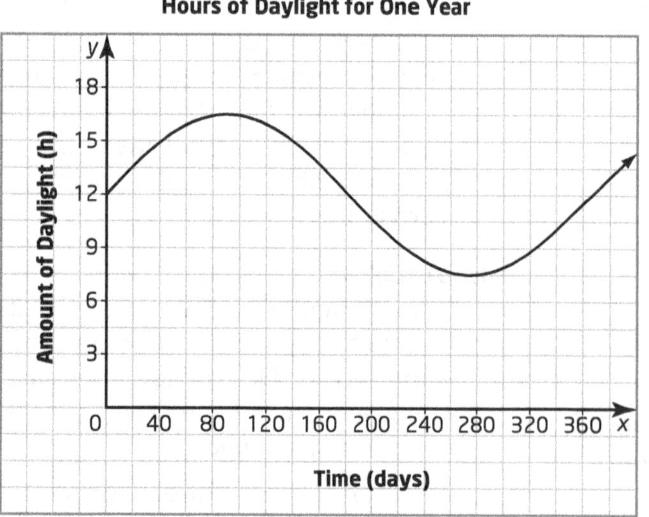

a) What is the number of daylight hours on December 21?
b) What is the number of daylight hours on June 21?
c) Determine the amplitude, the phase shift, the vertical shift, and the period of the graph.
d) Determine a sinusoidal equation that models the graph. Justify your answer.

Solution

a) December 21 is the shortest day, so it corresponds to the minimum number of daylight hours, which is approximately 7.5 h.

b) June 21 is the longest day, so it corresponds to the maximum number of daylight hours, which is approximately 16.5 h.

c) The amplitude is $\frac{16.5 - 7.5}{2}$, or 4.5. Therefore $a = 4.5$. Alternatively, determine the distance between the horizontal reference line and the maximum or minimum value.

Here the horizontal reference line is $y = 12$. Then, the distance from 12 to 16.5 is 4.5.
There is no phase shift since the graph begins at the y-axis. So, $d = 0$.
One way to determine the vertical displacement is to subtract the amplitude from the maximum value, that is, $16.5 - 4.5$, or 12. Another way to find the vertical displacement is to add the amplitude to the minimum value, that is, $7.5 + 4.5$, or 12. Therefore, $c = 12$.
The period of the graph is 365 days, since the pattern of number of daylight hours repeats on a yearly basis.

d) The equation will be of the form $y = a \sin [k(x - d)] + c$. Use the period to determine the value of k.

$$\frac{360}{k} = 365$$
$$k = \frac{360}{365}$$
$$k = \frac{72}{73}$$

Substitute $a = 4.5$, $k = \frac{72}{73}$, $d = 0$, and $c = 12$.
An equation that models the number of daylight hours in southern Ontario is
$y = 4.5 \sin \frac{72}{73}x + 12$.

A Practise

1. The sinusoidal function $h(t) = 7 \sin [30(t - 2.5)]$ models the height, h, of tides in a particular location on a particular day at t hours after midnight.

   a) Determine the maximum height and the minimum height of the tides.

   b) At what times do high tide and low tide occur?

   c) Use a cosine function to write an equivalent equation.

2. Refer to question 1. On a different day, the maximum height is 4.5 m, the minimum is −4.5 m, and low tide occurs at 5:00 a.m.

   a) Modify the sine function so that it matches the new data.

   b) Predict the times for the next low and high tides.

   c) Modify your equation from part a) so that low tide occurs at 5:30 a.m.

   d) Write an equivalent equation using a cosine function for your answer to part c).

3. The population of prey in a predator-prey relation is shown. Time is in years since 1985.

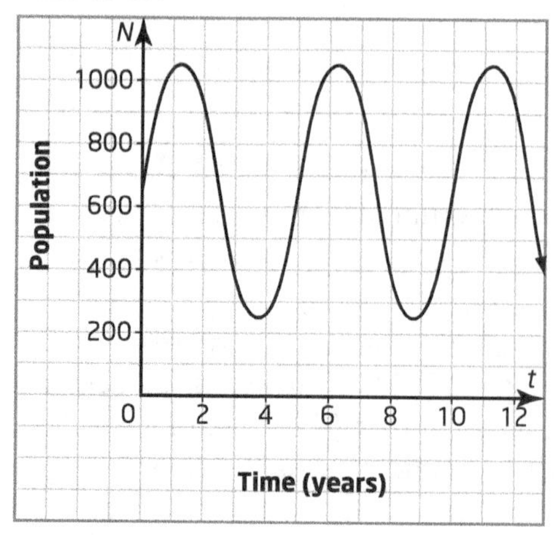

a) Determine the maximum and minimum values of the population. Use these to find the amplitude.

b) Determine the vertical shift, c.

c) Determine the phase shift, d.

d) Determine the period. Use the period to determine the value of k.

e) Model the population versus time with a sinusoidal function.

f) Graph your function. Compare it to the graph shown.

4. Refer to question 3. Suppose the period was 8 years. How would your equation in part e) change? Write the new equation.

B Connect and Apply

☆**5.** Refer to the Example at the beginning of this section. Use the equation you found in part d) to determine the number of hours of daylight on

a) April 1

b) September 1

☆**6.** The depth of the water at the end of a pier is 2 m at low tide and 12 m at high tide. There are 6 h between low tide and high tide. The first high tide occurs 6 h after midnight. One complete cycle takes 12 h.

a) Write a sinusoidal equation that represents the depth of the water.

b) Determine the depth of the water at 4:15 a.m. and 3:30 p.m.

c) Graph your equation from part a) and plot the points represented by your answers in part b).

7. The depth of water, d, in metres, of a seaside inlet on a given day can be modelled by the function $d = 7 \sin [30(t - 4)] + 11$, where t is the time past midnight, in hours.

a) Determine the maximum and minimum depths of water in the inlet.

b) What is the period between maximum values?

c) Graph the water level over a period of 24 h.

d) When is the water 5 m deep?

8. Angelina constructs a model alternating current (AC) generator in physics class and cranks it by hand at 5 revolutions per second. She is able to light up a flashlight bulb that is rated for 8 V.

a) What is the period of the AC produced by the generator?

b) Determine the value of k.

c) What is the amplitude of the voltage function?

d) Model the voltage with a suitably transformed sine function.

9. The number of sunlight hours on each day of the year for a particular location can be modelled by a periodic function. In London, Ontario, the maximum number of sunlight hours, 15.3 h, occurs on June 21. The minimum number of sunlight hours, 9.3 h, occurs on December 21.

a) Use a cosine function to model the number of sunlight hours in London, Ontario. Note that June 21 is day 172 and December 21 is day 355.

b) Determine the number of sunlight hours on April 1.

c) Determine a day when there are 14 h of sunlight.

10. The graph shows how the voltage, V, in volts, varies with time, t, in seconds, for the electricity provided to an electrical appliance.

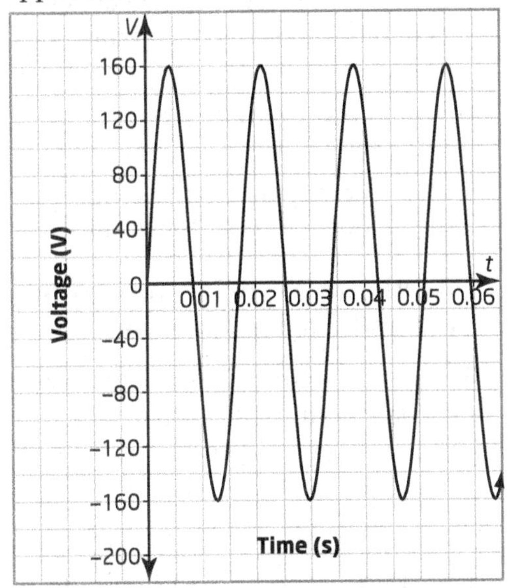

a) Identify the period and amplitude of the function.

b) What is the maximum voltage?

c) Write an equation to model this situation.

11. The table shows the temperature readings every 2 h over a 24-h period on an early summer day.

Time	Temperature (°C)
13:00	27.3
15:00	28.9
17:00	27.8
19:00	26.0
21:00	22.0
23:00	18.1
01:00	16.0
03:00	15.1
05:00	16.1
07:00	18.2
09:00	22.1
11:00	25.5
13:00	27.4

a) Use the data to write an equation that models the temperature over the 24-h period.

b) Explain how you can check the accuracy of your equation.

c) Use your equation to predict the temperature at the following times:

i) 04:00

ii) 16:00

iii) 20:30

12. The blades on a windmill turn at a frequency of 20 revolutions per minute. The length of each blade is 3.5 m, and the tips of the blades are 8 m off the ground when they are at their lowest point.

a) Use a sinusoidal function to model the height above the ground of one of the blade tips as a function of time.

b) Graph the function.

c) Determine the times in the first cycle when the tip of a blade is 10 m off the ground.

C Extend

13. Pistons in a vehicle engine move up and down many times each second. The graph shows how the height varies with time for the pistons in a 6-cylinder engine.

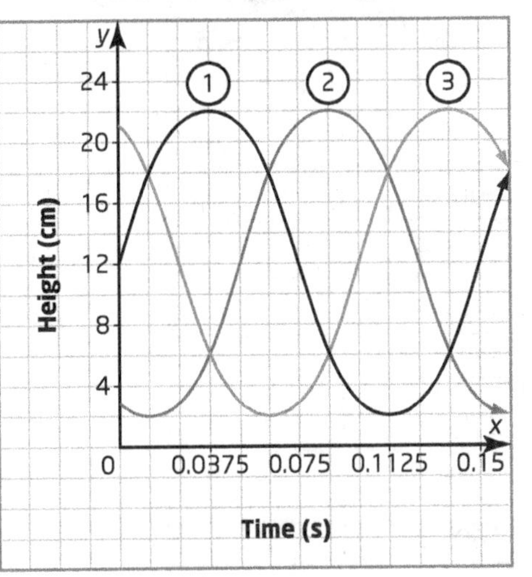

a) Determine an equation for each graph.

b) Determine the frequency of the motion.

Chapter 5 Review

5.1 Modelling Periodic Behaviour

1. Which of the following values do you expect to follow a periodic pattern? Justify your answer for each case.

a) the distance from the centre as a grandfather clock pendulum swings back and forth

b) the cost of sending a package by courier, which varies depending on the weight of the package

c) the value of a stock over a 1-year period

2. a) Sketch a periodic function, $f(x)$, with a maximum value of 8, a minimum of -5, and a period of 3.

b) Select a value a for x, and determine $f(a)$.

c) Determine two other values, b and c, such that $f(a) = f(b) = f(c)$.

5.2 The Sine Function and the Cosine Function

3. a) Copy and complete the table of values for $y = \sin 2x$.

x	$2x$	$y = \sin 2x$
0°		
45°		
90°		
135°		
180°		
225°		
270°		
315°		
360°		

b) Use the table values to sketch a graph of $y = \sin 2x$. On the same set of axes, sketch a graph of $y = \sin x$

c) Compare the graphs in part b). Describe the similarities and differences.

4. a) Predict what the graph of $y = -\csc x$ looks like. Use a table of values or technology to sketch the graph. Is your prediction correct?

b) Sketch the graph of $y = \csc x$ on the same set of axes.

c) Describe the similarities and differences between the graphs.

5.3 Investigate Transformations of Sine and Cosine Functions

5. Write two equations, one in the form $y = a \sin kx$ and one in the form $y = a \cos [k(x - d)]$, to match the graph.

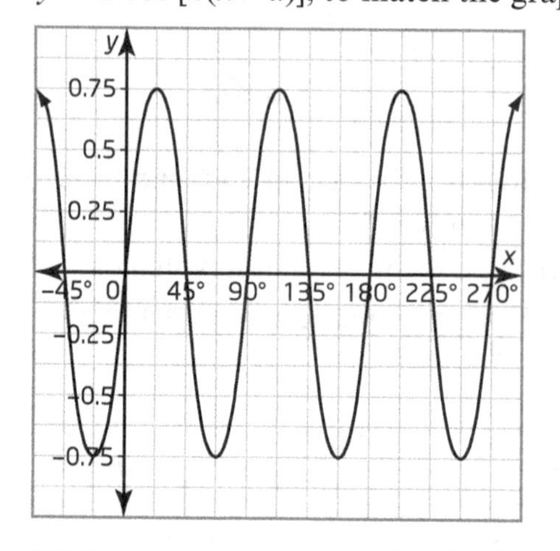

6. Write two equations, one in the form $y = a \cos kx$ and one in the form $y = a \sin [k(x - d)]$, to match the graph.

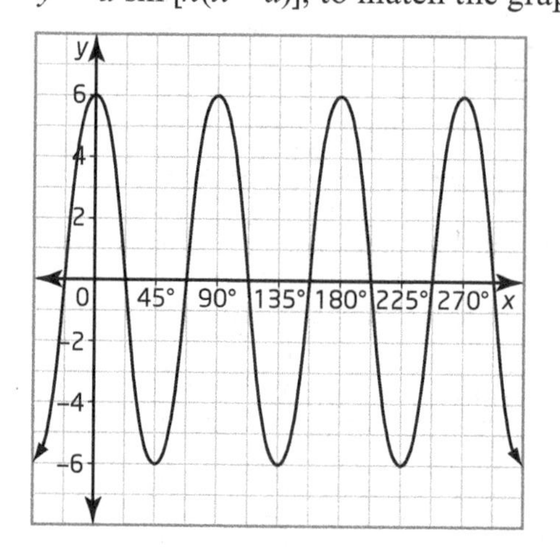

7. Determine the amplitude, the period, the phase shift, and the vertical shift of each function.

a) $y = 5 \sin [3(x - 40°)] + 6$
b) $y = \frac{1}{4} \cos [4x + 400°] - 2$
c) $y = -7 \sin \left[\frac{2}{3}(x + 75°)\right] - 1$
d) $y = 0.4 \cos [3.5(x - 60°)] + 5.6$

5.4 Graphing and Modelling With $y = a \sin [k(x - d)] + c$ and $y = a \cos [k(x - d)] + c$

8. **a)** Transform the graph of $f(x) = \sin x$ to $g(x) = -7 \sin \left[\frac{1}{2}(x - 30°)\right] + 1$. Show each step in the transformation.
b) State the domain and range of $f(x)$ and $g(x)$.

9. **a)** Transform the graph of $f(x) = \cos x$ to $g(x) = \frac{2}{3} \cos [5(x + 28°)] - 4$. Show each step in the transformation.
b) State the domain and range of $f(x)$ and $g(x)$.

10. **a)** Determine the equation of a sine function that represents the graph shown.

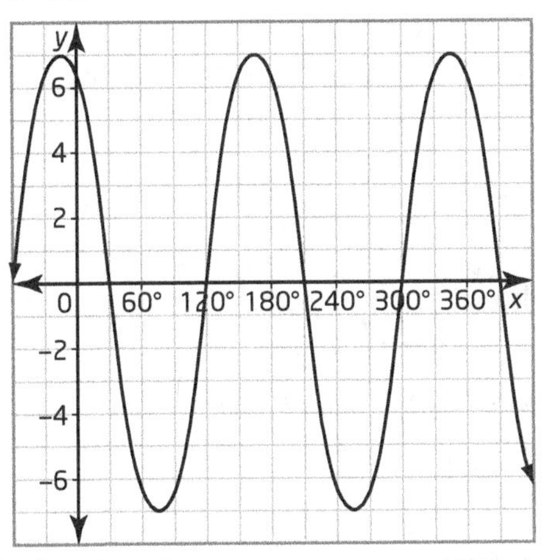

b) Determine the equation of a cosine function that represents the graph.

5.5 Data Collecting and Modelling

11. The table shows the mid-season high temperatures for winter, spring, summer, and fall over a 3-year period for a city in Ontario.

Month	Temperature (°C)
February	−9
May	16
August	25
November	3
February	−10
May	17
August	27
November	3
February	−10
May	16
August	26
November	3

a) Use the table to determine a sinusoidal model for the mid-season high temperature.
b) Graph the points in the table on the same axes as your model to verify the fit.
c) Is the fit as you expect? Explain any discrepancies.

5.6 Use Sinusoidal Functions to Model Periodic Phenomena Not Involving Angles

12. During a 12-h period, the tides in one area of the Bay of Fundy cause the water level to rise to 6 m above average sea level and to fall 6 m below average sea level. The depth of the water at low tide is 2 m.

a) Suppose the water is at average sea level at midnight and the tide is coming in. Draw a graph that shows the height of the tide over a 24-h period. Explain how you obtained the graph.
b) Determine an equation that represents the tide for part a) using
i) a sine function
ii) a cosine function
c) Suppose the water is at average sea level at 3 a.m. and the tide is coming in. Write an equation that represents this new situation. Explain your reasoning.

Chapter 5 Math Contest

1. Determine the value of x such that $\frac{8^{29} - 8^{28}}{7} = 2^x$.

A 29 **B** 84 **C** 58 **D** 56

2. The sum of $300 - 299 + 298 - 297 + 296 - 295 + \cdots - 3 + 2 - 1$ is

A 149 **B** 151 **C** 300 **D** 150

3. Determine the values of three positive integers x, y, and z given that
$x + \cfrac{1}{y + \cfrac{1}{z}} = \frac{38}{11}$.

4. If the fraction $\frac{5}{13}$ is written in expanded decimal form, what is the 153rd digit after the decimal point?

A 4 **B** 6 **C** 8 **D** 1

5. Three consecutive integers less than 20 have a sum of 27 and a product of 720. What are the numbers?

6. If $f(x) = \frac{1}{x^2 - 4}$ and $g(x) = \frac{2x}{x - 2}$, determine the value of x such that $(f + g)(x) = 2$.

A -2 **B** $-\frac{5}{2}$ **C** $-\frac{9}{4}$ **D** $\frac{7}{4}$

7. How many different-sized squares can be made on a 5-by-5 geoboard?

A 43 **B** 10 **C** 6 **D** 8

8. A sequence of numbers has the terms 0.3, 0.33, 0.333, 0.3333, ... What value does the sequence approach?

A 0.34 **B** 0.4 **C** $\frac{1}{3}$ **D** 1

9. A sequence of numbers has the terms $\sqrt{2}, \sqrt{2\sqrt{2}}, \sqrt{2\sqrt{2\sqrt{2}}}, \sqrt{2\sqrt{2\sqrt{2\sqrt{2}}}}, \ldots$. What is the limit of the value of the terms in the sequence?

A 2 **B** 1.5 **C** 3 **D** 1.4

10. When a number is divided by 18, the remainder is 13. What is the remainder when the number is divided by 6?

A 2 **B** 1 **C** 3 **D** 5

11. The period of $y = |5 \sin (4x - 120°)|$ is

A 45°

B 90°

C 120°

D 360°

12. If the number 6912 can be written in the form $2^x 3^y 4^z$, then the value of $x^2 + y^2 + z^2$ is

A 9 **B** 14 **C** 33 **D** 29

13. If $y = \sqrt[3]{x}$, what is the value of $x^{21} + 3\sqrt{2} - y^{63}$?

14. If $\binom{n}{r} = \frac{n!}{r!(n - r)!}$, where $n! = n \times (n - 1) \times (n - 2) \times \ldots 3 \times 2 \times 1$, determine the value of $\frac{\binom{100}{98}}{2}$.

A 4950

B 2475

C 9900

D 10 540

Chapter 6 Discrete Functions

6.1 Sequences as Discrete Functions

KEY CONCEPTS

- A sequence of numbers can be represented by a discrete function. The graph of a discrete function is a distinct set of points, not a smooth curve.
- The domain of a function representing a sequence is the set or a subset of the natural numbers, $\mathbb{N}$.
- Given the explicit formula for the *n*th term, t_n or $f(n)$, of a sequence, the terms can be written by substituting the term numbers for n. Examples of explicit formulas are $t_n = 3n + 2$ and $f(n) = 5n + 3$.
- An explicit formula for the *n*th term of a sequence can sometimes be determined by finding a pattern among the terms.

Example

Write the first four terms of a sequence that satisfies each of the following. Write an explicit formula for the *n*th term of each of your sequences using function notation.

a) The terms of the sequence are determined by adding a constant value.

b) The terms of the sequence are determined by dividing by a constant value.

Solution

a) Select a number for the first term, say 3. Select a constant value to be added to each term, say 7.

The first four terms of the sequence are 3, 10, 17, and 24.

The explicit formula is $f(n) = -4 + 7n$.

b) Select a number for the first term, say −20. Select a constant value that each term is divided by, say 4.

The first four terms of the sequence are $-20, -5, -\frac{5}{4}$, and $-\frac{5}{16}$.

The explicit formula is $f(n) = -\frac{20}{4^{n-1}}$, or $f(n) = -20(4^{-n+1})$.

A Practise

1. Write the first three terms of each sequence, given the explicit formula for the *n*th term of the sequence.

   a) $t_n = 2n + 1$

   b) $t_n = 4 - 3n$

   c) $f(n) = 1 + 2(n - 2)$

   d) $t_n = 7 + 2n$

   e) $t_n = 2^{n-1}$

   f) $f(n) = -2(3)^{n+1}$

2. Write the 16th term, given the explicit formula for the *n*th term of the sequence.

   a) $f(n) = 5 - 2n$

   b) $t_n = 3n + 2$

   c) $t_n = \sqrt{n} + 2$

   d) $f(n) = (-2)^{10-n}$

3. Describe the pattern in each sequence. Write the next three terms of each sequence.

   a) 5, 25, 125, 625, …

   b) 9, 7, 5, 3, …

   c) −4, −8, −16, −32, …

   d) 300, 30, 3, 0.3, …

   e) 3, 9, 27, 81, 243, …

   f) $ar^3, ar^2, ar, a, \ldots$

   g) 0.11, −0.33, 0.99, −2.97, …

4. For each sequence, make a table of values using the term number and term, and calculate the finite differences. Then, determine an explicit formula in function notation and specify the domain.

   a) 6, 12, 18, 24, …

   b) 7, 4, 1, −2, …

   c) 2, 5, 10, 17, …

   d) 4, 13, 26, 43, …

5. The graphs show the terms in a sequence. Write each sequence in function notation and specify the domain.

   a)

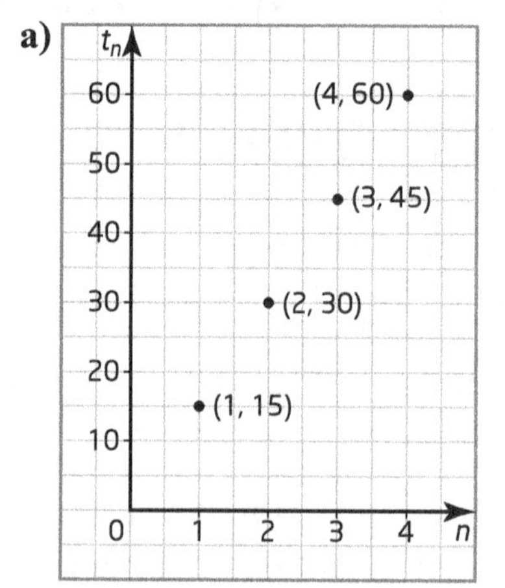

   b)

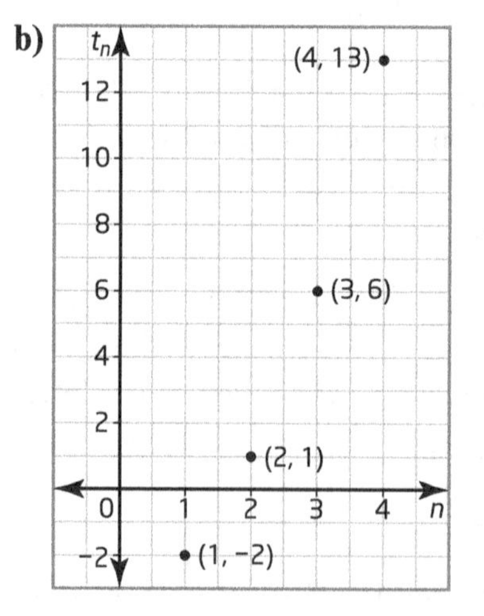

   c)

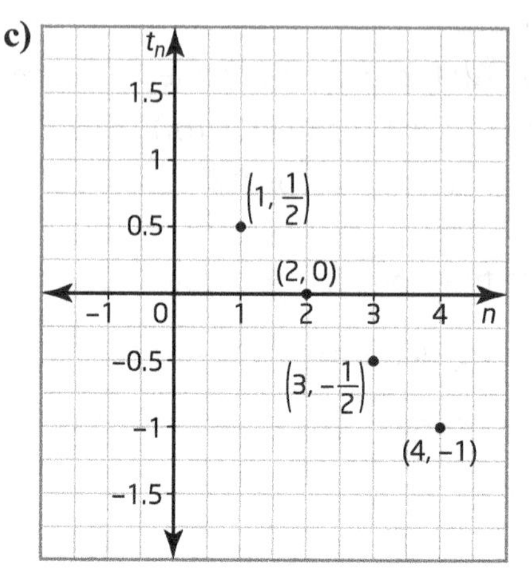

6. The graphs show the terms in a sequence. Write each sequence in function notation and specify the domain.

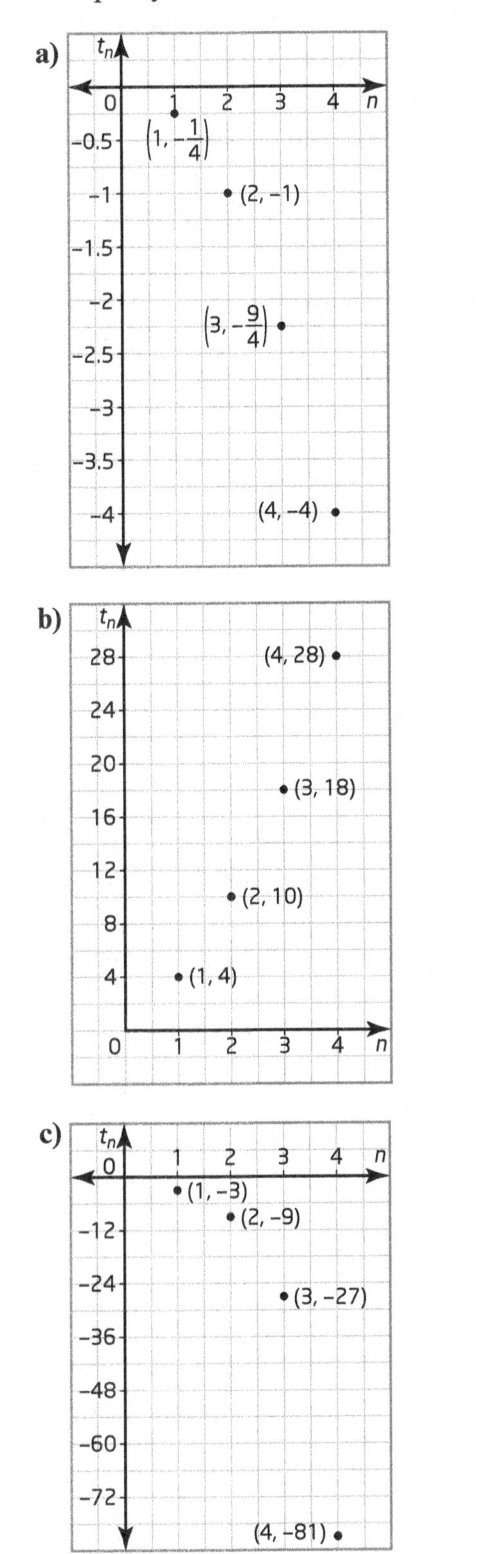

7. For each graph, specify whether the function is discrete or continuous and explain your choice.

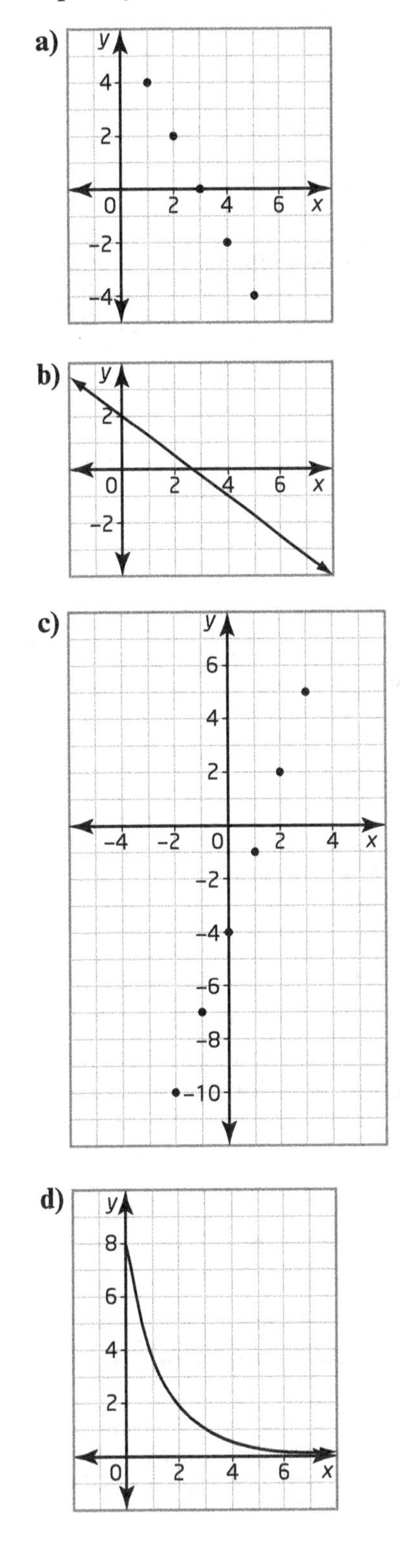

B Connect and Apply

★**8.** Describe the pattern in each sequence and write the next four terms.

a) $2, -5, 4, -10, 6, -15, 8, -20, 10, \ldots$

b) $-7, 9, -1, 2, 5, -5, 11, \ldots$

c) $4, \frac{1}{27}, 9, \frac{1}{9}, 14, \frac{1}{3}, 19, \ldots$

d) $8, -1, 0.8, -1, 0.08, -1, \ldots$

9. Consider the sequence 9, 18, 27, 36, ... Determine whether each of the following numbers is part of this sequence. Explain your thinking.

a) 135

b) 179

c) 653

d) 423

10. Determine an explicit formula for the *n*th term of each sequence. Use the formula to write the 15th term.

a) $-16, 8, -4, 2, \ldots$

b) $1, \frac{2}{3}, \frac{3}{5}, \frac{4}{7}, \ldots$

c) $2, \frac{2}{\sqrt{2}}, \frac{2}{\sqrt{3}}, 1, \ldots$

d) $1, 3, 9, 27, \ldots$

e) $2, \frac{3}{2}, \frac{4}{3}, \frac{5}{4}, \ldots$

11. Write the first four terms of a sequence that satisfies each of the following. Write an explicit formula for the *n*th term of each of your sequences in function notation.

a) The terms of the sequence are determined by subtracting a constant value.

b) The terms of the sequence are determined by multiplying a constant value.

★**12.** A new small business plans to triple its sales every day for the first 2 weeks. Sales on the first day are $20.

a) Write the sequence that represents the sales for the first 6 days according to the plan.

b) Write an explicit formula to determine the sales on any of the first 14 days.

c) Use your formula to determine the sales on the 14th day. Is this reasonable? Why or why not?

13. The number of tourists visiting a small seaside town each summer is decreasing. This year the number of visitors was 3400, and it has been predicted that every year there will be 260 fewer tourists.

a) Write an explicit formula to determine the number of tourists in any given year.

b) How many tourists are expected to visit in 6 years?

c) How long will it be before the number of tourists drops below 1500?

C Extend

14. Consider the sequence $\sqrt{5}, \sqrt{\sqrt{5}}, \sqrt{\sqrt{\sqrt{5}}}, \ldots$.

a) Write the next two terms of the sequence.

b) Express each of the five terms as a power.

c) Write an explicit formula, in function notation, to represent the terms in the sequence.

d) Express your formula in part c) in a different form.

e) Write a power to represent the 50th term in this sequence.

15. Determine a formula for the *n*th term of each sequence.

a) $1 \times 1, 3 \times 4, 5 \times 7, 7 \times 10, \ldots$

b) $\frac{3}{8}, \frac{15}{24}, \frac{35}{48}, \frac{63}{80}, \ldots$

6.2 Recursive Procedures

KEY CONCEPTS

- A recursive procedure is one where a process is performed on an initial object or number and then the result is put through the steps of the process again. This is repeated many times over.
- A sequence can be defined recursively if each term can be calculated from the previous term or terms.
- A recursion formula shows the relationship between the terms of a sequence.
- A sequence can be represented by a pattern, an explicit formula, or a recursion formula. Formulas can also be written using function notation.

  For example:

  Pattern: 1, 3, 5, 7, ...

  Explicit formula: $t_n = 2n - 1$ or $f(n) = 2n - 1$

  Recursion formula: $t_1 = 1$, $t_n = t_{n-1} + 2$, or $f(1) = 1, f(n) = f(n - 1) + 2$
- In an explicit or a recursion formula for a sequence, n is a natural number because it is a term number. To find the terms of a sequence using a recursion formula, begin with the next natural number that is not used in the formula.

Example

Aniia and Marco paid $350 000 for their first home. The real estate agent told them that the house will appreciate in value by 4% per year.

a) Copy and complete the table to show the value of the house for the next 8 years.

Year	House Value ($)
0	350 000
1	$350\ 000 + 0.04 \times 350\ 000 = 364\ 000$

b) Write the value of the house for the first 8 years as a sequence.

c) Write a recursion formula to represent the value of the house.

d) Predict the value after 25 years.

Solution

a)

Year	House Value ($)
0	350 000
1	350 000 + 0.04 × 350 000 = 364 000
2	364 000 + 0.04 × 364 000 = 378 560
3	378 560 + 0.04 × 378 560 = 393 702.40
4	393 702.40 + 0.04 × 393 702.40 = 409 450.50
5	409 450.50 + 0.04 × 409 450.50 = 425 828.52
6	425 828.52 + 0.04 × 425 828.52 = 442 861.66
7	442 861.66 + 0.04 × 442 861.66 = 460 576.13
8	460 576.13 + 0.04 × 460 576.13 = 478 999.18

b) The terms of the sequence are the final amounts in the second column of the table:
350 000, 364 000, 378 560, 393 702.40, 409 450.50, 425 828.52, 442 861.66, 460 576.13, 478 999.18.

c) The first term will be the house value in year 0, $350 000.
To find a recursion formula, note the pattern of calculations in each row and the common factor on the left side of the equation.
For example, in row 2 there is a common factor of 350 000 on the left side of the equation.

$$\begin{aligned} 350\,000 + 0.04 \times 350\,000 &= 350\,000(1 + 0.04) \\ &= 350\,000(1.04) \\ &= 364\,000 \end{aligned}$$

Similarly, the calculation in row 3 may also be written as 364 000(1.04) = 378 560, and so on for subsequent rows.
Therefore, a recursive formula to represent the value of the house is
$t_1 = 350\,000$, $t_n = 1.04t_{n-1}$.

d) The value of the house in 25 years can be obtained by multiplying the original amount by 1.04, 25 times, which is equivalent to multiplying by $(1.04)^{25}$.
$350\,000(1.04)^{25} = 933\,042.72$
In 25 years, the value of the house will be $933 042.72.

A Practise

1. Write the first four terms of each sequence, where $n \in \mathbb{N}$.

   a) $t_1 = 2,$
   $t_n = t_{n-1} + 6$

   b) $t_1 = 4,$
   $t_n = 3t_{n-1} - 2$

   c) $t_1 = -1,$
   $t_n = 0.5t_{n-1} + 0.5$

   d) $t_1 = 500,$
   $t_n = \frac{t_{n-1}}{5}$

   e) $t_1 = 3,$
   $t_n = 3n - 2t_{n-1}$

   f) $t_1 = 90,$
   $t_n = \frac{4t_{n-1}}{3}$

2. Write the first four terms of each sequence, where $n \in \mathbb{N}$.

   a) $f(1) = -3,$
   $f(n) = f(n-1) + 4$

   b) $f(1) = 0.25,$
   $f(n) = -2f(n-1)$

   c) $f(1) = 4,$
   $f(n) = \frac{f(n-1)}{n+1}$

   d) $f(1) = -7,$
   $f(n) = -f(n-1) + 3$

   e) $f(1) = -1.5,$
   $f(n) = f(n-1) + n$

3. Determine a recursion formula for each sequence.

   a) 2, 5, 11, 23, …

   b) 3, −1, −7, −15, …

   c) −2, −3, −5, −8, …

4. For each graph, write the sequence of terms and determine a recursion formula using function notation.

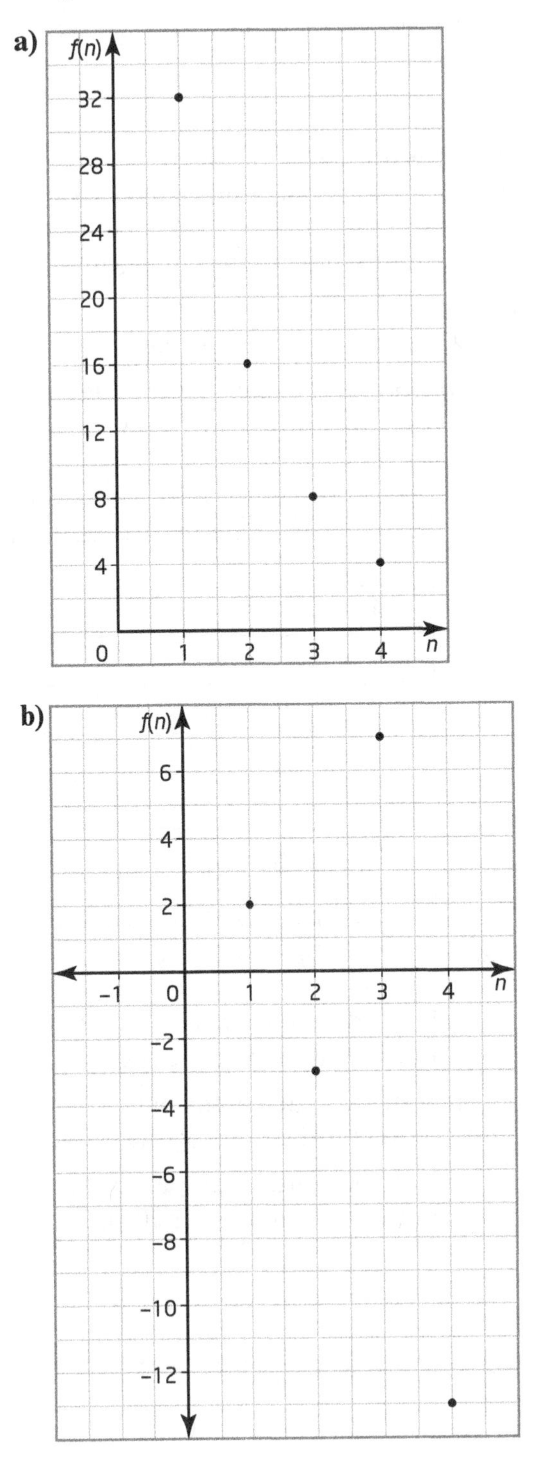

5. The first term of a constant sequence is $f(1) = 3.14$.

   a) State $f(n)$ for this sequence.

   b) Write the first five terms of this sequence.

B Connect and Apply

6. Annette and Gordon paid \$275 000 for a new home. They were told that they can expect the house to appreciate in value by 3.5% per year.

   a) Express 3.5% as a decimal.

   b) Copy and complete the table to show the value of the house for the next 8 years.

Year	House Value (\$)
0	275 000
1	
2	
3	
4	
5	
6	
7	
8	

   c) Write the value of the house for the first 8 years as a sequence.

   d) Write a recursion formula to represent the value of the house.

   e) Use your formula in part d) to predict the value after 20 years.

7. The auditorium in a new school has 42 seats in the first row, 51 in the second row, 65 in the third row, 84 in the next row, and so on.

   a) Represent the number of seats in the rows as a sequence.

   b) Describe the pattern in the number of seats per row.

   c) Write a recursion formula to represent the number of seats in any row.

☆8. A bacteria culture begins with 12 bacteria and doubles every hour.

   a) Write the sequence for the first 7 h.

   b) Write an explicit formula for the *n*th term of the sequence.

   c) Write a recursion formula to represent the number of bacteria.

   d) Which of the above formulas was easier to determine? Explain.

   e) Determine the number of bacteria in the culture after 12 h. Which formula did you use? Why?

   f) After how many hours will there be 1 572 864 bacteria?

9. Given the explicit formula of a sequence, write the first five terms and then determine a recursion formula for the sequence.

   a) $f(n) = 6n - 5$

   b) $t_n = 3n - 1$

   c) $t_n = (-2)^{-n}$

   d) $t_n = n(n - 2)$

10. Use the given recursion formula to determine the first five terms of each sequence.

a) $f(1) = 1,$
$f(2) = 1,$
$f(n) = f(n-1) + f(n-2)$

☆**b)** $f(1) = 4,$
$f(2) = -1,$
$f(n) = f(n-1) - 2f(n-2)$

c) $t_1 = 2,$
$t_2 = 3,$
$t_n = 3t_{n-2} - t_{n-1}$

d) $t_1 = -1,$
$t_2 = 4,$
$t_n = -2t_{n-2} + t_{n-1}$

e) $t_1 = 3,$
$t_2 = -2,$
$t_n = t_{n-2} \times t_{n-1} + n$

f) $t_1 = 5,$
$t_2 = 1,$
$t_3 = -1,$
$t_n = t_{n-3} - 2t_{n-2} + t_{n-1}$

11. Write the first four terms of each sequence.

a) $t_1 = 1,$
$t_n = 1 - (t_{n-1})^2$

b) $f(1) = 64,$
$f(n) = \frac{f(n-1)}{-4}$

c) $t_1 = -3,$
$t_n = -5t_{n-1}$

d) $t_1 = -2,$
$t_n = 11 + 3t_{n-1}$

e) $t_1 = \frac{1}{8},$
$t_n = 4t_{n-1} - 1$

f) $f(1) = a - 2b,$
$f(n) = f(n-1) + 3b$

g) $f(1) = 2c + 3d,$
$f(n) = f(n-1) - c$

h) $f(1) = m - 5n,$
$f(n) = f(n-1) + 2m + n$

12. Given the recursion formula, write the first four terms of the sequence and then determine the explicit formula for the sequence.

a) $t_1 = 4,$
$t_n = t_{n-1} - 7$

b) $t_1 = 81,$
$t_n = -\frac{1}{3}t_{n-1}$

c) $t_1 = 0,$
$t_n = t_{n-1} + 2n - 1$

d) $t_1 = -5,$
$t_n = t_{n-1} + 3$

C Extend

13. Write the first five terms of each sequence, starting at $f(1)$.

a) $f(2) = -5,$
$f(n) = -3f(n-1) + 1$

b) $f(3) = 7,$
$f(n) = f(n-1) - 2n$

14. Is it possible for a sequence to have two different recursion formulas? Justify your answer with an example.

6.3 Pascal's Triangle and Expanding Binomial Powers

KEY CONCEPTS

- Pascal's triangle is a triangular array of natural numbers in which the entries can be obtained by adding the two entries immediately above.
  $t_{n,r} = t_{n-1,r-1} + t_{n-1,r}$, where n is the horizontal row number and r is the diagonal row number.

- Many number patterns can be found in Pascal's triangle. For example, the sums of the terms of the rows form a sequence of the powers of 2 and the terms in diagonal row 2 are triangular numbers.

- The coefficients of the terms in the expansion of $(a + b)^n$ correspond to the terms in row n of Pascal's triangle.

Example

Write $t_{6,4}$ as the difference of two terms, each in the form $t_{n,r}$.

Solution

Use the formula $t_{n,r} = t_{n-1,r-1} + t_{n-1,r}$.
Since this formula involves a sum, rearrange the terms to create a formula that involves the difference of two terms. There are two possibilities.

i) $t_{n,r} - t_{n-1,r-1} = t_{n-1,r}$
ii) $t_{n,r} - t_{n-1,r} = t_{n-1,r-1}$

Formula i):

Let $t_{6,4}$ be represented by $t_{n-1,r-1}$ in the formula $t_{n,r} - t_{n-1,r} = t_{n-1,r-1}$.
Then, $n - 1 = 6$ and $r - 1 = 4$.
So, $n = 7$ and $r = 5$.
Therefore, $t_{6,4}$ can be expressed as the difference of two terms as $t_{6,4} = t_{7,5} - t_{6,5}$.

Formula ii):

Let $t_{6,4}$ be represented by $t_{n-1,r}$ in the formula $t_{n,r} - t_{n-1,r-1} = t_{n-1,r}$.
Then, $n - 1 = 6$ and $r = 4$.
So, $n = 7$ and $r - 1 = 3$.
Therefore, $t_{6,4}$ can be expressed as the difference of two terms as $t_{6,4} = t_{7,4} - t_{6,3}$.

A Practise

1. The following hockey stick pattern is one of many found in Pascal's triangle.

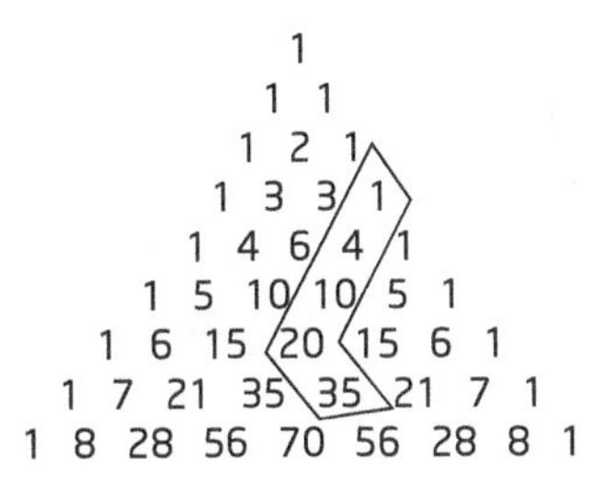

   a) Is this the only hockey stick pattern that has these numbers? Explain.

   b) Copy Pascal's triangle shown above and extend it to row 10. Use your triangle to list the numbers in a hockey stick pattern with each of the following sums.

   i) 84
   ii) 120
   iii) 56
   iv) 252

2. Determine the sum of the terms in each of the following rows of Pascal's triangle.

   a) row 11

   b) row 19

   c) row 22

   d) row 30

   e) row $n + 1$

3. Express as a single term from Pascal's triangle in the form $t_{n,\,r}$.

   a) $t_{5,\,7} + t_{5,\,8}$

   b) $t_{9,\,2} + t_{9,\,3}$

   c) $t_{3,\,4} + t_{3,\,5}$

   d) $t_{10,\,7} + t_{10,\,8}$

   e) $t_{15,\,9} + t_{15,\,10}$

   f) $t_{a+1,\,b} + t_{a+1,\,b+1}$

4. Write each as the sum of two terms, each in the form $t_{n,\,r}$.

   a) $t_{19,\,11}$

   b) $t_{25,\,16}$

   c) $t_{14,\,7}$

   d) $t_{a,\,2}$

   e) $t_{x+2,\,x-3}$

5. Use Pascal's triangle to expand each power of a binomial.

   a) $(x + 1)^8$

   b) $(y - 2)^7$

   c) $(2 + t)^6$

   d) $(1 - m^2)^4$

   e) $(a + 2b)^3$

6. How many terms will there be in each expansion?

   a) $(6a - 7b)^7$

   b) $(8x + 11)^{20}$

   c) $(9t - 4)^1$

   d) $(-7x + 2)^{38}$

   e) $\left(\frac{1}{x} + 3\right)^{54}$

   f) $(5b + 2a)^{n+1}$

   g) $(2t^2 + 3t - 5)^0$

7. Use patterns in the terms of the expansion to determine the value of k in each term of $(x + y)^{10}$.

   a) ky^{10}

   b) $252x^ky^5$

   c) $128x^7y^k$

   d) kx^6y^4

   e) kx^2y^8

   f) $210x^ky^6$

B Connect and Apply

8. What row number of Pascal's triangle has each indicated row sum?

   a) 32 768

   b) 128

   c) 131 072

   d) 1024

   e) 1 048 576

   f) 8192

   g) 512

   h) 4096

9. Write each as the difference of two terms, each in the form $t_{n,\,r}$.

a) $t_{7,\,3}$

b) $t_{9,\,5}$

c) $t_{13,\,2}$

d) $t_{26,\,17}$

e) $t_{24,\,3}$

f) $t_{10,\,10}$

g) $t_{n,\,r}$

10. Look for patterns in Pascal's triangle. What are the missing numbers in each diagram?

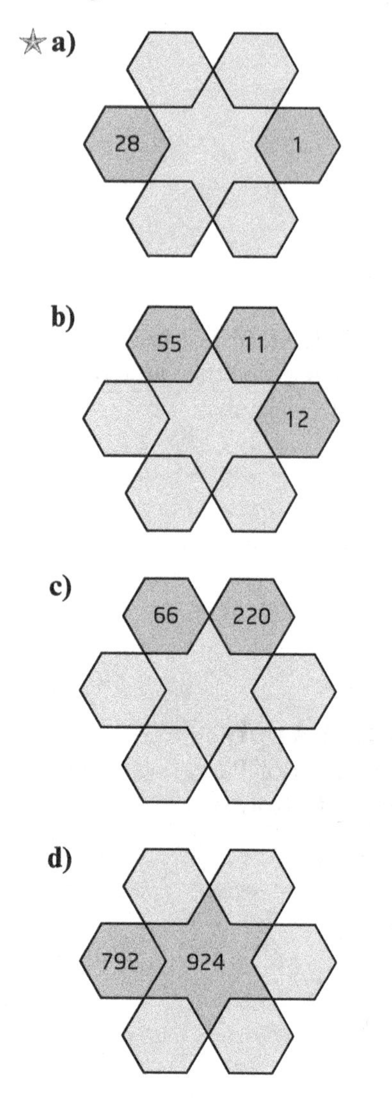

e)

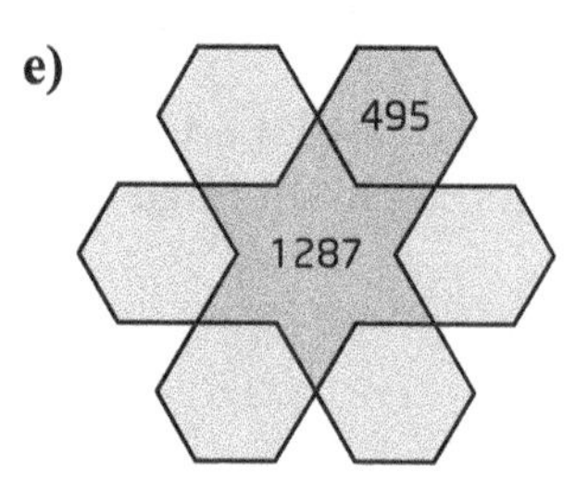

11. Use Pascal's triangle to expand and simplify.

a) $(x + y)^4 + (x - y)^4$

b) $(x + y)^4 - (x - y)^4$

12. Use Pascal's triangle to expand each power of a binomial.

a) $\left(2x + \frac{3}{x}\right)^6$

b) $\left(\sqrt{x} - \frac{2}{\sqrt{x}}\right)^6$

C Extend

★ 13. a) Describe how Pascal's triangle can be used to expand and simplify $(a + b + c)^3$.

b) Apply your method from part a) to expand and simplify the trinomial $(a + b + c)^3$.

14. The first three terms in the expansion of $(1 + ax + bx^2)^4$ are 1, $8x$, and $32x^2$. Determine the value(s) of a and b.

15. Determine the coefficient of x^{14} in the expansion of $(x^4 + 3)^3(2 - x^2)^5$.

16. The coefficients of $(a + b)^n$ in Pascal's triangle may be written in the form $\binom{n}{r}$, where $\binom{n}{r} = \frac{n!}{r!\,(n-r)!}$, $n! = n \times (n-1) \times (n-2) \times \ldots \times 3 \times 2 \times 1$, $0! = 1$, and $0 \leq r \leq n$.

a) Show that the above is true for $(a + b)^5$.

b) Write the coefficients of $(a + b)^{10}$ in the form $\binom{n}{r}$.

6.4 Arithmetic Sequences

KEY CONCEPTS

- An arithmetic sequence is a sequence in which the difference between consecutive terms is a constant.
- The difference between consecutive terms of an arithmetic sequence is called the common difference.
- The formula for the general term of an arithmetic sequence is $t_n = a + (n - 1)d$, where a is the first term, d is the common difference, and n is the term number.

Example

Determine the number of terms in the arithmetic sequence −28, −22, −16, …, 260.

Solution

First, determine the general term of the sequence.
The first term is $a = -28$ and the common difference is $d = 6$.
Substitute the values into the formula for the general term.

$$\begin{aligned} t_n &= a + (n - 1)d \\ &= -28 + (n - 1)(6) \\ &= -28 + 6n - 6 \\ &= -34 + 6n \end{aligned}$$

A formula for the general term is $t_n = -34 + 6n$.

To find the number of terms in the sequence, solve for n when $t_n = 260$.

$$\begin{aligned} 260 &= -34 + 6n \\ 294 &= 6n \\ n &= 49 \end{aligned}$$

There are 49 terms in the sequence.

A Practise

1. For each arithmetic sequence, determine the values of a and d. Then, write the next four terms.

   a) 5, 8, 11, …

   b) −3, 2, 7, …

   c) 1.5, 0.7, −0.1, …

   d) 33, 31.2, 29.4, …

   e) $\frac{1}{4}, \frac{1}{2}, \frac{3}{4}, \ldots$

   f) 0.25, 0.26, 0.27, …

2. State whether or not each sequence is arithmetic. Justify your answer.

   a) 1, 4, 7, 10, …

   b) 3, 2, 3, 4, …

   c) −12, −5, 2, 9, …

   d) 0.41, 0.32, 0.23, …

   e) $-\frac{5}{4}, -\frac{4}{3}, -\frac{3}{2}, \ldots$

   f) $\frac{19}{12}, \frac{5}{4}, \frac{11}{12}, \ldots$

3. Given the values of a and d, write the first three terms of the arithmetic sequence. Then, write the formula for the general term.

   a) $a = 12, d = -5$

   b) $a = -9, d = 2$

   c) $a = 11, d = -\frac{7}{8}$

   d) $a = -\frac{2}{3}, d = \frac{1}{2}$

   e) $a = x^2, d = 1.3x^2$

4. Given the formula for the general term of an arithmetic sequence, determine t_{16}.

   a) $t_n = 2n + 7$

   b) $f(n) = 3 - 5n$

   c) $t_n = -\frac{3}{4}n + 3$

   d) $f(n) = 16 - 2.8n$

   e) $t_n = 4n + 11$

   f) $f(n) = 19 - 12n$

5. Given the formula for the general term of an arithmetic sequence, write the first five terms. Graph the discrete function that represents each sequence.

   a) $t_n = 4n - 1$

   b) $f(n) = -n + 3$

   c) $f(n) = 2(1 - 5n)$

   d) $t_n = -6n + 17$

   e) $f(n) = \frac{3n + 2}{2}$

   f) $t_n = 0.9n + 0.3$

   g) $f(n) = 0.1(3 + 2n)$

6. Which term in the arithmetic sequence −15, −8, −1, … has the value 125?

7. Determine the number of terms in each arithmetic sequence.

   a) 5, 11, 17, …, 179

   b) 8, 16, 24, …, 424

   c) −13, −9, −5, …, 327

   d) 8, 3, −2, …, −152

   e) $\frac{11}{5}, -\frac{4}{5}, -\frac{19}{5}, \ldots, -\frac{949}{5}$

   f) $2x^2 + x, 3x^2 + 6x, 4x^2 + 11x, \ldots, 39x^2 + 186x$

B Connect and Apply

☆8. a) Verify that the sequence determined by the recursion formula $t_1 = -5$, $t_n = t_{n-1} + 3$ is arithmetic.

   b) Determine the formula for the general term of the sequence.

9. For each sequence, determine the values of a and d and write the next three terms.

   a) $\frac{1}{5}, \frac{7}{15}, \frac{11}{15}, \ldots$

   b) $-1, -\frac{5}{3}, -\frac{7}{3}, \ldots$

   c) $2, \frac{5}{4}, \frac{1}{2}, \ldots$

   d) $-\frac{3}{8}, \frac{1}{2}, \frac{11}{8}, \ldots$

   e) $-4x + y, -3x + 5y, -2x + 9y, \ldots$

   f) $3m - \frac{5}{6}n, -3m - \frac{2}{3}n, -9m - \frac{1}{2}n, \ldots$

10. Determine a and d, and then write the formula for the nth term of each arithmetic sequence with the given terms.

   a) $t_3 = 11$ and $t_8 = 46$

   b) $t_{12} = 52$ and $t_{22} = 102$

   c) $t_{50} = 140$ and $t_{70} = 180$

   d) $t_{34} = 96$ and $t_{46} = 132$

   e) $t_{21} = 34.5$ and $t_{38} = 60$

   f) $t_{19} = -91.8$ and $t_{41} = -223.8$

   g) $t_9 = 29 + 41x$ and $t_{16} = 29 + 76x$

   h) $t_5 = -x^3 - 6$ and $t_{18} = -14x^3 - 19$

11. Write a recursion formula for each sequence in question 10.

12. Eight fence posts are to be equally spaced between two corner posts that are 117 m apart.

   a) What should be the distance between two posts?

   b) Write a sequence to represent this situation.

   c) Write the formula for the general term of the sequence in part b).

   d) How is the value you found in part a) related to the general term of the formula you found in part c)?

☆13. An architect's starting salary is $73 000. The company has guaranteed a raise of $2275 every 6 months with satisfactory performance.

   a) Write a sequence to represent this situation. Is this sequence arithmetic? Explain.

   b) State the general term of the sequence in part a).

   c) Write a recursion formula for the sequence in part a).

   d) What will the architect's salary be after 8 years?

   e) When will the architect's salary be $127 600?

14. A number, m, is called an arithmetic mean between a and b if a, m, and b form an arithmetic sequence.

   a) Determine the arithmetic mean between 3 and 27.

   b) Determine five arithmetic means between 5 and 29.

15. Determine the general term of an arithmetic sequence such that the 11th term is 53 and the sum of the 5th and 7th terms is 56.

C Extend

16. An original painting is purchased for $230, and each year it increases in value by 22% of its original value.

   a) What is the painting's value after 12 years?

   b) When is the painting worth $1242?

17. Determine all possible arithmetic sequences formed by the numbers p, q, and r such that $q = 3$ and $p^2 + r^2 = 68$.

18. The sum of the first three terms of an arithmetic sequence is 15. The sum of their squares is 147. Determine the sequence.

KEY CONCEPTS

- A geometric sequence is a sequence in which the ratio of consecutive terms is a constant.
- The ratio between consecutive terms of a geometric sequence is called the common ratio.
- The formula for the general term of a geometric sequence is $t_n = a(r)^{n-1}$, where a is the first term, r is the common ratio, and n is the term number.

Example

In a geometric sequence, the fifth term is 1875 and the seventh term is 46 875.

a) Determine the formula for the general term of the sequence.

b) Write the first four terms of the sequence.

Solution

a) The formula for the general term of a geometric sequence is $t_n = ar^{n-1}$.
The fifth term occurs when $n = 5$.
Therefore, $t_5 = ar^4$ and $ar^4 = 1875$. ①
The seventh term occurs when $n = 7$.
Therefore, $t_7 = ar^6$ and $ar^6 = 46\ 875$. ②
To determine the common ratio, divide ② by ①.

$$\frac{ar^6}{ar^2} = \frac{46\ 875}{1875}$$ Simplify each side.

$$r^2 = 25$$

$$r = \pm 5$$

There are two possible geometric sequences, one with $r = 5$ and the other with $r = -5$.
Determine a for each value of r using $ar^4 = 1875$.
Since $5^4 = (-5)^4$, you only need to check one value of r.

$$a(5)^4 = 1875$$

$$625a = 1875$$

$$a = 3$$

The formula for the general term is $t_n = 3(5)^{n-1}$ or $t_n = 3(-5)^{n-1}$.

b) The first four terms of the sequence $t_n = 3(5)^{n-1}$ are 3, 15, 75, and 375.
The first four terms of the sequence $t_n = 3(-5)^{n-1}$ are 3, −15, 75, and −375.

A Practise

1. Determine whether the sequence is arithmetic, geometric, or neither. Give a reason for your answer.

   a) 7, 5, 3, 1, ...

   b) 4, −16, 64, −256, ...

   c) 3, 0.3, 0.03, 0.003, ...

   d) 8, 8.8, 8.88, 8.888, ...

   e) 1, 3, 9, 27, ...

   f) $ab, ab^2, ab^3, ab^4, \ldots$

2. State the common ratio for each geometric sequence and write the next three terms.

   a) 3, 6, 12, 24, ...

   b) −5, 20, −80, 320, ...

   c) $\frac{1}{2}, -1, 2, -4, \ldots$

   d) 8000, 800, 80, 8, ...

   e) $-\frac{1}{6}, -\frac{1}{2}, -\frac{3}{2}, -\frac{9}{2}, \ldots$

   f) 2.5, 0.5, 0.1, 0.02, ...

   g) $\frac{(x+3)^2}{3}, \frac{(x+3)^5}{12}, \frac{(x+3)^8}{48}, \frac{(x+3)^{11}}{192}, \ldots$

3. For each geometric sequence, determine the formula for the general term and use it to determine the indicated term.

   a) 4096, 1024, 256, ..., t_8

   b) 12, 6, 3, ..., t_{12}

   c) $6, -2, \frac{2}{3}, \ldots, t_8$

   d) 13.45, 2.69, 0.538, ..., t_{10}

   e) $\frac{1}{32}, \frac{1}{8}, \frac{1}{2}, \ldots, t_{13}$

   f) $\frac{a^2}{b}, \frac{a^3}{2b}, \frac{a^4}{4b}, \ldots, t_{16}$

4. Write the first four terms of each geometric sequence.

   a) $t_n = 3(-1)^{n-1}$

   b) $a = 22, r = -2$

   c) $f(n) = \frac{1}{3}(2)^{n-1}$

   d) $f(n) = 4(\sqrt{5})^{n-1}$

   e) $a = -2, r = \frac{2}{3}$

   f) $t_n = -1111(-0.3)^{n-1}$

5. Determine the number of terms in each geometric sequence.

   a) 2, −10, 50, ..., −156 250

   b) $64, 32, 16, \ldots, \frac{1}{256}$

   c) $12, 4, \frac{4}{3}, \ldots, \frac{4}{729}$

   d) 5, 35, 245, ..., 588 245

   e) $a, ab, ab^2, \ldots, ab^{12}$

B Connect and Apply

6. Determine if each sequence is arithmetic, geometric, or neither. If it is arithmetic, state the values of a and d. If it is geometric, state the values of a and r.

   a) $3m, 7m, 11m, \ldots$

   b) $-1, -\frac{2}{x}, -\frac{4}{x^2}, \ldots$

   c) $3x - 4y, 5x - 6y, 7x - 8y, \ldots$

   d) 5.440, 54.40, 544.0, ...

   e) $\frac{8}{7}, \frac{6}{5}, \frac{4}{3}, \ldots$

   f) $7, 4 + s, 1 + 2s, \ldots$

7. Find the unknown terms, m and n, in each geometric sequence.

   a) $7, m, 63, n$

   b) $-2, -10, m, n$

   c) $\frac{2}{9}, m, \frac{1}{2}, n$

   d) $m, 6, n, 216$

   e) $m, n, 2, \frac{1}{2}$

   f) $4, m, n, 500$

☆8. Which term of the geometric sequence $\frac{2}{81}, \frac{4}{27}, \frac{8}{9}, \ldots$ has a value of 6912?

9. Which term of the geometric sequence $5, 1, \frac{1}{5}, \ldots$ has a value of $\frac{1}{78\,125}$?

☆**10.** Without writing the terms of the sequence, determine the general term of the geometric sequence that corresponds to each recursion formula.

a) $t_1 = 4$, $t_n = -3xt_{n-1}$

b) $t_1 = -28m^3$, $t_n = \frac{1}{2}t_{n-1}$

c) $t_1 = \frac{5}{3}$, $t_n = \left(\frac{3}{4} + c\right)t_{n-1}$

11. Chad, a champion show dog, had 2 parents one generation ago, 4 grandparents two generations ago, 8 great-grandparents three generations ago, and so on.

a) Write the general term of the geometric sequence that represents this situation.

b) Determine how many ancestors Chad had each number of generations ago.
i) 6
ii) 10
iii) 14

c) How many generations ago did Chad have 8192 ancestors?

12. In a bacteria strain, the number of bacteria doubles every 20 min. There were 8 bacteria to start with.

a) How many bacteria will there be after 3 h?

b) Write an expression to represent the term that corresponds to the number of bacteria after 1 day.

13. The geometric mean of a set of n numbers is the nth root of the product of the numbers. For example, given two non-consecutive terms of a geometric sequence, 6 and 24, their product is 144 and the geometric mean is $\sqrt{144}$, or 12. The numbers 6, 12, 24 form a geometric sequence. Determine the geometric mean of

a) 2 and 200

b) 8 and 128

14. A super bouncy ball is thrown from a balcony that is 180 m above the ground. When it hits the ground the ball bounces back to 0.75 of its original height.

a) How high does the ball bounce after the 8th bounce?

b) On which bounce is the ball's height 5.7 m?

C Extend

15. Determine the value of y if $y - 2$, $5y + 10$, and $y - 50$ are consecutive terms in

a) a geometric sequence

b) a arithmetic sequence

16. Determine the values of p, q, r, and s such that $\frac{1}{18}$, p, q, r, s, 432 forms a geometric sequence.

17. The product of the first two terms of a geometric sequence is 27, and the product of the first three terms is also 27.

a) State the general term of the sequence.

b) Which term in the sequence is $\frac{1}{729}$?

18. Determine the first three terms of a geometric sequence such that the sum of the second and third terms is 24 and the sum of the seventh and eighth terms is 5832.

19. Determine the first five terms of two different geometric sequences that satisfy the given conditions.

a) The sum of the first two terms of the sequence is 3 and the sum of the next two terms is $\frac{4}{3}$.

b) The sum of the first three terms of the sequence is 3 and the sum of the third, fourth, and fifth terms is 12.

6.6 Arithmetic Series

KEY CONCEPTS

- An arithmetic series is the indicated sum of the terms of an arithmetic sequence. For example, 4, 9, 14, 19, … is an arithmetic sequence, while $4 + 9 + 14 + 19 + \cdots$ is an arithmetic series.
- Given the first term, the last term, and the number of terms of an arithmetic series, the sum of the series can be found using the formula $S_n = \frac{n}{2}(a + t_n)$ or the formula $S_n = \frac{n}{2}[2a + (n - 1)d]$.
- Given the first terms of an arithmetic series, the sum of the first n terms can be found using the formula $S_n = \frac{n}{2}[2a + (n - 1)d]$.

Example

Determine an expression for the sum, S_n, of the terms of an arithmetic series where the terms are represented by $t_n = 6n - 14$.

Solution

To determine t_1, or a, substitute $n = 1$ into the general term $t_n = 6n - 14$.

$$\begin{aligned} t_1 &= 6(1) - 14 \\ &= 6 - 14 \\ &= -8 \end{aligned}$$

The last term is $t_n = 6n - 14$, and there are n terms in the series.

Since there is no specified number of terms for the series, the expression for the sum of the series is found by substituting $a = -8$ and $t_n = 6n - 14$ into the formula $S_n = \frac{n}{2}(a + t_n)$.

$$\begin{aligned} S_n &= \frac{n}{2}(a + t_n) \\ &= \frac{n}{2}(-8 + 6n - 14) \\ &= \frac{n}{2}(-22 + 6n) \\ &= -11n + 3n^2 \end{aligned}$$

An expression for the sum of the series is $S_n = 3n^2 - 11n$.

A Practise

1. Determine the sum of each arithmetic series.

   a) $a = 3, t_n = 15, n = 8$

   b) $a = 14, d = -3, n = 16$

   c) $a = 2, t_n = -34, n = 15$

   d) $a = -1, t_n = 11, n = 21$

   e) $a = \frac{4}{3}, d = \frac{1}{4}, n = 8$

   f) $a = 7x, t_n = 32x, n = 17$

2. For each arithmetic series, state the values of a and of d. Then, determine the sum of the first 10 terms.

   a) $3 + 7 + 11 + \cdots$

   b) $5 + 12 + 19 + \cdots$

   c) $2 + 8 + 14 + \cdots$

   d) $6 + 18 + 30 + \cdots$

   e) $\frac{3}{2} + \frac{1}{2} - \frac{1}{2} - \cdots$

   f) $5.6 + 5.9 + 6.2 + \cdots$

3. The first and last terms in each arithmetic series are given. Determine the sum of the series.

   a) $a = \frac{1}{3}, t_8 = 729$

   b) $a = 6, t_{15} = 62$

   c) $a = -3, t_{36} = -73$

   d) $a = 6.6, t_{23} = -19.8$

   e) $a = -\sqrt{5}, t_{24} = 15\sqrt{5}$

   f) $a = 9, t_9 = -\frac{1}{729}$

4. Determine the sum of each arithmetic series.

   a) $2 + 4 + 6 + \cdots + 2000$

   b) $4 + 8 + 12 + \cdots + 400$

   c) $-2 - 8 - 14 - \cdots - 128$

   d) $-17 - 10 - 3 + \cdots + 74$

   e) $2 + 7 + 12 + \cdots + 62$

   f) $4 + 2.5 + 1 + \cdots - 33.5$

5. Determine the sum of each arithmetic series.

   a) $5 + 10 + 15 + \cdots + 265$

   b) $-20 - 18 - 16 - \cdots - 2$

   c) $1 + 0.9 + 0.8 + \cdots - 5.3$

   d) $\frac{1}{6} + \frac{1}{3} + \frac{1}{2} + \cdots + \frac{5}{3}$

   e) $\sqrt{3} + 2\sqrt{3} + 3\sqrt{3} + \cdots + 20\sqrt{3}$

   f) $1 + 5 + 9 + \cdots + 77$

B Connect and Apply

6. Find the specified sum for each arithmetic series.

   a) S_{16} for $3 + 7 + 11 + \cdots$

   b) S_{20} for $100 + 85 + 70 + \cdots$

   c) S_{11} for $2 + 10 + 18 + \cdots$

   d) S_{10} for $1 + 6 + 11 + \cdots$

   e) S_{20} for $-21 - 19 - 17 - \cdots$

   f) S_{15} for $2 - 1 - 4 - \cdots$

   g) S_{18} for $\frac{2}{3} + 1 + \frac{4}{3} + \cdots$

   h) S_{21} for $a + (2a + b) + (3a + 2b) + \cdots$

   i) S_{15} for $5 + 9 + 13 + \cdots$

7. Determine the number of terms, n, for each arithmetic series with the given sum.

   a) $1 + 2 + 3 + \cdots + t_n = 78$

   b) $3 + 7 + 11 + \cdots + t_n = 1830$

   c) $15 + 20 + 25 + \cdots + t_n = 1250$

   d) $10 + 8 + 6 + \cdots - t_n = -350$

   e) $-30 - 26 - 22 - \cdots - t_n = -120$

   f) $5 + 1 - 3 - \cdots - t_n = -345$

   g) $28 + 26 + 24 + \cdots + t_n = 154$

   h) $8 + 2 - 4 - \cdots - t_n = -300$

   i) $19 + 15 + 11 + \cdots - t_n = -441$

8. Find the specified sum for each arithmetic series with the given general term.

   a) $t_n = 2n - 1$; S_{100}

   b) $t_n = 2n$; S_{2000}

   c) $t_n = 3n - 2$; S_{80}

9. The general term and the sum of the first n terms of each arithmetic series is given. Determine the value of n.

a) $t_n = 3n - 1$; $S_n = 950$

b) $t_n = 2n - 1$; $S_n = 1\,234\,321$

10. The sum of the first 5 terms of an arithmetic sequence is 625 and the sum of the first 10 terms is 100. Determine the sum of the first 15 terms.

11. The third term of an arithmetic sequence is 18 and the seventh term is 30. Find the sum of the first 23 terms.

12. Determine the sum of each arithmetic series.

a) $-8\sqrt{6} - 6\sqrt{6} - 4\sqrt{6} - \cdots + 34\sqrt{6}$

b) $53x + 47x + 41x - \cdots - 55x$

c) $(9a - 5b) + (12a - 4b) + (15a - 3b) + \cdots + (93a + 23b)$

d) $\frac{1}{x^2} + \frac{4}{x^2} + \frac{7}{x^2} + \cdots + \frac{94}{x^2}$

13. Which are arithmetic series? Justify your answers.

a) $-5 - 10 - 14 - 17 - \cdots$

b) $6x^2 + 2x^2 - 2x^2 + \cdots$

c) $3m + (5m - b) + (7m - 2b) + \cdots$

d) $-\frac{8}{b} + \frac{4}{b} - \frac{2}{b} + \cdots$

14. In a grocery store, soup cans are displayed in a triangular formation. There are 55 cans in the bottom row and 1 can in the top row. Each row has 1 can less than the previous row. How many cans are in this display?

☆ **15.** Cool Juices makes a profit of \$350 in the first week of a 16-week summer season. After the first week, the profit increases by \$75 per week.

a) Explain why the total profit for the season represents an arithmetic series.

b) Determine the total profit for the season.

☆ **16.** Bashira has a choice between two summer jobs, each for a period of 16 weeks.
Job A: He would be paid \$450 every two weeks.
Job B: He would be paid \$100 the first week and then an additional \$25 per week for each successive week.
Which job should Bashira accept to earn the most money? Justify your answer.

17. Determine an expression for the sum, S_n, of the terms of an arithmetic series where the terms are represented by

a) $t_n = 5 + 2(n - 1)$

b) $t_n = 4n + 1$

c) $t_n = 5n - 2$

d) $t_n = 7n + 4$

e) $t_n = 12 - 3n$

18. Determine an expression for the sum of

a) the first n even natural numbers

b) the first n odd natural numbers

19. Determine an arithmetic series such that the fifth term of the series is 16 and the sum of the first 10 terms is 145.

C Extend

20. The sum of the first 10 terms of an arithmetic sequence is 250. All the terms are positive. Determine the general term for a sequence that satisfies this condition.

21. A formula for the sum of the first n terms of an arithmetic series is $S_n = n^2 + 4n$. Determine the first four terms of the series.

22. Determine an arithmetic series such that $t_{12} = 35$ and $S_{20} = 610$.

23. The sum of an arithmetic series is $S_n = \frac{1}{2}(3n^2 - n)$. Determine the general term for the series.

6.7 Geometric Series

KEY CONCEPTS

- A geometric series is the sum of the terms in a geometric sequence. For example, $-3 + 6 - 12 + 24 - \cdots$ is a geometric series.
- The formula for the sum of the first n terms of a geometric series with first term a and common ratio r is $S_n = \frac{a(r^n - 1)}{r - 1}$, $r \neq 1$.

Example

Find the third term of a geometric series given that the first term is 7, the last term is 448, and the sum of the series is 889.

Solution

The formula for the general term of a geometric series is $t_n = ar^{n-1}$, and $t_1 = 7$, $t_n = 448$, and $S_n = 889$.

Since $a = t_1$, then $a = 7$.

Since $t_n = ar^{n-1}$, then $ar^{n-1} = 448$. ①

Since $S_n = 889$, then $\frac{a(r^n - 1)}{r - 1} = 889$. ②

Substitute $a = 7$ in ①.

$7r^{n-1} = 448$

$r^{n-1} = 64$

Now, 64 may be expressed as **i)** 2^6 or **ii)** $(-2)^6$.

Case i):

$r^{n-1} = 2^6$, $r = 2$, and $n - 1 = 6$, or $n = 7$.

Substitute $a = 7$, $r = 2$, and $n = 7$ in ② to check if these values satisfy the sum of the series.

$$
\begin{aligned}
\text{L.S.} &= \frac{a(r^n - 1)}{r - 1} \qquad\qquad \text{R.S.} = 889 \\
&= \frac{7(2^7 - 1)}{2 - 1} \\
&= 7(127) \\
&= 889
\end{aligned}
$$

L.S. = R.S.

The values $a = 7$, $r = 2$, and $n = 7$ satisfy the sum of the series.

Case ii):

$r^{n-1} = (-2)^6$, $r = -2$, and $n - 1 = 6$, or $n = 7$.

Substitute $a = 7$, $r = -2$, and $n = 7$ in ② to check if these values satisfy the sum of the series.

$$\text{L.S.} = \frac{a(r^n - 1)}{r - 1} \qquad \text{R.S.} = 889$$

$$= \frac{7[(-2)^7 - 1]}{-2 - 1}$$

$$= \frac{7[-128 - 1]}{-2 - 1}$$

$$= \frac{-903}{-3}$$

$$= 301$$

L.S. $\neq$ R.S.

The sum of the series is not satisfied by $r = -2$.

The general term is $t_n = 7(2)^{n-1}$ and $t_3 = 7(2)^2$, or 28.

A Practise

1. Determine whether each series is geometric, arithmetic, or neither. Justify your answer.
   a) $1 + 10 + 100 + \cdots$
   b) $6 + 12 + 18 + 24 + \cdots$
   c) $-4 + 8 - 16 + 32 - \cdots$
   d) $7 - 8 - 10 - 13 - \cdots$
   e) $6571 - 2187 + 729 - 243 + \cdots$
   f) $\frac{1}{8} + \frac{1}{7} + \frac{1}{6} + \frac{1}{5} + \cdots$

2. For each geometric series, determine the values of a and r. Then, determine the specified sum.
   a) S_9 for $3 + 6 + 12 + \cdots$
   b) S_{12} for $5 - 10 + 20 - \cdots$
   c) S_8 for $\frac{1}{8} + \frac{1}{4} + \frac{1}{2} + \cdots$
   d) S_{13} for $-0.2 + 0.6 - 1.8 + \cdots$
   e) S_{50} for $9 - 9 + 9 - \cdots$
   f) S_{17} for $2 + 0.2 + 0.02 + \cdots$

3. Determine S_n for each geometric series.
   a) $a = \frac{1}{81}$, $r = 3$, $n = 7$
   b) $f(1) = 6$, $r = -\frac{1}{2}$, $n = 11$
   c) $f(1) = 4$, $r = -2$, $n = 10$
   d) $f(1) = -6$, $r = 4$, $n = 9$
   e) $a = 16$, $r = 5$, $n = 8$
   f) $a = -2$, $r = 2$, $n = 13$
   g) $f(1) = 0.4$, $r = 1.5$, $n = 6$
   h) $a = -4$, $r = -1$, $n = 20$
   i) $a = 20$, $r = 6$, $n = 5$

4. Determine the sum of each geometric series.
   a) $1 + 5 + 25 + \cdots + 3125$
   b) $3 + 9 + 27 + \cdots + 59\,049$
   c) $\frac{1}{3} + 1 + 3 + \cdots + 6561$
   d) $5 + 20 + 80 + \cdots + 20\,480$
   e) $-4 + 12 - 36 + \cdots + 8748$
   f) $2700 + 270 + 27 + \cdots + 0.0027$
   g) $243 + 81 + 27 + \cdots + \frac{1}{27}$

5. Determine the sum of each geometric series.

a) $2 + 1 + \frac{1}{2} + \cdots + \frac{1}{128}$

b) $3 + 9 + 27 + \cdots + 6561$

c) $100 + 25 + 6.25 + \cdots + 0.390\,625$

d) $5 + \frac{5}{2} + \frac{5}{4} + \cdots + \frac{5}{512}$

e) $5 - \frac{5}{2} + \frac{5}{4} - \cdots - \frac{5}{512}$

B Connect and Apply

6. Determine the specified sum for each geometric series.

a) S_8 for $\sqrt{5} - 5 + 5\sqrt{5} - \cdots$

☆ b) S_{13} for $x + x\sqrt{7} + 7x + 7\sqrt{7}x + \cdots$

c) S_{14} for $4 + 4x + 4x^2 + \cdots$

d) S_{11} for $2 + 2x^2 + 2x^4 + \cdots$

7. Determine the sum of each geometric series.

a) $1 + \frac{5}{2} + \frac{25}{2} + \cdots + \frac{15\,625}{64}$

b) $3\sqrt{6} - 18 + 18\sqrt{6} - \cdots + 839\,808\sqrt{6}$

c) $500 + 500(1.2) + 500(1.2)^2 + \cdots + 500(1.2)^{11}$

d) $8 + 16x^3 + 32x^6 + \cdots + 32\,768x^{36}$

8. Find an expression for the sum of the first n terms of the series with the given general term. Then, use your expression to find the sum when $n = 9$.

☆ a) $t_n = -2(3)^{n-1}$

b) $t_n = 18\left(\frac{2}{3}\right)^{n-1}$

c) $t_n = x^2(x^2)^{n-1}$

9. Determine the sum of the first 10 terms of a geometric series with common ratio 2 and whose tenth term is 16.

10. The sum of the first seven terms of a geometric series is 70 993 and the common ratio is 4. Determine the first term.

11. Determine the fourth term of a geometric series given that the sum of the first seven terms of the series is 1093 and the common ratio is 3^{-1}.

12. Tatiana is training for a marathon that will take place in four months. This week she ran 45 km and intends to increase her distance by 10% each week. Determine the total distance that Tatiana will have run after 10 weeks.

13. In a lottery, the first ticket drawn wins a prize of $25, the second ticket drawn receives a prize of $75, the third ticket drawn receives a prize of $225, and so on. How many prizes can be given out if the total amount of prize money is $1 million?

14. Kayla tried to convince her dad that during the month of April he should pay her allowance in the following manner: 1 penny on the first day of the month, 2 pennies on the second day of the month, 4 pennies on the third day, 8 pennies on the fourth day, and so on until the last day of the month. What is the total allowance Kayla would receive if her dad agrees to her idea? Do you think he will agree? Explain.

15. If the second term of a geometric series is 15 and the sum of the first three terms is 93, determine the general term of the series.

C Extend

16. Show that the sum of $4 + 2 + 1 + 0.5 + 0.25 + \cdots + t_n$ is always less than 8 for any natural number n.

17. Determine the sum of the factors of 3^8.

18. a) Determine an expression for the sum of the first n terms of a series with general term $t_n = 2^n - 3^{n-1}$.

b) Use your expression from part a) to find the sum of the first six terms of the series with the given general term.

Chapter 6 Review

6.1 Sequences as Discrete Functions

1. Write the first three terms of each sequence, given the explicit formula for the nth term of the sequence.

   a) $f(n) = 3^{-n}$

   b) $t_n = \frac{n + 2}{n + 1} + 1$

2. Write the 16th term, given the explicit formula for the nth term of the sequence.

   a) $f(n) = n^2 - 6$

   b) $t_n = \frac{n - 2}{n}$

3. Describe the pattern in each sequence. Write the next three terms of each sequence.

   a) $7, -14, 21, -28, \ldots$

   b) $-\frac{1}{2}, \frac{1}{4}, -\frac{1}{8}, \frac{1}{16}, \ldots$

   c) $3x, 6x^2, 12x^3, 24x^4, \ldots$

4. For each sequence, create a table of values using the term number and term, and calculate the finite differences. Then, determine an explicit formula, in function notation, and specify the domain.

   a) $-5, -10, -15, -20, \ldots$

   b) $22, 23, 18, 7, \ldots$

6.2 Recursive Procedures

5. Write the first four terms of each sequence, where $n \in \mathbb{N}$.

   a) $f(1) = 2, f(n) = 5n - f(n - 1)$

   b) $f(1) = 5, f(n) = 0.4f(n - 1)$

   c) $f(1) = 10, f(n) = \frac{f(n - 1)}{1 - n}$

6. Determine a recursion formula for each sequence.

   a) $1, 4, 13, 40, \ldots$

   b) $3, 5, 7, 9, \ldots$

   c) $-2, 2, -10, 26, \ldots$

7. Write the first four terms of each sequence.

   a) $t_1 = \frac{1}{8}, t_n = 4t_{n-1} - 1$

   b) $f(1) = a - 2b, f(n) = f(n - 1) + 3b$

8. Anita convinces her dad to increase her allowance by 12% per week. In the first week she receives $5.

   a) Write a sequence to represent Anita's allowance for 4 weeks.

   b) Write a recursion formula to represent her weekly allowance.

   c) Write an explicit formula for the nth term of the sequence.

   d) What will her allowance be after 10 weeks?

   e) After how many weeks will her allowance be $75.89?

6.3 Pascal's Triangle and Expanding Binomial Powers

9. Use Pascal's triangle to list the numbers in a hockey stick pattern with each of the following sums.

   a) 210

   b) 70

   c) 126

10. Determine the sum of the terms in each of these rows of Pascal's triangle.

    a) row 21

    b) row 18

11. Express as a single term from Pascal's triangle in the form $t_{n, r}$.

    a) $t_{8, 6} + t_{8, 7}$

    b) $t_{12, 2} + t_{12, 3}$

    c) $t_{23, 21} + t_{23, 22}$

12. Use Pascal's triangle to expand each power of a binomial.

  a) $(a + 1)^5$

  b) $(4x^2 - 3y^3)^4$

  c) $\left(1 - \frac{1}{x}\right)^5$

6.4 Arithmetic Sequences

13. For each arithmetic sequence, determine the values of a and d and the formula for the general term. Then, write the next four terms.

  a) $-19, -25, -31, \ldots$

  b) $\frac{8}{3}, \frac{34}{15}, \frac{28}{15}, \ldots$

14. Given the formula for the general term of an arithmetic sequence, determine t_{16}.

  a) $f(n) = 1 + \frac{1}{2}n$

  b) $t_n = 3.2n + 0.8$

15. A jogger running along a path that goes up a hill runs a distance of 423 m in the first minute. As the hill becomes steeper, the jogger runs 14 m less in each subsequent minute.

  a) Determine the general term for the sequence that represents this situation.

  b) How far does the jogger run in the 12th minute?

  c) In which minute does the jogger run 157 m?

6.5 Geometric Sequences

16. Determine whether the sequence is arithmetic, geometric, or neither. Give a reason for your answer.

  a) $\frac{3}{5}, \frac{5}{7}, \frac{7}{9}, \frac{9}{11}, \ldots$

  b) $2, 2\sqrt{3}, 6, 6\sqrt{3}, \ldots$

  c) $x + 7y, 2x + 10y, 3x + 13y, \ldots$

17. For each geometric sequence, determine the formula for the general term and use it to determine the specified term.

  a) $-3, 15, -75, \ldots, t_9$

  b) $-\frac{2}{625}, \frac{2}{125}, -\frac{2}{25}, \ldots, t_{11}$

18. A chain e-mail starts with three people each sending out five e-mail messages. Each of the recipients sends out five messages, and so on. How many e-mail messages will be sent in the ninth round of e-mailing?

6.6 Arithmetic Series

19. For each arithmetic series, state the values of a and d. Then, determine the sum of the first 10 terms.

  a) $21 + 15 + 9 + \cdots$

  b) $-4 - 9 - 14 - \cdots$

20. Determine the sum of each arithmetic series.

  a) $52 + 47 + 42 + \cdots - 48$

  b) $3 + 5.5 + 8 + \cdots + 133$

21. A ball picks up speed as it rolls down a long steep hill. The ball travels 0.75 m in the first second, 1.25 m in the second, 1.75 m in the next second, and so on. Determine the total distance travelled by the ball in 40 s.

22. Determine an arithmetic series such that the sum of the first 9 terms of the series is 162 and the sum of the first 12 terms is 288.

6.7 Geometric Series

23. For the geometric series $100 - 200 + 400 - \cdots$, determine the values of a and r. Then, determine S_8.

24. Determine the sum of each geometric series.

  a) $2 + 6 + 18 + \cdots + 1458$

  b) $1 - \frac{1}{3} + \frac{1}{9} - \cdots - \frac{1}{19\,683}$

25. The sum of the first two terms of a geometric series is 12 and the sum of the first three terms is 62. Determine the series.

Chapter 6 Math Contest

1. Given $f(x) = 5^x$ and $f(x + 3) - f(x + 2) = mf(x)$, determine the value of m.

A 125 **B** 100 **C** 25 **D** 5

2. Solve the equation $\sqrt{x + 30} = 12 - x$.

A −5 **B** 5 **C** −6 **D** 6

3. When $f(x)$ is divided by $4x + 1$, a quotient of $2x - 3$ and a remainder of 8 are obtained. Determine $f(x)$.

4. Determine the smallest positive integers x and y such that $\frac{1}{x} + \frac{x}{y} + \frac{1}{xy} = \frac{11}{10}$.

5. A quadratic equation $f(x)$ satisfies $f(1) = 6$, $f(-2) = -9$, and $f(0) = -3$. Determine the value of $f(-3)$.

A 9 **B** −8 **C** −6 **D** 4

6. Given that $m = x + y$ and $n = xy$, determine $x^2 + y^2$ in terms of m and n.

A $m^2 - 2n$

B $m^2 + 2n$

C $n^2 - 2m$

D $n^2 + 2m$

7. Without using a calculator, determine which of the following is equivalent to 2^{200}.

A $2^{100} + 2^{100}$

B $2^{40} \times 2^{50}$

C 400

D 16^{50}

8. Determine the sum of the series $300 - 299 + 298 - 297 + 296 - \cdots + 2 - 1$.

A 1 **B** 150 **C** 151 **D** 300

9. The sum of the first n terms of a sequence is $S_n = (2n + 1)(n - 1)$. Determine the 15th term of the sequence.

A 57 **B** 434 **C** 377 **D** 61

10. State an explicit formula for the general terms of two different geometric sequences, such that the sum of the first two terms is 2 and the sum of the first three terms is 3.

11. Consider the sequence 4, −6, x, y. The first three terms of this sequence form an arithmetic sequence. The last three terms form a geometric sequence. Determine the values x and y.

12. Find the sum of the 52 terms in the series $\sin 90° + \sin 180° + \sin 270° + \sin 360° + \sin 450° + \cdots + \sin 4590° + \sin 4680°$.

A 0 **B** −1 **C** 26 **D** 1

13. Determine two different geometric sequences such that $t_1 + t_2 + t_3 = 3$ and $t_3 + t_4 + t_5 = 12$.

14. Find the sum of the factors of 2^{10}.

A 2047

B 20

C 2104

D 1024

15. How many four-digit numbers greater than 5000 can be formed from 1, 3, 5, and 7 if the numbers can be repeated?

A 98 **B** 12 **C** 128 **D** 102

16. A school has 8 doors that lead outside. In how many ways can a student enter the school through one door and leave through a different door?

A 65 **B** 56 **C** 16 **D** 7

Chapter 7 Financial Applications

7.1 Simple Interest

KEY CONCEPTS

- Simple interest, I, in dollars, can be calculated by multiplying the principal, P, in dollars, by the annual interest rate, r, expressed as a decimal, and by the time, t, in years.
  $I = Prt$
- The amount, A, of an account earning simple interest is the sum of the principal, P, and the interest, I.
  $A = P + I$
- The amount in an account earning simple interest can be represented using
  - a table of values
  - a partial variation equation
  - a linear graph
  - an arithmetic sequence

Example

Ester buys a $2700 annual interest Step-Up Canada Savings Bond (CSB). This bond offers increasing interest rates each year for 5 years, as shown in the table. Determine the amount of the bond at the end of the 5 years.

Year	Annual Interest Rate (%)
1	3.5
2	3.7
3	3.9
4	4.1
5	4.9

Solution

To determine the amount, first determine the interest earned each year.
Year 1:

Substitute $P = 2700$, $r = 0.035$, and $t = 1$ into the formula $I = Prt$.

$$\begin{aligned} I &= Prt \\ &= 2700 \times 0.035 \times 1 \\ &= 95.50 \end{aligned}$$

The interest earned in year 1 is $95.50.

Year 2:

Substitute $P = 2700$, $r = 0.037$, and $t = 1$ into the formula $I = Prt$.

$$\begin{aligned} I &= Prt \\ &= 2700 \times 0.037 \times 1 \\ &= 99.90 \end{aligned}$$

The interest earned in year 2 is \$99.90.

Year 3:

Substitute $P = 2700$, $r = 0.039$, and $t = 1$ into the formula $I = Prt$.

$$\begin{aligned} I &= Prt \\ &= 2700 \times 0.039 \times 1 \\ &= 105.30 \end{aligned}$$

The interest earned in year 3 is \$105.30.

Year 4:

Substitute $P = 2700$, $r = 0.041$, and $t = 1$ into the formula $I = Prt$.

$$\begin{aligned} I &= Prt \\ &= 2700 \times 0.041 \times 1 \\ &= 110.70 \end{aligned}$$

The interest earned in year 4 is \$110.70.

Year 5:

Substitute $P = 2700$, $r = 0.049$, and $t = 1$ into the formula $I = Prt$.

$$\begin{aligned} I &= Prt \\ &= 2700 \times 0.049 \times 1 \\ &= 132.30 \end{aligned}$$

The interest earned in year 5 is \$132.30.

$$\begin{aligned} \text{Total interest} &= \$95.50 + \$99.90 + \$105.30 + \$110.70 + \$132.30 \\ &= \$543.70 \end{aligned}$$

$$\begin{aligned} A &= P + I \\ &= 2700 + 543.70 \\ &= 3243.70 \end{aligned}$$

At the end of 5 years, the amount of the bond is \$3243.70.

A Practise

1. Determine the simple interest earned on each investment.

   a) $480 is deposited for 5 years and earns 4.5% per year simple interest.

   b) $950 is deposited for 7 months at 6% per year simple interest.

   c) $600 is invested at 3.75% annual simple interest for 42 weeks.

   d) $1320 is invested at 7.4% per year, simple interest, for 90 days.

2. $500 is deposited into an account that earns 7% simple interest annually.

   a) Determine the amount of the investment after 1, 2, 3, 4, and 5 years.

   b) Identify the first term, a, and the common difference, d, of this arithmetic sequence.

   c) Write an equation to represent the nth term of this sequence. What is the significance of the nth term?

3. The table shows the amount of a simple interest GIC over a period of several years.

Time (years)	Amount ($)
1	1040
2	1080
3	1120
4	1160
5	1200
6	1240

   a) Calculate the first differences. What do these values represent?

   b) What is the principal of this investment? How do you know?

   c) What is the annual rate of simple interest?

4. Refer to the table in question 3.

   a) Develop a linear model to represent the amount in the GIC versus time.

   b) Explain why the model in part a) is a partial variation. Identify the fixed part and the variable part.

   c) How long will it take for this investment to double from its initial value?

☆5. IOU Credit Card Company charges an annual simple interest rate of 18% on unpaid account balances. Calculate the amount of interest that the company would charge when a balance of $2100 is paid 23 days late.

6. The graph shows the amount of an investment earning simple interest.

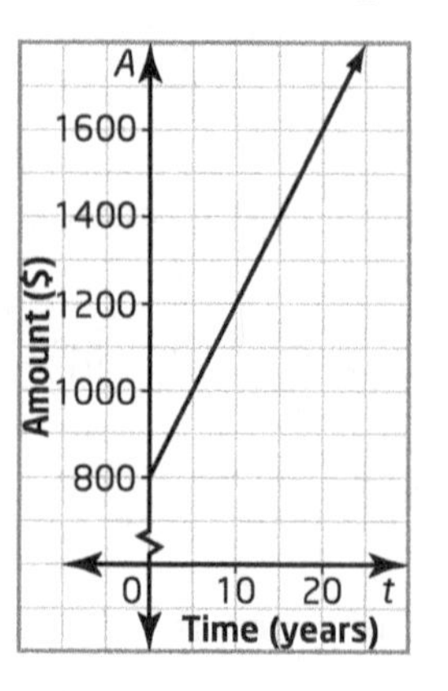

   a) What is the principal?

   b) What is the annual interest rate?

   c) Write an equation to relate the amount to time.

   d) Use your equation to determine how long it will take for the original investment to double.

B Connect and Apply

7. Refer to question 6.

   a) Write an equation to relate the interest to time.

   b) Use your equation to determine how long it will take for the original investment to double. Compare this result with your answer to question 6d).

☆**8.** Katio paid \$165 in interest for borrowing a sum of money at an interest rate of $2\frac{3}{4}\%$ for 4 years. How much did he borrow?

9. To save for a new bike, Sasha deposits \$320 into a savings account that earns 5.5% per year, simple interest.

a) Write an equation to relate the amount of the investment to time.

b) Graph the function.

c) How long will it take, to the nearest month, for the amount to reach \$450?

d) What interest rate is required for the amount to reach \$450 in 2 years less than your answer in part c)?

☆**10.** Lorilo borrows \$1350 for 8 months to buy a new riding lawn mower. He pays \$38.50 in interest on the loan. What was the annual interest rate of Lorilo's loan?

11. Rosalie borrows \$3800 at an annual rate of 7.25% simple interest to buy new appliances. She plans to repay the loan in 18 months.

a) What amount must she pay back?

b) How much interest will she pay?

c) How much sooner should Rosalie repay the loan if she wants to pay no more than \$280 in interest charges?

12. Martin took out a loan for \$1050 at an annual rate of 9.5% simple interest. When he repaid the loan, the amount was \$1848. How long did Martin hold this loan?

13. Arash wants to borrow \$4500 to buy a motorcycle. He is considering the following two options:

- Borrow from the bank at 8.5% per year simple interest.
- Borrow from the motorcycle dealership at 8% per year simple interest, plus a \$150 administration fee due upon repayment date.

a) Write an equation for each option to relate the amount, A, to time, t, in years.

b) Graph the amount payable versus time for each option on the same set of axes.

c) Which option is the better deal? Explain.

14. After 3 years, Taylor's investment is worth \$1041.25. Fours years later the amount has reached \$1296.25.

a) How much simple interest is Taylor's investment earning per year?

b) What is the principal?

c) What is the annual simple interest rate per year?

C Extend

15. Abraham's loan payment of \$650 is due in 10 months. How much should Abraham invest now, at 7.5% simple interest, to meet the payment?

16. Rebecca's best friend moves to Australia and Rebecca promises to visit her in 5 years. She knows the trip will cost her \$3300. How much should Rebecca invest now at a simple interest rate of 7.5% so that she will have \$3300 in 5 years?

17. Suppose you invest \$1000 at an interest rate of 7.25% per year.

a) Determine the amount in your account after 5 years if the interest is calculated on the sum of the principal plus the interest at the end of each year.

b) How much more interest is earned using the method in part a) than the simple interest on the same amount?

c) Why do you think this type of interest is called *compound* interest?

KEY CONCEPTS

- Compound interest investments or loans add the interest from one compounding period to the previous principal and use the sum as the principal for the next compounding period.
- The compounding effect causes an amount to grow exponentially over time. The amounts after each compounding period produce a geometric sequence.
- The compound interest formula $A = P(1 + i)^n$ can be used to calculate the amount, A, if the principal, P; the interest rate per compounding period, i; and the number of compounding periods, n, are known.
- The table shows common methods of compounding.

Frequency of Compounding	Number of Times Interest Is Added During a Year
annual	1 (every year)
semi-annual	2 (every 6 months)
quarterly	4 (every 3 months)
monthly	12 (every month)
bi-weekly	26 (every 2 weeks)
daily	365 (every day)

Example

Carmine has the option of the following compounding periods for his $1000 investment. The interest rate is 4% per annum and the time is 6 years.

a) semi-annually

b) quarterly

c) monthly

Which compounding period should he select? Justify your choice.

Solution

The principal is $1000. This means $P = 1000$.

a) When the interest is compounded semi-annually, it is added twice a year.

The semi-annual rate is $\frac{4\%}{2}$, or 2%. This means $i = 0.02$.

In 6 years, there are 6×2, or 12 compounding periods. This means $n = 12$.

Substitute the known values into the compound interest formula.

$$\begin{aligned} A &= P(1 + i)^n \\ &= 1000(1 + 0.02)^{12} \\ &= 1000(1.02)^{12} \\ &\doteq 1268.24 \end{aligned}$$

The amount after 6 years is $1268.24.

b) When the interest is compounded quarterly, it is added four times a year.

The quarterly rate is $\frac{4\%}{4}$, or 1%. This means $i = 0.01$.

In 6 years, there are 6×4, or 24 compounding periods. This means $n = 24$.

Substitute the known values into the compound interest formula.

$$\begin{aligned} A &= P(1 + i)^n \\ &= 1000(1 + 0.01)^{24} \\ &= 1000(1.01)^{24} \\ &\doteq 1269.73 \end{aligned}$$

The amount after 6 years is \$1269.73.

c) When the interest is compounded monthly, it is added 12 times a year.

The monthly rate is $\frac{4\%}{12}$, or $\frac{1}{3}\%$. This means $i \doteq 0.003\ 333\ 3$.

In 6 years, there are 6×12, or 72 compounding periods. This means $n = 72$.

Substitute the known values into the compound interest formula.

$$\begin{aligned} A &= P(1 + i)^n \\ &= 1000(1 + 0.003\ 333\ 3)^{72} \\ &= 1000(1.003\ 333\ 3)^{72} \\ &\doteq 1270.74 \end{aligned}$$

The amount after 6 years is \$1270.74.

The amounts for each compounding period are
- semi-annually: \$1268.24
- quarterly: \$1269.73
- monthly: \$1270.74

Since the largest amount occurs when the interest is compounded monthly, Carmine should choose this option to invest his \$1000.

A Practise

1. \$650 is invested for 7 years at 5% interest per year, compounded annually.

a) Determine the amount in the account after 7 years.

b) How much interest was earned?

2. \$975 is borrowed at a rate of 8.5% interest per year, compounded annually, for 5 years.

a) Determine the amount to be repaid after 5 years.

b) How much interest was charged?

3. For each compounding condition, determine the interest rate per compounding period, expressed as a decimal.

a) 7% per year, compounded monthly

b) 9% per annum, compounded quarterly

c) 8% annual interest, compounded semi-annually

d) 11% per year, compounded bi-weekly

4. For each compounding condition, determine the number of compounding periods.
   a) quarterly compounding for 4 years
   b) semi-annual compounding for 5 years
   c) monthly compounding for $\frac{2}{3}$ of a year
   d) daily compounding for 3 weeks
   e) annual compounding for 7 years

5. Determine the total number, n, of compounding periods and the interest rate, i, as a decimal, per compounding period for each scenario.
   a) 8.5% per year, compounded annually for 4 years
   b) 7% per annum, compounded quarterly for 5 years
   c) 3.6% per year, compounded monthly for 3 years
   d) 5.5% per annum, compounded semi-annually for 6.5 years
   e) 6.2% per year, compounded daily for 2 years

6. Matteo invests $1300 into a GIC that earns 5.25% interest per year, compounded quarterly, for 4 years.
   a) Determine the amount in the account after 4 years.
   b) How much interest was earned?
   c) Compare this to the amount of interest that would have been earned if simple interest had been earned at the same rate.

7. Moira's chequing account earns 4.8% interest per year, compounded daily. How much interest will she earn if she has $1670 in the account for 40 days?

B Connect and Apply

☆**8.** Richard invested $6800 at 5.2% compounded semi-annually.
   a) Determine the amount of the investment after
   i) 4 years
   ii) 7 years
   b) How much interest was earned on the investment between the 4th year and the 7th year?

9. Kara borrows $1000 for 6 years at $9\frac{1}{4}$% interest per year.
   a) Compare the interest charges under each condition.
   i) simple interest
   ii) annual compounding
   iii) semi-annual compounding
   iv) quarterly compounding
   v) monthly compounding
   vi) daily compounding
   b) Which is the best scenario for Kara? Which is the worst?
   c) Explain the effect of the compounding period on this loan.

☆**10.** Isabella has $5000 to invest in a GIC that earns 6% per year, compounded daily. How long will it take, to the nearest month, for Isabella's investment to double?

☆**11.** Meg has $8000 to invest in an RESP (Registered Education Savings Plan) for 7 years.
   a) Which of the following investment options should she choose? Justify your reasoning.
   Option 1: 6% compounded semi-annually
   Option 2: 7.5% simple interest
   b) What type of function is represented by each of the above options? Explain.

12. Krista borrows $12 000 as start-up capital for her new business. She plans to repay the loan in 3 years, at which point she will owe $14 803.80. What rate of interest is Krista being charged, assuming that it is compounded annually?

13. Paolo borrows $650 for 5 years at an interest rate that is compounded quarterly. At the end of the 5 years, he repays $866.87. What annual, quarterly compounded interest rate was Paolo charged?

14. The Rule of 72 states that the number of years required for an investment to double when interest is compounded annually can be estimated by dividing 72 by the annual interest rate.

a) Use the Rule of 72 to determine how many years it will take for an amount to double when invested at each interest rate, compounded annually.

i) 4%

ii) 3%

iii) 6%

b) Verify your results in part a) using the compound interest formula. Is the Rule of 72 exact? Explain.

15. Isam invested $850 in an account that earned 6.75% interest per year, compounded quarterly. When he closed the account, there was $1358.03 in it. How long did Isam invest his money?

16. Maxime has inherited $5000 and would like to invest the money so she can use it to purchase a new car 4 years from now. She has two options:

Option A: invest the money for 4 years at 5.5% compounded annually

Option B: invest the money for 2 years at 3% compounded semi-annually and then, at the end of 2 years, take the amount and invest it for the remaining 2 years at 8% compounded annually

Which option should Maxime select? Justify your answer.

C Extend

17. Describe an investment that could be represented by the function $f(x) = 1200(1.065)^x$.

18. Determine the time it takes to double an investment in an account that pays interest at 4% per annum, compounded quarterly.

19. Mark estimates that the cost of tuition for his first year in university will be $6780. How much should he invest now, at 4.5% compounded quarterly, so that he will have the required amount in 5 years?

20. An investment grows more quickly when the interest is compounded more frequently. There are two types of interest rates that are often available. The *nominal* interest rate is the one usually quoted. The *effective* interest rate is the annual interest rate that produces the amount of interest that is equivalent to the nominal interest rate. For example, $2000 is invested at 12% per annum compounded monthly. The amount of the investment at the end of 1 year is

$A = 2000(1.01)^{12}$
$\doteq 2253.65$

The interest earned is $253.65

The nominal interest rate is 12%.

The effective rate of interest is determined as follows:

$\frac{253.65}{2000} \times 100 \doteq 12.68\%$

The effective rate of interest is 12.68%.

a) Determine the effective rate of interest for the following nominal rates.

i) 6% per annum compounded semi-annually

ii) 8% per annum compounded quarterly

b) Does the principal amount invested influence the effective interest rate? Explain.

KEY CONCEPTS

- Present value refers to the principal that must be invested today to grow to a known future amount under specified interest and time conditions.
- The formula $PV = \frac{FV}{(1 + i)^n}$ can be used to calculate the present value, PV, if the future value, FV; number of compounding periods, n; and interest rate, i, as a decimal, per compounding period are known.

Example

Mandy earned $7500 from her very first summer job and plans to invest it for 10 years. At the end of 10 years she would like to have $20 000. What rate of interest, to the nearest hundredth of a percent, compounded monthly, does Mandy need to achieve her goal?

Solution

Method 1: Apply Algebraic Techniques

Let i represent the annual interest rate, as a decimal. Then $\frac{i}{12}$ represents the monthly rate.
Substitute the known values, $PV = 7500$, $FV = 20\ 000$, and $n = 120$, into $PV = \frac{FV}{\left(1 + \frac{i}{12}\right)^n}$. Then, rearrange to solve for i.

$$7500 = \frac{20\ 000}{\left(1 + \frac{i}{12}\right)^{120}}$$

$$\left(1 + \frac{i}{12}\right)^{120} = \frac{20\ 000}{7500}$$

$$\left(1 + \frac{i}{12}\right)^{120} = \frac{8}{3}$$

$$1 + \frac{i}{12} = \sqrt[120]{\frac{8}{3}}$$

Note that $\sqrt[120]{\frac{8}{3}} = \left(\frac{8}{3}\right)^{\frac{1}{120}}$.

$$\frac{i}{12} = \sqrt[120]{\frac{8}{3}} - 1$$

$$i = 12\left(\sqrt[120]{\frac{8}{3}} - 1\right)$$

$$i \doteq 0.0985$$

The annual rate of interest is approximately 9.85% per annum, compounded monthly.

Method 2: Use a TVM Solver

To access the Time Value of Money (TVM) Solver on a graphing calculator, press [APPS], select **1:Finance**, and then select **1:TVM Solver...**.

Enter the values in the fields as shown.

The investment is for 10 years, so N = 10.

Since Mandy must pay $7500 for the investment, PV = −7500.

The amount wanted in 10 years is $20 000, so FV = 20 000.

Since the investment is one time only, P/Y = 1.

The interest is compounded monthly, so C/Y = 12.

The interest is calculated at the end of each compounding period, so select **END**.

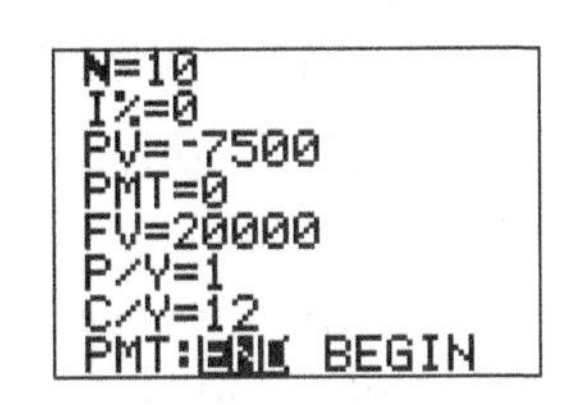

To solve for the unknown interest, move the cursor to the **I%** field and press [ALPHA] [ENTER] for [SOLVE]. The interest will be calculated.

To achieve her goal Mandy needs an interest rate of approximately 9.85% per annum, compounded monthly.

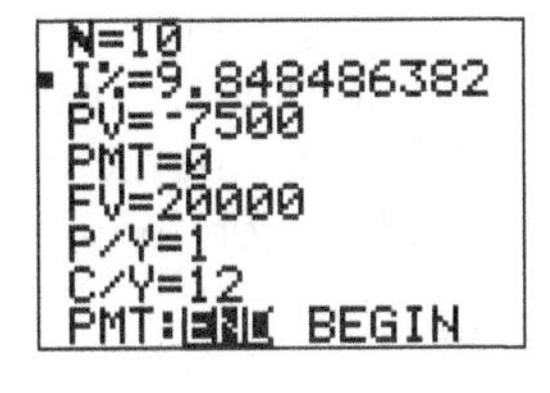

A Practise

1. Determine the present value of each future amount for the given conditions.

   a) In 4 years, an investment earning 6% per year, compounded annually, will have a value of $800.

   b) Three years from now, an investment earning 4.2% annual interest, compounded quarterly, will have a value of $1076.86.

2. In 5 years, an investment will be worth $66.21. If interest is earned at a rate of 7% per year, compounded annually, what is the present value of this investment?

3. In 6 years, money invested at 6.5% per annum, compounded semi-annually, will grow to $1614.63.

   a) How much money was invested?

   b) How much interest will be earned in 6 years?

4. Sam receives a financial gift from his grandparents, which he invests at 9.2% annual interest, compounded quarterly. He is advised that the investment will be worth $3151.68 in 5 years.

   a) What is the amount of the gift?

   b) How much interest will be earned?

☆5. How much money should Tara invest now at a rate of 6.3% per year, compounded monthly, to have $10 000 in 5 years?

B Connect and Apply

6. A bond will be worth $950 when it becomes due in 5 years. If the bond is purchased today for $700 at 6.15% per year, determine how frequently the interest was compounded.

7. Simon invests $2000 at 9.5% per year, compounded semi-annually. When the account is closed, its value will be $3829.89. How long will Simon's money be invested?

★**8.** Paula would like to have $8000 in 6 years to use as a down payment for a house. She is considering two investment options:

Investment A: 5.5% annual interest, compounded quarterly

Investment B: 5.3% annual interest, compounded monthly

a) Compare the present values of each option.

b) Which investment is the better choice for Paula? Explain your reasoning.

9. Five years ago, money was invested at 8% per year. Today the investment is worth $6000. Determine the amount originally invested for each compounding period.

a) annually

b) semi-annually

c) quarterly

10. Three and a half years ago, some money was invested in a fund that paid an annual interest rate of 8%, compounded quarterly. Today, the account has a value of $1000. What was the amount of the original deposit?

11. Leah borrows $800 to buy a treadmill. She agrees to repay $875 in a year and a half. What annual rate of interest, compounded monthly, is Leah being charged?

12. Tim wants to have $4450 in 2.5 years to finish his basement.

a) How much money must he invest today at 6.8% annual interest, compounded quarterly, to have enough money?

b) Tim only has $3500 today. What interest rate must he obtain to have enough money to finish his basement on time?

13. A 4-L container of milk costs $4.75 in 2009.

a) What would the price of a 4-L container of milk have been in 1989, assuming an average inflation rate of 3% per year, compounded annually?

b) How much would a similar volume of milk have cost in 1929?

14. A financial institution is owed $100 000, due in 10 years. The financial institution is willing to sell the debt today discounted at 7.2% per year, compounded semi-annually. What is the value of the debt today?

C Extend

15. Nine years ago Amelia inherited a certain amount of money. For the first 5 years the money was invested at a rate of 10% per annum, compounded semi-annually. For the next 4 years the money was invested at a rate of 12% per annum, compounded quarterly. Now, the investment is worth $20 000. How much money did Amelia inherit?

16. Tate plans to buy a new small car in 3 years. The base price of the model he prefers is currently $21 800. The dealership anticipates that in 3 years the price of a similar new model will have increased by 18%. They also guarantee that he will receive a $6200 trade-in allowance on his current vehicle. How much money should Tate invest today at a rate of 6.4% per year, compounded quarterly, so that he will have enough to purchase the car in 3 years?

17. Dean needs $1000 one year from now to purchase a new laptop and printer. He plans on making two equal deposits, one now and the other in 6 months, into an account that pays 7.5% per year, compounded semi-annually. What is the amount of each deposit?

7.4 Annuities

KEY CONCEPTS

- An annuity is an investment in which regular payments are deposited into an account.
- An ordinary simple annuity is one in which payments are made at the end of every payment period and interest is compounded at the end of the same payment period.
- The amount, A, of an annuity can be calculated using the formula $A = \frac{R[(1 + i)^n - 1]}{i}$, where R represents the regular payment; i represents the interest rate per compounding period, as a decimal; and n represents the number of compounding periods.

Example

Clarissa would like to purchase a cottage in no more than 10 years from now. She wants to have at least $50 000 for the down payment. So, she deposits $100 at the end of each week into an investment plan that pays 4.55% per year, compounded weekly. In how many years will Clarissa have enough money to make the down payment?

Solution

Draw a time line to represent this annuity.
Determine the interest per compounding period.

$$i = \frac{0.0455}{52}$$
$$= 0.000\,875$$
$$n = ?$$
$$R = 100$$

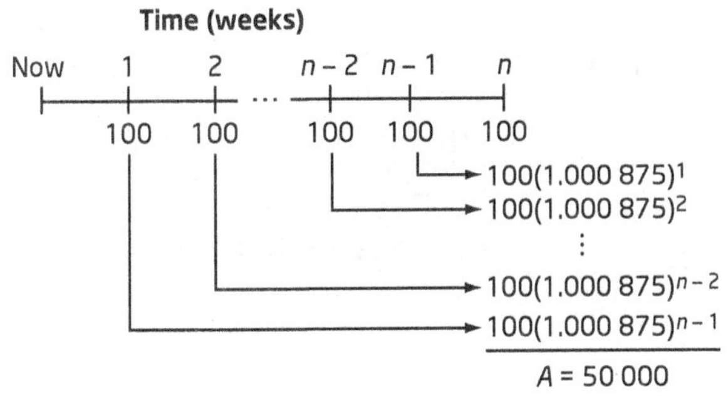

Time (weeks)

Now 1 2 ... $n - 2$ $n - 1$ n

100 100 100 100 100

$100(1.000\,875)^1$
$100(1.000\,875)^2$
⋮
$100(1.000\,875)^{n-2}$
$100(1.000\,875)^{n-1}$

$A = 50\,000$

Method 1: Apply Algebraic Techniques

Substitute the known values into the formula $A = \frac{R[(1 + i)^n - 1]}{i}$ and solve for n.

$A = 50\,000$, $i = 0.000\,875$, and $R = 100$.

$$50\,000 = \frac{100[(1 + 0.000\,875)^n - 1]}{0.000\,875}$$

$$43.75 = 100[(1.000\,875)^n - 1]$$

$$0.4375 = (1.000\,875)^n - 1$$

$$1.4375 = (1.000\,875)^n$$

Use systematic trial to find the value of n.

Use a table to organize your work. Try $n = 400$ to start.

Estimate, n	$(1.000\,875)^n$	Analysis
400	$(1.000\,875)^{400} \doteq 1.418\,85$	Too low. Try a higher value.
425	$(1.000\,875)^{425} \doteq 1.450\,22$	Too high. Try a lower value.
420	$(1.000\,875)^{420} \doteq 1.443\,89$	Close, but a little high.
410	$(1.000\,875)^{410} \doteq 1.431\,31$	Close, but a little low.
415	$\mathbf{(1.000\,875)^{415} \doteq 1.437\,59}$	**That's it.**

Since there are 52 weeks in a year, it will take approximately 415 ÷ 52, or 8 years, for Clarissa to have enough money to make the down payment.

Method 2: Use a TVM Solver

Access the TVM Solver on a graphing calculator and enter the values, as shown.

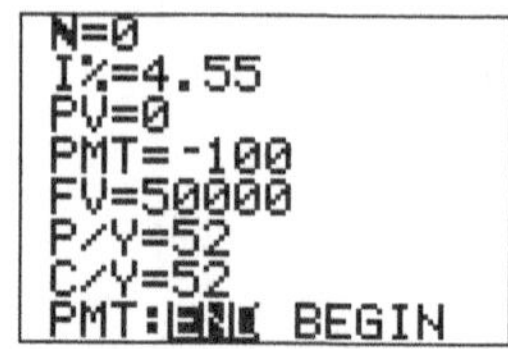

Move the cursor to the **N** field and press ALPHA [SOLVE].

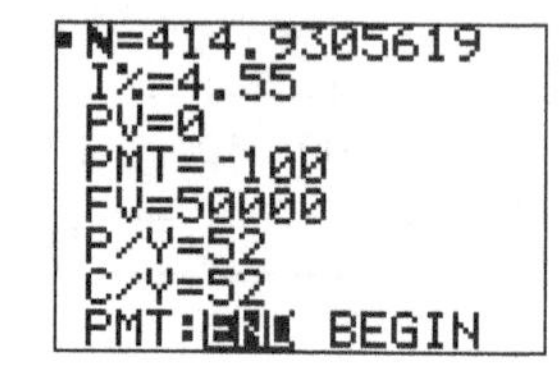

Since there are 52 weeks in a year, it will take approximately 415 ÷ 52, or 8 years, for Clarissa to have enough money to make the down payment.

A Practise

1. The time line shows an annuity with an annual interest rate of 10%.

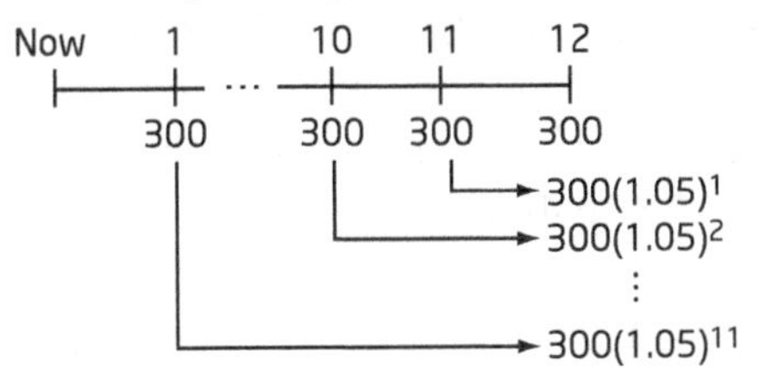

   a) How often is interest compounded? Justify your answer.

   b) What is the duration of the annuity? Justify your answer.

   c) Calculate the amount of the annuity.

2. The time line shows an annuity with an annual interest rate of 8%.

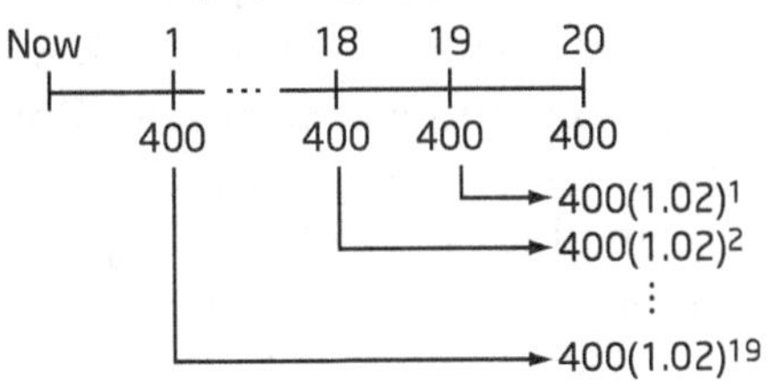

   a) How often is interest compounded? Justify your answer.

   b) What is the duration of the annuity? Justify your answer.

   c) Calculate the amount of the annuity.

3. Anita deposits $1200 in an investment account every 6 months, for 5 years. The plan pays 7.5% annual interest, compounded semi-annually.

   a) Draw a time line to represent this annuity.

   b) Determine the amount of the annuity at the end of 5 years.

   c) Verify the amount in part b) using the formula.

   d) How much interest has been earned?

4. At the end of every month, for 2 years, Martino deposits $40 into an account that earns 6% per year, compounded monthly.

   a) Draw a time line to represent this annuity.

   b) Determine the amount of the annuity.

   c) How much interest was earned?

5. How much must be invested every 6 months, for 4 years, in order to achieve an amount of $8000, if interest is earned at a rate of 6% per year, compounded semi-annually?

6. Lucinda wants to have $30 000 in her account 4 years from now to renovate her home. How much must she invest per month if her account earns 5.5% annual interest, compounded monthly?

B Connect and Apply

7. At the end of every quarter, Simon deposits $450 in an account that earns interest that is compounded quarterly. After 1.5 years, Simon will have $2874.48 in the account.

   a) How much total interest will have been earned?

   b) Determine the annual rate of interest, compounded quarterly.

8. How many years will it take Grace to save $25 000 for the car of her dreams if she deposits $130 each week into an account that pays 7.3% annual interest, compounded weekly?

9. Every 6 months, Allen deposits $250 into an investment account that pays 4.5% per annum, compounded semi-annually.

   a) How long will it take him to save $1586.95?

   b) How much interest is earned in that time period?

☆10. Daniel plans to retire in 35 years and at that time he would like to have saved $500 000 in his RRSP (Registered Retirement Savings Plan). Determine the monthly deposits he should make into his RRSP if the rate of interest earned is fixed at 5.6% per year, compounded monthly.

11. Three sisters, Anna, Donella, and Tina, make regular deposits in individual investment accounts that pay 6% per year, compounded monthly. Anna deposits $400 per month for 5 years, Donella deposits $200 per month for 10 years, and Tina deposits $100 per month for 20 years.

   a) How much does each sister deposit in the investment account?

   b) Without making calculations, predict which annuity is greatest, or whether they are all equal.

   c) Determine the amount of each annuity. Was your prediction in part b) accurate?

12. Mick would like to retire at age 65 and is considering the following investment options:

    Option A: Invest $1000 per month beginning at age 25.

    Option B: Invest $4000 per month beginning at age 45.

    In both cases, the interest is 8% per annum, compounded monthly.

   a) What is the total amount deposited for each option?

   b) Which option should Mick choose? Justify your answer.

☆13. Compare the amounts at age 65 that would result from making an annual deposit of $1000 starting at age 20, or from making an annual deposit of $3000 starting at age 50, to an RRSP that earns 6% interest per annum, compounded annually. What is the total of the deposits in each situation?

C Extend

14. a) Gordon deposits $1000 at the *beginning* of each year into an investment account that pays 6% compounded annually. How much will he have saved after 10 years?

   b) How much would Gordon have saved if he had made the deposits at the end of each year instead of the beginning?

   c) The annuity in part a) is an example of an *annuity due* because the payments are made at the beginning of each compounding period. Predict a formula for the amount of an annuity due of R dollars per period after n periods at an interest rate I per period.

15. Austin deposits $50 on the first of each month in an investment account that pays 9% compounded monthly. How much will Austin have in the account after 5 years?

16. Justin makes semi-annual deposits of $150 from November 1, 2003, to May 1, 2009, in an investment account that averages 11.75% compounded semi-annually. If Justin plans on leaving the money in the account for another 4 years, what will be the value of his investment?

17. Corinne deposits $100 at the end of each year in an account that pays 7.5% compounded semi-annually. How much will Corinne have saved after 9 years?

7.5 Present Value of an Annuity

KEY CONCEPTS

- The present value of an annuity is the total amount that can finance a series of regular withdrawals over a specific period of time.
- The present value, PV, of an annuity can be calculated using the formula $PV = \frac{R[1-(1+i)^{-n}]}{i}$, where R represents the regular withdrawal; i represents the interest rate per compounding period, as a decimal; and n represents the number of compounding periods.

Example

Andrew would like to withdraw $500 per month from a retirement fund for 15 years after he retires. If he can earn $9\frac{3}{4}\%$ annual interest, compounded monthly, on this fund, how much money must Andrew have in this account when he retires?

Solution

Draw a time line to represent this annuity.

Determine the interest per compounding period and the number of compounding periods.

$$i = \frac{0.0975}{12}$$
$$= 0.008\,125$$
$$n = 15 \times 12$$
$$= 180$$
$$R = 500$$

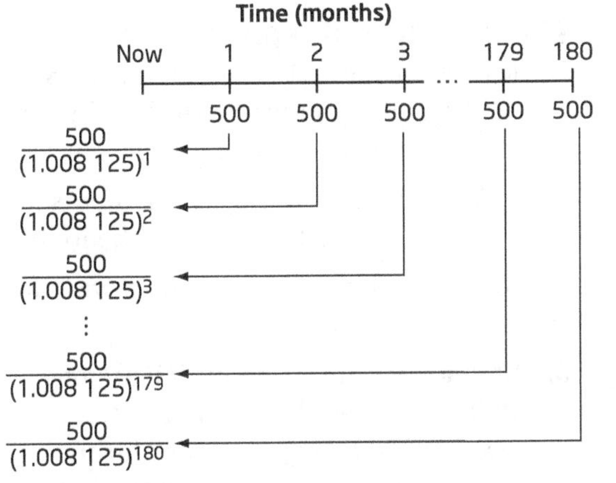

Substitute $R = 500$, $i = 0.008\,125$, and $n = 180$ into the formula $PV = \frac{R[1-(1+i)^{-n}]}{i}$.

$$PV = \frac{500[1-(1+0.008\,125)^{-180}]}{0.008\,125}$$
$$= \frac{500[1-(1.008\,125)^{-180}]}{0.008\,125}$$
$$\doteq 47\,198.19$$

Therefore, Andrew will need $47 198.19 in his retirement fund.

A Practise

1. The time line shows an annuity from which semi-annual withdrawals are made for 2 years. Interest is compounded semi-annually.

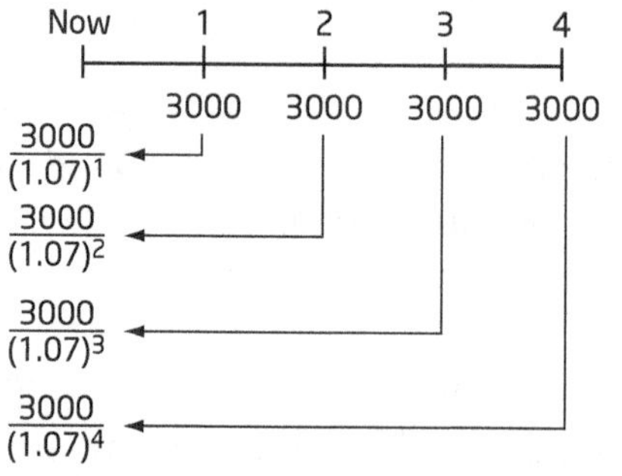

   a) What is the annual rate of interest? Justify your answer.

   b) How many withdrawals will be made, in total? Justify your answer.

   c) Calculate the present value of the annuity.

2. The time line shows an annuity from which quarterly withdrawals are made for 10 years. Interest is compounded quarterly.

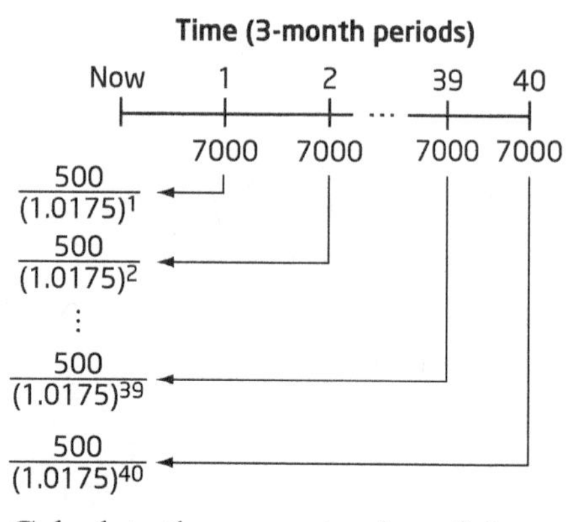

   Calculate the present value of the annuity.

3. $500 is to be withdrawn at the end of every year, for 5 years, from an account that earns 9% interest, compounded annually.

   a) Draw a time line to represent this annuity.

   b) Determine the present value of the annuity.

4. $300 is to be withdrawn at the end of every month, for 3 years, from an account that earns 6.9% interest, compounded monthly.

   a) Draw a time line to represent this annuity.

   b) Determine the present value of the annuity.

   c) How much interest is earned?

5. An annuity has an initial balance of $7500 in an account that earns 7% interest, compounded quarterly. What amount can be withdrawn at the end of each quarter of the 6.5 years of this annuity?

6. Adam uses $60 000 of savings to purchase an annuity that pays 6.8% interest, compounded semi-annually.

   a) What semi-annual withdrawals can Adam make for the next 20 years if the first payment is made 6 months from now?

   b) How much interest will the account earn?

B Connect and Apply

☆7. Jessica borrows $12 000 at a rate of 8% per year, compounded monthly, for her school expenses for a year.

   a) What are her monthly payments if it takes 5 years to pay back the loan?

   b) How much interest is she paying in total?

8. Brendon is converting his RRSP into an income fund. He would like to receive $1500 every 6 months for the next 20 years, starting 6 months from now. The interest rate is 6.25% per year, compounded semi-annually.

   a) How much must Brendon convert now to pay for the annuity?

   b) How much interest does the annuity earn over the 20 years?

☆9. A charitable organization is having a contest to raise money. The winner will receive \$100 per month for 10 years.

a) How much money is needed to fund this prize if the organization plans to draw from an account that pays 6% annual interest, compounded monthly?

b) What is the total amount of money that the winner receives?

c) How much of the total winnings are earned as interest?

☆10. A customer needs to borrow \$7500 to purchase a used car. The car dealer arranges with a finance company to lend the customer the money at 2.9% per year, compounded monthly for 3 years. What will the customer's monthly payment be?

11. A department store has a five-piece leather living-room set on sale for \$2799.95, including taxes. It can be purchased with 24 payments of \$129 per month. What annual interest rate compounded monthly is the store charging?

12. An electronics store is promoting the sale of their DVD players by offering the following deal: no money down and 24 equal monthly payments of \$23. The interest charged is 10% per year, compounded monthly. Determine the equivalent cash price of the DVD player.

13. An annuity has an initial balance of \$4000. Annual withdrawals are made in the amount of \$1000 for 5 years, at which point the account balance is zero. What annual rate of interest, compounded annually, was earned over the duration of this annuity?

14. Astil wants to borrow \$35 000 to purchase a new vehicle. The car dealership offers loans at 8% compounded monthly for 48 months. Clients who apply for the loan online will receive a 0.5% reduction in the interest rate.

a) Calculate Astil's monthly payments at each interest rate.

b) What is the total amount Astil would have to repay for each loan?

c) How much interest would Astil save if he applies for the loan online?

15. On her 30th birthday, Eileen decides she wants to save enough money so that on her 55th birthday she can purchase an annuity that pays \$1000 per month, at a rate of 6% per annum, compounded monthly, until her 85th birthday. How much money should Eileen deposit annually, starting on her 30th birthday, at a rate of 5.5% per annum, compounded annually, so that she can achieve her goal on her 55th birthday?

C Extend

16. Liam just won \$1 000 000 in a lottery! He set aside \$100 000 for immediate spending money. The remaining amount was invested in an account that earned 6% per annum, compounded monthly. Liam made regular withdrawals of \$10 000 per month from this account. Determine the number of years that Liam would be able to withdraw this monthly income.

17. In an ordinary annuity, the first payment is automatically received one period from now. In a *deferred annuity*, the first payment is delayed to a later time. Dana has invested her \$25 000 inheritance in an account that earns 8.5% per year, compounded annually. Her plan is that, starting 4 years from now, she will withdraw equal yearly payments from the account, for 10 years. What is the amount of each withdrawal?

Chapter 7 Review

7.1 Simple interest

1. Calculate the missing information in the chart.

Principal, P	Interest Rate, r	Time, t	Simple Interest, I
\$627.00	6.5%	2 months	
	9.25%	58 days	\$5.72
\$270.00		3 years	\$64.80
\$425.00	$7\frac{1}{2}$%		\$12.66
\$380.21	$4\frac{3}{4}$%	6 months	\$9.03
\$178.50	8.6%		\$10.30
\$3200.00		4.5 months	\$138.00

2. MONEY Loan Company charges an annual interest rate of 15.5% on unpaid account balances. Calculate the amount of interest that the company would charge when a balance of \$1850 is paid 37 days late.

3. Arianna's financial advisor has recommended that she invest at least 30% of her money in treasury bonds, at a fixed rate of return (interest rate). Following this recommendation, Arianna invests \$4000 in a treasury bond for 5 years at a rate of 4.8% per year simple interest. She cannot access this money before the end of the 5 years without paying a financial penalty.

   a) Determine the interest earned over the term of the bond.

   b) Determine the amount of this investment at the end of 5 years.

7.2 Compound Interest

4. Describe the difference between simple interest and compound interest. What type of growth does each represent? Explain.

5. Glen purchases a \$1500 GIC that earns 6.25% interest each year for 8 years.

   a) Determine the total interest earned at the end of each year under simple interest.

   b) Determine the total interest earned at the end of each year under compound interest.

   c) How much extra interest is earned under compound interest?

   d) Determine the amount of the investment under

   i) simple interest

   ii) compound interest

6. To buy a new laptop for her home business, Brianna borrows \$1600 at an interest rate of 3.5% per annum, compounded annually. She plans to pay back the loan in 3 years.

   a) How much will Brianna owe after 3 years?

   b) How much interest will Brianna pay for the loan?

7.3 Present Value

7. How much should Stephen invest today at 9.5% annual interest, compounded semi-annually, so that he will have \$2500 in 6 years?

8. Andrew invests $150 in an account in which the interest is compounded semi-annually. In 8 years Andrew will have $275. What is the interest rate?

9. Sarah invests $300 at a rate of 8% per year, compounded monthly. How long will it take for her investment to grow to $1000?

10. Suppose the value of a debt owed to a financial institution today is $35 000. What interest rate is required, compounded semi-annually, so that it will be worth $100 000 in 10 years?

7.4 Annuities

11. Amir deposited $500 in an account at the end of every 3 months for $5\frac{1}{2}$ years. The account paid 6% per year, compounded quarterly.

a) Determine the amount in the account on the date of the last deposit.

b) Determine the amount of interest earned in this account.

12. Karrington would like to save $48 000 at the end of 4 years. How much should she deposit at the end of each month into a savings account that pays $3\frac{1}{2}$% annual interest, compounded monthly?

13. Nathan would like to have $15 000 in 10 years, and can afford to deposit $500 every 6 months in an investment account. What interest rate, compounded semi-annually, does he need to achieve his goal?

7.5 Present Value of an Annuity

14. Due to the high cost of post-secondary education, many students apply to the Ontario Student Assistance Program (OSAP) for a loan to help pay their tuition fees. Students must begin to make payments to repay their loans 6 months after graduating. Kieran completed his university undergraduate degree 6 months ago. His loan payments of $250 are withdrawn at the end of each month from an account that is earning 6.5% interest, compounded monthly.

a) How much must Kieran deposit in the account today so that the loan payments can be withdrawn for 1 year?

b) What is the amount paid for the loan?

c) How much of this amount is earned in interest?

15. Yasmine's grandparents set up an annuity for her. She will be paid $500 at the end of each month for the next 5 years. The first payment will be made 1 month from now. How much must Yasmine's grandparents deposit to provide for the annuity if the account earns 5.7% per annum, compounded monthly?

16. Chen-Chi has invested $20 000 into an annuity from which she plans to withdraw $1094.41 every 3 months for the next 5 years. If at the end of this time period the balance of the annuity is zero, what annual rate of interest, compounded quarterly, did this account earn?

Chapter 7 Math Contest

1. Determine the values of x and y such that $x^m y^n = \left(\frac{2}{3}\right)^{m-n}$ and $x^n y^m = \left(\frac{2}{3}\right)^{n-m}$ for all real numbers m, n.

   A $x = \frac{2}{3}, y = \frac{2}{3}$

   B $x = \frac{2}{3}, y = \frac{3}{2}$

   C $x = \frac{3}{2}, y = \frac{2}{3}$

   D $x = \frac{3}{2}, y = \frac{3}{2}$

2. Solve the equation $\sqrt{6 - \frac{1}{a}} = 6 - \frac{1}{a}$.

   A $a = -1$ or $a = 1$

   B $a = \frac{1}{6}$ or $a = 1$

   C $a = \frac{1}{5}$ or $a = \frac{1}{6}$

   D $a = -\frac{1}{5}$ or $a = \frac{1}{5}$

3. Determine the largest possible value of $ab + bc + cd + ad$ given that the values of a, b, c, and d are 3, 4, 5, and 6, but not necessarily in that order.

   A 80

   B 81

   C 360

   D 77

4. Solve for x given that $(4^{3x-1})(16^{2x+3}) = 64^{5x+2}$.

5. A quadratic equation $f(x)$ satisfies $f(0) = 2, f(-1) = 13$, and $f(2) = 4$. Determine the value of $2f\left(\frac{1}{2}\right)$.

   A -1

   B $-\frac{1}{2}$

   C -3

   D 2

6. Determine the sum, S, and product, P, of the roots of the equation $\frac{2}{x-1} + \frac{3}{x+2} = 3$.

   A $S = \frac{7}{3}, P = -\frac{2}{3}$

   B $S = -\frac{2}{3}, P = -\frac{7}{3}$

   C $S = \frac{7}{3}, P = \frac{2}{3}$

   D $S = \frac{2}{3}, P = -\frac{7}{3}$

7. Determine the value of m so that the roots of $mx^2 - 25x + 12 = 0$ are reciprocals.

8. Determine the real value of x that satisfies the equation $14x + 29\sqrt{x} - 15 = 0$.

9. Determine the values of x such that $13^{x^3 + 4x^2 - 21x} = 1$.

10. State an explicit formula for the general terms of two different geometric sequences such that the sum of the first two terms is 2 and the sum of the first three terms is 3.

11. Determine the smallest positive angle θ, in degrees, such that $(8^{\sin^2\theta})(8^{\cos^2\theta})(8^{\tan^2\theta}) = 16$.

12. If θ is an angle such that $\tan\theta + \sec\theta = 2$, then what is the value of $\cos\theta$?

    A 1

    B $\frac{4}{5}$

    C $\frac{1}{2}$

    D $\frac{1}{\sqrt{2}}$

Functions 11 Practice Exam

Part A Short Answer

1. Evaluate $\left(-\frac{3}{5}\right)^4$. Express your answer as a fraction.

2. Simplify $(-7)^{43} \times (-7)^{52} \div (-7)^{30}$. Express your answer as a power.

3. Express $\left(\frac{x^4}{y^6}\right)^7$ as a quotient of powers.

4. Express 5^{-9} using a positive exponent.

5. Express $\sqrt[5]{48}$ as a power.

6. Evaluate $\left(\sqrt[5]{-32}\right)^3$.

7. What type of function is represented by $y = 8^x$?

8. State the y-intercept of the graph of $y = \left(\frac{1}{5}\right)^x$.

9. State the equation of the horizontal asymptote of the graph of $y = 9^x$.

10. State the range of the graph of $y = \left(\frac{3}{4}\right)^x$.

11. State the equation that represents the graph of $y = 2^x$ after it is translated 3 units to the right.

12. State the equation that represents the graph of $f(x) = 6^x$ after it is compressed horizontally by a factor of $\frac{1}{2}$.

13. Is the graph of $y = 5^x$ increasing or decreasing?

14. Express $y = \left(\frac{1}{8}\right)^x$ in terms of an equivalent equation using base 2.

15. State the equation of the horizontal asymptote for $y = 3^{x+2} - 1$.

16. For each graph, write a corresponding equation in terms of sine.

a)

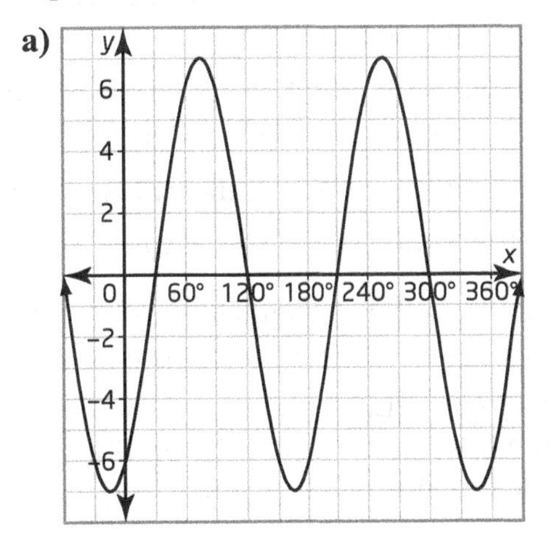

b)

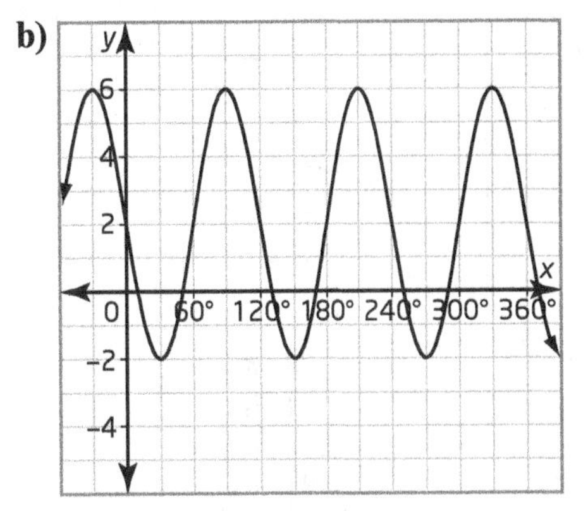

Part B Extended Answer

17. Simplify $\frac{9x}{x^2 - 5x + 6} - \frac{4x}{x^2 + x - 12}$ and state any restrictions on the variable.

18. Determine whether $f(x) = (2x - 3)^2 - (4x + 5)(x - 7)$ is equivalent to $g(x) = \frac{11x^2 - 33x - 44}{x + 1}$. Justify your answer.

19. Identify the parameters and use them to describe the transformations that must be applied to the graph of each base function to obtain the transformed function. Write the transformed equation in simplified form.

a) $f(x) = \sqrt{x}$, to obtain the transformed function $y = -f[4(x + 3)] - 1$

b) $f(x) = \frac{1}{x}$, to obtain the transformed function $y = \frac{1}{2}f[-(x + 5)] + 2$

20. Each graph represents a transformation of one of the base functions $f(x) = x$, $f(x) = x^2$, $f(x) = \sqrt{x}$, or $f(x) = \frac{1}{x}$. State the base function and the equation of the transformed function.

a)

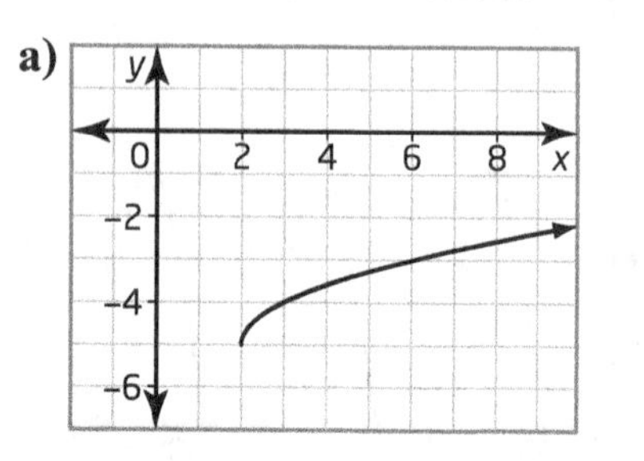

b)

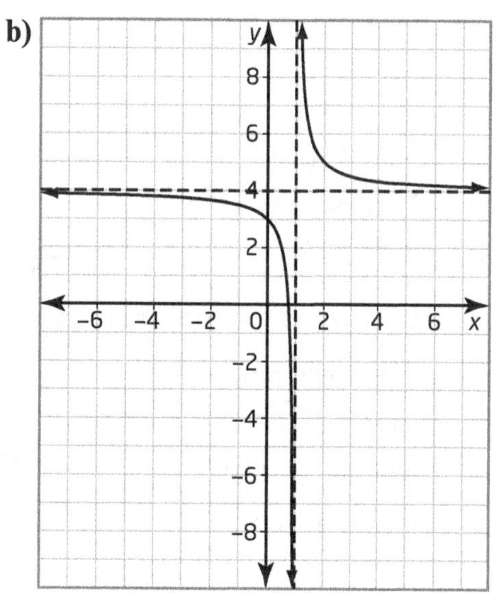

21. Consider these functions:

i) $f(x) = \frac{1}{2 - x}$

ii) $f(x) = 3x^2 + 1$

For each function,

a) state the domain and range of $f(x)$

b) evaluate $f(-5)$

c) determine the equation of the inverse function

22. Determine the vertex of each quadratic function by completing the square. Verify your answer by using partial factoring. State if the vertex is a maximum or minimum.

a) $f(x) = -3x^2 + 6x + 4$

b) $f(x) = 2x^2 - 8x + 7$

23. Find an equation in standard form for the quadratic function with zeros $x = 3 \pm \sqrt{5}$ and containing the point (2, –8).

24. State the value of the discriminant and determine the number of points of intersection of each. Justify your answers.

a) the line $y = 2x + 1$ and the quadratic function $f(x) = x^2 - 3x + 3$

b) the line $y = -3x + 2$ and the quadratic function $f(x) = x^2 - 4x + 9$

25. Andrew and David are on a canoe trip between three campsites located at different points on a lake. Starting at campsite A, they canoe 11 km to campsite B. From that site, they canoe 20 km to campsite C. If the angle from campsite A to campsite C to campsite B is 30°, how far must Andrew and David canoe in order to return directly to campsite A?

26. A squash player hits a ball 2.3 m to the side wall. The ball rebounds at an angle of 100° and travels 3.1 m to the front wall. How far is the ball from the player when it hits the front wall? Assume the player does not move after her shot.

27. State the amplitude, the period, the phase shift, and the range of the graph of each sinusoidal function. Then, sketch a graph of the function.

a) $y = 5 \sin [4(x - 30°)] - 2$

b) $y = -2 \sin [3(x + 45°)] + 5$

28. Sarah is standing on a balcony that is 10 m above the ground. From her position, the angle of elevation to the top of a tower across the street is 45°. Liz is standing on a balcony that is 20 m higher than Sarah's. From Liz's position, the angle of elevation to the top of the same tower is 30°. Determine the height of the tower. Express your answer using exact values.

29. Prove each.

a) $\frac{\csc \theta + \cot \theta}{\csc \theta - \cot \theta} = \frac{1 + 2\cos \theta + \cos^2 \theta}{\sin^2 \theta}$

b) $\frac{\cos \theta}{\sec \theta} - \frac{\sin \theta}{\cot \theta} = \frac{\cot \theta \cos \theta - \tan \theta}{\csc \theta}$

30. The equation $T = 18 \sin [30(t - 4)] + 11$ models the average monthly temperature for a city in southwestern Ontario. In this equation, t denotes the number of months, with January represented by 1, and T is the temperature, in degrees Celsius.

a) Determine the city's maximum average monthly temperature. When does this occur?

b) Determine the city's minimum average monthly temperature. When does this occur?

c) What is the difference between the maximum and minimum average monthly temperatures?

d) What is the relationship between your answer in part c) and the coefficient of the sine term in the equation?

e) What is the sum of the maximum and minimum average monthly temperatures?

f) What is the relationship between your answer in part e) and the value of the constant term in the equation?

g) What is the average monthly temperature in October?

h) When is the average monthly temperature 20 °C?

31. Write $t_{18,8}$ as the difference of two terms, each in the form $t_{n,r}$.

32. Use Pascal's triangle to expand $(4x - y)^5$.

33. Determine the number of terms in each arithmetic sequence.

a) 16, 23, 30, …, 583

b) $x + 2, x - 1, x - 4, \ldots, x - 52$

34. Determine a and d and then write the formula for the nth term of each arithmetic sequence with $t_8 = 79$ and $t_{21} = 235$.

35. Determine the number of terms in the geometric sequence $-36, -18, -9, \ldots, -\frac{9}{128}$.

36. Determine an arithmetic series such that the sum of the first five terms of the series is 85 and the sum of the first six terms of the series is 123.

37. A jogger runs 300 m in the first minute. The distance the jogger covers decreases by 20 m in each succeeding minute. What distance does the jogger cover in the 7th minute?

38. A ball bounces to $\frac{5}{6}$ of its height when dropped on a hard surface. Suppose the ball is dropped from a height of 40 m.

a) What height does the ball bounce back up to after the 7th bounce?

b) What is the total distance travelled by the ball after 10 bounces?

39. There is a legend that the inventor of chess chose the following for his reward: 1 grain of wheat on the first square, 2 grains of wheat on the second square, 4 on the third, 8 on the fourth, and so on, for all 64 squares on the chessboard. Find an expression for the amount of wheat required to fulfill his request.

40. Identify whether each series is arithmetic or geometric. Justify your answer. Then, determine the sum of each series.

a) $100 + 90 + 80 + \cdots - 220$

b) $1 + 3 + 9 + \cdots + 2187$

41. In a geometric series, $t_2 = 10$ and $t_5 = 1250$. Determine t_4 and S_6.

42. Matteo is very excited about his new sports car! Although he paid \$24 800 for the car, its resale value will depreciate (decline) by 22% of its current value every year. The equation relating the car's depreciated value, v, in dollars, to the time, t, in years, since its purchase is $v(t) = 24\,800(0.78^t)$.

a) Explain the significance of each part of this equation.

b) How much will Matteo's car be worth in
i) 2 years?
ii) 5 years?

c) Explain why this is an example of exponential decay.

d) How long will it take for the value of Matteo's sports car to decline to 40% of its original cost?

43. Timothy invests \$2500 in an 18-month term deposit that pays simple interest at an annual rate of 3.5%. How much interest does Timothy earn?

44. Amanda buys a \$5000 guaranteed investment certificate (GIC) that will earn simple interest at the rate of 5.8% per year for 7 years.

a) Determine the amount of interest that Amanda will earn on the GIC.

b) What is the amount of the GIC at the end of 7 years?

45. Victoria invests \$5000 in a registered retirement savings plan (RRSP) that earns interest at the rate of 6.95% per annum, compounded monthly. What is the value of the RRSP at the end of 7 years?

46. Katip wants to have \$16 000 in 5 years in order to buy a new motorcycle. If Katip has \$10 000 to invest today, what rate of interest, to the nearest hundredth of a percent, compounded quarterly, does he need to achieve his goal?

47. On his 21st birthday, Carmine receives \$5000 from his grandparents, the accumulated amount of an investment they made for him when he was born. What was the original amount of the investment if it earned interest at the rate of 8.75% per year, compounded monthly?

48. How long does it take \$100 to grow to \$500 if the amount is invested at a rate of 13.5% per annum, compounded semi-annually?

49. David invests \$25 000 in an annuity that earns 7.5% interest per year, compounded semi-annually. If the annuity is to pay David twice a year for 10 years, starting 6 months from now, what is the amount of each semi-annual payment?

Answers
Chapter 1 Functions

1.1 Functions, Domain, and Range

1. **a)** Yes, no vertical line will pass through more than one point.
   b) No, any vertical line between $x = -6$ and $x = 6$ will pass through two points.

2. **a)** function

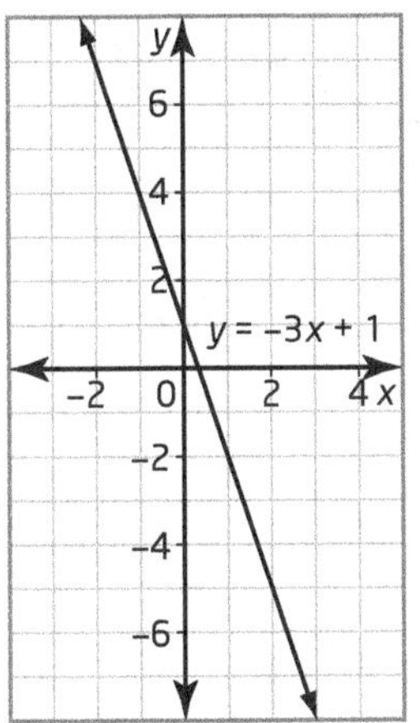

b) not a function

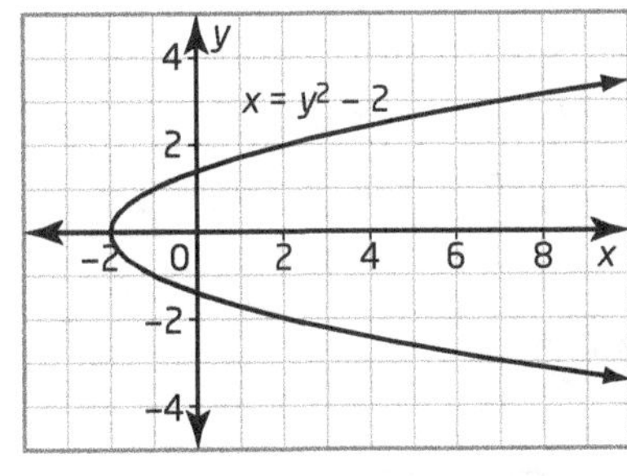

c) function

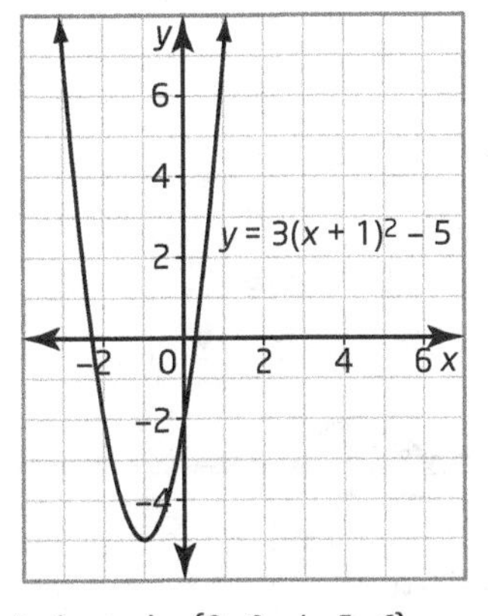

3. **a)** domain {2, 3, 4, 5, 6}, range {4, 6, 8, 10, 12}; function; for every element of the domain there is only one corresponding element of the range
   b) domain {−6, −5, −4, −3}, range {2}, function; for every element of the domain there is only one corresponding element of the range
   c) domain {5}, range {−4, −2, 0, 2, 4}; not a function; the single element of the domain corresponds with more than one element of the range

4. **a)** not a function; there are more range values than domain values
   b) function; each domain value has only one range value

5. **a)** domain $\{x \in \mathbb{R}, -7 \leq x \leq 7\}$, range $\{y \in \mathbb{R}, -7 \leq y \leq 7\}$
   b) domain $\{x \in \mathbb{R}, x \neq 5\}$, range $\{y \in \mathbb{R}, y \neq 0\}$

6. Answers may vary.

7. **a)** $A = -2x^2 + 60x$
   b) domain $\{x \in \mathbb{R}, 0 < x < 30\}$, range $\{y \in \mathbb{R}, 0 < y < 450\}$

8. **a)** range {8}
   b) range {−27, −18, −11, −6, −3}
   c) range $\left\{\frac{8}{3}, 2, \frac{8}{5}, \frac{4}{3}, \frac{8}{7}\right\}$

9. **a)** domain $\{x \in \mathbb{R}\}$, range $\{y \in \mathbb{R}\}$
   b) domain $\{x \in \mathbb{R}\}$, range $\{y \in \mathbb{R}, y \geq -1\}$
   c) domain $\{x \in \mathbb{R}, x \leq 3\}$, range $\{y \in \mathbb{R}\}$
   d) domain $\{x \in \mathbb{R}, x \neq 4\}$, range $\{y \in \mathbb{R}, y \neq 0\}$

10. **a)** the graph is not a function; there are fewer elements in the domain than in the range
    b) the graph is a function; for each value in the domain there is exactly one value in the range

11. **a) i)** domain $\{x \in \mathbb{R}, -4 \leq x \leq 4\}$, range $\{y \in \mathbb{R}, -4 \leq y \leq 4\}$; not a function

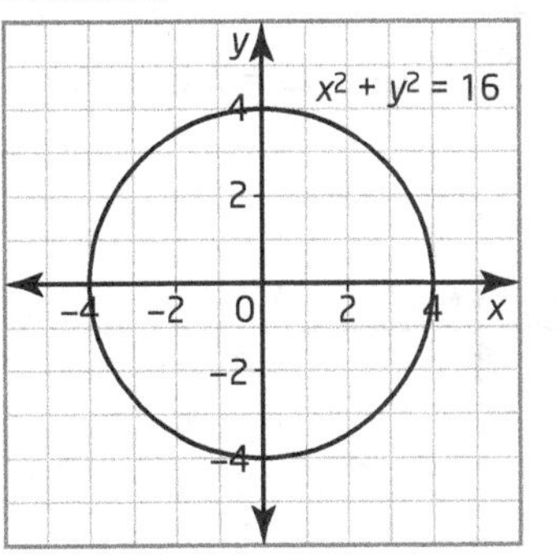

ii) domain $\{x \in \mathbb{R}, -4 \le x \le 4\}$,
range $\{y \in \mathbb{R}, 0 \le y \le 4\}$, function

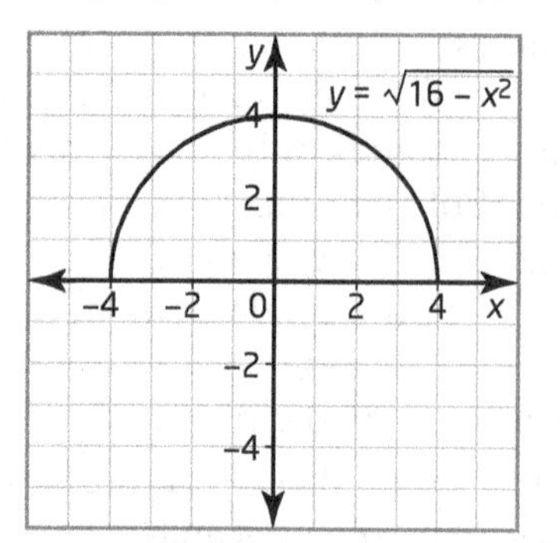

iii) domain $\{x \in \mathbb{R}, -4 \le x \le 4\}$,
range $\{y \in \mathbb{R}, -4 \le y \le 0\}$; function

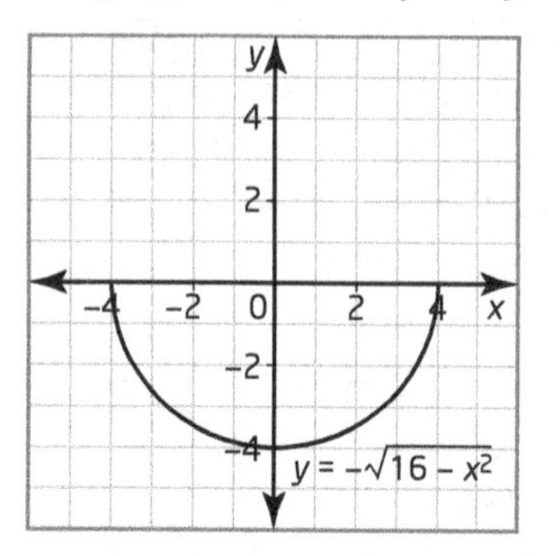

b) Together, the semicircles in graphs ii) and iii) form the circle in graph i).

12. a) domain $\{x \in \mathbb{R}\}$,
range $\{y \in \mathbb{R}, -3 \le x \le 7\}$; function

b) domain $\{y \in \mathbb{R}, x \le -3 \text{ or } x \le 3\}$,
range $\{y \in \mathbb{R}\}$; not a function

1.2 Functions and Function Notation

1. a) $\frac{16}{5}, \frac{7}{5}, \frac{17}{10}; f: x \rightarrow -\frac{3}{5}x + 2$

b) $35, 5, \frac{5}{2}; f: x \rightarrow 6x^2 - 4x + 3$

c) $-5, -14, -\frac{35}{4}; f: x \rightarrow -3(x + 1)^2 - 2$

d) $7, 7, 7; f: x \rightarrow 7$

e) $-\frac{1}{7}, \frac{1}{5}, \frac{1}{3}; f: x \rightarrow \frac{1}{4x + 1}$

f) $\sqrt{7}, 1, \sqrt{2}; f: x \rightarrow \sqrt{3 - 2x}$

2. a) -1

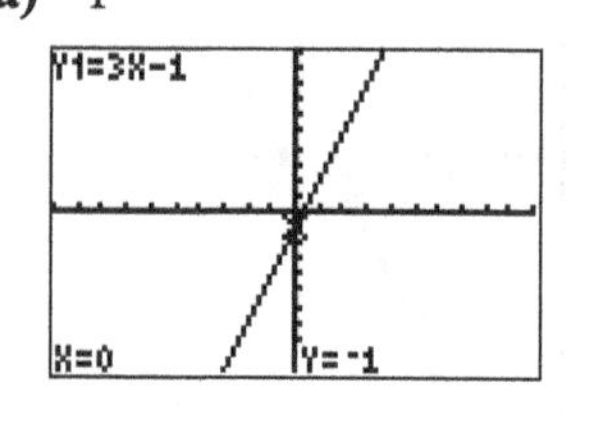

b) 0

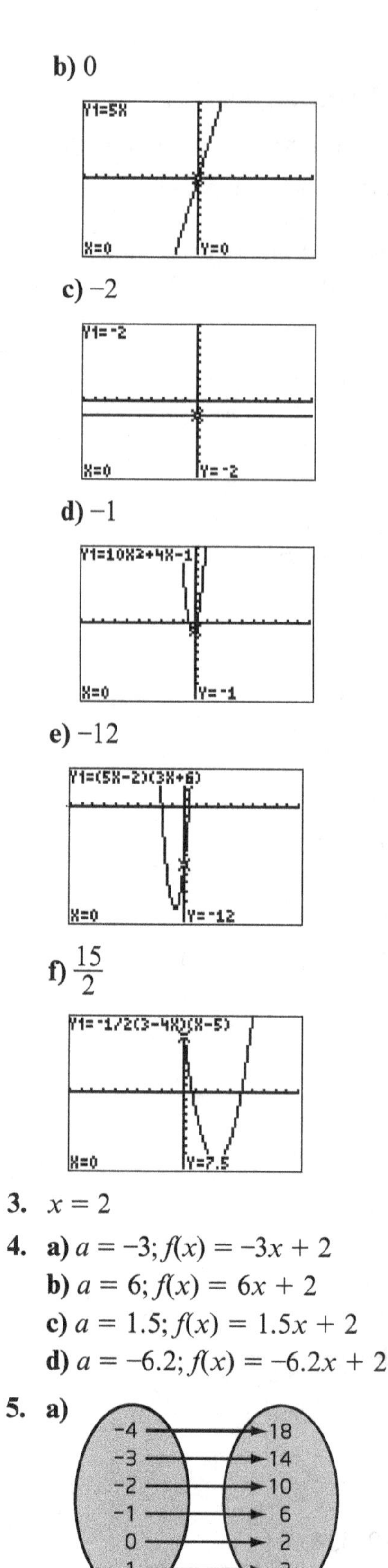

3. $x = 2$

4. a) $a = -3; f(x) = -3x + 2$

b) $a = 6; f(x) = 6x + 2$

c) $a = 1.5; f(x) = 1.5x + 2$

d) $a = -6.2; f(x) = -6.2x + 2$

5. a)

Domain		Range
−4	→	18
−3	→	14
−2	→	10
−1	→	6
0	→	2
1	→	−2

b)

c)

d)

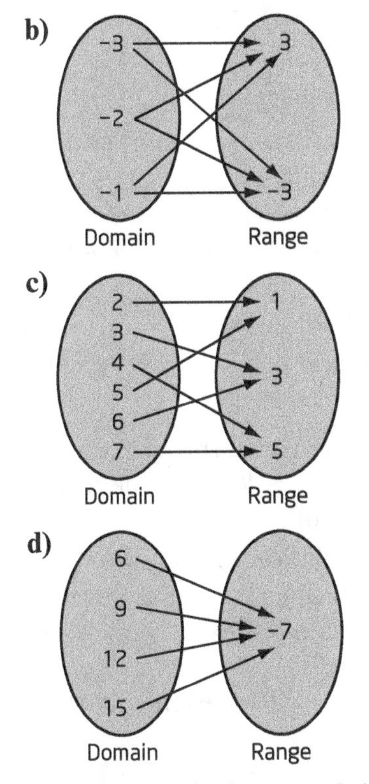

6. **a)** function; each element of the domain corresponds with only one element of the range
   b) not a function; some elements of the domain correspond with more than one element of the range
   c) function; each element of the domain corresponds with only one element of the range
   d) function; each element of the domain corresponds with only one element of the range

7. **a)** $\{(-8, 3), (-3, 1), (-1, 3), (2, 5), (2, -9)\}$
   b) $\{(0, 3), (2, 8), (5, 7), (11, 3)\}$
   c) $\{(-5, -2), (-2, 4), (0, 4), (7, -7), (7, -2)\}$
   d) $\{(-5, 0), (-4, 2), (-3, 5), (-2, 6), (0, 7)\}$
   e) $\{(-1, -3), (2, -3), (5, -3), (9, -3)\}$

8. **a)** not a function; some elements of the domain correspond with more than one element of the range
   b) function; each element of the domain corresponds with only one element of the range
   c) not a function; some elements of the domain correspond with more than one element of the range
   d) function; each element of the domain corresponds with only one element of the range
   e) function; each element of the domain corresponds with only one element of the range

9. **a)** $f: x \to -7x + 1$
   b) $g: x \to x^2 + 7x - 5$
   c) $h: b \to \sqrt{9b + 9}$
   d) $r: k \to \dfrac{1}{5k - 3}$

10. **a)** Substitute $\ell = 1.8$ in each equation.
    Earth:
    $T = 2\sqrt{1.8}$
    $\doteq 2.7$
    On Earth the period is approximately 2.7 s.
    Moon:
    $T = 5\sqrt{1.8}$
    $\doteq 6.7$
    On the moon the period is approximately 6.7 s.
    Pluto:
    $T = 8\sqrt{1.8}$
    $\doteq 10.7$
    On Pluto the period is approximately 10.7 s.
    b) Substitute $T = 3$ in each equation and solve for ℓ.
    Earth:
    $5 = 2\sqrt{\ell}$
    $2.5 = \sqrt{\ell}$ Square both sides.
    $6.25 = \ell$
    On Earth the length of the pendulum is 6.25 m.
    Moon:
    $5 = 5\sqrt{\ell}$
    $1 = \sqrt{\ell}$
    $1 = \ell$
    On the moon the length of the pendulum is 1 m.
    Pluto:
    $5 = 8\sqrt{\ell}$
    $\frac{5}{8} = \sqrt{\ell}$ Square both sides.
    $\frac{25}{64} = \ell$ or $\ell \doteq 0.4$

On Pluto the length of the pendulum is approximately 0.4 m.

c) domain $\{\ell \in \mathbb{R}, \ell \geq 0\}$, range $\{T \in \mathbb{R}, T \geq 0\}$

d)

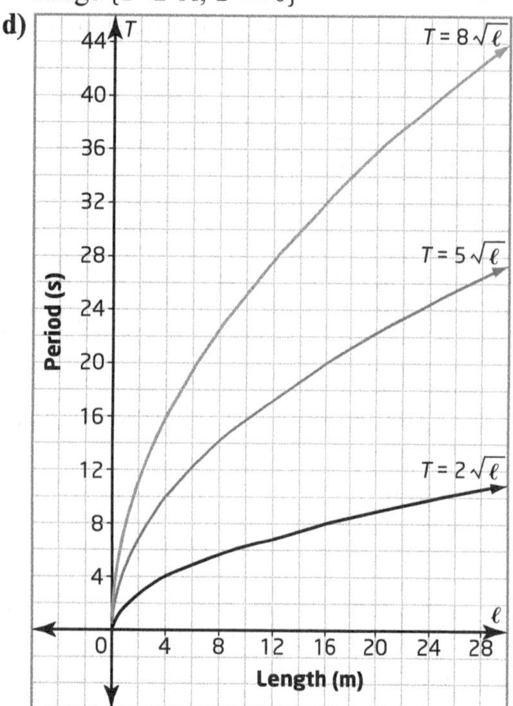

e) all are functions; each x-value corresponds with one y-value

f) $T: \ell \rightarrow 2\sqrt{\ell}$
$T: \ell \rightarrow 5\sqrt{\ell}$
$T: \ell \rightarrow 8\sqrt{\ell}$

11. a) 60 000 **b) i)** 76 552 **ii)** 77 727
c) 2020 **d)** Yes

12. a)

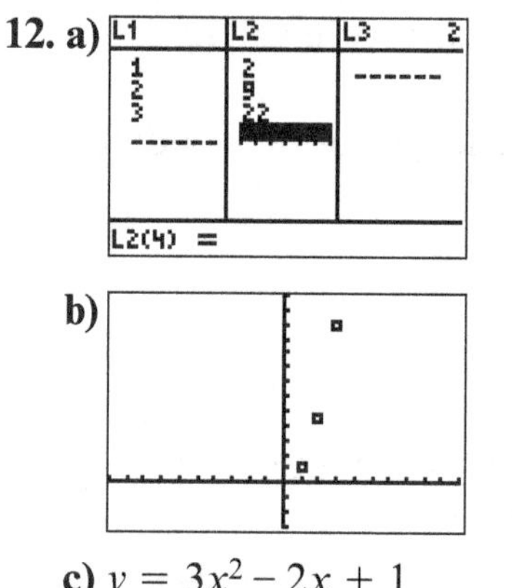

b)

c) $y = 3x^2 - 2x + 1$

d) $f(-4) = 57, f(0) = 1, f(6) = 97$

13. a) domain $\{i \in \mathbb{R}, i \geq 0\}$, range $\{A \in \mathbb{R}, 0 \leq A \leq 500\}$
b) Yes **c) i)** \$462.28 **ii)** \$428.67
d) i) 19.5% **ii)** 11.8%

14. a) Earth: $t: h \rightarrow \sqrt{\frac{80 - h}{4.9}}$;
Jupiter: $t: h \rightarrow \sqrt{\frac{80 - h}{12.8}}$

b) In each case, the expression under the radical sign cannot be less than zero. Since the denominators are both constants, $80 - h \geq 0$. Both h and t must be positive.
$80 - h \geq 0$ and $h \geq 0$
$-h \geq -80$ and $h \geq 0$
$0 \leq h \leq 80$
For both relations, the domain is $\{h \in \mathbb{R}, 0 \leq h \leq 80\}$ and the range is $\{t \in \mathbb{R}, t \geq 0\}$.

c) Yes; both relations are square root functions. For each relation, every value of the domain has exactly one value in the range.

d) Substitute $h = 10$ in each equation and solve for t.
Earth:
$$t(10) = \sqrt{\frac{80 - 10}{4.9}}$$
$$\doteq 3.8$$
Jupiter:
$$t(10) = \sqrt{\frac{80 - 10}{12.8}}$$
$$\doteq 2.3$$
On Earth, the object reaches a height of 10 m after 3.8 s. On Jupiter, the object reaches a height of 10 m after 2.3 s.

15. a) Answers may vary. Sample answer: $f(x) = 4x^2 - 3$
b) $f(x) = -0.5x^2 + 3$

16. a)

Function	Domain	Range
$f(x) = 2x$	$\{x \in \mathbb{R}\}$	$\{y \in \mathbb{R}\}$
$g(x) = 2^x$	$\{x \in \mathbb{R}\}$	$\{y \in \mathbb{R}, y \geq 0\}$
$h(x) = x^2$	$\{x \in \mathbb{R}\}$	$\{y \in \mathbb{R}, y \geq 0\}$
$q(x) = \frac{x}{2}$	$\{x \in \mathbb{R}\}$	$\{y \in \mathbb{R}\}$
$p(x) = \frac{2}{x}$	$\{x \in \mathbb{R}, x \neq 0\}$	$\{y \in \mathbb{R}, y \neq 0\}$

b) 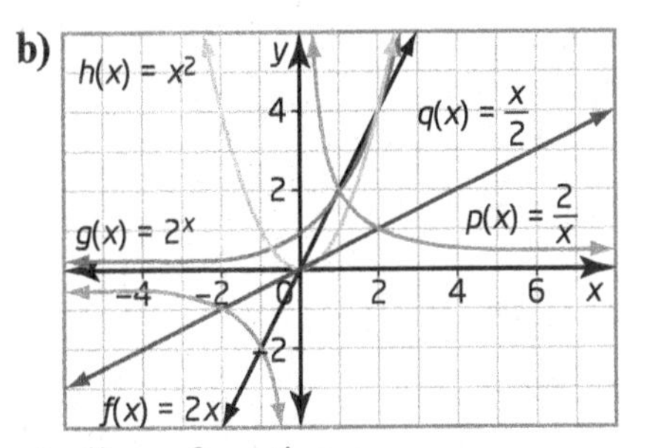

c) all are functions

d) $f(2) = g(2) = h(2) = 4$; $q(2) = p(2) = 1$

e) $f(0) = h(0) = q(0) = 0$;
$f(1) = g(1) = p(1) = 2$;
$g(-0.77) = h(-0.77) \doteq 0.59$;
$h(0.5) = q(0.5) = 0.25$;
$q(-2) = p(-2) = -1$;
$h(1.26) = p(1.26) \doteq 1.6$;
$f(-1) = p(-1) = -2$

17. a) $g(x) = \dfrac{-2}{x+3}$; $h(x) = 4x^2 - 5x$

b) i) −2 **ii)** −8 **iii)** 3 **iv)** 7

18. $f(x) = 2x^2 - 3x + 5$

1.3 Maximum or Minimum of a Quadratic Function

1. a) $y = (x-4)^2 - 16$

b) $f(x) = (x+8)^2 - 68$

c) $f(x) = \left(x + \frac{5}{2}\right)^2 + \frac{3}{4}$

d) $g(x) = \left(x - \frac{1}{2}\right)^2 + \frac{7}{4}$

e) $y = (x-4)^2 - 22$

f) $y = \left(x - \frac{7}{2}\right)^2 - \frac{89}{4}$

2. a) (−2, −3); minimum

b) (3, 25); maximum

c) (−1, 8); maximum

d) $\left(\frac{5}{2}, -4\right)$; minimum

e) (2, 3); minimum

f) (−1, −1); maximum

3. a) (1, −3); minimum

b) (−3, 2); maximum

c) (−4, 5); maximum

d) (1, 3); minimum

e) (6, 0); minimum

f) (5, 11); maximum

4. Answers may vary.

5. \$850 over cost

6. a) Let x represent the number of \$1.25 price decreases and $D(x)$ represent the amount of the donation, in dollars.

$D(x) =$ (ticket price) × (number of tickets sold)
$D(x) = (31.25 - 1.25x)(104 + 8x)$
Since the equation is in factored form, solve $D(x) = 0$.
$0 = (31.25 - 1.25x)(104 + 8x)$
$31.25 - 1.25x = 0$ or $104 + 8x = 0$
$x = 25$ or $x = -13$
The maximum occurs at the average of the two zeros.
$x = \dfrac{25 - 13}{2}$
$= 6$
Tickets sold $= 104 + 8x$
$= 104 + 8(6)$
$= 152$
The maximum donation occurs when 152 tickets are sold.

b) ticket price $= 31.25 - 1.25x$ Substitute $x = 6$.
$= 31.25 - 1.25 \times 6$
$= 23.75$
The ticket price that maximizes the donation is \$23.75.

c) $D(6) = 23.75 \times 152$
$= 3610$
The maximum donation is \$3610.

7. a) 3.7 m **b)** after 0.8 s

8. 10 m by 20 m

9. a) Let x represent the larger number and let y represent the smaller number.
$x - y = 8$, so $y = x - 8$
Let $p(x)$ represent the product of the two numbers.
$p(x) = xy$
$= x(x - 8)$
$= x^2 - 8x$
Complete the square to determine the maximum product.
$p(x) = x^2 - 8x$
$= x^2 - 8x + 16 - 16$
$= (x - 4)^2 - 16$
The maximum product is −16.

b) The maximum product occurs when $x = 4$.
$y = 4 - 8$
$= -4$
The two numbers that produce the maximum product are 4 and −4.

10. a) 13 and 13 **b)** 338

11. 28.1 cm^2

12. a) 66.25 m **b)** 1.5 s **c)** 55 m

13. a) \$15.50 **b)** \$4805

14. a) 34.52 m **b)** 55 m

15. a) $y = -\frac{13}{16}x(x - 10)$
b) 20.3 m

16. a) 10.125 **b)** 2.25

17. $\frac{v^2}{2g} + h_0$

18. a) minimum = 1.875 V; maximum = 17 V
b) minimum: 2.25 min; maximum: 5 min

19. b must be an even integer

20. b must be divisible by 8

1.4 Skills You Need: Working With Radicals

1. a) $14\sqrt{3}$ **b)** $3\sqrt{30}$ **c)** $-4\sqrt{33}$
d) $-16\sqrt{21}$ **e)** $-15\sqrt{6}$ **f)** $6\sqrt{22}$
g) $-6\sqrt{35}$ **h)** $-49\sqrt{30}$

2. a) $3\sqrt{6}$ **b)** $7\sqrt{2}$ **c)** $12\sqrt{2}$
d) $5\sqrt{3}$ **e)** $6\sqrt{2}$ **f)** $5\sqrt{5}$
g) $4\sqrt{6}$ **h)** $3\sqrt{14}$ **i)** $4\sqrt{2}$ **j)** $6\sqrt{5}$

3. a) $13\sqrt{2}$ **b)** $14\sqrt{3}$
c) $-2\sqrt{11}$ **d)** $-4\sqrt{5} + 31\sqrt{6}$

4. a) $-33\sqrt{3}$ **b)** $-37\sqrt{2}$ **c)** $-23\sqrt{5}$
d) $31\sqrt{2}$ **e)** $-5\sqrt{3}$ **f)** $\sqrt{3} - 5\sqrt{5}$
g) $-6\sqrt{3} - 9\sqrt{2}$ **h)** $47\sqrt{2} - \sqrt{7}$

5. a) $5\sqrt{10}$ **b)** $-30\sqrt{2}$ **c)** $70\sqrt{2}$
d) $-240\sqrt{3}$ **e)** -126 **f)** -28
g) $-30\sqrt{10}$ **h)** $-162\sqrt{2}$

6. a) $2\sqrt{3} - \sqrt{6}$ **b)** $2\sqrt{15} - 4\sqrt{3}$
c) $6\sqrt{5} - 3\sqrt{10}$ **d)** $-2\sqrt{15} - 6\sqrt{21}$
e) $\sqrt{30} - 5\sqrt{2}$ **f)** $12\sqrt{22} + 20\sqrt{26}$
g) $6\sqrt{10} - 8\sqrt{15}$ **h)** $36\sqrt{3} - 72\sqrt{2}$

7. a) $1 - 5\sqrt{7}$ **b)** $2 + 6\sqrt{3}$
c) -43 **d)** $52 - 38\sqrt{2}$
e) $67 - 42\sqrt{2}$ **f)** 33

8. a) $-3\sqrt{3} - \frac{3}{2}\sqrt{2}$ **b)** $-4\sqrt{2}$

9. a)
$$\begin{aligned} A &= \frac{1}{2}bh \\ &= \frac{1}{2}(3\sqrt{5})(\sqrt{15}) \\ &= \frac{3}{2}(\sqrt{75}) \\ &= \frac{3}{2}\sqrt{25 \times 3} \\ &= \frac{3}{2}(5\sqrt{3}) \\ &= \frac{15\sqrt{3}}{2} \end{aligned}$$

b)
$$\begin{aligned} A &= \ell w \\ &= 7\sqrt{6}(3\sqrt{8}) \\ &= 21\sqrt{48} \\ &= 21\sqrt{16 \times 3} \\ &= 21(4\sqrt{3}) \\ &= 84\sqrt{3} \end{aligned}$$

c)
$$\begin{aligned} A &= \frac{h}{2}(b_1 + b_2) \\ &= \frac{\sqrt{20}}{2}(\sqrt{147} + \sqrt{48}) \\ &= \frac{\sqrt{4 \times 5}}{2}(\sqrt{49 \times 3} + \sqrt{16 \times 3}) \\ &= \frac{2\sqrt{5}}{2}(7\sqrt{3} + 4\sqrt{3}) \\ &= \sqrt{5}(11\sqrt{3}) \\ &= 11\sqrt{15} \end{aligned}$$

d)
$$\begin{aligned} A &= s^2 \\ &= (\sqrt{28} + \sqrt{54})^2 \\ &= (\sqrt{4 \times 7} + \sqrt{9 \times 6})^2 \\ &= (2\sqrt{7} + 3\sqrt{6})^2 \\ &= (2\sqrt{7})^2 + 2(2\sqrt{7})(3\sqrt{6}) + (3\sqrt{6})^2 \\ &= 4(7) + 12\sqrt{42} + 9(6) \\ &= 82 + 12\sqrt{42} \end{aligned}$$

10. $12\sqrt{35}$; explanations may vary

11. $6\sqrt{21}$ cm

12.
$$\begin{aligned} x^2 + x^2 &= (32\sqrt{2})^2 \\ 2x^2 &= 2048 \\ x^2 &= 1024 \\ x &= 32 \end{aligned}$$

The side length of the square game board is 32 cm.
Divide by 4 to determine the number of small squares along each side.
$32 \div 4 = 8$
Each side has 8 squares, so there are 64 squares in total.

13. $\sqrt{100-64}$ According to BEDMAS, subtract first, then take the square root.

$= \sqrt{36}$
$= 6$

$\sqrt{100} - \sqrt{64}$ According to BEDMAS, take the square root then subtract.

$= 10 - 8$
$= 2$

The order of the operations is reversed, so the answers are not the same.

14. a) $\frac{4+\sqrt{11}}{6}$ b) $\frac{7-2\sqrt{6}}{8}$ c) $\sqrt{13}$
d) $\frac{5+2\sqrt{7}}{9}$ e) $\frac{-2+\sqrt{5}}{4}$

15. a) i) $4\sqrt[3]{5}$ ii) $5\sqrt[3]{7}$ iii) 14
b) i) $2\sqrt[4]{15}$ ii) $3\sqrt[4]{10}$ iii) $6\sqrt[4]{7}$

16. a) $25\sqrt{m}$ b) $17\sqrt{c} - \sqrt{7ab}$
c) $8a\sqrt{5ab} + 10mn\sqrt{3n}$
d) $4b\sqrt{3ab} + 9c\sqrt{d}$

1.5 Solving Quadratic Equations

1. a) −3, 2 b) −3, −4 c) −5, 5
d) −9, 3 e) $-\frac{5}{3}$, 3 f) $\frac{2}{3}$, −5

2. a) $x = \frac{3}{2}$ or $-\frac{1}{3}$ b) $x = \frac{-3 \pm \sqrt{6}}{3}$
c) $x = \frac{-3 \pm \sqrt{3}}{2}$ d) $x = \frac{-7 \pm \sqrt{13}}{6}$
e) $x = -3 \pm \sqrt{5}$

3. a) no roots b) two roots
c) two roots d) one root
e) no roots f) no roots

4. a) $x = \frac{-5 \pm \sqrt{17}}{4}$ b) $x = 3 \pm \sqrt{2}$
c) $x = 3 \pm \sqrt{21}$ d) $x = \frac{10 \pm 2\sqrt{10}}{3}$
e) $x = \frac{24 \pm 4\sqrt{41}}{5}$

5. a) two distinct real roots
b) two equal real roots
c) no real roots
d) two distinct real roots
e) two equal real roots

6. Methods may vary.
a) $-\frac{3}{2}$, 4 b) $\pm\frac{9}{2}$ c) $\frac{-5 \pm 2\sqrt{41}}{4}$
d) 0, $\frac{3}{2}$ e) 3.78, −1.15 f) $\frac{2}{3}$, 1
g) $\frac{5 \pm \sqrt{7}}{2}$ h) $-\frac{3}{4}$, 1

7. a) $k = \pm 4$
b) $k > 4$ or $k < -4$
c) $-4 < k < 4$

8. a)

x	$y = f(x)$
−2	−12
−1	−4
0	2
1	6
2	8
3	8
4	6
5	2
6	−4
7	−12

b), c)

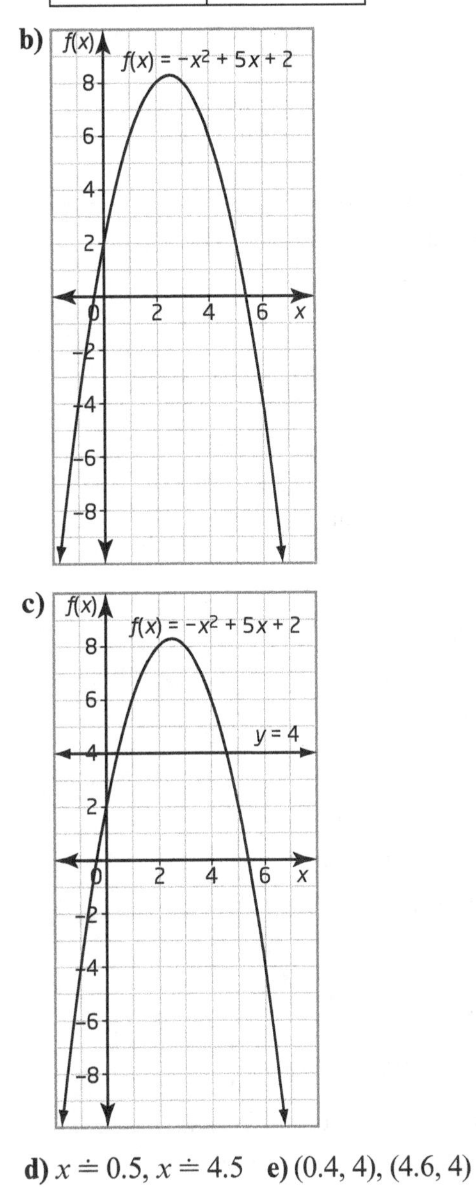

d) $x \doteq 0.5$, $x \doteq 4.5$ e) (0.4, 4), (4.6, 4)

9. **a)** $k = \pm 9, \pm 15$ **b)** $k = \pm 3, \pm 9$
c) Answers may vary. Possible values of k are -4, -6, 14.

10. Find the values of t when the height is 0.
Solve $h(t) = 0$.
$-4.9t^2 + 21.8t + 1.5 = 0$
Use the quadratic formula.
$$t = \frac{-21.8 \pm \sqrt{21.8^2 - 4(-4.9)(1.5)}}{2(-4.9)}$$
$$\doteq -0.068 \text{ or } 4.517$$
Time must be positive, so the ball will be in the air for approximately 4.5 s.

11. **a)** approximately 50 km/h
b) approximately 70 km/h
c) 100 km/h

12. Let x represent one of the numbers and let y represent the other number.
The sum of the numbers is 24, so $x + y = 24$.
Isolate y: $y = 24 - x$ ①
The sum of the squares of the numbers is 306, so $x^2 + y^2 = 306$. ②
Substitute ① in ②.
$x^2 + (24 - x)^2 = 306$ Expand and simplify.
$x^2 + (576 - 48x + x^2) = 306$
$2x^2 - 48x + 270 = 0$ Divide by 2.
$x^2 - 24x + 135 = 0$
$(x - 9)(x - 15) = 0$
$x = 9$ or $x = 15$
The two numbers are 9 and 15.

13. **a)** 498 m **b)** 10 s
c) 20 s **d)** 8 m

14. 9 cm, 12 cm

15. 5 cm

16. 11 and 12

17. 7.2 m by 7.2 m

18. 7, 8, 9 or −7, −8, −9

19. 18.6 A and 5.4 A

20. **a)** $x = \pm 3, \pm 1$ **b)** $x = -1 \pm \sqrt{3}$
c) $x = \dfrac{-1 \pm \sqrt{37}}{6}$

21. **a)** $x = -1 \pm \sqrt{3}$ **b)** $x = \dfrac{2}{3}$

22. $a > 3 + 2\sqrt{2}$ and $a < 3 - 2\sqrt{2}$, $a \neq 0$

1.6 Determine a Quadratic Equation Given Its Roots

1. **a)** $f(x) = a(x - 1)(x + 4)$

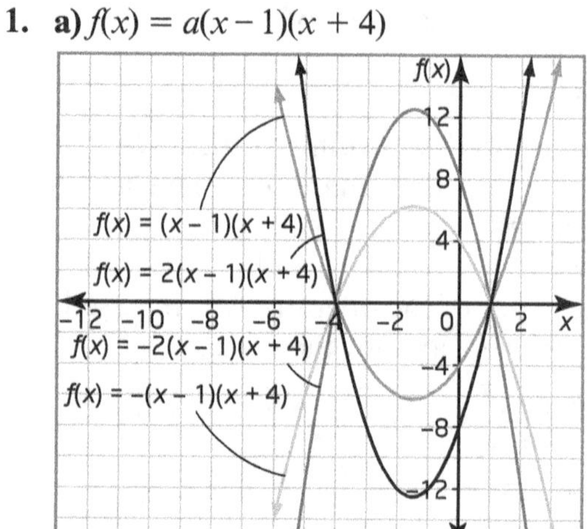

b) $f(x) = a(x + 3)(x + 6)$

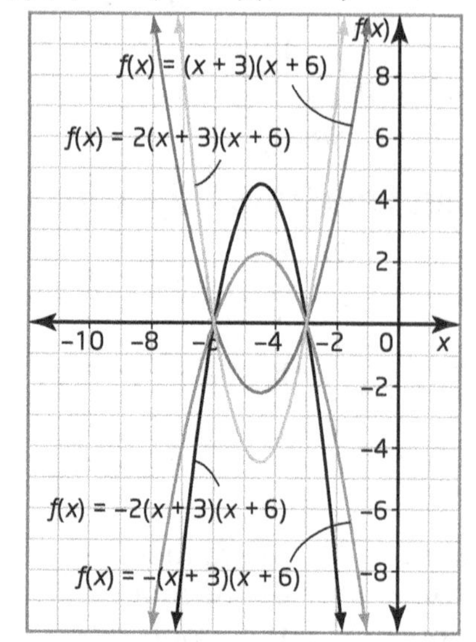

c) $f(x) = a(x - 5)(x + 2)$

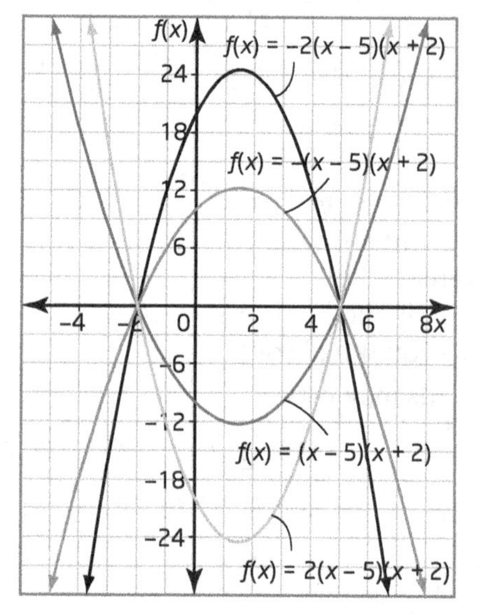

2. **a)** $f(x) = a(x^2 + 3x - 4)$
b) $f(x) = a(x^2 + 9x + 18)$
c) $f(x) = a(x^2 - 3x - 10)$

3. **a)** $y = 2(x - 4)(x + 3)$
b) $y = -0.5(x + 2)(x - 5)$
c) $y = 4x(3x - 2)$

4. **a)** $y = 2x^2 - 2x - 24$
b) $y = -0.5x^2 + 1.5x + 5$
c) $y = 12x^2 - 8x$

5. **a)** $y = -3x^2 + 12x + 3$
b) $y = -2x^2 - 12x - 6$
c) $y = 3x^2 - 24x + 52$
d) $y = -0.5x^2 - x + 6$

6. **a)** $y = 3(x - 2)^2 - 27$
b) $y = -2\left(x + \frac{1}{2}\right)^2 + \frac{49}{2}$
c) $y = 2(x + 1)^2 - 8$
d) $y = -3(x + 2)^2 + 48$

7. **a)** $y = -\frac{1}{32}x^2 + \frac{49}{8}$
b) $\frac{49}{8}$ m or 6.125 m
c) 14 m **d)** $y = -\frac{1}{32}x^2 + \frac{7}{8}x$
e) The graph of $y = -\frac{1}{32}x^2 + \frac{7}{8}x$ is the graph of $y = -\frac{1}{32}x^2 + \frac{49}{8}$ translated 14 m to the right.
f)

8. **a)** $y = -\frac{3}{16}x^2$ **b)** $y = \frac{1}{5}(x - 3)^2$
c) $y = -(x + 6)^2$ **d)** $y = -\frac{2}{3}(x - 4)^2$
e) $y = 5(x + 1)^2$

9. **a)** $y = -5x^2 - 5x + 10$
b) $y = 2x^2 - 2x - 12$
c) $y = \frac{3}{4}x^2 - 3x - 9$

10. If my graphs pass through the given points and have the same vertex and direction of opening as the given graphs, I know my equations are correct.

11. $ac > 9$

12. **a)** The width of the arch is 32 m, so half of the width is 16 m. When the vertex is on the y-axis, the x-intercepts are −16 and 16. A point that is 8 m from one end of the arch and 18 m high is (8, 18); another point on the other side is (−8, 18). The height of the arch is unknown.

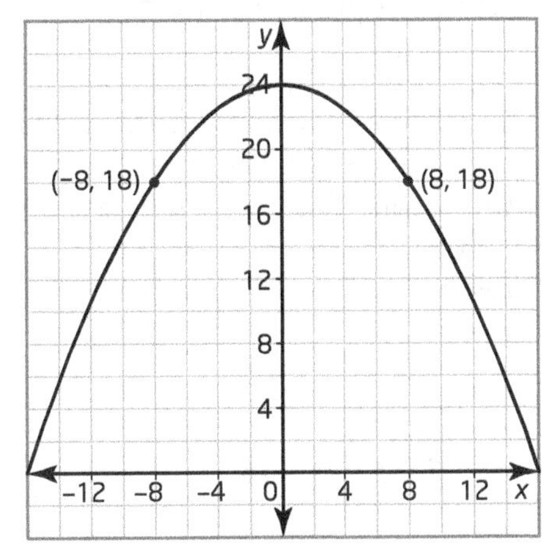

b) Use the x-intercepts and the coordinates of the known point, (8, 18), to determine the factored form of the equation.

$y = a(x - 16)(x + 16)$ Substitute (8, 18) to find the value of a.

$18 = a(8^2 - 256)$
$18 = -192a$
$a = -\frac{3}{32}$

$f(x) = -\frac{3}{32}(x - 16)(x + 16)$ is the factored form of the equation. The standard form, which in this case is also the vertex form, is $f(x) = -\frac{3}{32}x^2 + 24$.

c) The vertex is (0, 24), so the maximum height of the arch is 24 m.

13. **a)** In this situation the x-intercepts are 0 and 32, and a point that is 8 m from one end of the arch is (8, 18). Use this information to write the factored form of the equation.

$y = ax(x - 32)$ Substitute $x = 8$ and $y = 18$.

$18 = a(8)(8 - 32)$
$18 = a(8)(-24)$
$18 = -192a$
$a = -\frac{18}{192}$

$a = -\frac{3}{32}$

The factored form of the equation is $y = -\frac{3}{32}x(x - 32)$.

In standard form the equation is $y = -\frac{3}{32}x^2 + 3x$.

b) The maximum height occurs at the vertex, which is halfway between the x-intercepts. The x-coordinate of the vertex is $x = 16$.
Substitute this value into the equation and solve for y.

$$y = -\frac{3}{32}x^2 + 3x$$
$$= -\frac{3}{32}(16)^2 + 3(16)$$
$$= 24$$

The maximum height of the arch is 24 m. The height is the same as the one found in question 12, which makes sense since only the orientation has changed, not the size of the arch represented by the function.

14. Yes. Explanations may vary.

15. a) $f(x) = -2(x - 2)(x + 1)(x - 4)$; $f(x) = -2x^3 + 10x^2 - 4x - 16$
b) $f(x) = a(2x - 1)(x + 2)(x - 3)$
c) $f(x) = -\frac{4}{3}x^3 + 2x^2 + \frac{22}{3}x - 4$

1.7 Solve Linear-Quadratic Systems

1. a) (3, 24), (−2, −1) **b)** $\left(-\frac{4}{3}, -9\right), \left(\frac{5}{2}, \frac{5}{2}\right)$
c) $\left(\frac{3}{4}, \frac{5}{8}\right)$, (−1, 2) **d)** (−7, −15), (2, −6)

2. Answers may vary.

3. a) no intersection
b) two points of intersection
c) one point of intersection
d) two points of intersection

4. a)

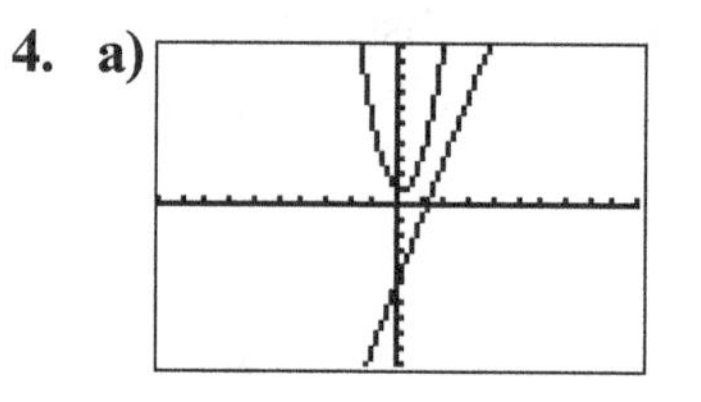

b) **c)** **d)**

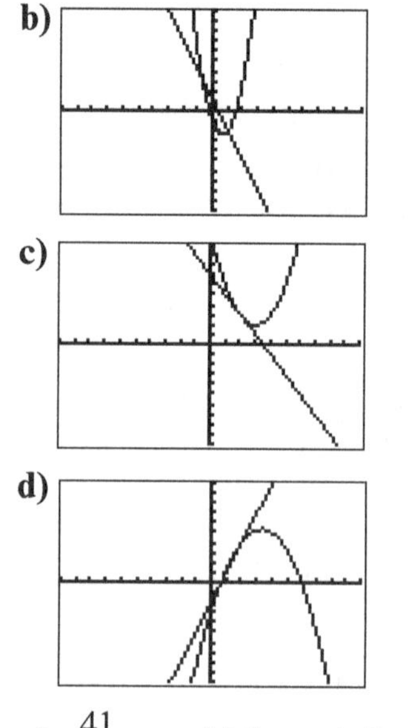

5. a) $-\frac{41}{8}$ **b)** 3 **c)** 5 **d)** 8

6. Answers may vary.

7. (4, 12), (−5, 57)

8. To determine if the two paths intersect, set the equations equal.

$-8x^2 + 720x + 56\,800 = -960x + 145\,000$
$-8x^2 + 1680x - 88\,200 = 0$ Divide by −8.
$x^2 - 210x + 11\,025 = 0$ Factor or use the quadratic formula.
$(x - 105)^2 = 0$
$x = 105$

Substitute $x = 105$ into $y = -960x + 145\,000$ and solve for y.
$y = -960(105) + 145\,000$
$= 44\,200$

The paths will intersect at (105, 44 200).

9. Answers may vary.

10. a) $k > -\frac{4}{3}$ **b)** $k = -\frac{4}{3}$ **c)** $k < -\frac{4}{3}$

11. Equate the expressions and simplify.
$kx^2 + 3x + 10 = -5x + 3$
$kx^2 + 8x + 7 = 0$ Use the discriminant; $a = k, b = 8, c = 7$.

$b^2 - 4ac$
$= 8^2 - 4(k)(7)$
$= 64 - 28k$

a) Two points of intersection occur when the discriminant is positive.
$64 - 28k > 0$
$64 > 28k$
$k < \frac{16}{7}$

b) One point of intersection occurs when the discriminant is zero.

$$64 - 28k = 0$$
$$64 = 28k$$
$$k = \frac{16}{7}$$

c) No points of intersection occur when the discriminant is negative.

$$64 - 28k < 0$$
$$64 < 28k$$
$$k > \frac{16}{7}$$

12. (−16.8, −2.2), (24.5, 0.7)

13. Answers may vary. Sample answer: The line $x = 3$ is a vertical line that intersects or cuts through the parabola such that part of the line is above the parabola and part of it is below.

14. a)

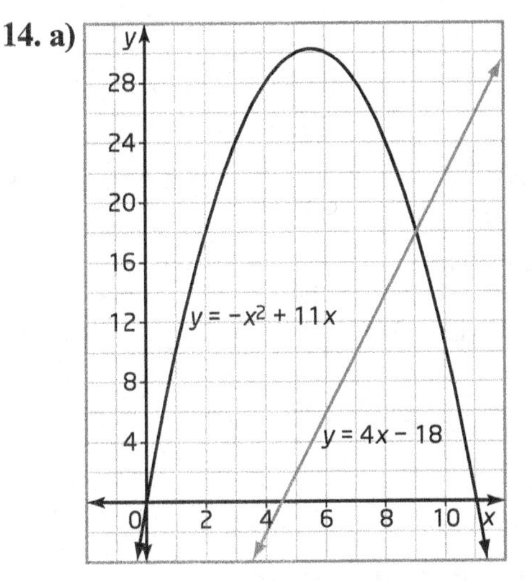

b) (9, 18)

15. $10{:}30 < x < 14{:}30$, or between 10:30 a.m. and 2:30 p.m.

16. a) 7.1 s **b)** 112.8 m

17. 90 m by 160 m

18. $y = x - 10$

19. Two parabolas may have two, one, or no points of intersection. Equations and sketches will vary.

20. a) Estimates will vary. Sample answer: (−8, 6), (9.6, −2.8)

b) Estimates will vary. Sample answer: (3.5, 0.9), (1.5, −3)

21. There are no real roots.

Chapter 1 Review

1. a) Yes; vertical line test is satisfied

b) No; vertical line test is not satisfied

2. a) Yes; each domain value has only one range value

b) No; the domain value has four range values

3. a) domain $\{x \in \mathbb{R}\}$, range $\{y \in \mathbb{R}, y \leq 2\}$

b) domain $\left\{x \in \mathbb{R}, x \leq \frac{4}{3}\right\}$, range $\{y \leq 0, y \in \mathbb{R}\}$

4. Answers may vary.

5. a) range {−5, −1, 3, 4, 11}

b) range {−7, −5, 1}

6. a) 16

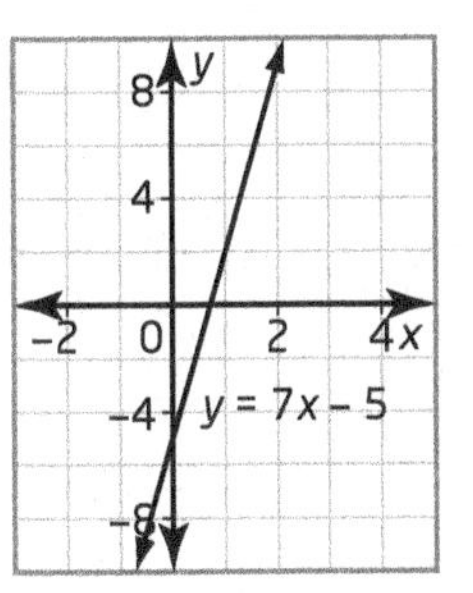

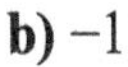

b) −1

y
2
−6 −4 −2 0 2 4 6 x
−2
y = −1

c) 9

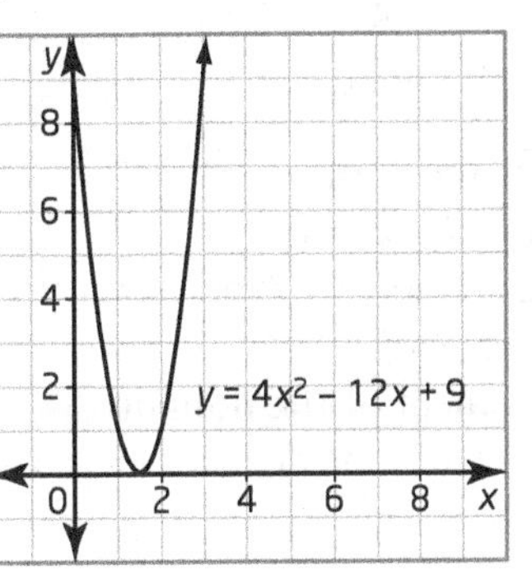

d) 0

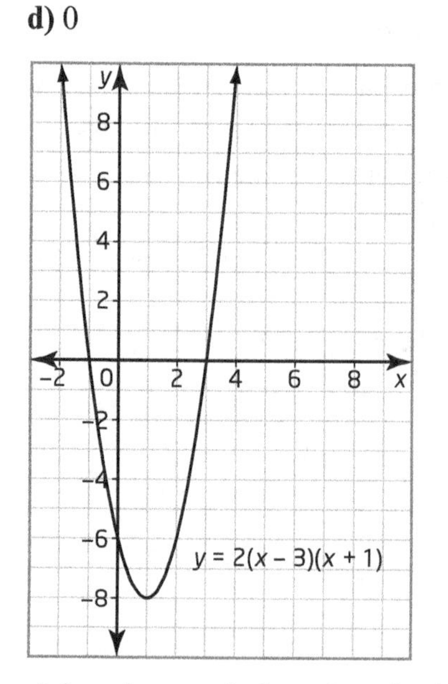

7. **a)** function; each domain value has a single range value

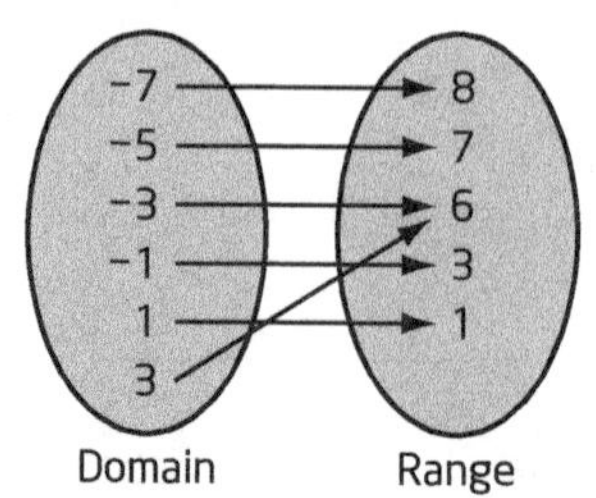

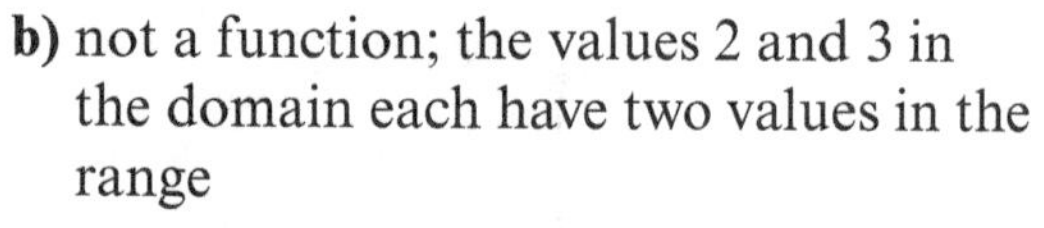

b) not a function; the values 2 and 3 in the domain each have two values in the range

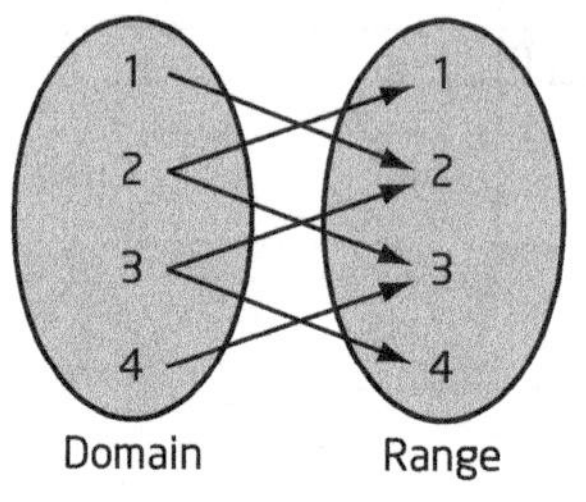

8. **a)** the width of the pool
   b) domain $\{x \in \mathbb{R}, x > 0.2\}$, range $\{w \in \mathbb{R}, x \geq 0\}$, where w is the width of the pool
   c) Yes; each element of the domain corresponds with one element of the range
   d) $w = 18$ ft

9. **a)** $(-3, 29)$; maximum
   b) $\left(\frac{3}{2}, 16\right)$; maximum
   c) $(-6, 1)$; minimum

10. **a)** $\left(\frac{1}{2}, -3\right)$; minimum
    b) $\left(-\frac{3}{4}, 2\right)$; minimum

11. **a)** \$25 000 **b)** \$3000

12. **a)** $7\sqrt{3}$ **b)** $2\sqrt{15}$

13. **a)** $2\sqrt{7} - 2\sqrt{3}$ **b)** $41\sqrt{6} + 36\sqrt{7}$
    c) $-16\sqrt{2} - 2\sqrt{7}$ **d)** $36 - 40\sqrt{3}$
    e) $48\sqrt{3} - 96\sqrt{2} - 96$ **f)** $\sqrt{10} - 2$
    g) $3\sqrt{5}$

14. $A = 128$

15. $x = \frac{1}{3}$ or $-\frac{1}{6}$

16. $x = \frac{3 \pm \sqrt{7}}{2}$

17. two distinct real roots

18. 68.4 m by 131.6 m

19. **a)** $y = -24x^2 + 42x + 45$
    b) $y = -x^2 + 10x - 22$

20. Answers may vary. Sample answer: $h = -4.8(x - 5)^2 + 120$

21. $y = 5(x + 1)^2$

22. $\left(-\frac{5}{2}, -17\right)$, $(1, -3)$

23. one

24. −3

25. after 8.3 s

Chapter 1 Math Contest

1. B
2. D
3. A
4. B
5. C
6. A
7. C
8. B
9. D
10. C

Chapter 2 Transformation of Functions

2.1 Functions and Equivalent Algebraic Expressions

1. a) 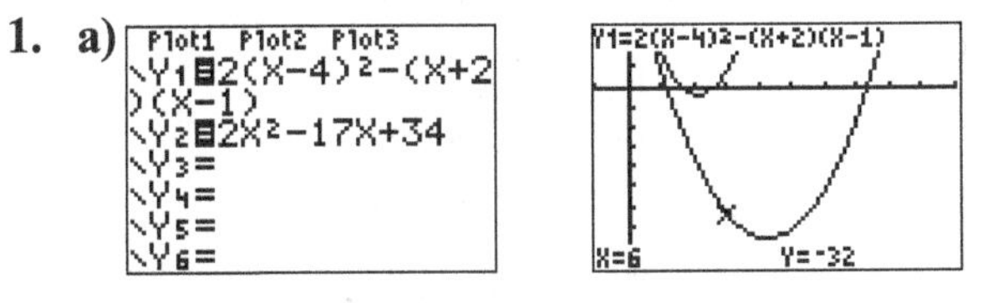

No. The functions do not appear to be equivalent.

b) Plot1 Plot2 Plot3
\Y1=-3(X²+4X-1)+
(2X-5)²
\Y2=X²-32X+28
\Y3=
\Y4=
\Y5=
\Y6=

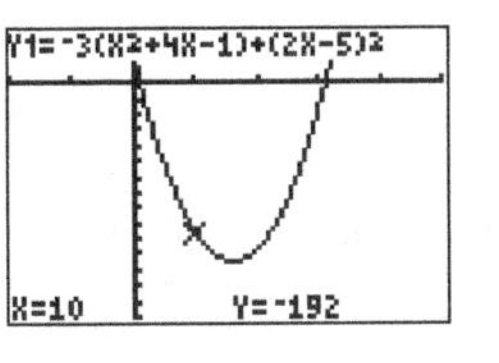

Yes. The functions appear to be equivalent.

c) 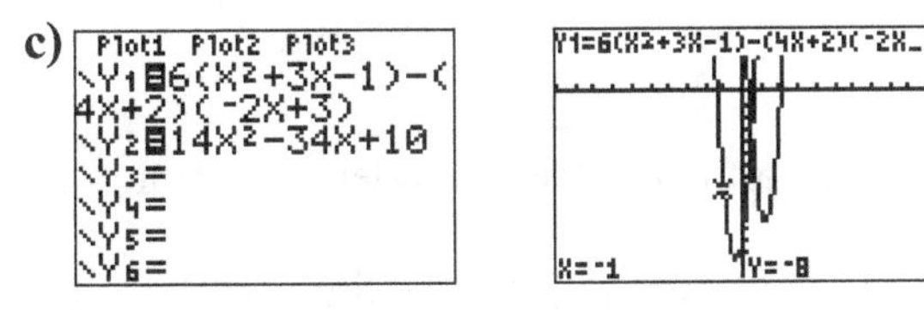

No. The functions do not appear to be equivalent.

d) Plot1 Plot2 Plot3
\Y1=(X+1)²-4(2-X
)(X+3)
\Y2=-(X+3)(X-4)+
2(X+3)²
\Y3=
\Y4=
\Y5=

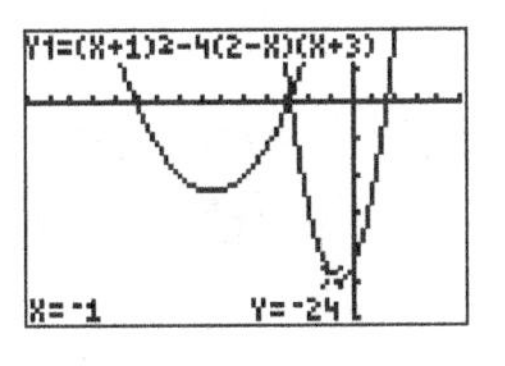

No. The functions do not appear to be equivalent.

e) Plot1 Plot2 Plot3
\Y1=(X-2)(3X+1)(
X+4)
\Y2=3X³+5X²-5X-8
\Y3=
\Y4=
\Y5=

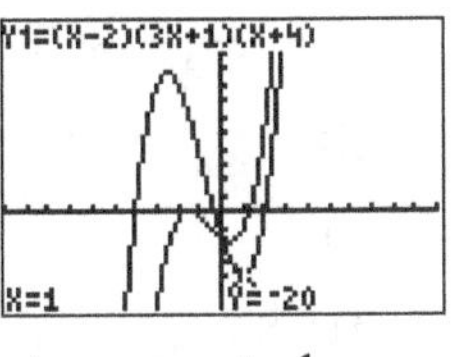

No. The functions do not appear to be equivalent.

f) 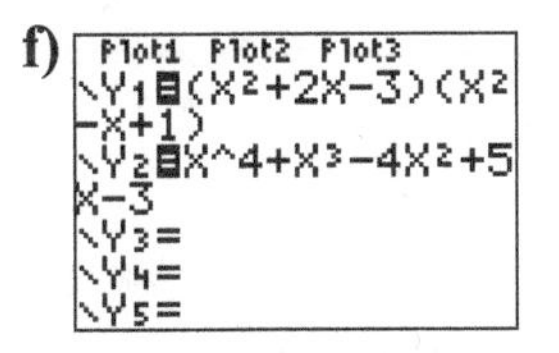

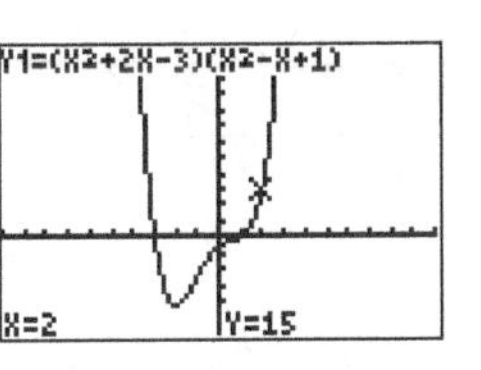

Yes. The functions appear to be equivalent.

2. a) $f(6) = -32$; $g(0) = 4$
   b) Answers may vary.
   c) $f(0) = -12$; $g(0) = 10$
   d) $s(0) = -23$; $t(0) = 30$
   e) $f(1) = -20$; $g(0) = -5$
   f) Answers may vary.

3. a) $x \neq -3$
   b) $x \neq -4$

4. a) $x \neq 3, x \geq 2$
   b) $x \neq -2, x \neq 2$

5. a) Yes; $x \neq -5$
   b) No; $g(x) = \frac{x+6}{x+3}$; $x \neq -6$; $x \neq -3$
   c) No; $g(x) = x + 1$; $x \neq -5$
   d) Yes; $x \neq -3$; $x \neq -\frac{1}{3}$

6. a) $\frac{1}{x+3}$; $x \neq -3, x \neq 7$
   b) $-\frac{x+3}{2}$; $x \neq -3, x \neq 4$
   c) $\frac{x+5}{x+3}$; $x \neq \frac{3}{2}, x \neq -3$
   d) $\frac{x+4}{x+5}$; $x \neq -5, x \neq 9$
   e) $\frac{x}{x+1}$; $x \neq -1, x \neq 2$
   f) $\frac{2x-1}{2(x+1)}$; $x \neq -1, x \neq \frac{2}{3}$
   g) $\frac{2x+1}{2x-1}$; $x \neq -\frac{1}{2}, x \neq \frac{1}{2}$
   h) $\frac{x-17}{3-x}$; $x \neq -3, x \neq 0, x \neq 3$

7. a)

x	y
−4	7
−2	19
0	31
3	49
10	91

b)

x	y
−4	undefined
−2	undefined
0	0
3	$\frac{72}{5}$
10	$\frac{75}{2}$

$x \neq -4, x \neq -2$

c)

x	y
-4	0
-2	$-\frac{1}{6}$
0	undefined
3	$-\frac{7}{2}$
10	$\frac{7}{6}$

$x \neq 0$

d)

x	y
-4	39
-2	-11
0	9
3	24
10	-11

8. a) Area of large circle is $A = \pi r^2$
The diameter of the small circle is 8 cm, so the radius is 4 cm.
The area of the small circle is
$A = \pi(4)^2$
$= 16\pi$
Subtract the area of the small circle from the area of the large circle.
Shaded Area $= \pi r^2 - 16\pi$

b) Shaded Area $= \pi r^2 - 16\pi$
$= \pi(r^2 - 16)$
$= \pi(r - 4)(r + 4)$

c) Since this function represents area, it is restricted to positive r-values that result in positive area. The domain is $\{x \in \mathbb{R}, x > 4\}$.

9. a) $V = \pi(2x + 1)^2(x - 2)$;
$V = \pi(4x^3 - 4x^2 - 7x - 2)$

b) $SA = 2\pi(2x + 1)^2 + 2\pi(2x + 1)(x - 2)$;
$SA = 2\pi(6x^2 + x - 1)$

c) 56.5 m^3; 245.0 m^2

d) $\{x \in \mathbb{R}, x > 2\}$

10. a) $V(x) = (3x + 2)(2x - 0.5)(x + 1)$

b) $SA(x) = 2(3x + 2)(2x - 0.5) + 2(2x - 0.5)(x + 1) + 2(3x + 2)(x + 1)$

c) 25.875 m^3, 57.875 m^2; 84 m^3, 125 m^2; 149.625 m^3, 183.5 m^2

11. Expand and simplify each function.

$$f(x) = x^2 + \left[\frac{1}{2}(x - 1)(x + 1)\right]^2$$
$$= x^2 + \left[\frac{1}{2}(x^2 - 1)\right]^2$$
$$= x^2 + \frac{1}{4}(x^2 - 1)^2$$
$$= x^2 + \frac{1}{4}(x^4 - 2x^2 + 1)$$
$$= x^2 + \frac{1}{4}x^4 - \frac{1}{2}x^2 + \frac{1}{4}$$
$$= \frac{1}{4}x^4 + \frac{1}{2}x^2 + \frac{1}{4}$$
$$g(x) = \left[\frac{1}{2}(x^2 + 1)\right]^2$$
$$= \frac{1}{4}(x^2 + 1)^2$$
$$= \frac{1}{4}(x^4 + 2x^2 + 1)$$
$$= \frac{1}{4}x^4 + \frac{1}{2}x^2 + \frac{1}{4}$$

$f(x)$ and $g(x)$ are equivalent expressions.

12. The graph of $f(x)$ is the line $y = 2x + 1$, with slope 2, y-intercept 1, and two holes, one at $\left(-\frac{2}{3}, -\frac{1}{3}\right)$ and the other at (4, 9).

2.2 Skills You Need: Operations With Rational Expressions

1. a) $\frac{16y^2}{x^2}$; $x \neq 0$

b) $48x^4$; $x \neq 0$

c) $12b^3$; $b \neq 0$

d) $\frac{1}{3x}$; $x \neq 0, y \neq 0$

e) $16ab$; $a \neq 0, b \neq 0$

f) $18pr^2$; $p \neq 0, q \neq 0, r \neq 0$

2. a) 4; $x \neq 6$

b) 9; $x \neq -2, x \neq 0$

c) $\frac{x - 8}{x - 6}$; $x \neq -2, x \neq 6$

d) $\frac{7x}{x + 4}$; $x \neq -4, x \neq -\frac{1}{2}, x \neq 0$

e) $\frac{4x}{x + 6}$; $x \neq -6, x \neq 0, x \neq 5$

f) $\frac{x + 1}{x + 3}$; $x \neq -8, x \neq -4, x \neq -3$

g) $\frac{1}{x-4}$; $x \neq -2, x \neq -1, x \neq 1, x \neq 4$

h) $\frac{x-3}{x+6}$; $x \neq -6, x \neq -2, x \neq 4$

3. a) 2; $x \neq -1, x \neq 0$

b) x; $x \neq 3$

c) $\frac{x-5}{x+10}$; $x \neq -12, x \neq -10, x \neq 5$

d) $\frac{x+15}{4}$; $x \neq -6, x \neq 0$

e) $\frac{1}{6}$; $x \neq 0, x \neq 9$

f) $\frac{5x(x+13)}{x-5}$; $x \neq -2, x \neq 0, x \neq 5$

g) $\frac{3}{x+1}$; $x \neq -2, x \neq -1, x \neq 2$

h) $\frac{x+7}{x+5}$; $x \neq -5, x \neq -2, x \neq 1, x \neq 4$

4. a) $\frac{5x-2}{12}$

b) $\frac{-2x+75}{21}$

c) $-\frac{1}{28x}$; $x \neq 0$

d) $\frac{8+9a}{2ab}$; $a \neq 0, b \neq 0$

e) $\frac{44a-21b^2}{48a^2b^2}$; $a \neq 0, b \neq 0$

f) $\frac{3+7a}{10a}$; $a \neq 0$

g) $\frac{-3(x-7)}{(x-3)(x+3)}$; $x \neq -3, x \neq 3$

h) $\frac{9(2x+1)}{(x+4)(x-5)}$; $x \neq -4, x \neq 5$

i) $\frac{20x+37}{(x-2)(x+5)}$; $x \neq -5, x \neq 2$

5. a) $\frac{2x^2-3x+3}{(x-6)(x-3)}$; $x \neq 3, x \neq 6$

b) $\frac{-3x^2-8x-7}{(x-5)(x+3)}$; $x \neq -3, x \neq 5$

c) $\frac{2x^2+4x-3}{(x-2)(x+2)}$; $x \neq -2, x \neq 2$

d) $\frac{3x^2+4x}{(x-1)(x+2)}$; $x \neq -2, x \neq 1$

e) $\frac{-x-10}{(x+8)(x+6)}$; $x \neq -8, x \neq -6, x \neq -5,$ $x \neq -3$

f) $\frac{4x-7}{(x-4)(x+5)}$; $x \neq -7, x \neq -5, x \neq 4$

g) $\frac{1}{x+2}$; $x \neq -3, x \neq -2, x \neq 1$

h) $\frac{4x^2-37x+21}{(x+7)(x-10)}$; $x \neq -7, x \neq 2, x \neq 5,$ $x \neq 10$

6. a) Use the formula for time: $t = \frac{d}{v}$.
The total distance is 40 km, so half the total distance is 20 km.
Let t_1 represent David's time for the first half of the race and let t_2 represent David's time for the second half of the race. Let t represent the total time for the race.
The time for the first half of the race is represented by $t_1 = \frac{20}{x}$.
The time for the second half of the race is represented by $t_2 = \frac{20}{x-8}$.

$$\begin{aligned} t &= t_1 + t_2 \\ &= \frac{20}{x} + \frac{20}{x-8} \\ &= \frac{20(x-8)+20x}{x(x-8)} \\ &= \frac{20x-160+20x}{x(x-8)} \\ &= \frac{40x-160}{x(x-8)} \end{aligned}$$

The total time taken for the race is given by $t = \frac{40x-160}{x(x-8)}$.

b) Substitute $x = 35$ in t.

$$\begin{aligned} t &= \frac{40(35)-160}{35(35-8)} \\ &\doteq 1.3 \end{aligned}$$

David completed the race in approximately 1.3 h, which is 1 h and 18 min.

7. a) $\frac{2}{x-5}$; $x \neq 5$

b) $\frac{x+4}{x-4}$; $x \neq 4$

c) $\frac{2a-3}{5-2a}$; $a \neq \frac{5}{2}$

d) $\frac{b-4}{2b-3}$; $b \neq \frac{3}{2}$

e) $\frac{5x+2}{x-2}$; $x \neq 2$

f) $\frac{-x-1}{4x-3}$; $x \neq \frac{3}{4}$

g) $\frac{5b-8}{b+2}$; $x \neq -2$

h) $\frac{-3c+1}{5c-1}$; $x \neq \frac{1}{5}$

8. **a)** The dimensions of the box are
$\ell = 120 - 2x$, $w = 100 - 2x$, and $h = x$.
$V = \ell wh$
$V(x) = (120 - 2x)(100 - 2x)x$

b) $SA(x) = \ell w + 2\ell h + 2wh$
$SA(x) = (120 - 2x)(100 - 2x) + 2(120 - 2x)x + 2(100 - 2x)x$

c) The side length of the square must be positive, so $x > 0$. The shortest side is 100 cm, so $x < 50$ cm, since it would be impossible to cut two squares with sides larger than 50 cm from a side that is only 100 cm long. The domain is $\{x \in \mathbb{R}, 0 < x < 50\}$.

$$\frac{V}{SA} = \frac{x(120-2x)(100-2x)}{(120-2x)(100-2x) + 2x(120-2x) + 2x(100-2x)}$$
$$= \frac{4x(60-x)(50-x)}{4(60-x)(50-x) + 4x(60-x) + 4(50-x)}$$
$$= \frac{x(3000 - 60x - 50x + x^2)}{3000 - 6x - 50x + x^2 + 60x - x^2 + 50x - x^2}$$
$$= \frac{x^3 - 110x^2 + 3000x}{x^2 + 3000}$$

e) The denominator cannot be zero. The restrictions are $x \neq \pm\sqrt{3000}$, or $x \neq \pm 54.77$.

9. **a)** $\dfrac{6x^2 + x - 12}{10x - 2}$

b) $x \neq -\dfrac{3}{2}, x \neq \dfrac{1}{5}$

10. **a)** 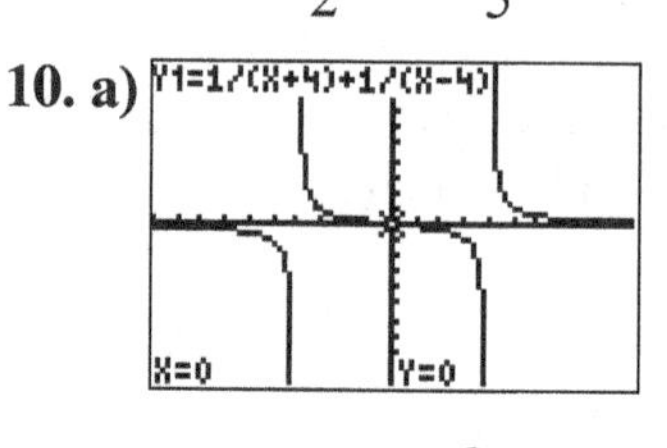

b) $f(x) = \dfrac{2x}{(x-4)(x+4)}$

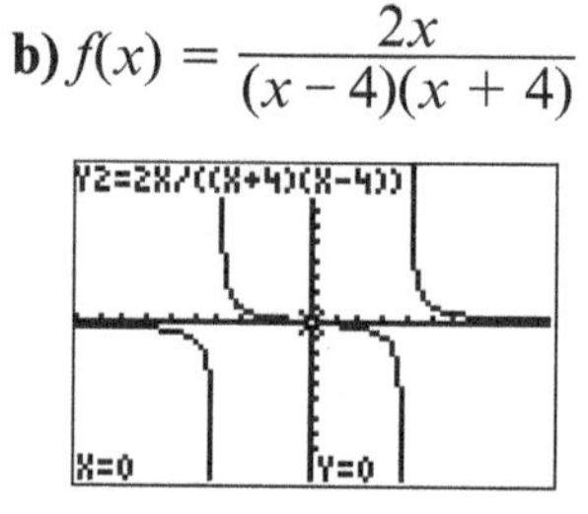

c) Answers may vary. Sample answer: The two graphs are the same. The restrictions for both graphs are $x \neq -4$ and $x \neq 4$. These are the vertical asymptotes of the graph.

11. $\dfrac{-19x}{3(x-1)}$; $x \neq -4, x \neq -3, x \neq -\dfrac{4}{3}, x \neq -1, x \neq 0, x \neq \dfrac{3}{2}, x \neq 1, x \neq 4$

12. **a)** $\dfrac{x + y}{y - x}$; $x \neq 0, y \neq 0, x \neq y$

b) $\dfrac{x^2 + y^2}{y^2 - x^2}$; $x \neq 0, y \neq 0, y \neq \pm x$

13. **a)** $\dfrac{-2a - 3}{(a + 2)^2}$; $a \neq -2$

b) $\dfrac{2a + 3}{3a + 5}$; $a \neq -2, a \neq -\dfrac{5}{3}$

2.3 Horizontal and Vertical Translations of Functions

1. **a)**

x	$f(x) = \sqrt{x}$	$r(x) = f(x) - 4$	$s(x) = f(x + 5)$
0	0	−4	$\sqrt{5}$
1	1	−3	$\sqrt{6}$
4	2	−2	3
9	3	−1	$\sqrt{14}$

b) 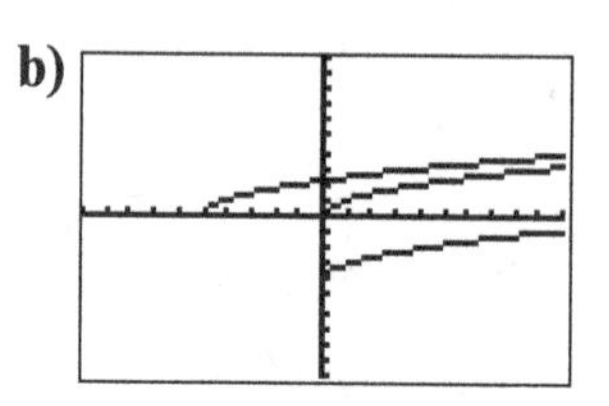

c) $r(x)$ translates the points 4 units down. $s(x)$ translates the points 5 units to the left.

2. **a)** A′(−8, 3), B′(−5, 1), C′(−2, 1), D′(1, 10), E′(3, 10), F′(6, 8), G′(8, 8)

b) A′(−8, −7), B′(−5, −9), C′(−2, −9), D′(1, 0), E′(3, 0), F′(6, −2), G′(8, −2)

c) A′(−5, −3), B′(−2, −5), C′(1, −5), D′(4, 4), E′(6, 4), F′(9, 2), G′(11, 2)

d) A′(−9, −3), B′(−6, −5), C′(−3, −5), D′(0, 4), E′(2, 4), F′(5, 2), G′(7, 2)

e) A′(−7, 6), B′(−4, 4), C′(−1, 4), D′(2, 13), E′(4, 13), F′(7, 11), G′(9, 11)

f) A′(−10, −7), B′(−7, −12), C′(−4, −12), D′(−1, −3), E′(1, −3), F′(4, −5), G′(6, −5)

3. **a)** $f(x) = x$; $y = f(x) - 7$; translate the graph of $f(x)$ down 7 units;
$f(x)$: domain $\{x \in \mathbb{R}\}$, range $\{y \in \mathbb{R}\}$;
$g(x)$: domain $\{x \in \mathbb{R}\}$, range $\{y \in \mathbb{R}\}$

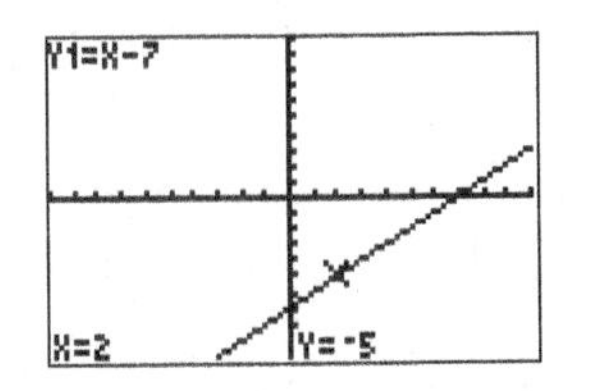

b) $f(x) = x^2$; $y = f(x) + 3$; translate the graph of $f(x)$ up 3 units;
$f(x)$: domain $\{x \in \mathbb{R}\}$,
range $\{y \in \mathbb{R}, y \geq 0\}$;
$g(x)$:domain $\{x \in \mathbb{R}\}$,
range $\{y \in \mathbb{R}, y \geq 3\}$

c) $f(x) = \sqrt{x}$; $y = f(x) + 9$; translate the graph of $f(x)$ up 9 units;
$f(x)$: domain $\{x \in \mathbb{R}, x \geq 0\}$,
range $\{y \in \mathbb{R}, y \geq 0\}$;
$g(x)$: domain $\{x \in \mathbb{R}, x \geq 0\}$,
range $\{y \in \mathbb{R}, y \geq 9\}$

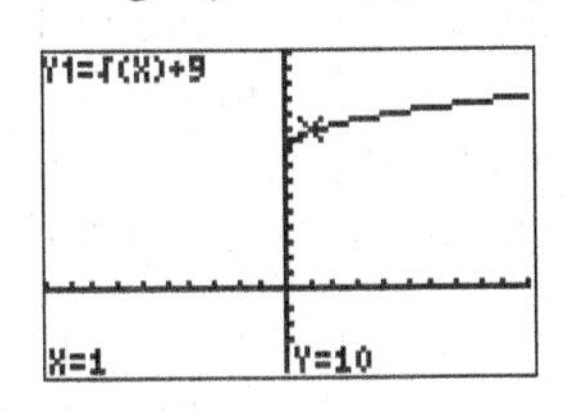

d) $f(x) = x^2$; $y = f(x - 5)^2$; translate the graph of $f(x)$ right 5 units;
$f(x)$: domain $\{x \in \mathbb{R}\}$,
range $\{y \in \mathbb{R}, y \geq 0\}$;
$g(x)$: domain $\{x \in \mathbb{R}\}$,
range $\{y \in \mathbb{R}, y \geq 0\}$

e) $f(x) = \frac{1}{x}$; $y = f(x) + 2$; translate the graph of $f(x)$ up 2 units;
$f(x)$: domain $\{x \in \mathbb{R}, x \neq 0\}$,
range $\{y \in \mathbb{R}, y \neq 0\}$;
$g(x)$: domain $\{x \in \mathbb{R}, x \neq 0\}$,
range $\{y \in \mathbb{R}, y \neq 0\}$

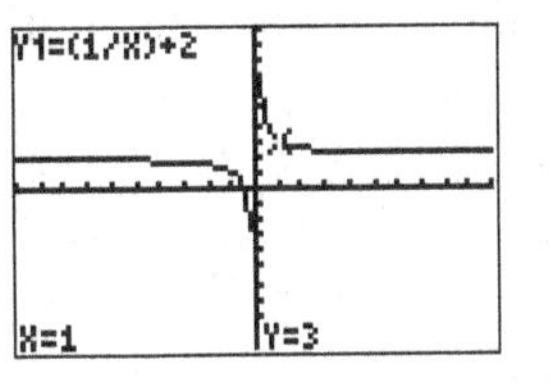

f) $f(x) = \sqrt{x}$; $y = f(x + 3)$; translate the graph of $f(x)$ left 3 units;
$f(x)$: domain $\{x \in \mathbb{R}, x \geq 0\}$,
range $\{y \in \mathbb{R}, y \geq 0\}$;
$g(x)$: domain $\{x \in \mathbb{R}, x \geq -3\}$,
range $\{y \in \mathbb{R}, y \geq 0\}$

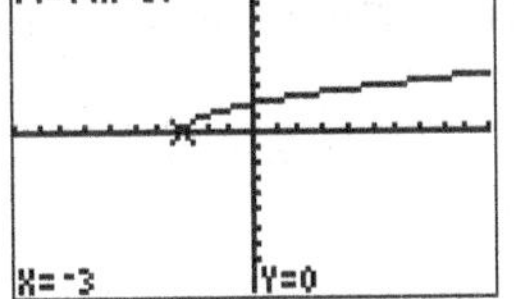

g) $f(x) = \frac{1}{x}$; $g(x) = f(x - 8)$; translate the graph of $f(x)$ right 8 units;
$f(x)$: domain $\{x \in \mathbb{R}, x \neq 0\}$,
range $\{y \in \mathbb{R}, y \neq 0\}$;
$g(x)$: domain $\{x \in \mathbb{R}, x \neq 8\}$,
range $\{y \in \mathbb{R}, y \neq 0\}$

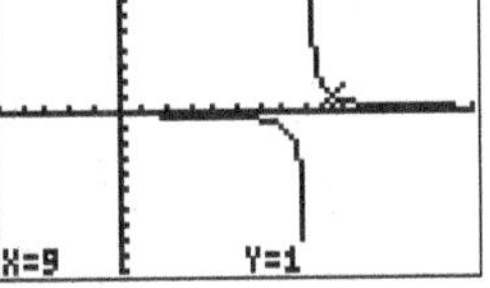

4. a) translate $f(x)$ left 3 units and up 1 unit;
$g(x) = f(x + 3) + 1$;
$f(x)$: domain $\{x \in \mathbb{R}\}$,
range $\{y \in \mathbb{R}, y \geq 0\}$;
$g(x)$: domain $\{x \in \mathbb{R}\}$,
range $\{y \in \mathbb{R}, y \geq 1\}$

b) translate $f(x)$ right 4 units and down 7 units; $g(x) = f(x - 4) - 7$;
$f(x)$: domain $\{x \in \mathbb{R}, x \geq 0\}$,
range $\{y \in \mathbb{R}, y \geq 0\}$;
$g(x)$: domain $\{x \in \mathbb{R}, y \geq 4\}$,
range $\{y \in \mathbb{R}, y \geq -7\}$

c) Answers may vary. Sample answer: translate $f(x)$ down 6 units;
$g(x) = f(x) - 6$; $f(x)$: domain $\{x \in \mathbb{R}\}$,
range $\{y \in \mathbb{R}\}$; $g(x)$: domain $\{x \in \mathbb{R}\}$,
range $\{y \in \mathbb{R}\}$

5. a) translate $f(x)$ right 4 units and up 3 units; $g(x) = f(x - 4) + 3$;
$f(x)$: domain $\{x \in \mathbb{R}, x \neq 0\}$, range $\{y \in \mathbb{R}, y \neq 0\}$;
$g(x)$:domain $\{x \in \mathbb{R}, x \neq 4\}$, range $\{y \in \mathbb{R}, y \neq 3\}$

b) translate $f(x)$ left 2 units and down 2 units; $g(x) = f(x + 2) - 2$;
$f(x)$: domain $\{x \in \mathbb{R}\}$, range $\{y \in \mathbb{R}, y \geq 0\}$;
$g(x)$: domain $\{x \in \mathbb{R}\}$, range $\{y \in \mathbb{R}, y \geq -2\}$

c) translate $f(x)$ left 3 units and up 5 units; $g(x) = f(x + 3) + 5$;
$f(x)$: domain $\{x \in \mathbb{R}, x \geq 0\}$, range $\{y \in \mathbb{R}, y \geq 0\}$;
$g(x)$: domain $\{x \in \mathbb{R}, x \geq -3\}$, range $\{y \in \mathbb{R}, y \geq 5\}$

6. a) $b(x) = x + 2$
b) $h(x) = x - 5$
c) $m(x) = x + 9$
d) $n(x) = x - 10$
e) $r(x) = x + 10$
f) $s(x) = x - 6$
g) $t(x) = x - 4$

7. a) $b(x) = (x + 2)^2$
b) $h(x) = x^2 - 5$
c) $m(x) = x^2 + 9$
d) $n(x) = (x - 3)^2 - 7$
e) $r(x) = (x + 4)^2 + 6$
f) $s(x) = (x + 2)^2 - 8$
g) $t(x) = (x - 5)^2 + 1$

8. a) $b(x) = \sqrt{(x + 2)}$
b) $h(x) = \sqrt{x} - 5$
c) $m(x) = \sqrt{x} + 9$
d) $n(x) = \sqrt{x - 3} - 7$
e) $r(x) = \sqrt{x + 4} + 6$
f) $s(x) = \sqrt{x + 2} - 8$
g) $t(x) = \sqrt{x - 5} + 1$

9. a) $b(x) = \dfrac{1}{x + 2}$
b) $h(x) = \dfrac{1}{x} - 5$
c) $m(x) = \dfrac{1}{x} + 9$
d) $n(x) = \dfrac{1}{x - 3} - 7$
e) $r(x) = \dfrac{1}{x + 4} + 6$
f) $s(x) = \dfrac{1}{x + 2} - 8$
g) $t(x) = \dfrac{1}{x - 5} + 1$

10. a) False. The order does not matter. For example, if the base function $y = x^2$ is translated left 2 units and then up 1 unit, the image of the point (2, 4) is (0, 5). Similarly, if (2, 4) is translated up 1 unit and then left 2 units, the image point is also (0, 5). This will be true for all points on $y = x^2$.

b) True. Consider the point (2, 2) on the graph of $y = x$. A translation of 2 units right results in the image point (4, 2), which is on the graph of $y = x - 2$. If the same point is translated 2 units down, the resulting point is (2, 0), which is also on the graph of $y = x - 2$. Thus, when translated horizontally the image points of the points on the line $y = x$ lie on the line $y = x - 2$. Similarly, when translated vertically the image points of the points on the line $y = x$ lie on the line $y = x - 2$.

11. When $f(x) = x$ is translated 5 units to the left the transformed function is
$g(x) = f(x + 5)$
$g(x) = x + 5$

a) Equivalent; the transformed function is
$g(x) = f(x) + 5$
$= x + 5$

b) Not equivalent; the transformed function is
$g(x) = f(x) - 5$
$= x - 5$

c) Not equivalent; the transformed function is
$g(x) = f(x - 2) + 3$
$= (x - 2) + 3$
$= x + 1$

d) Equivalent; the transformed function is
$g(x) = f(x + 3) + 2$
$= (x + 3) + 2$
$= x + 5$

e) Not equivalent; the transformed function is

$g(x) = f(x - 4) + 1$
$= (x - 4) + 1$
$= x - 3$

12. a) base function: $f(x) = x$; transformed function: $g(x) = x + 3$

b) base function: $f(x) = x^2$; transformed function: $g(x) = (x + 1)^2 + 2$

c) base function: $f(x) = \frac{1}{x}$; transformed function: $g(x) = \frac{1}{x - 2} + 3$

d) base function: $f(x) = \sqrt{x}$; transformed function: $g(x) = \sqrt{x - 1} + 4$

13. a) domain $\{x \in \mathbb{R}, x \geq 0\}$, the number of units of the product; range $\{y \in \mathbb{R}, y \geq 400\}$, the cost associated with producing x number of units

b) $g(x) = \sqrt{x - 8} + 400$

c) translate right 8 units

d) domain $\{x \in \mathbb{R}, x \geq 8\}$, range $\{y \in \mathbb{R}, y \geq 400\}$

14. a) translate 6 units left and 5 units up

$f(x)$	$g(x) = f(x + 6) + 5$
$f(x) = x$	$g(x) = x + 11$
$f(x) = x^2$	$g(x) = (x + 6)^2 + 5$
$f(x) = \sqrt{x}$	$g(x) = \sqrt{x + 6} + 5$
$f(x) = \frac{1}{x}$	$g(x) = \frac{1}{x + 6} + 5$

b) translate 4 units right and 3 units down

$g(x)$	$h(x) = g(x - 4) - 3$
$g(x) = x + 11$	$h(x) = x + 4$
$g(x) = (x + 6)^2 + 5$	$h(x) = (x + 2)^2 + 2$
$g(x) = \sqrt{x + 6} + 5$	$h(x) = \sqrt{x + 2} + 2$
$g(x) = \frac{1}{x + 6} + 5$	$h(x) = \frac{1}{x + 2} + 2$

c) $p(x) = f(x + 2) + 2$; Answers may vary.

2.4 Reflections of Functions

1. a)

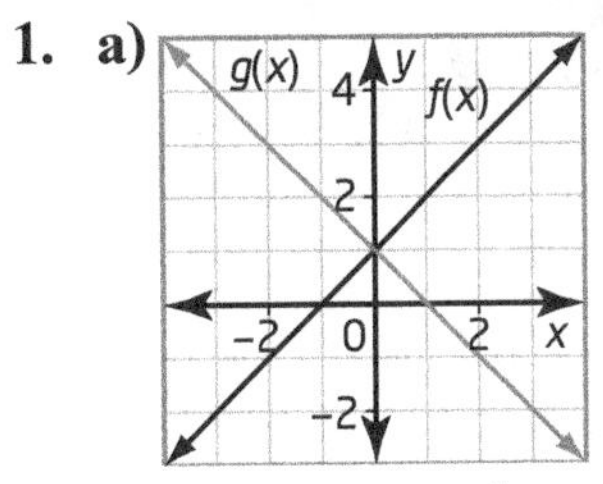

$f(x)$: domain $\{x \in \mathbb{R}\}$, range $\{y \in \mathbb{R}\}$; $g(x)$: domain $\{x \in \mathbb{R}\}$, range $\{y \in \mathbb{R}\}$

b)

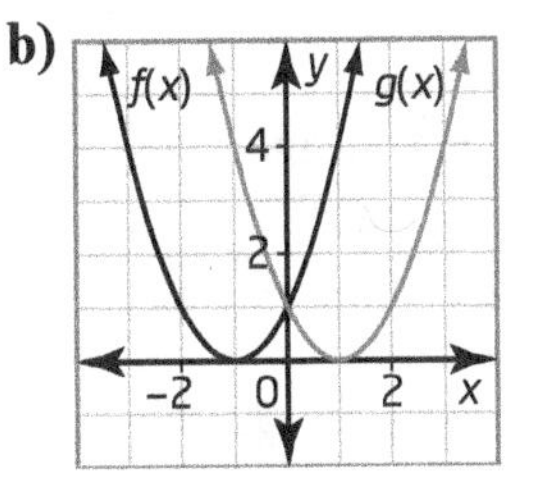

$f(x)$: domain $\{x \in \mathbb{R}\}$, range $\{y \in \mathbb{R}, y \geq 0\}$; $g(x)$: domain $\{x \in \mathbb{R}\}$, range $\{y \in \mathbb{R}, y \geq 0\}$

c)

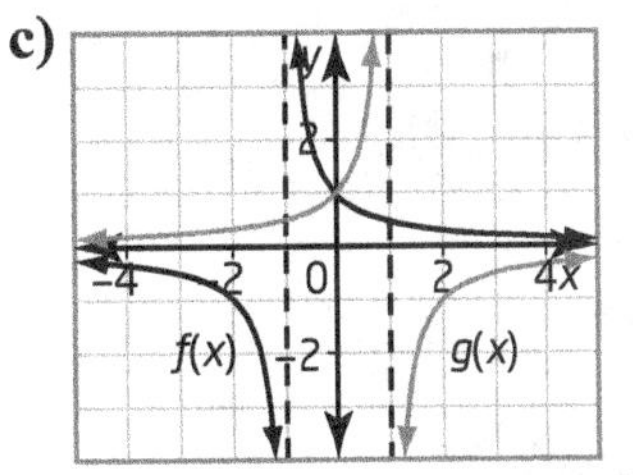

$f(x)$: domain $\{x \in \mathbb{R}, x \neq -1\}$, range $\{y \in \mathbb{R}, y \neq 0\}$; $g(x)$: domain $\{x \in \mathbb{R}, x \neq 1\}$, range $\{y \in \mathbb{R}, y \neq 0\}$

d)

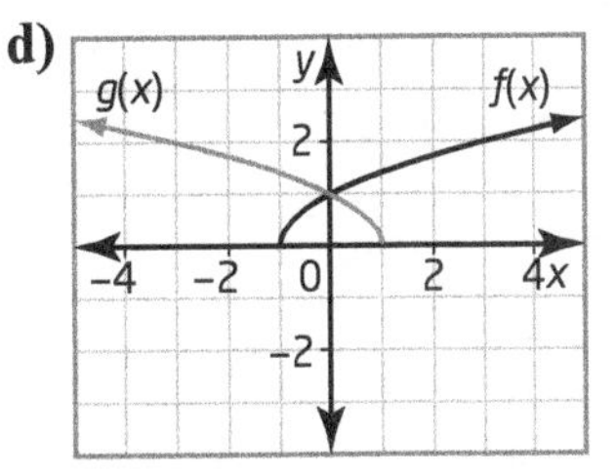

$f(x)$: domain $\{x \in \mathbb{R}, x \geq -1\}$, range $\{y \in \mathbb{R}, y \geq 0\}$; $g(x)$: domain $\{x \in \mathbb{R}, x \leq 1\}$, range $\{y \in \mathbb{R}, y \geq 0\}$

e)

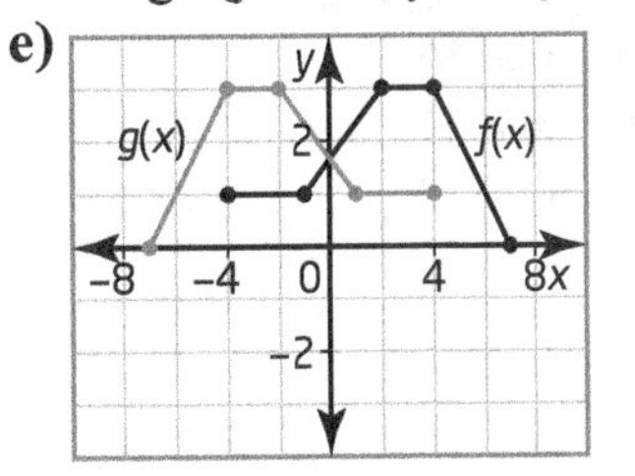

$f(x)$: domain $\{x \in \mathbb{R}, -4 \leq x \leq 7\}$,
range $\{y \in \mathbb{R}, 0 \leq y \leq 3\}$;
$g(x)$: domain $\{x \in \mathbb{R}, -7 \leq x \leq 4\}$,
range $\{y \in \mathbb{R}, 0 \leq y \leq 3\}$

2. a)

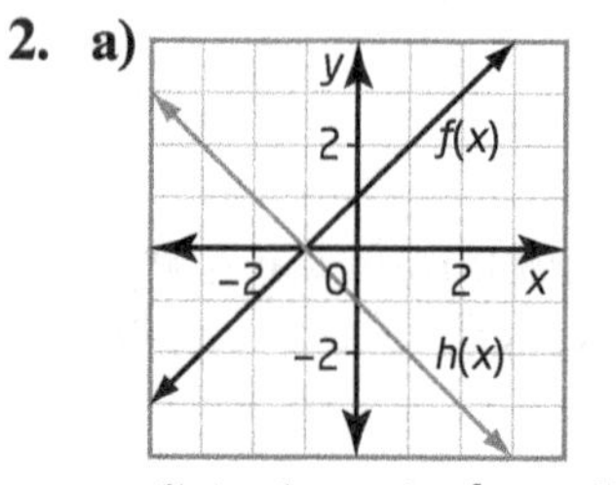

$f(x)$: domain $\{x \in \mathbb{R}\}$, range $\{y \in \mathbb{R}\}$;
$h(x)$: domain $\{x \in \mathbb{R}\}$, range $\{y \in \mathbb{R}\}$

b)

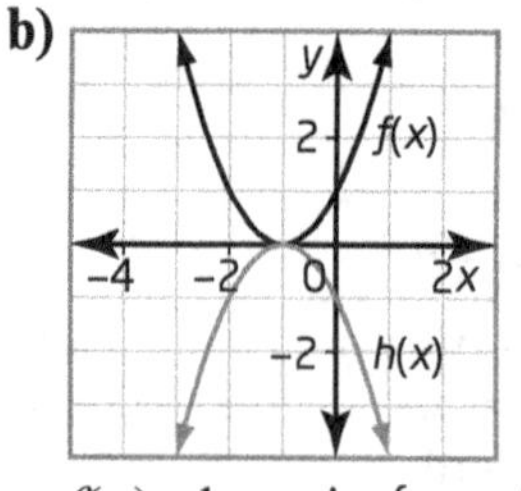

$f(x)$: domain $\{x \in \mathbb{R}\}$,
range $\{y \in \mathbb{R}, y \geq 0\}$;
$h(x)$: domain $\{x \in \mathbb{R}\}$,
range $\{y \in \mathbb{R}, y \leq 0\}$

c)

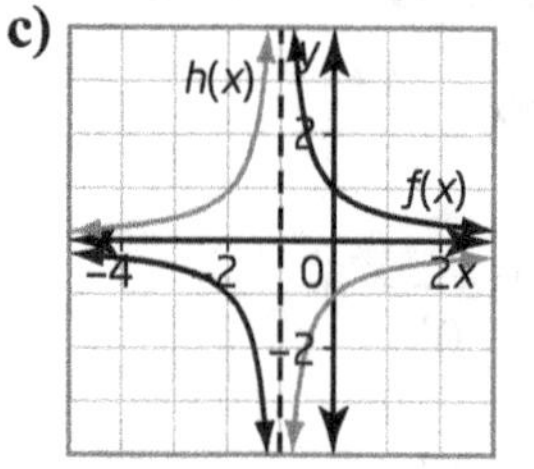

$f(x)$: domain $\{x \in \mathbb{R}, x \neq -1\}$,
range $\{y \in \mathbb{R}, y \neq 0\}$;
$h(x)$: domain $\{x \in \mathbb{R}, x \neq -1\}$,
range $\{y \in \mathbb{R}, y \neq 0\}$

d)

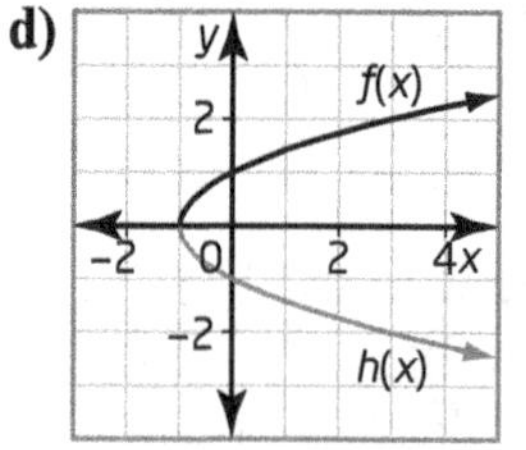

$f(x)$: domain $\{x \in \mathbb{R}, x \geq -1\}$,
range $\{y \in \mathbb{R}, y \geq 0\}$;
$h(x)$: domain $\{x \in \mathbb{R}, x \geq -1\}$,
range $\{y \in \mathbb{R}, y \leq 0\}$

e)

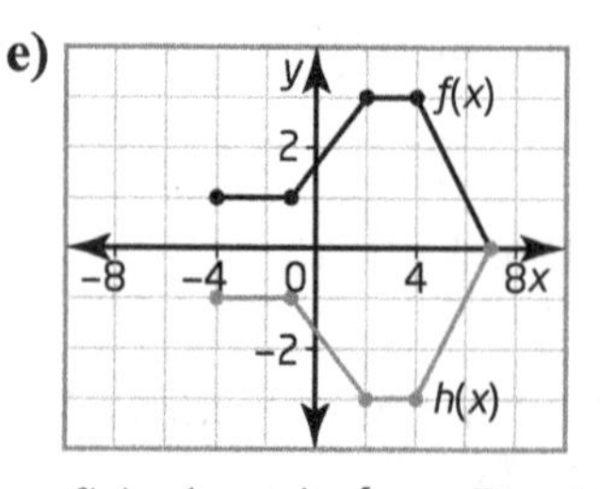

$f(x)$: domain $\{x \in \mathbb{R}, -4 \leq x \leq 7\}$,
range $\{y \in \mathbb{R}, 0 \leq y \leq 3\}$;
$h(x)$: domain $\{x \in \mathbb{R}, -4 \leq x \leq 7\}$,
range $\{y \in \mathbb{R}, -3 \leq y \leq 0\}$

3. A reflection in the x-axis is represented by $k(x) = -f(-x)$.

a)

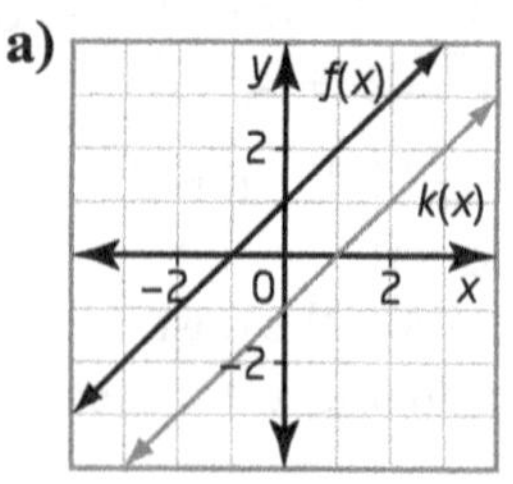

$f(x)$: domain $\{x \in \mathbb{R}\}$, range $\{y \in \mathbb{R}\}$;
$k(x)$: domain $\{x \in \mathbb{R}\}$, range $\{y \in \mathbb{R}\}$

b)

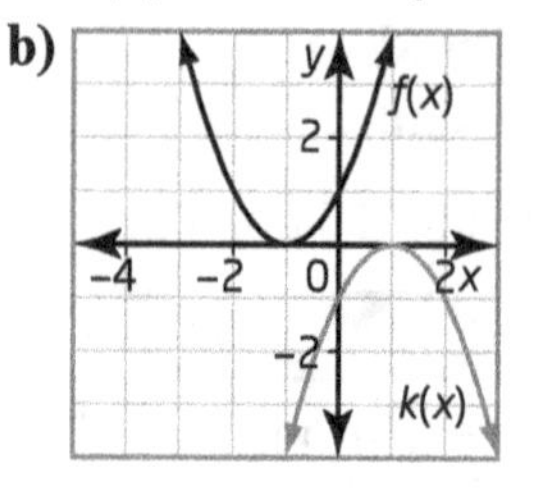

$f(x)$: domain $\{x \in \mathbb{R}\}$,
range $\{y \in \mathbb{R}, y \geq 0\}$;
$k(x)$: domain $\{x \in \mathbb{R}\}$,
range $\{y \in \mathbb{R}, y \leq 0\}$

c)

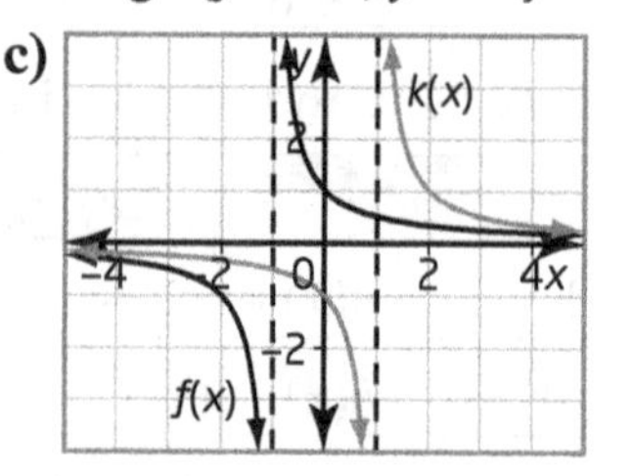

$f(x)$: domain $\{x \in \mathbb{R}, x \neq -1\}$,
range $\{y \in \mathbb{R}, y \neq 0\}$;
$k(x)$: domain $\{x \in \mathbb{R}, x \neq 1\}$,
range $\{y \in \mathbb{R}, y \neq 0\}$

d)

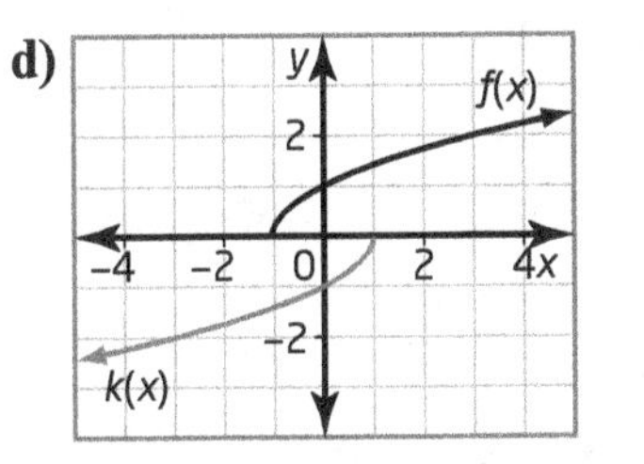

$f(x)$: domain $\{x \in \mathbb{R}, x \geq -1\}$, range $\{y \in \mathbb{R}, y \geq 0\}$;
$k(x)$: domain $\{x \in \mathbb{R}, x \leq 1\}$, range $\{y \in \mathbb{R}, y \leq 0\}$

e)

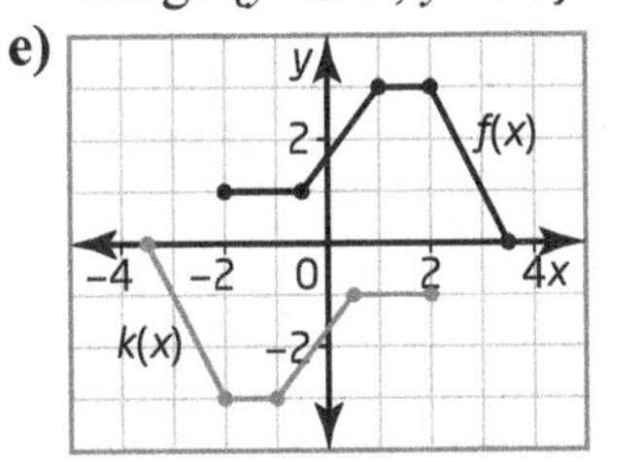

$f(x)$: domain $\{x \in \mathbb{R}, -4 \leq x \leq 7\}$, range $\{y \in \mathbb{R}, 0 \leq y \leq 3\}$;
$k(x)$: domain $\{x \in \mathbb{R}, -7 \leq x \leq 4\}$, range $\{y \in \mathbb{R}, -3 \leq y \leq 0\}$

4. a) $g(x) = -\sqrt{x-21} - 9$
b) $g(x) = (-x + 8)^2 - 17$
c) $g(x) = -(x + 1)^2 - 11$
d) $f(x) = \dfrac{1}{x-6} + 5$

Since $g(x) = -f(-x)$, replace x with $-x$ in $f(x)$ and multiply $f(x)$ by -1.

$g(x) = -\left[\dfrac{1}{(-x)-6} + 5\right]$

$= -\left[\dfrac{1}{-x-6} + 5\right]$

$= -\left[\dfrac{1}{-(x+6)} + 5\right]$ Common factor -1 in the denominator.

$= -\dfrac{1}{-(x+6)} - 5$ Multiply each term in the brackets by -1.

$= \dfrac{1}{x+6} - 5$ Simplify.

Therefore, $g(x) = \dfrac{1}{x+6} - 5$.

e) $g(x) = -\sqrt{-x+4} + 19$
f) $g(x) = \dfrac{1}{8-x} - 3$
g) $g(x) = x - 18$

5. a) $g(x) = f(-x)$; reflection in y-axis
b) $g(x) = -f(x)$; reflection in x-axis
c) $g(x) = -f(-x)$; reflection in x- and y-axes

6. a) i) (0, 8)
ii) (−4, 0) and (−2, 0)
iii) There are no invariant points.
b) Answers may vary. Sample answer: The graph of $y = ax^2$, $\{a \in \mathbb{R}, a \neq 0\}$, will have (0, 0) as an invariant point under each type of reflection.

7. a) No
b) Yes; $-f(x)$
c) Yes; $f(-x)$
d) Yes; $-f(-x)$
e) No
f) Yes; $f(-x)$

8. a) Use a graphing calculator.

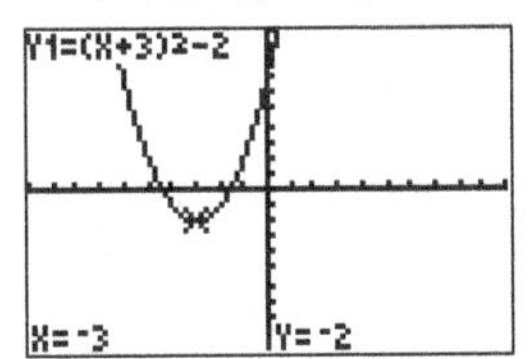

b) $g(x) = f(-x)$
$g(x) = (-x + 3)^2 - 2$

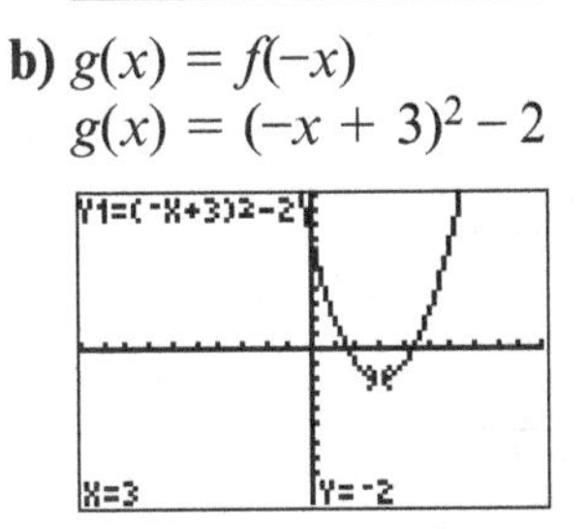

c) translate $f(x)$ 6 units to the right
d) $f(x - 6) = (x + 3 - 6)^2 - 2$
$= (x - 3)^2 - 2$
$g(x) = (-x + 3)^2 - 2$ Common factor -1.
$= [-1(x - 3)]^2 - 2$
$= (-1)^2(x - 3)^2 - 2$ Apply the laws of exponents for powers.
$= (x - 3)^2 - 2$
$= f(x - 6)$

A reflection of $f(x)$ in the y-axis is equivalent to a translation of 6 units right, $f(x - 6)$.

e) This would not be true for reflections in the x-axis because the direction of opening of the parabola would change, whereas translations do not change the direction of opening.
f) This would work for functions that have a vertical line as axis of symmetry. In this case reflection in the y-axis can

be obtained by applying a translation. For example, the quadratic function in part a) has a vertical line that passes through the vertex (–3, –2) as an axis of symmetry. A cubic function such as $f(x) = (x + 3)^3 - 2$ does not have a vertical line of symmetry, and so a reflection in the y-axis cannot be expressed as a translation.

9. a) i) $f(x) = \frac{1}{x}$

ii) $f(x) = \sqrt{x}$

b) i) translate 9 units right and 4 units up

ii) translate 5 units left and 7 units down

c) i) $k(x) = \frac{1}{9 - x} - 4$; $p(x) = \frac{-1}{x + 9} + 4$; $q(x) = \frac{1}{x + 9} - 4$

ii) $k(x) = -\sqrt{x + 5} + 7$; $p(x) = \sqrt{-x + 5} - 7$; $q(x) = -\sqrt{-x + 5} + 7$

10. a) i) $g(x) = \sqrt{-(x + 2)}$

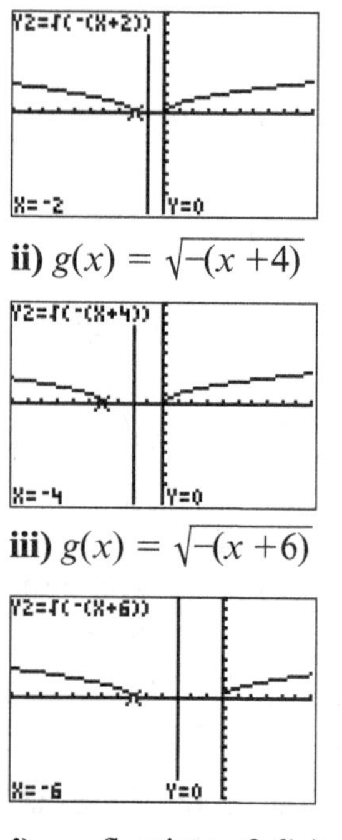

ii) $g(x) = \sqrt{-(x + 4)}$

iii) $g(x) = \sqrt{-(x + 6)}$

b) i) a reflection of $f(x) = \sqrt{x}$ in the y-axis and a translation of 2 units left

ii) a reflection of $f(x) = \sqrt{x}$ in the y-axis and a translation of 4 units left

iii) a reflection of $f(x) = \sqrt{x}$ in the y-axis and a translation of 6 units left

c) Yes; explanations may vary; $g(x) = \sqrt{-(x - 2a)}$

11. a) $f(-x) = \sqrt{16 - x^2}$; $f(-x) = -\sqrt{16 - x^2}$; $-f(-x) = -\sqrt{16 - x^2}$;
$f(x) = f(-x)$ and $-f(x) = -f(-x)$ are equivalent

b) invariant points: (–4, 0) and (4, 0)

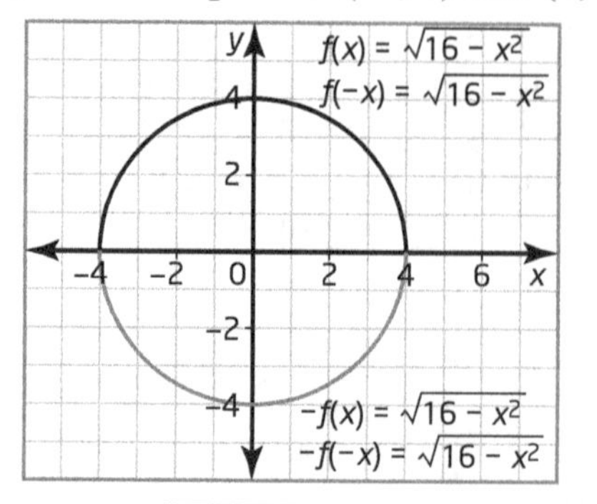

c) $f(x) = \sqrt{16 - x^2}$ and $f(-x) = -\sqrt{16 - x^2}$:
domain $\{x \in \mathbb{R}, -4 \le x \le 4\}$,
range $\{y \in \mathbb{R}, 0 \le y \le 4\}$
$-f(x) = -\sqrt{16 - x^2}$ and $-f(-x) = -\sqrt{16 - x^2}$:
domain $\{x \in \mathbb{R}, -4 \le x \le 4\}$,
range $\{y \in \mathbb{R}, -4 \le y \le 0\}$

12. a) All points are invariant under each reflection.

b) only true for circles with centre (0, 0)

2.5 Stretches of Functions

1. a)

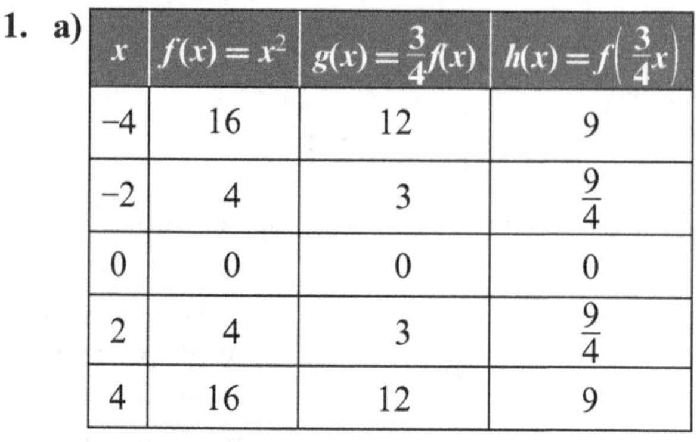

x	$f(x) = x^2$	$g(x) = \frac{3}{4}f(x)$	$h(x) = f\left(\frac{3}{4}x\right)$
–4	16	12	9
–2	4	3	$\frac{9}{4}$
0	0	0	0
2	4	3	$\frac{9}{4}$
4	16	12	9

b)

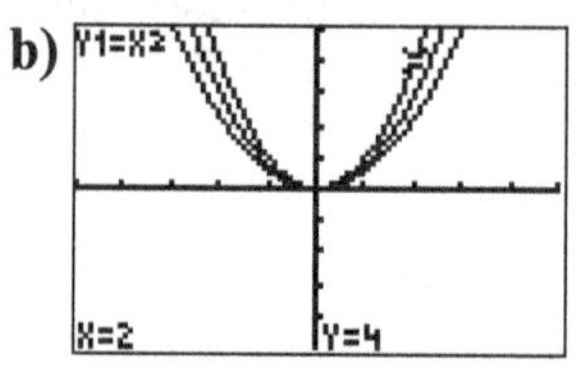

c) $g(x)$ represents a vertical compression of $f(x)$ by a factor of $\frac{3}{4}$; $h(x)$ represents a horizontal stretch of $f(x)$ by a factor of $\frac{4}{3}$

2. a) b) c) d)

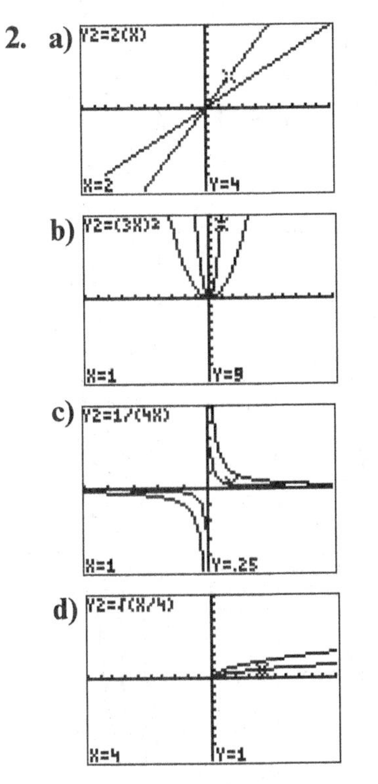

3. a) $a = 8$; $g(x)$ is a vertical stretch by a factor of 8 of $f(x)$
   b) $k = 6$; $g(x)$ is a horizontal compression by a factor of $\frac{1}{6}$ of $f(x)$
   c) $a = \frac{2}{3}$; $g(x)$ is a vertical compression by a factor of $\frac{2}{3}$ of $f(x)$
   d) $k = \frac{1}{9}$; $g(x)$ is a horizontal stretch by a factor of 9 of $f(x)$

4. a) $g(x)$ is a vertical stretch by a factor of 12 of $f(x) = x$

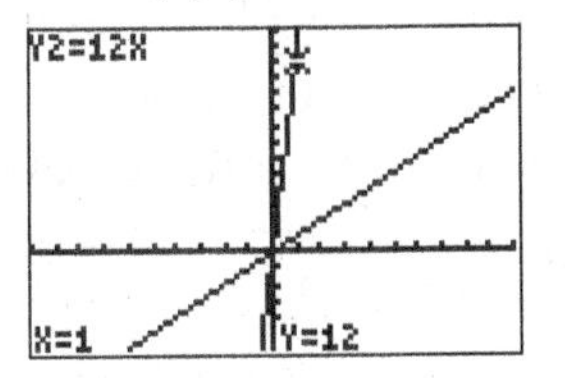

   b) $g(x)$ is a horizontal compression by a factor of $\frac{1}{4}$ of $f(x) = x^2$

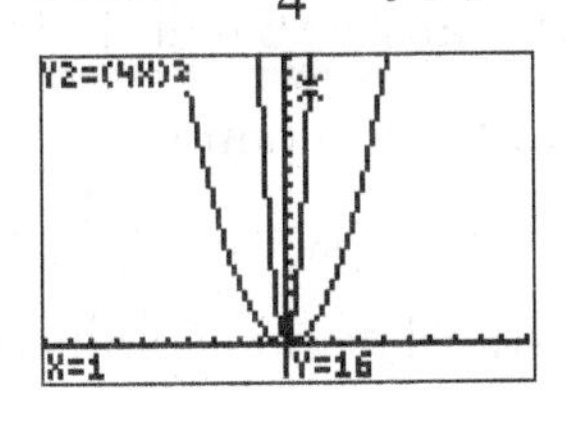

   c) $g(x)$ is a horizontal stretch by a factor of 6 of $f(x) = \sqrt{x}$

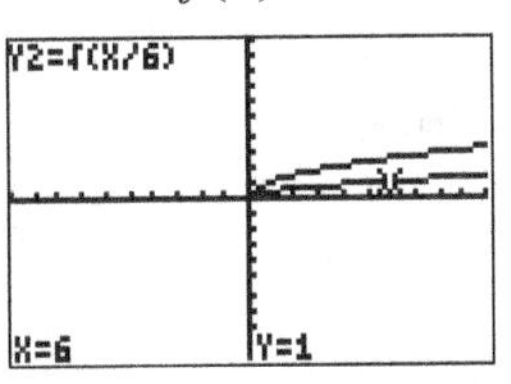

   d) $g(x)$ is a vertical stretch by a factor of 7 of $f(x) = \frac{1}{x}$

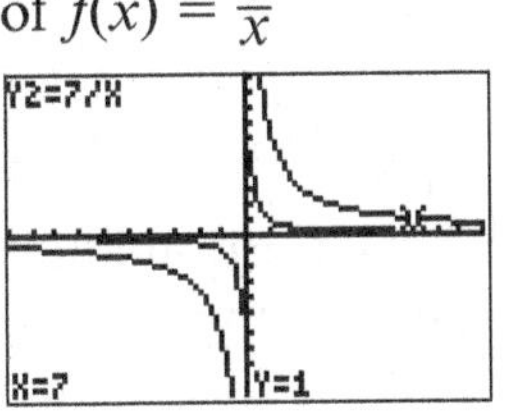

   e) $g(x)$ is a horizontal compression by a factor of $\frac{1}{25}$ of $f(x) = \sqrt{x}$

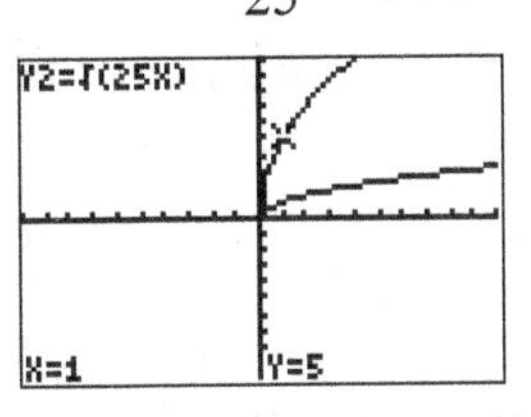

   f) $g(x)$ is a vertical compression by a factor of $\frac{1}{8}$ of $f(x) = x$

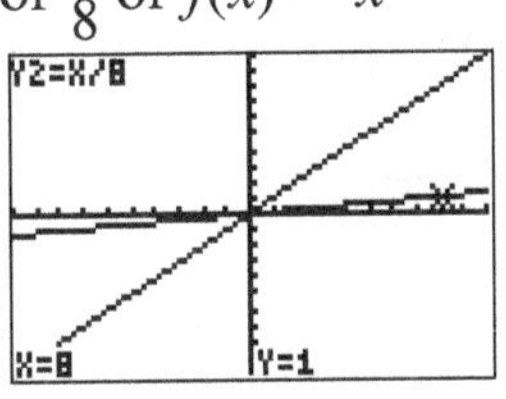

5. a) $g(x) = 2x^2$

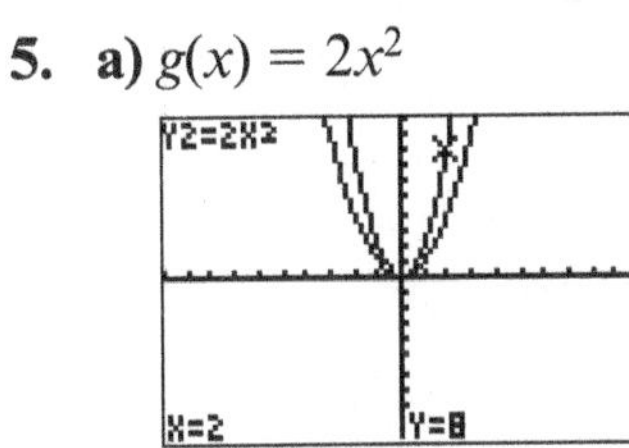

   b) $g(x) = \sqrt{\frac{3}{2}x}$

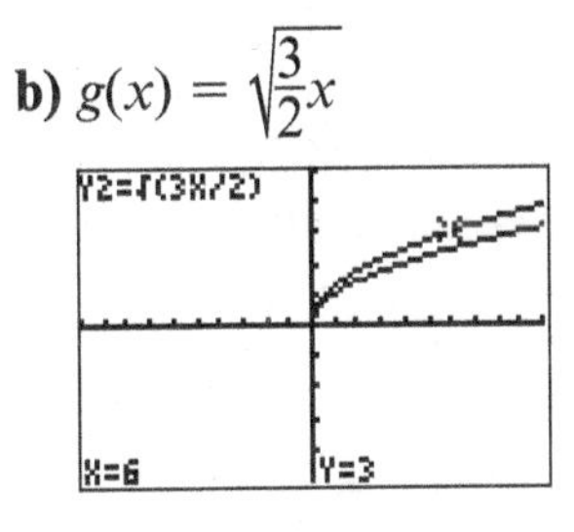

c) $g(x) = \frac{2}{x}$

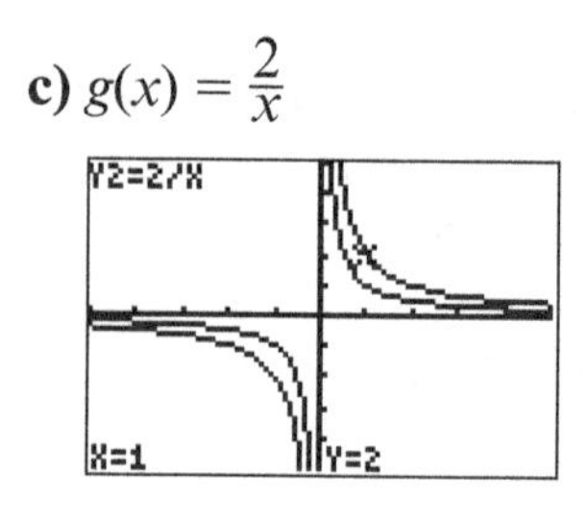

6. a) The base function is $f(t) = t^2$.
   b) vertical stretch by a factor of $\frac{a}{2}$
   c) Earth: $d(t) = 4.9t^2$;
      Neptune: $d(t) = 5.7t^2$;
      Mercury: $d(t) = 1.8t^2$
   d) For all three planets, the domain is $\{t \in \mathbb{R}, t \geq 0\}$ and the range is $\{d \in \mathbb{R}, d \geq 0\}$.
7. a) compress $f(x)$ horizontally by a factor of $\frac{1}{8}$; $g(x) = \sqrt{8x}$
   b) stretch $f(x)$ vertically by a factor of 7; $g(x) = \frac{7}{x}$
8. a) $g(x) = 2\sqrt{25 - x^2}$;
   domain $\{x \in \mathbb{R}, -5 \leq x \leq 5\}$,
   range $\{y \in \mathbb{R}, 0 \leq x \leq 10\}$

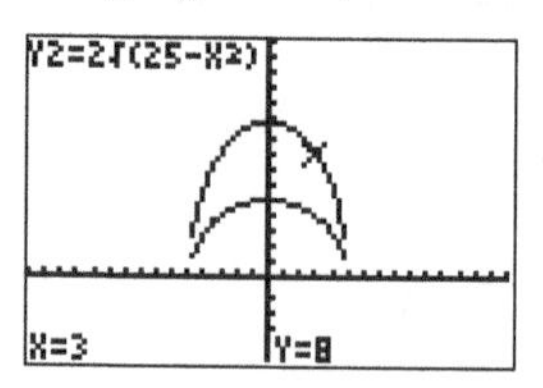

   b) $g(x) = \sqrt{25 - 4x^2}$;
   domain $\{x \in \mathbb{R}, -2.5 \leq x \leq 2.5\}$,
   range $\{y \in \mathbb{R}, 0 \leq x \leq 5\}$

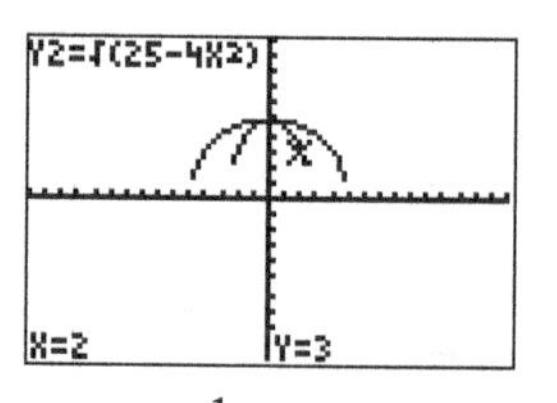

   c) $g(x) = \frac{1}{2}\sqrt{25 - x^2}$;
   domain $\{x \in \mathbb{R}, -5 \leq x \leq 5\}$,
   range $\{y \in \mathbb{R}, 0 \leq x \leq 2.5\}$

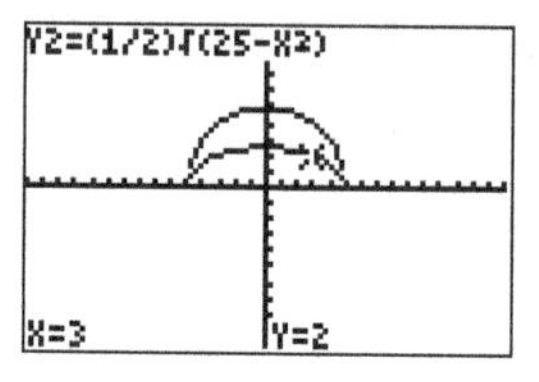

   d) $g(x) = \sqrt{25 - \frac{1}{4}x^2}$;
   domain $\{x \in \mathbb{R}, -10 \leq x \leq 10\}$,
   range $\{y \in \mathbb{R}, 0 \leq y \leq 5\}$

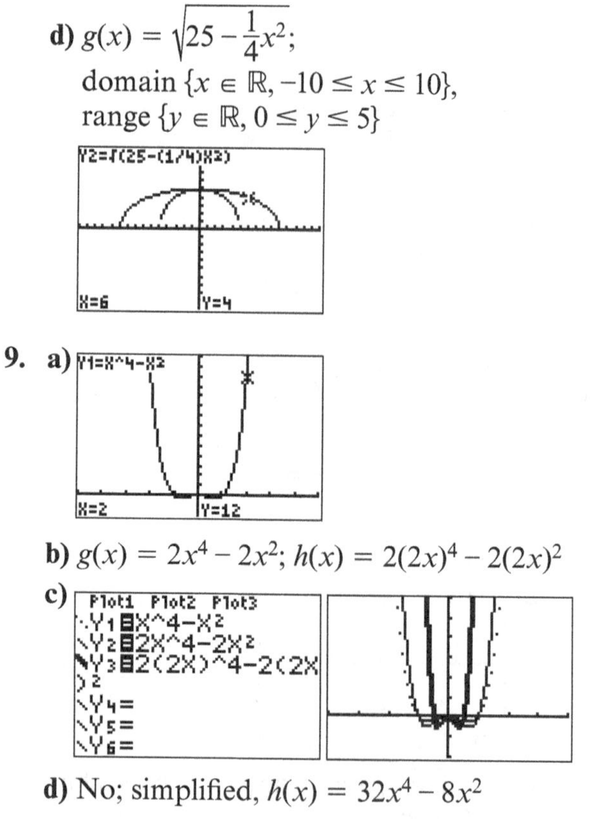

9. a) (graph)
   b) $g(x) = 2x^4 - 2x^2$; $h(x) = 2(2x)^4 - 2(2x)^2$
   c) (screens)
   d) No; simplified, $h(x) = 32x^4 - 8x^2$
10. The value of the parameter c is 18 in both $f(x)$ and $g(x)$.
    In $g(x)$, the term $-10x^2$ may be written as follows:
    $$-10x^2 = -(0.4 \times 25x^2)$$
    $$= -0.4(25x^2)$$
    $$= -0.4(5x)^2$$
    So $g(x) = f(5x)$,
    since $f(5x) = -0.4(5x)^2 + 18$.
    $$f(5x) = -0.4(25x^2) + 18$$
    $$= -10x^2 + 18$$
    To obtain the graph of $g(x)$, apply a horizontal compression by a factor of $\frac{1}{5}$ to the graph of $f(x)$.

2.6 Combinations of Transformations

1. a) $a = 3$, $d = 5$; vertically stretch $f(x)$ by a factor of 3, then translate 5 units right
   b) $a = \frac{1}{4}$, $c = 4$; vertically compress $f(x)$ by a factor of $\frac{1}{4}$, then translate 4 units up
   c) $d = -6$, $c = 2$; translate $f(x)$ 6 units left and 2 units up

d) $k = \frac{1}{3}$, $c = 7$; horizontally stretch $f(x)$ by a factor of 3, then translate 7 units up

e) $k = 2$, $c = -8$; horizontally compress $f(x)$ by a factor of $\frac{1}{2}$, then translate down 8 units

f) $a = 5$, $c = -3$; vertically stretch $f(x)$ by a factor of 5, then translate down 3 units

2. a) $a = 4$, $k = 3$, $c = -2$; vertically stretch by a factor of 4, horizontally compress by a factor of $\frac{1}{3}$, and then translate 2 units down

b) $a = -5$, $c = 6$; vertically stretch by a factor of 5, reflect in the x-axis, and then translate 6 units up

c) $a = \frac{1}{3}$, $d = 8$, $c = 1$; vertically compress by a factor of $\frac{1}{3}$, then translate 8 units right and 1 unit up

d) $k = -2$, $c = 6$; horizontally compress by a factor of $\frac{1}{2}$, reflect in the y-axis, and then translate 6 units up

e) $a = -1$, $k = \frac{1}{4}$, $c = -1$; reflect in the x-axis, horizontally stretch by a factor of 4, and then translate 1 unit down

f) $a = \frac{2}{5}$, $k = 5$, $c = -7$; vertically compress by a factor of $\frac{2}{5}$, horizontally compress by a factor of $\frac{1}{5}$, and then translate 7 units down

3. a) vertically stretch by a factor of 2 and horizontally compress by a factor of $\frac{1}{4}$; $g(x) = 2\sqrt{4x}$

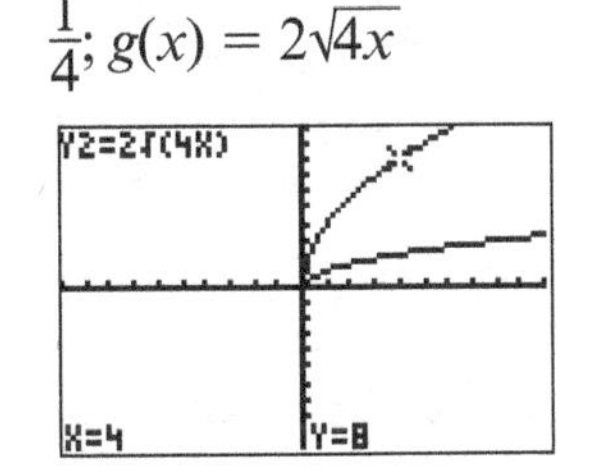

b) vertically stretch by a factor of 3, reflect in the x-axis, and then translate 1 unit right and 7 units up; $g(x) = \frac{-3}{x-1} + 7$

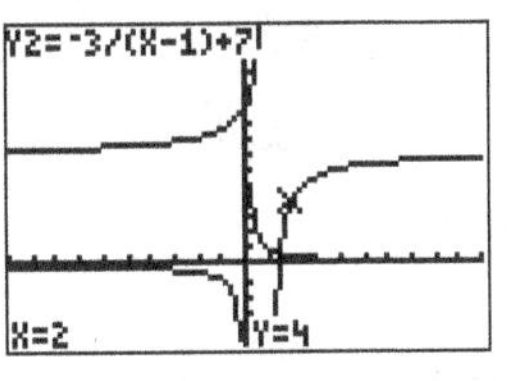

c) horizontally stretch by a factor of 2, then translate 1 unit left; $g(x) = \frac{1}{4}(x+1)^2$

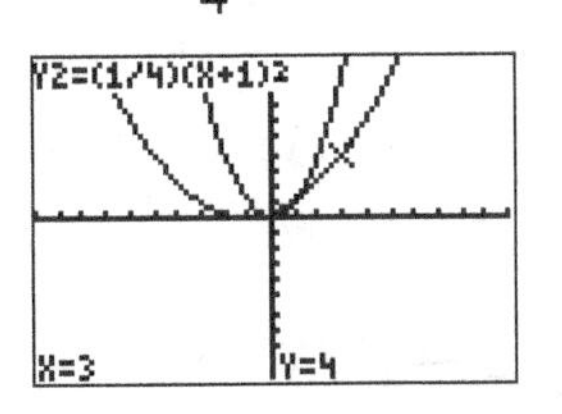

d) vertically stretch by a factor of 4, reflect in the x-axis, and then translate 6 units down; $g(x) = -4x - 6$

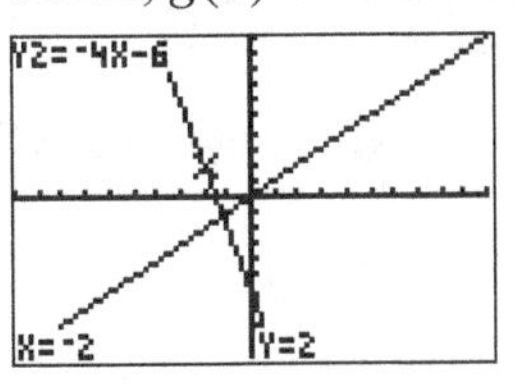

4. a) vertically compress by a factor of $\frac{1}{3}$, reflect in the x-axis, horizontally compress by a factor of $\frac{1}{3}$, and then translate 2 units left and 4 units down; $g(x) = -x - 6$

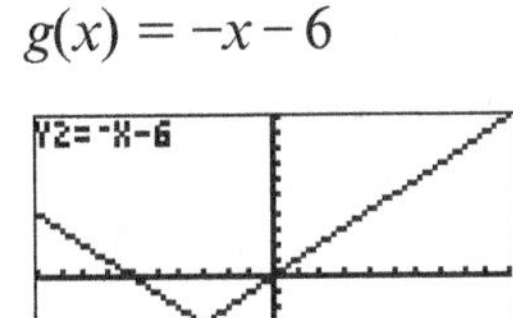

b) vertically stretch by a factor of 4, reflect in the x-axis, horizontally compress by a factor of $\frac{1}{2}$, and then translate 1 unit right and 6 units up; $g(x) = -16(x-1)^2 + 6$

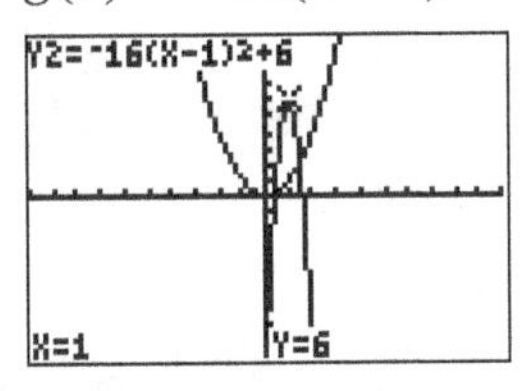

c) vertically compress by a factor of $\frac{1}{3}$, horizontally compress by a factor of

$\frac{1}{2}$, and then translate 5 units left and 4 units up; $g(x) = \frac{1}{3}\sqrt{2(x + 5)} + 4$

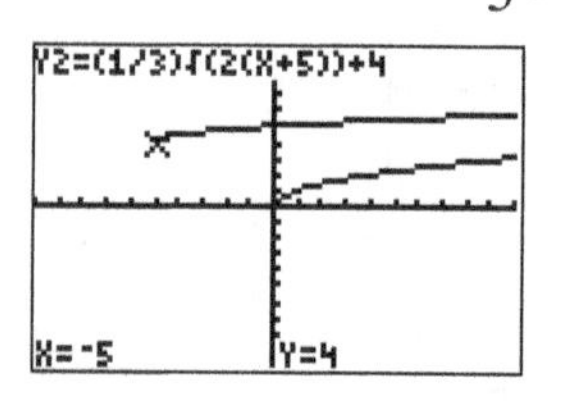

d) vertically stretch by a factor of 5, reflect in the y-axis, and then translate 1 unit right and 2 units up; $g(x) = \frac{5}{1 - x} + 2$

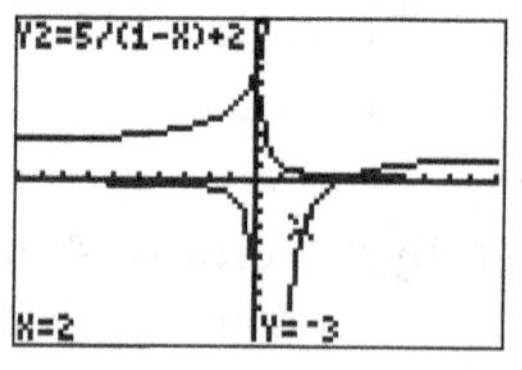

5. a) $f(x) = x$; $f(x)$: domain $\{x \in \mathbb{R}\}$, range $\{y \in \mathbb{R}\}$;
$g(x)$: domain $\{x \in \mathbb{R}\}$, range $\{y \in \mathbb{R}\}$

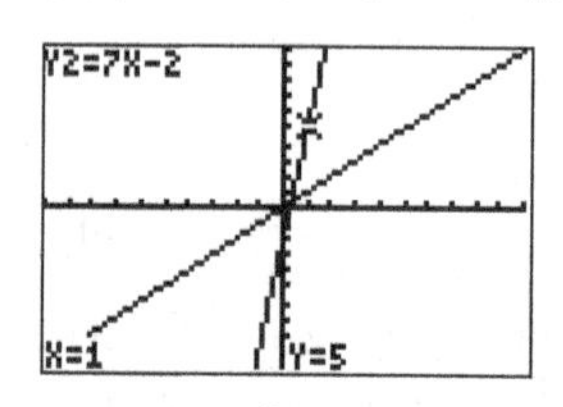

b) $f(x) = x^2$; $f(x)$: domain $\{x \in \mathbb{R}\}$, range $\{y \in \mathbb{R}, y \geq 0\}$;
$g(x)$: domain $\{x \in \mathbb{R}\}$, range $\{y \in \mathbb{R}, y \geq -3\}$

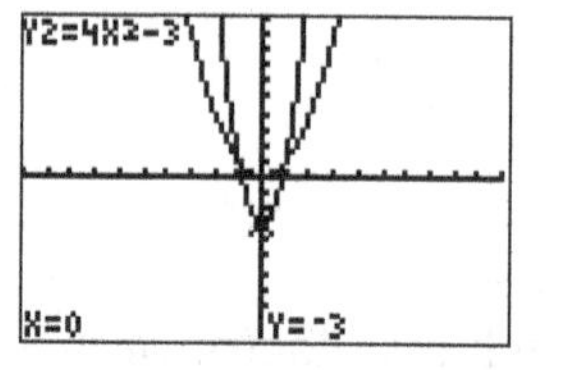

c) $f(x) = x^2$; $f(x)$: domain $\{x \in \mathbb{R}\}$, range $\{y \in \mathbb{R}, y \geq 0\}$;
$g(x)$: domain $\{x \in \mathbb{R}\}$, range $\{y \in \mathbb{R}, y \geq 0\}$

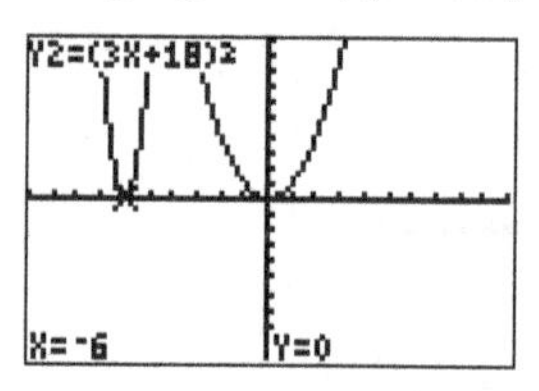

d) $f(x) = \sqrt{x}$; $f(x)$: domain $\{x \in \mathbb{R}, x \geq 0\}$, range $\{y \in \mathbb{R}, y \geq 0\}$;
$g(x)$: domain $\{x \in \mathbb{R}, x \geq 3\}$, range $\{y \in \mathbb{R}, y \geq 0\}$

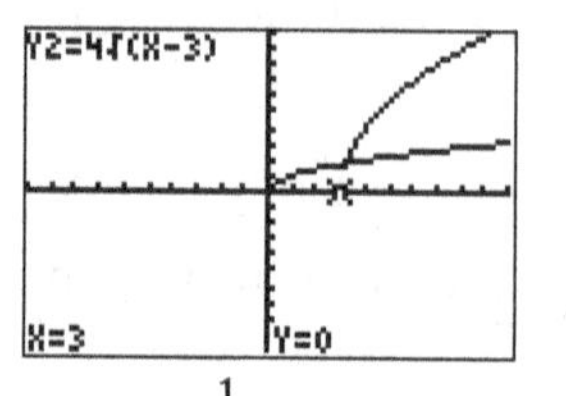

e) $f(x) = \frac{1}{x}$; $f(x)$: domain $\{x \in \mathbb{R}, x \neq 0\}$, range $\{y \in \mathbb{R}, y \neq 0\}$;
$g(x)$: domain $\{x \in \mathbb{R}, x \neq -9\}$, range $\{x \in \mathbb{R}, x \neq 0\}$

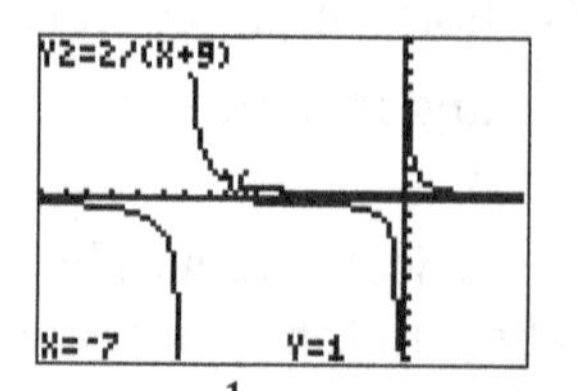

f) $f(x) = \frac{1}{x}$; $f(x)$: domain $\{x \in \mathbb{R}, x \neq 0\}$, range $\{y \in \mathbb{R}, y \neq 0\}$;
$g(x)$: domain $\{x \in \mathbb{R}, x \neq 4\}$, range $\{x \in \mathbb{R}, x \neq 6\}$

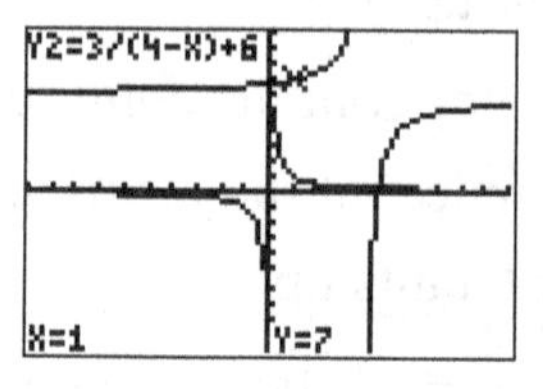

6.

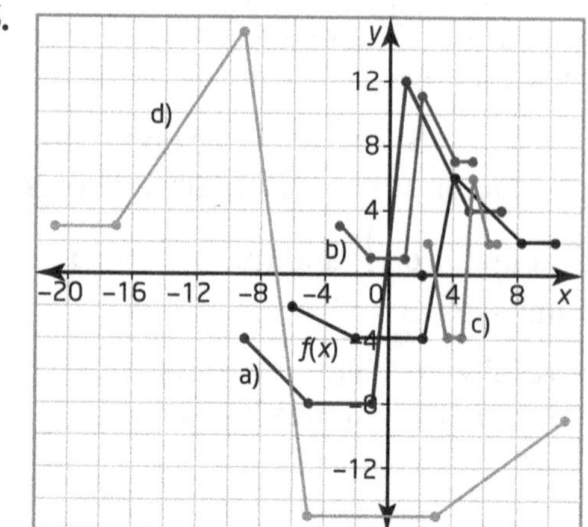

7. a) $y = \frac{2}{x + 4} - 3$; graph ii)

b) $y = \frac{1}{2}\sqrt{-x + 4} + 3$; graph iv)
The equation $y = \frac{1}{2}\sqrt{-x + 4} + 3$ may be expressed as $y = \frac{1}{2}\sqrt{-(x - 4)} + 3$.
This equation matches graph iv) because the base function for graph iv) is $f(x) = \sqrt{x}$. The graph of $f(x) = \sqrt{x}$ is reflected in the y-axis,

vertically compressed by a factor of $\frac{1}{2}$, and then translated right 4 units and up 3 units. The point (0, 4) satisfies the equation.

c) $y = 3\sqrt{x-2} + 1$; graph i)

d) $y = \left[\frac{1}{4}(x-5)\right]^2 + 2$; graph iii)

8. a) $y = -\frac{2}{x+3} + 1$; graph ii)

b) $y = 2\sqrt{-x+4} - 1$; graph i)

c) $y = \frac{4}{-x+2} + 1$; graph iv)

d) $y = \frac{1}{2}\sqrt{x+5} - \frac{5}{2}$; graph iii)

9. a) Since s is in the denominator, each time function is a reciprocal function, so the base function is $f(s) = \frac{1}{s}$.

b) In $t_1 = \frac{24}{s}$, $a = 24$, so t_1 is a vertical stretch by a factor of 24 of $f(s)$.

In $t_2 = \frac{18}{s-4}$, $a = 18$ and $d = 4$, so t_2 is a vertical stretch of $f(s)$ by a factor of 18 and a translation of 4 units right.

In $t_3 = \frac{36}{s+3}$, $a = 36$ and $d = -3$, so t_3 is a vertical stretch of $f(s)$ by a factor of 36 and a translation of 3 units left.

c)

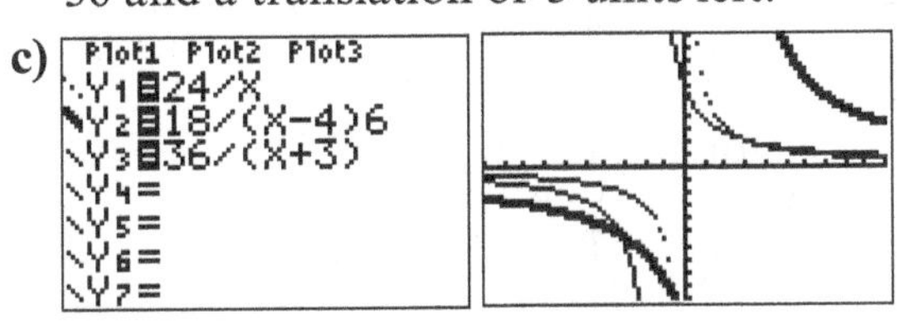

d) Substitute $s = 6$ in each time function.

$t_1 = \frac{24}{6}$
$= 4$ It will take Andrew and David 4 h to travel across the lake.

$t_2 = \frac{18}{6-4}$
$= 9$ It will take Andrew and David 9 h to travel up the river.

$t_3 = \frac{36}{6+3}$
$= 4$ It will take Andrew and David 4 h to travel down the river.

10. a) domain $\{t \in \mathbb{R}, t \geq 0\}$, range $\{V \in \mathbb{R}, 0 \leq V \leq 4000\}$

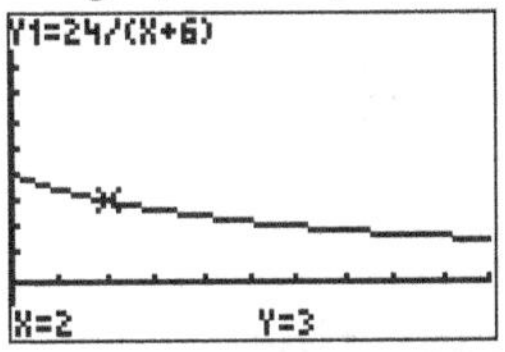

b) \$4000

c) i) \$3429

ii) \$2667

iii) \$1846

11. i)

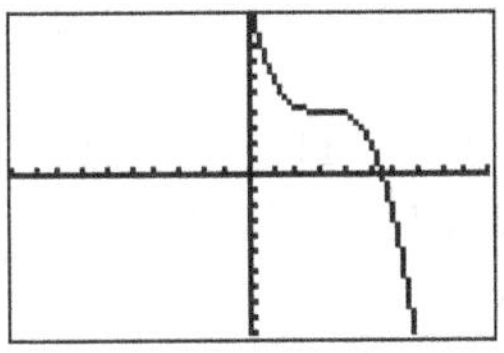

ii)

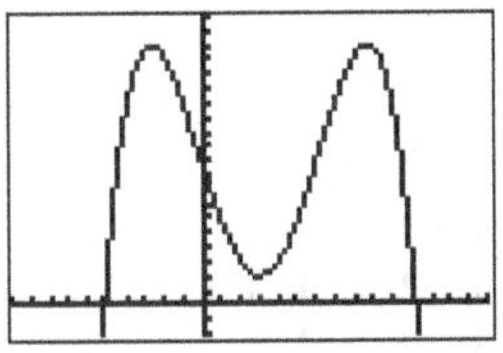

12. a)

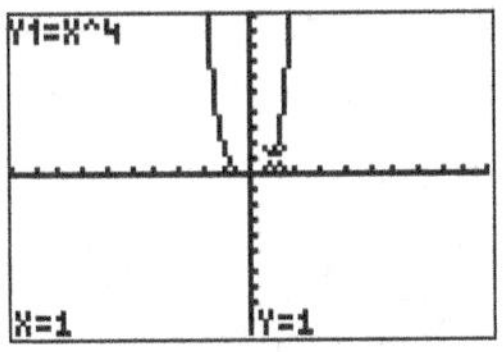

b) i) $g(x) = 4(-x+5)^4$

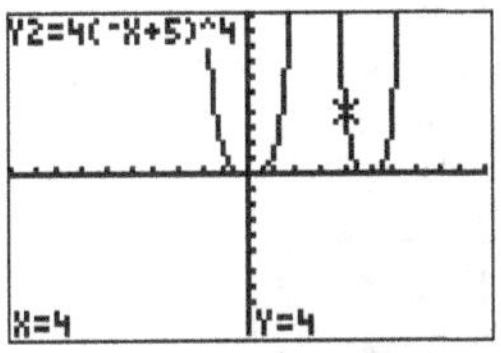

ii) $h(x) = -\frac{1}{256}(x-4)^4 + 3$

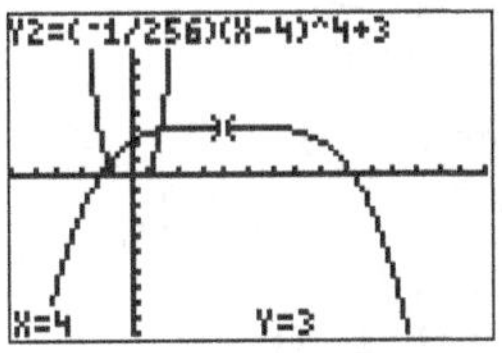

13. a) translate 3 units right and 5 units up

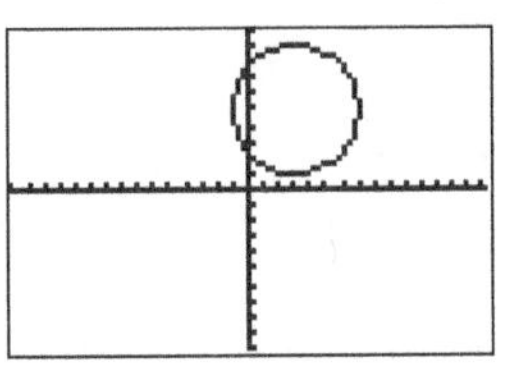

b) translate 2 units left and 7 units up

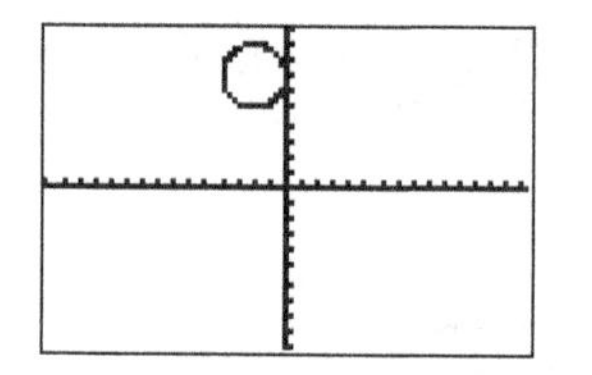

2.7 Inverse of a Function

1. a) $\{(6, 2), (1, 3), (-1, 4), (2, 5)\}$;
function: domain $\{2, 3, 4, 5\}$,
range $\{6, 1, -1, 2\}$;
inverse: domain $\{6, 1, -1, 2\}$,
range $\{2, 3, 4, 5\}$

b) $\{(7, -3), (5, -2), (-2, -1), (-6, 0)\}$;
function: domain $\{-3, -2, -1, 0\}$,
range $\{7, 5, -2, -6\}$;
inverse: domain $\{7, 5, -2, -6\}$,
range $\{-3, -2, -1, 0\}$

c)

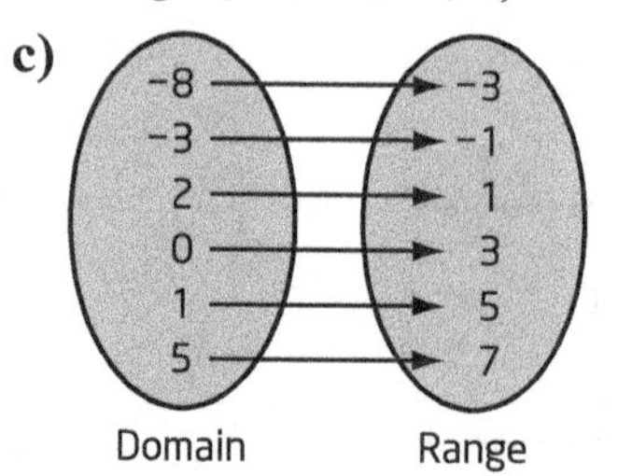

function: domain $\{-3, -1, 1, 3, 5, 7\}$,
range $\{-8, -3, -2, 0, 1, 5\}$;
inverse: domain $\{-8, -3, -2, 0, 1, 5\}$,
range $\{-3, -1, 1, 3, 5, 7\}$

d)

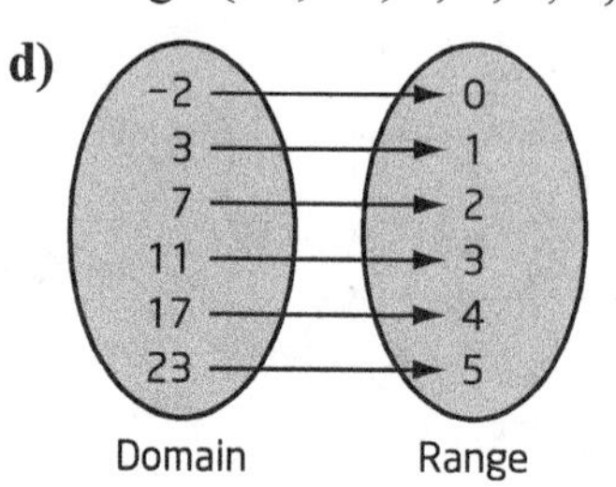

function: domain $\{0, 1, 2, 3, 4, 5\}$,
range $\{-2, 3, 7, 11, 17, 23\}$;
inverse: domain $\{-2, 3, 7, 11, 17, 23\}$,
range $\{0, 1, 2, 3, 4, 5\}$

2. a)

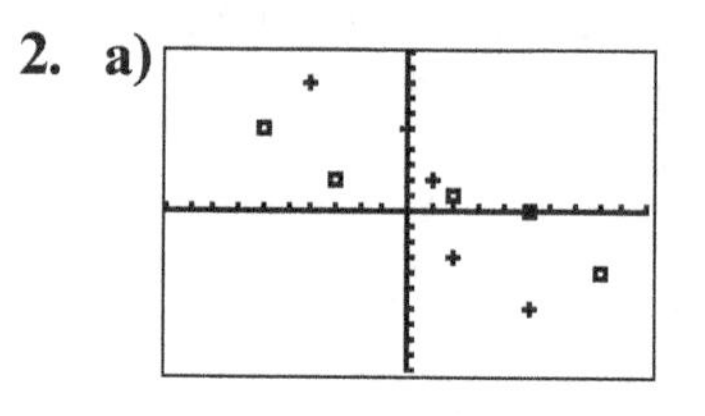

function: domain $\{-6, -3, 2, 5, 8\}$,
range $\{-4, 0, 1, 2, 5\}$;
inverse: domain $\{-4, 0, 1, 2, 5\}$,
range $\{-6, -3, 2, 5, 8\}$

b)

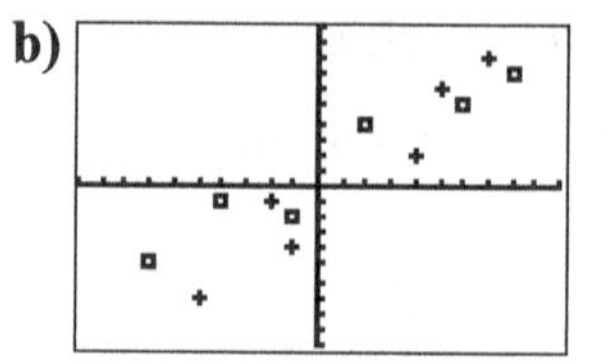

function: domain $\{-7, -4, -1, 2, 6, 8\}$,
range $\{-5, -1, -2, 4, 5, 7\}$;
inverse: domain $\{-5, -1, -2, 4, 5, 7\}$,
range $\{-7, -4, -1, 2, 6, 8\}$

3. a)

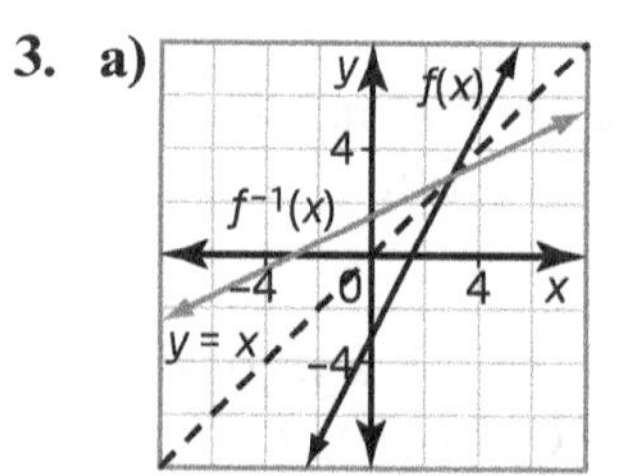

function

b)

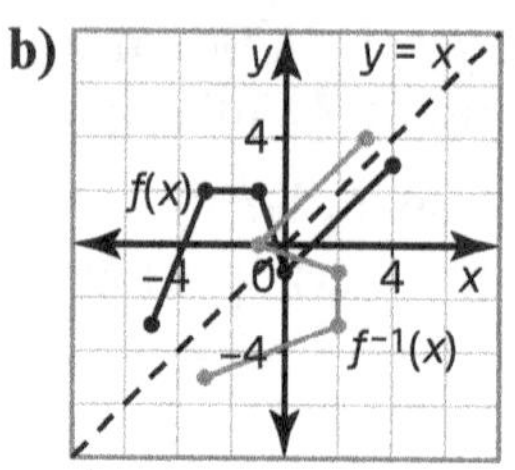

not a function

c)

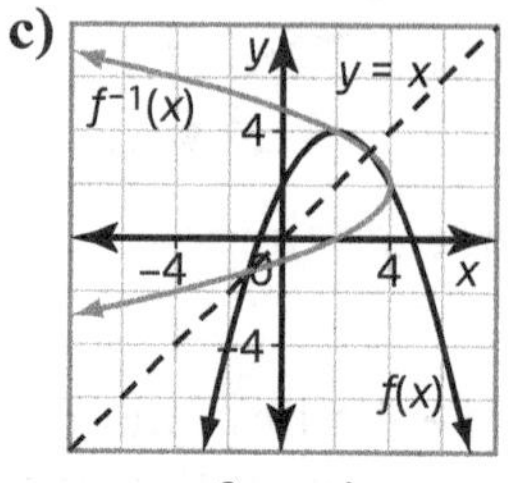

not a function

4. a) $f^{-1}(x) = \frac{x}{5}$

b) $f^{-1}(x) = \frac{x + 3}{4}$

c) $f^{-1}(x) = -x + 7$

d) $f^{-1}(x) = \frac{-3x + 1}{2}$

5. a) $f^{-1}(x) = \pm\sqrt{x - 5}$

b) $f^{-1}(x) = \pm\sqrt{\frac{x}{7}}$

c) $f^{-1}(x) = \pm\sqrt{x} - 3$

d) $f^{-1}(x) = \pm\sqrt{3(x + 4)}$

6. a) $f(x) = (x - 2)^2 - 1$
$f^{-1}(x) = 2 \pm\sqrt{x + 1}$
b) $f(x) = -(x - 7)^2 + 10$
$f^{-1}(x) = 7 \pm \sqrt{-x + 10}$
c) $f(x) = 2(x + 4)^2 - 2$
$f^{-1}(x) = -4 \pm \sqrt{\dfrac{x + 2}{2}}$
d) $f(x) = -3(x + 4)^2 - 52$
$f^{-1}(x) = -4 \pm \sqrt{\dfrac{-x - 52}{3}}$

7. a) i) $f^{-1}(x) = \dfrac{-x + 5}{4}$
ii)
iii) function
b) i) $f^{-1}(x) = 2x + 12$
ii)
iii) function
c) i) $f^{-1}(x) = 3 \pm \sqrt{x - 8}$
ii)
iii) not a function
d) i) $f^{-1}(x) = 8 \pm \sqrt{-x + 3}$
ii)
iii) not a function

8. a) domain $\{r \in \mathbb{R}, r \geq 0\}$,
range $\{S \in \mathbb{R}, S \geq 0\}$
b) $r(S) = \sqrt{\dfrac{S}{4\pi}}$; domain $\{S \in \mathbb{R}, S \geq 0\}$,
range $\{r \in \mathbb{R}, r \geq 0\}$

9. a) Let s represent Aubrey's weekly sales and let e represent her weekly earnings.
The equation that represents her weekly earnings is $e = 450 + 0.08s$, where 450 corresponds to the \$450 she earns each week and $0.08s$ represents 8% of her sales.
b) To find the inverse, solve the equation for s.
$$e = 450 + 0.08s$$
$$e - 450 = 0.08s$$
$$\frac{e - 450}{0.08} = s$$
$$s = 12.5e - 5625$$
c) The inverse represents Aubrey's weekly sales.
d) Substitute 1025 in s.
$$s = 12.5(1025) - 5625$$
$$= 7187.50$$
Aubrey's sales for the week were \$7187.50.

10. a) $u = 0.89c$
b) $c = 1.12u$; the value of the Canadian dollar in U.S. dollars
c) \$280.00

11. a) Since time must be positive, the domain is restricted to $t \geq 0$.
domain $\{t \in \mathbb{R}, t \geq 0\}$,
range $\{h \in \mathbb{R}, 0 \leq h \leq 100\}$

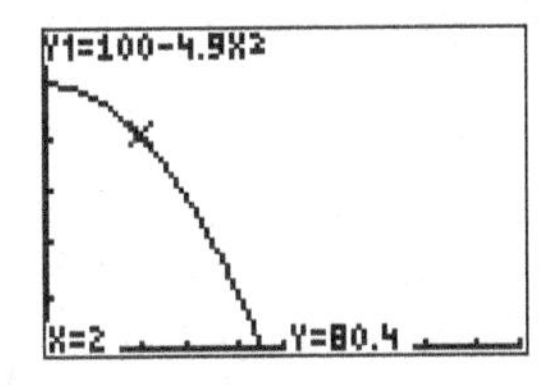

b) Isolate t to determine the inverse.
$$h = 100 - 4.9t^2$$
$$h - 100 = -4.9t^2$$
$$t^2 = \frac{100 - h}{4.9}$$
$$t = \sqrt{\frac{100 - h}{4.9}}$$
Time is positive, so ignore the negative root.

domain $\{h \in \mathbb{R}, 0 \leq h \leq 100\}$,
range $\{t \in \mathbb{R}, t \geq 0\}$

c) The inverse represents the time for an object to fall from a height of 100 m above the ground.

d) The object hits the ground when the height is 0 m. Substitute $h = 0$ in the inverse function and solve for t.

$t = \sqrt{\frac{100 - 0}{4.9}}$
$= 4.5$

The object hits the ground after 4.5 s.

12. a) Yes; $g(x)$ is a reflection of $f(x)$ in $y = x$
b) Yes; $g(x)$ is a reflection of $f(x)$ in $y = x$
c) No; $g(x)$ is a reflection of $f(x)$ in the x-axis

13. a) $f^{-1}(x) = \frac{x^2 + 5}{2}$
b) $f(x)$: domain $\left\{x \in \mathbb{R}, x \geq \frac{5}{2}\right\}$, range $\{y \in \mathbb{R}, y \geq 0\}$; $f^{-1}(x)$: domain $\{x \in \mathbb{R}, x \geq 0\}$, range $\left\{y \in \mathbb{R}, y \geq \frac{5}{2}\right\}$
c)

14. a) $f^{-1}(x) = \frac{2 + x}{3x}$
b) $f(x)$: domain $\left\{x \in \mathbb{R}, x \neq \frac{1}{3}\right\}$, range $\{y \in \mathbb{R}, y \neq 0\}$; $f^{-1}(x)$: domain $\{x \in \mathbb{R}, x \neq 0\}$, range $\left\{y \in \mathbb{R}, y \neq \frac{1}{3}\right\}$

15. a) $n(a) = \frac{360}{180 - a}$
b) function: domain $\{n \in \mathbb{N}, n \geq 3\}$, range $\{a \in \mathbb{R}, 60 \leq a < 180\}$; inverse: domain $\{a \in \mathbb{R}, 60 \leq a < 180\}$, range $\{n \in \mathbb{N}, n \geq 3\}$
c)

Chapter 2 Review

1. a) No
b) Yes
c) No

2. a) Yes; $x \neq \frac{1}{4}, x \neq 0$
b) No; $g(x) = \frac{2x + 1}{x}; x \neq 2, x \neq 0$

3. a) $\frac{1}{x + 2}; x \neq -8, x \neq -2$
b) $\frac{2x - 3}{x + 6}; x \neq -\frac{3}{4}, x \neq -6$

4. a) $24a^2b; a \neq 0, b \neq 0$
b) $\frac{5ab}{18c}; a \neq 0, b \neq 0, c \neq 0$
c) $2; x \neq -9, x \neq \frac{4}{3}$
d) $\frac{x - 8}{x + 4}; x \neq -4, x \neq -3, x \neq 5$
e) $-2; x \neq 4, x \neq 3$
f) $\frac{x + 8}{x - 8}; x \neq -3, x \neq 1, x \neq 8$

5. a) $\frac{19}{15x}; x \neq 0$
b) $\frac{7a + 4a - ab}{12ab^2}; a \neq 0, b \neq 0$
c) $\frac{2x^2 + 8x + 23}{(x - 1)(x + 2)}; x \neq -2, x \neq 1$
d) $\frac{-2x^2 + 13x}{(x - 3)(x - 4)}; x \neq 3, x \neq 4$
e) $\frac{4x^2 - 10x - 9}{(x - 3)(x + 3)}; x \neq -3, x \neq 3$
f) $\frac{-5}{(x + 2)}; x \neq -5, x \neq -2, x \neq 2$

6. a) $s(x) = x - 6$
b) $t(x) = x - 4$

7. i) a) $s(x) = (x + 2)^2 - 8$
b) $t(x) = (x - 5)^2 + 1$
ii) a) $s(x) = \sqrt{x + 2} - 8$
b) $t(x) = \sqrt{x - 5} + 1$
iii) a) $s(x) = \frac{1}{x + 2} - 8$
b) $t(x) = \frac{1}{x - 5} + 1$

8. a) base function: $f(x) = \frac{1}{x}$; transformed function: $g(x) = \frac{1}{x + 6} - 3$
b) base function: $f(x) = \sqrt{x}$; transformed function: $g(x) = \sqrt{x + 4} + 1$

9. a) No
b) Yes; $g(x) = f(-x)$

c) No
d) Yes; $g(x) = -f(x)$

10. a) $g(x) = -\sqrt{x-1} - 8$
b) $g(x) = -(x + 3)^2 - 10$
c) $g(x) = \frac{1}{x-7} + 2$

11. a) $a = 9$; vertical stretch by a factor of 9
b) $k = 3$; horizontal compression by a factor of $\frac{1}{3}$
c) $a = \frac{2}{5}$; vertical compression by a factor of $\frac{2}{5}$
d) $k = \frac{1}{7}$; horizontal stretch by a factor of 7

12. a) vertical stretch of $f(x) = x$ by a factor of 13

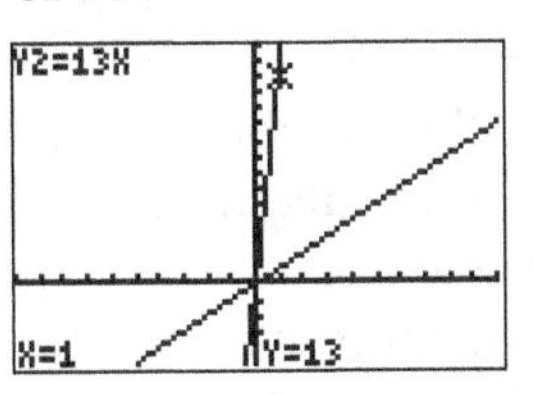

b) horizontal compression of $f(x) = x^2$ by a factor of $\frac{1}{5}$

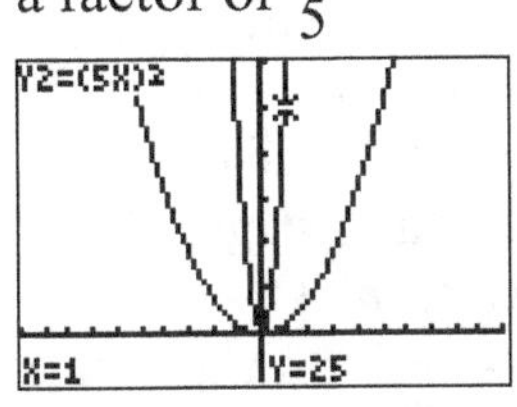

c) horizontal stretch of $f(x) = \sqrt{x}$ by a factor of 3

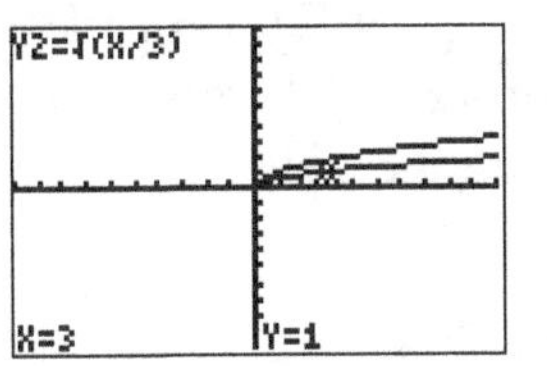

d) vertical stretch of $f(x) = \frac{1}{x}$ by a factor of 6

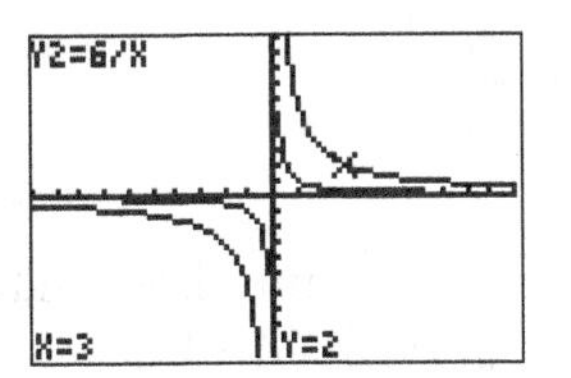

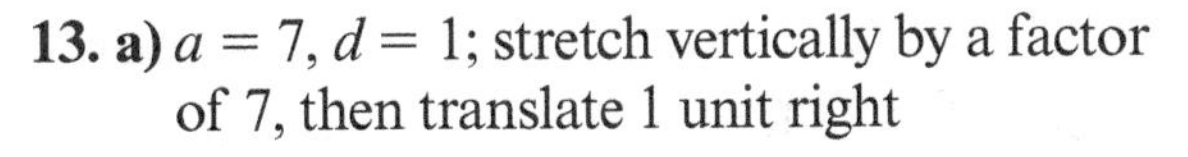

13. a) $a = 7$, $d = 1$; stretch vertically by a factor of 7, then translate 1 unit right
b) $a = \frac{1}{5}$, $c = -3$; compress vertically by a factor of $\frac{1}{5}$, then translate 3 units down
c) $d = -9$, $c = 8$; translate 9 units left and 8 units up
d) $k = \frac{1}{2}$, $c = 10$; stretch horizontally by a factor of 2, then translate 10 units up

14. a) $g(x) = 3\sqrt{2x}$

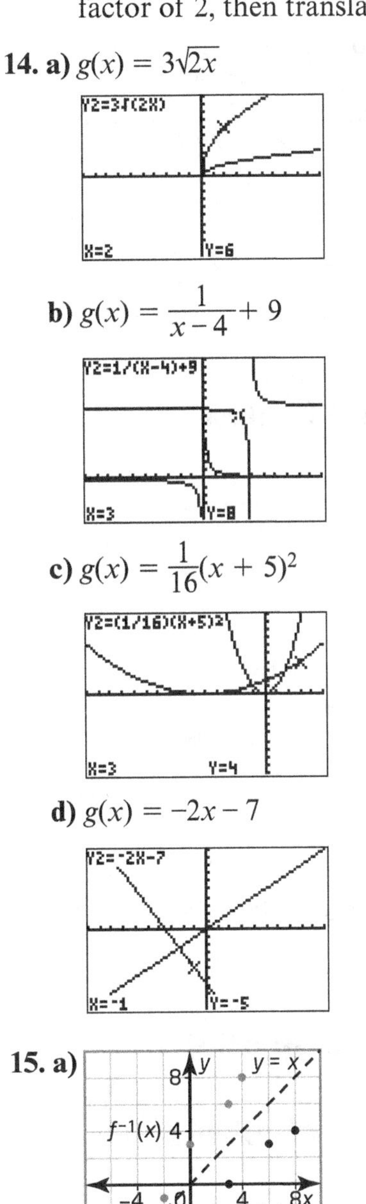

b) $g(x) = \frac{1}{x-4} + 9$
c) $g(x) = \frac{1}{16}(x + 5)^2$
d) $g(x) = -2x - 7$

15. a)

function: domain $\{-4, -1, 3, 6, 8\}$, range $\{-6, -2, 0, 3, 4\}$;
inverse: domain $\{-6, -2, 0, 3, 4\}$, range $\{-4, -1, 3, 6, 8\}$

b) 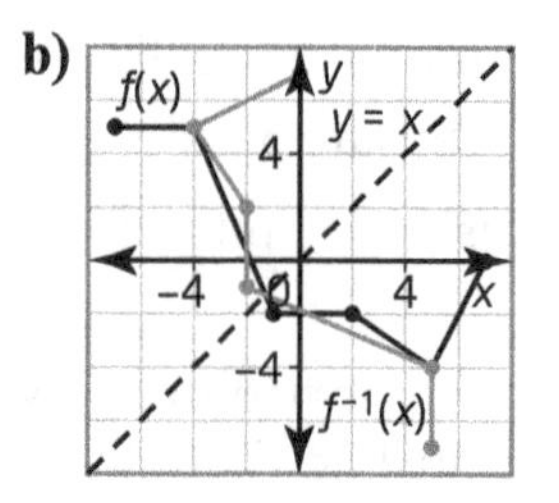

function: domain $\{x \in \mathbb{R}, -7 \le x \le 7\}$, range $\{y \in \mathbb{R}, -4 \le x \le 5\}$;
inverse: domain $\{x \in \mathbb{R}, -4 \le x \le 5\}$, range $\{y \in \mathbb{R}, -7 \le y \le 7\}$

16. a) $f^{-1}(x) = \frac{-x + 7}{2}$

b) $f^{-1}(x) = \frac{4x + 3}{5}$

c) $f^{-1}(x) = 3 \pm \sqrt{x - 1}$

d) $f^{-1}(x) = \pm 2\sqrt{9 - x}$

Chapter 2 Math Contest

1. C
2. C
3. B
4. D
5. C
6. A
7. D
8. A
9. C
10. B
11. 8
12. $\frac{4b - 3a}{8a - 6b}$
13. 50; 50 = 1 + 49; 50 = 25 + 25
14. −25
15. 540

Chapter 3 Exponential Functions

3.1 The Nature of Exponential Growth

1. a)

Day	Population	First Differences	Second Differences
0	25		
1	75	50	
2	225	150	100
3	675	450	300
4	2025	1350	900
5	6075	4050	2700

b) Yes. For each additional day the ant population increases by a common factor of 3.

c) The ratio of the first differences is 3. The ratio of the second differences is also 3.

d) Answers may vary. Sample answer: Yes, the pattern will continue.

e)

Day	Population	First Differences	Second Differences	Third Differences	Fourth Differences
0	25				
1	75	50			
2	225	150	100		
3	675	450	300	200	
4	2025	1350	900	600	400
5	6075	4050	2700	1800	1200

2. a) The value 5 and the variable x have different positions in each function. In particular the value 5 is the coefficient in $y = 5x$, the exponent in $y = x^5$, and the base in $y = 5^x$. The variable x is multiplied with the 5 in $y = 5^x$, is the base in $y = x^5$ and is the exponent in $y = 5x$. The graph of $y = 5x$ is a straight line with slope 5. The graph of $y = x^5$ is a polynomial function of degree 5 and extends from quadrant 3 to quadrant 1. The graph of $y = 5^x$ is an exponential function that extends from quadrant 2 to quadrant 1.

b) $y = 5x$: domain $\{x \in \mathbb{R}\}$, range $\{y \in \mathbb{R}\}$
$y = x^5$: domain $\{x \in \mathbb{R}\}$, range $\{y \in \mathbb{R}\}$
$y = 5^x$: domain $\{x \in \mathbb{R}\}$, range $\{y \in \mathbb{R}, y > 0\}$

3. Justifications may vary.

4. a) $\frac{a^5}{a^5} = \frac{a \times a \times a \times a \times a}{a \times a \times a \times a \times a}$

b) 1

c) a^0 **d)** $a^0 = 1$

5. a) B

b) The constant 15 is the initial population. The power 4^n represents the daily quadrupling.

6. a)–e) 1 **f)** −1

7. **a)** exponential: $f(x) = 8^x$ is of the form $y = a^x$, where the base a is a constant, such that $a > 0$, and the exponent is a variable

b) linear: $f(x) = 11 - 9x$ can be rewritten as $f(x) = -9x + 11$, which is of the form $y = mx + b$

c) none of linear, quadratic, or exponential: $f(x) = \sqrt{x}$ is a square root function

d) quadratic

8. Determine the first and second differences for each table of values.

a)

x	y	First Differences	Second Differences	Ratio of First and Second Differences
−4	16			
−3	8	−8		
−2	4	−4	4	
−1	2	−2	2	0.5
0	1	−1	1	0.5
1	0.5	−0.5	0.5	0.5
2	0.25	−0.25	0.25	0.5

The table represents an exponential function. Neither the first differences nor the second differences are constant; however, the ratio of the first and second differences is constant.

b)

x	y	First Differences
−4	13	
−3	10	−3
−2	7	−3
−1	4	−3
0	1	−3
1	−2	−3
2	−5	−3

The table represents a linear function because the first differences are constant.

c)

x	y	First Differences	Second Differences
−4	−18		
−3	−11	7	
−2	−6	5	−2
−1	−3	3	−2
0	−2	1	−2
1	−3	−1	−2
2	−6	−3	−2

The table represents a quadratic function because the second differences are constant.

d)

x	y	First Differences	Second Differences	Ratio of First and Second Differences
−4	625			
−3	125	−500		
−2	25	−100	400	
−1	5	−20	80	0.2
0	1	−4	16	0.2
1	0.2	−0.8	3.2	0.2
2	0.04	−0.16	0.64	0.2

The table represents an exponential function. Neither the first differences nor the second differences are constant; however, the ratio of the first and second differences is constant.

e)

x	y	First Differences	Second Differences
−4	2.2		
−3	0.8	−1.4	
−2	−0.2	−1	0.4
−1	−0.8	−0.6	0.4
0	−1	−0.2	0.4
1	−0.8	0.2	0.4
2	−0.2	0.6	0.4

The table represents a quadratic function because the second differences are constant.

9. **a)** Answers may vary.

b) Answers may vary. First 4 terms are 1, 4, 16, 64.

c) i) 1024 **ii)** 4 194 304

d) 5 terms **e)** 6 terms

f) The answers differ by 1 term. This is an exponential function in which each term is multiplied by 4.

10.**a)** The initial population is 32; since it doubles every 30 minutes, multiply 32 by 2 for each 30-min interval. The equation is $p(t) = 32 \times 2^t$.

b)

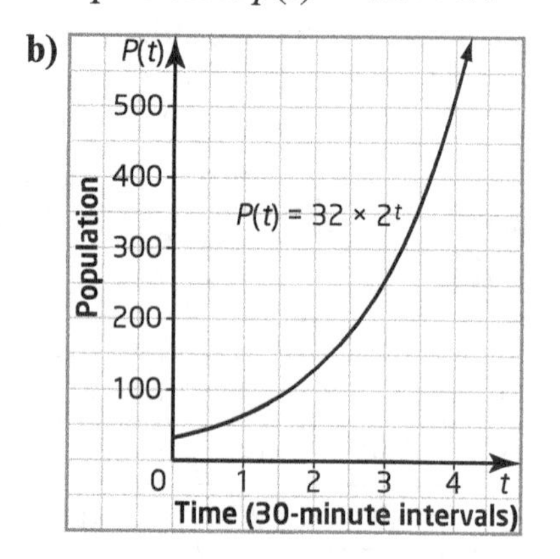

c) Answers may vary. Sample answer: Since there are two 30-min intervals in each hour, 1 h on the graph corresponds to $t = 2$. By moving up to the curve and then across to the vertical axis, it can be estimated that at $t = 2$ the population is approximately 130 bacteria.

This can be checked in the equation. To use the equation, substitute $t = 2$ to obtain $p(2) = 32 \times 2^2 = 128$, which is very close to 130.

d) Since the graph does not extend to 3.5 h, it is easier to use the equation. In 3.5 h, there are seven 30-min intervals. Substitute $t = 7$ in $p(t) = 32 \times 2^t$:

$p(7) = 32 \times 2^7$

$= 4096$

After 3.5 h there are 4096 bacteria.

11. **a)** $A(n) = 200(1.045)^n$

b)

Number of Compounding Periods (years)	Amount ($)
0	200.00
1	209.00
2	218.41
3	228.23
4	238.50
5	249.24
6	260.45

c)

Number of Compounding Periods (years)	Amount ($)	First Differences	Second Differences
0	200.00		
1	209.00	9.00	
2	218.41	9.41	0.41
3	228.23	9.82	0.41
4	238.50	10.27	0.45
5	249.24	10.74	0.47
6	260.45	11.21	0.47

Neither. The first differences are not equal, nor are the second differences.

d) The ratio of the first differences and second differences is approximately 1.04. The function is exponential.

e) In the equation the constant ratio is represented by the value 1.045.

f) No. The amount remains the same between compounding periods and increases only at the end of each compounding period.

12. **a)** $1663.08 **b)** $1975.21

13. **a) i)** 500 **ii)** 12 500

b) $r(n) = 4 \times 5^n$, where r is the number of residents called in each interval, n

c) approximately 5.4 intervals

d) This is an example of exponential growth, because the number of residents notified increases by a factor of 5 with each interval.

14. **a)** approximately 13 years; Answers may vary. Sample answer: Systematic trial.

b) 5.18 or approximately 6 more years (since the interest is paid at the end of the year)

15. Prize A. The value of Prize A at week 26 alone is \$335 544.32. The value of Prize B for all 26 weeks is only \$260 000.

16.a) 6 days; population of A is 6400; population of B is 8192

b) 2 days sooner, on the 4th day

17. a) 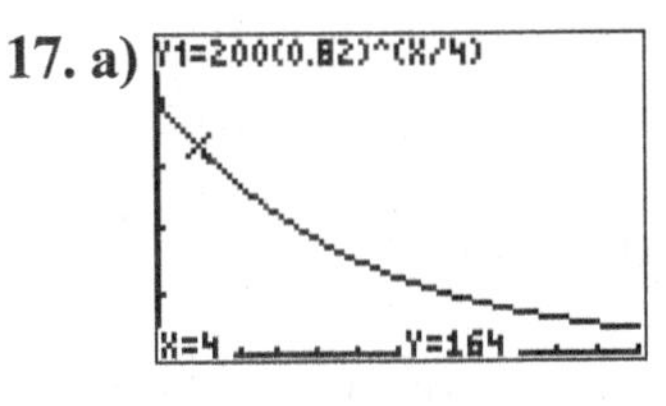

b) approximately 14 h

c) For $h = 14$, $M \doteq 99.9$.

d) approximately 107 h

3.2 Exponential Decay: Connecting to Negative Exponents

1. a) $\frac{1}{7}$ b) $\frac{1}{10^2}$ c) $\frac{1}{a^4}$

d) $\frac{1}{mn}$ e) $-\frac{1}{4}$ f) $\frac{1}{2b}$

2. a) a^{-3} b) $2x^{-5}$

c) $-x^{-9}$ d) $\frac{2}{5}b^{-6}$

3. a) $\frac{1}{25}$ b) $\frac{1}{81}$ c) $\frac{1}{1000}$

d) $\frac{1}{16}$ e) $-\frac{1}{16}$ f) $-\frac{1}{64}$

g) $\frac{4}{81}$ h) $\frac{5}{48}$

4. a) 25 b) $\frac{1}{512}$ c) 729

d) $\frac{1}{36}$ e) 24 f) 64

5. a) a^4 b) $-\frac{12}{v^7}$

c) a^{10} d) $\frac{3}{m^2}$

6. a) 6 b) $\frac{49}{16}$

c) $\frac{64}{27}$ d) $\frac{81}{625}$

7. a) x^3y^3 b) $121b^2$

c) $\frac{b^8}{a^{12}}$ d) $\frac{8n^{12}}{125m^6}$

8. a)

Number of 20-day Intervals, n	Amount Remaining (mg)
0	40
1	20
2	10
3	5
4	2.5
5	1.25

Half the amount remains after each 20-day interval.

b) $A = 40\left(\frac{1}{2}\right)^n$, where n is the number of half-life periods, in 20-day intervals, and A is the amount of polonium-210 remaining, in milligrams

c) Plot the points from the table. Connect them with a smooth curve.

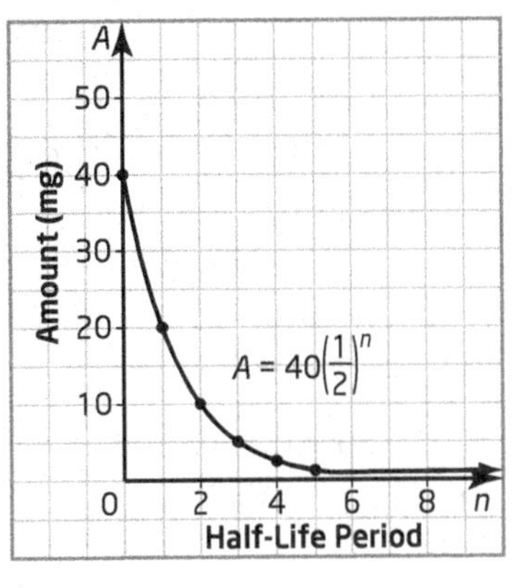

The graph starts at point (0, 40), decreases by a factor of $\frac{1}{2}$ with each 20-day interval, and has a horizontal asymptote, $y = 0$.

d) Since there are 7 days in a week, 10 weeks = 70 days. This represents 3.5 half-life periods. Substitute $n = 3.5$ into the equation to determine the amount remaining:

$$A = 40\left(\frac{1}{2}\right)^{3.5}$$
$$= 3.54$$

Approximately 3.54 mg of polonium-210 will remain after 10 weeks.

e) Answers may vary. Sample answer:
Determine 8% of 40 mg:
8% = 0.08, so 0.08(40) mg = 3.2 mg
Substitute $A = 6$ into the equation and solve for n:

$3.2 = 40\left(\frac{1}{2}\right)^n$ Divide each side by 40.

$0.08 = \left(\frac{1}{2}\right)^n$

Use systematic trial to solve for n.
Observe the chart in part a). Note that when $n = 3$ the amount remaining is 5 mg, and when $n = 4$ the amount remaining is 2.5 mg. Therefore, for 3.2 mg, the value of n is between 3 and 4.

Try $n = 3.5$ in $\left(\frac{1}{2}\right)^n$: $\left(\frac{1}{2}\right)^{3.5} \doteq 0.088$, which is a bit high.

Try $n = 3.64$ to get $\left(\frac{1}{2}\right)^{3.64} \doteq 0.0802$, which is very close, so $n = 3.64$.
Multiply to find the number of days.
$3.64(20) \doteq 73$ days
Therefore, it takes approximately 73 days for polonium-210 to decay to 8% of its initial mass.

f) Since $\frac{1}{2} = 2^{-1}$, an equivalent way to write the equation is $A = 40(2^{-1})^n$ or $A = 40(2^{-n})$.

Since $\frac{1}{2} = 0.5$, another equivalent way to write the equation is $A = 40(0.5)^n$.

9. a) In the formula 13 500 represents the initial value of the motorcycle. Since the value depreciates by 20% per year, 80% of the value remains. This amount is represented by the decimal 0.8.
b) i) $10 800 ii) $3538.94
c) Answers may vary. Sample answer: The equation is of the form $f(x) = ab^x$, where 0.8 is the constant ratio. This value is less than 1, so the initial amount is decreasing.
d) 3.1 years, or approximately 3 years 1 month

10. $2720.63

11. a) The initial deposit was made 5 years ago, so determine the amount in the account when $n = 5$.
Substitute $A = 4200$, $i = 0.075$, and $n = 5$ in the formula $P = A(1 + i)^{-n}$.
$P = 4200(1 + 0.075)^{-5}$
$\doteq 2925.55$
Denise's initial deposit was $2925.55.
b) Substitute $A = 4200$, $i = 0.075$, and $n = 2$ in the formula $P = A(1 + i)^{-n}$.
$P = 4200(1 + 0.075)^{-2}$
$\doteq 3634.40$
The amount in the account 2 years ago was $3634.40.
c) Use the formula $A = P(1 + i)^n$ to determine the amount in the account 2 years from now. Substitute $P = 4200$, $i = 0.075$, and $n = 2$, and solve for A.
$A = 4200(1 + 0.075)^2$
$\doteq 4853.63$
Two years from now the amount in the account will be $4853.63.
To determine the total interest earned, subtract the initial deposit from the amount at this point.
$4853.63 – $2925.55 = $1928.08
The total interest earned up to this point is $1928.08.

12. approximately 17.3%

13. a) $c = 100\left(2^{-\frac{t}{5}}\right)$
b) i) 16 h 36 min ii) 33 h 12 min

14. a) $T = 80\left(2^{-\frac{t}{5}}\right) + 20$ b) 15 min

3.3 Rational Exponents

1. a) 6 b) −11
c) $\frac{5}{7}$ d) $\frac{4}{9}$

2. a) 5 b) 2
c) 3 d) −4

3. a) $32^{\frac{3}{5}} = \left(32^{\frac{1}{5}}\right)^3$
$= (\sqrt[5]{32})^3$
$= 2^3$
$= 8$

b) $(-64)^{\frac{2}{3}} = \left(-64^{\frac{1}{3}}\right)^2$
$= (\sqrt[3]{-64})^2$
$= (-4)^2$
$= 16$

c) $64^{\frac{5}{6}} = \left(64^{\frac{1}{6}}\right)^5$
$= (\sqrt[6]{64})^5$
$= 2^5$
$= 32$

d) $6561^{\frac{5}{8}} = \left(6561^{\frac{1}{8}}\right)^5$
$= (\sqrt[8]{6561})^5$
$= 3^5$
$= 243$

4. a) $1728^{-\frac{1}{3}} = \frac{1}{1728^{\frac{1}{3}}}$
$= \frac{1}{(\sqrt[3]{1728})}$
$= \frac{1}{12}$

b) $36^{-\frac{3}{2}} = \frac{1}{36^{\frac{3}{2}}}$
$= \frac{1}{\left(36^{\frac{1}{2}}\right)^3}$
$= \frac{1}{(\sqrt{36})^3}$
$= \frac{1}{6^3}$
$= \frac{1}{216}$

c) $\left(-\frac{8}{125}\right)^{\frac{5}{3}} = \frac{1}{\left(-\frac{8}{125}\right)^{\frac{5}{3}}}$
$= \frac{1}{\left(-\frac{8^{\frac{1}{3}}}{125^{\frac{1}{3}}}\right)^5}$
$= \frac{1}{\left(-\frac{(\sqrt[3]{8})}{(\sqrt[3]{125})}\right)^5}$
$= \frac{1}{\left(-\frac{2}{5}\right)^5}$
$= \frac{1}{-\frac{32}{3125}}$
$= -\frac{3125}{32}$

d) $\left(\frac{1024}{243}\right)^{-\frac{3}{5}} = \frac{1}{\left(\frac{1024}{243}\right)^{\frac{3}{5}}}$
$= \frac{1}{\left(\frac{\sqrt[5]{1024}}{\sqrt[5]{243}}\right)^3}$
$= \frac{1}{\left(\frac{4}{3}\right)^3}$
$= \frac{1}{\frac{64}{27}}$
$= \frac{27}{64}$

5. a) $8^{\frac{1}{3}} \times 8^{\frac{2}{3}}$
$= 8^{\frac{1}{3} + \frac{2}{3}}$ Use the product rule for exponents.
$= 8^{\frac{3}{3}}$
$= 8$

b) $16^{\frac{1}{4}} \div 16^{\frac{1}{2}} \times 16^{\frac{3}{4}}$
$= 16^{\frac{1}{4} - \frac{1}{2} + \frac{3}{4}}$ Find a common denominator for the fractional exponents.
$= 16^{\frac{1}{4} - \frac{1}{2} + \frac{3}{4}}$
$= 16^{\frac{2}{4}}$ Reduce the exponent.
$= 16^{\frac{1}{2}}$
$= \sqrt{16}$
$= 4$

c) $64^{\frac{1}{3}} \times 64^{\frac{1}{6}} \div 64^{\frac{2}{3}}$
$= 64^{\frac{1}{3} + \frac{1}{6} - \frac{2}{3}}$ Find a common denominator for the exponents.
$= 64^{\frac{2}{6} + \frac{1}{6} - \frac{4}{6}}$
$= 64^{\frac{1}{6}}$
$= \frac{1}{64^{\frac{1}{6}}}$ Take the reciprocal.
$= \frac{1}{\sqrt[6]{64}}$
$= \frac{1}{2}$

d) $3^{\frac{2}{3}} \times 27^{\frac{4}{9}}$
$= 3^{\frac{2}{3}} \times (3^3)^{\frac{4}{9}}$

$= 3^{\frac{2}{3}} \times 3^{\frac{4}{9}}$

$= 3^{\frac{2}{3}} \times 3^{\frac{4}{3}}$

$= 9$

6. **a)** $x^{\frac{2}{3}}$ **b)** $a^{\frac{7}{6}}$

c) $\frac{a^{\frac{8}{3}}}{b^{\frac{3}{2}}}$ **d)** $z^{\frac{8}{15}}$

7. **a)** $b^{\frac{2}{15}}$ **b)** $\frac{1}{a^{\frac{13}{12}}}$

c) $w^{\frac{4}{11}}$ **d)** $2a^{\frac{1}{2}}$

8. 1652.7 cm^3

9. **a)** $C = 2\pi\left(\frac{A}{\pi}\right)^{\frac{1}{2}}$ **b)** $C = 2(\pi A)^{\frac{1}{2}}$

c) **i)** 62.8 cm **ii)** 108.0 cm **iii)** 136.1 cm

d) Answers may vary.

10. **a)** 400 **b)** approximately 2 h 40 min

c) Yes. The exponents are equivalent because $\frac{t}{0.5} = 2t$.

d) Answers may vary.

11. **a)** $N = 1000(2^{\frac{t}{3}})$, where t is the time, in minutes

b) 32 000 **c)** approximately 18 min

12. **a)** **i)** 23 beats per min **ii)** 43 beats per min **iii)** 159 beats per min

b) **i)** 5 breaths per min **ii)** 10 breaths per min **iii)** 35 breaths per min

c) **i)** 5.08 kg **ii)** 0.987 kg or 987 g **iii)** 0.03 kg or 30.4 g

d) **i)** the larger the animal, the fewer beats per min

ii) the larger the animal, the fewer breaths per min

iii) the larger the animal, the greater the brain mass

e) Answers may vary.

13. **a)** $f^{-1}(x) = x^{\frac{2}{3}}$; 16

b) $f^{-1}(x) = (x + 2)^{\frac{5}{4}}$; 243

c) $f^{-1}(x) = \sqrt[4]{x^3 + 4}$; 268.014

14. **a)** $x^{\frac{29}{30}}$

b) $\frac{1}{x^{\frac{37}{12}}}$

c) $\frac{9}{7m}$

d) $\frac{1}{6b^{9x + 1}}$

e) $a^{\frac{5x}{8}}$

15. **a)** $P = P_0(10)^{\frac{t}{20}}$

b) approximately 3.2 times greater

16. **a)** No. Answers may vary.

b) No. Answers may vary.

3.4 Properties of Exponential Functions

1. Graph a) matches **B** $y = 3\left(\frac{1}{3}\right)^x$

Graph b) matches **D** $y = -3^x$

Graph c) matches **C** $y = \frac{1}{3}(3^x)$

Graph d) matches **A** $y = 3(3^x)$

2. Graph a) matches **C** $y = \frac{1}{2}(4)^x$

Graph b) matches **A** $y = -4(2)^x$

Graph c) matches **D** $y = 4\left(\frac{1}{2}\right)^x$

Graph d) matches **B** $y = -2(4)^x$

3. **a)** Answers may vary.

b) No. The conditions are satisfied by any curve whose equation is of the form $y = 2b^x$, where $b > 1$.

4. **a)** Answers may vary.

b) No. The conditions are satisfied by any curve whose equation is of the form $y = -3b^x$, where $b > 1$.

5. $y = 6 \times 2^x$

6. $y = 8 \times \left(\frac{1}{2}\right)^x$

7. **a)** C **b)** 9.5 mg

8. **a)**

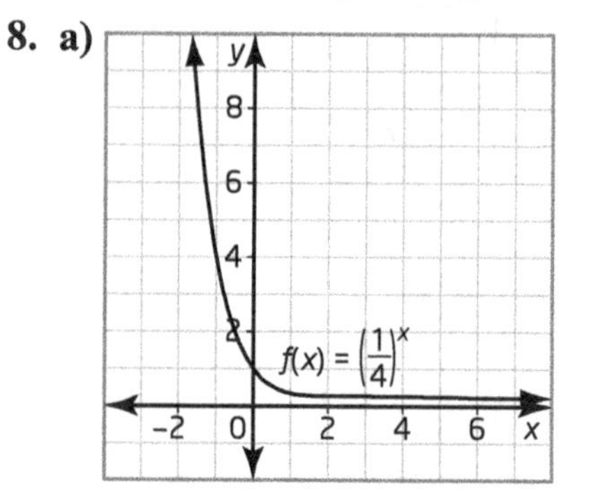

i) domain $\{x \in \mathbb{R}\}$
ii) range $\{y \in \mathbb{R}, y > 0\}$
iii) The y-intercept is 1. There is no x-intercept.
iv) The y-values are getting closer to zero as the x-values increase, so the graph is decreasing for $x \in \mathbb{R}$.
v) The equation of the horizontal asymptote is $y = 0$, which is the x-axis.

b)

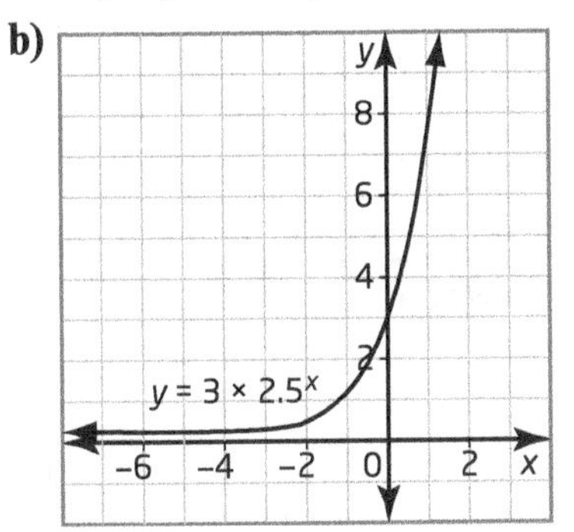

i) domain $\{x \in \mathbb{R}\}$
ii) range $\{y \in \mathbb{R}, y > 0\}$
iii) The y-intercept is 3. There is no x-intercept.
iv) The y-values are increasing as the x-values increase, so the graph is increasing for $x \in \mathbb{R}$.
v) The horizontal asymptote is $y = 0$, which is the x-axis.

c)

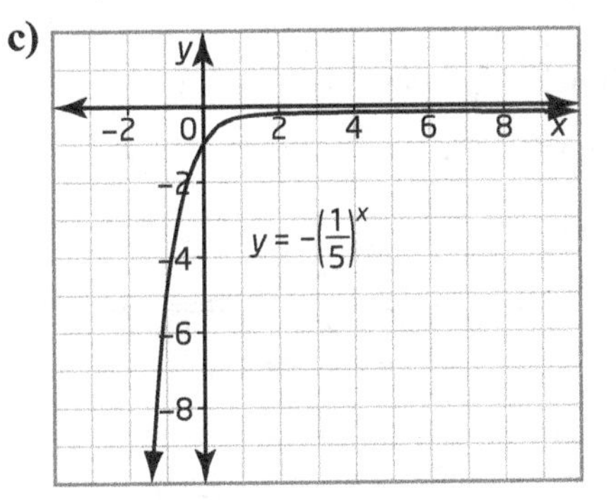

i) domain $\{x \in \mathbb{R}\}$
ii) range $\{y \in \mathbb{R}, y < 0\}$
iii) The y-intercept is −1. There is no x-intercept.
iv) The y-values are increasing as the x-values increase, so the graph is increasing for $x \in \mathbb{R}$.
v) The horizontal asymptote is $y = 0$, which is the x-axis.

9. a)

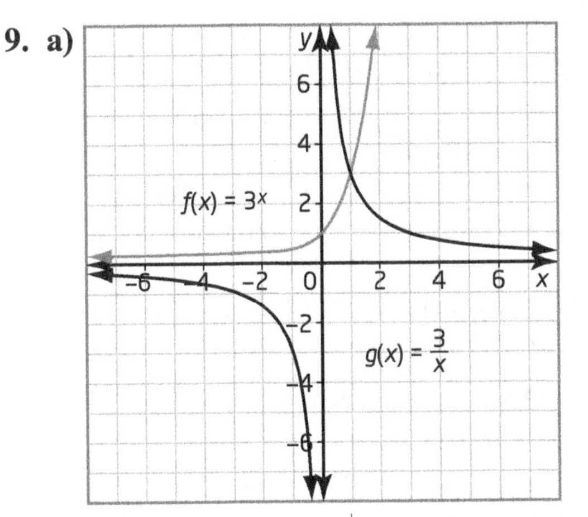

b) i) They have the same horizontal asymptote, $y = 0$. Both graphs pass through the point (1, 3). The curves have a similar shape, one end near the x-axis and the other end moving away from it, either upward or downward.

ii) Differences:

- the graph of $f(x) = 3x$ increases as x increases, it has only one branch, and has no vertical asymptotes
- the graph of $g(x) = \frac{3}{x}$ decreases as x increases, it has two branches, and has a vertical asymptote, $x = 0$

c) Both graphs have $y = 0$ (the x-axis) as a horizontal asymptote. The graph of $g(x) = \frac{3}{x}$ also has a vertical asymptote at $x = 0$ (the y-axis).

10.a)

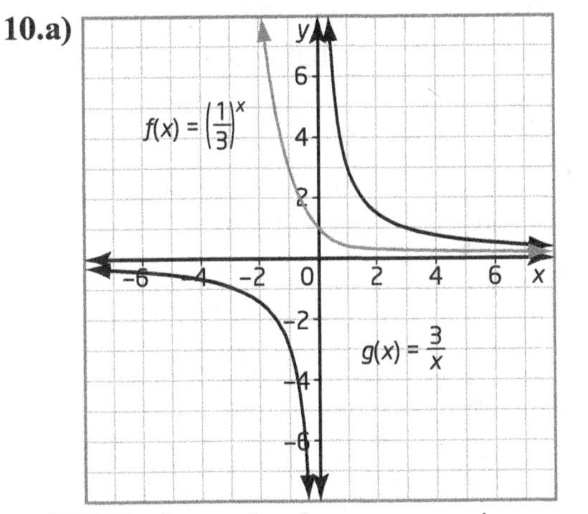

b) i) Both graphs decrease as x increases. They have the same horizontal asymptote, $y = 0$. The curves have a similar shape, one end near the x-axis and the other end moving away from it, either upward or downward.

ii) Differences:
- the graph of $f(x) = \left(\frac{1}{3}\right)^x$ has only one branch and no vertical asymptotes
- the graph of $g(x) = \frac{3}{x}$ has two branches and a vertical asymptote, $x = 0$

c) Both graphs have $y = 0$ (the x-axis) as a horizontal asymptote. The graph of $g(x) = \frac{3}{x}$ also has a vertical asymptote at $x = 0$ (the y-axis).

11. a) The graphs are the same.

b)

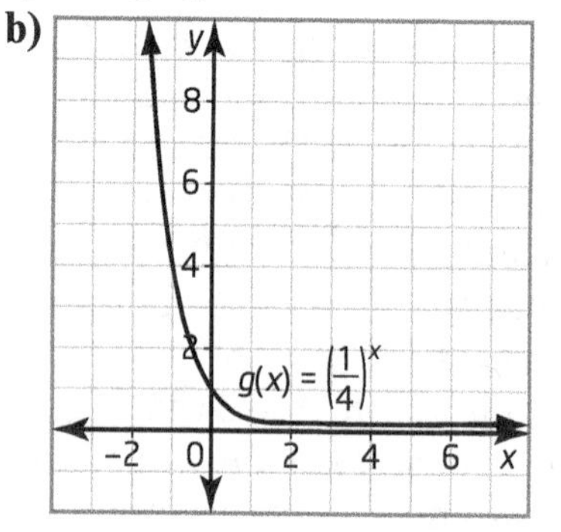

c) $f(x) = 4^{-x}$

$= \frac{1}{4x}$

$= \left(\frac{1}{4}\right)^x$

$= g(x)$

12. a) $P(t) = 100\left(\frac{10}{23}\right)^t$

b) The common ratio $\frac{10}{23}$ is a proper fraction (value is between 0 and 1), so when multiplied with 100 will make the value smaller.

c)

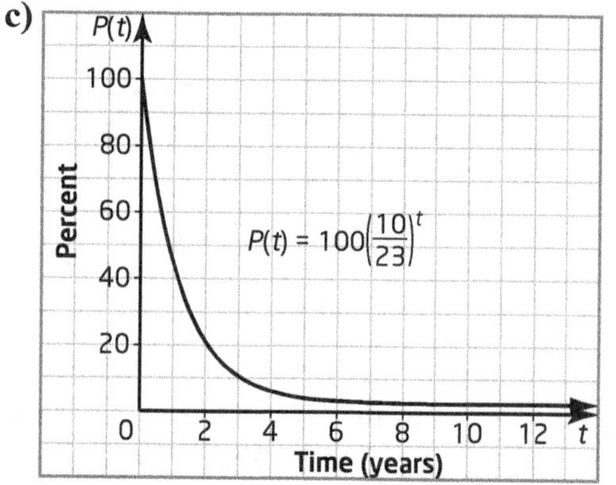

The graph falls from left to right, which means that as time passes the percent of radioactive substance remaining is decreasing.

d) domain $\{t \in \mathbb{R}, t \geq 0\}$, range $\{P \in \mathbb{R}, 0 < P \leq 100\}$

e) As time passes the percent remaining of the substance decreases, becoming closer to 0 but never actually reaching 0.

f) i) Answers may vary. Approximately 3% of the initial amount of the substance remains.

ii) $P(4) = 3.6\%$

13. a)

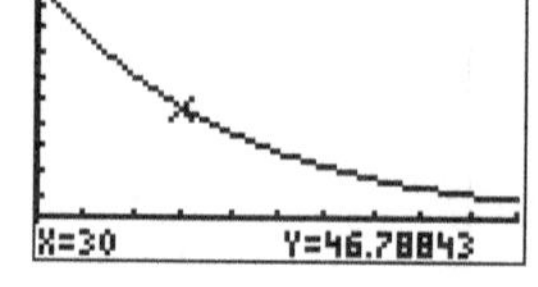

b) 27 m

14. a) 372 m^3

b) $S(V) = (3V)^{\frac{2}{3}}(4\pi)^{\frac{1}{3}}$

c) 137 m^2

15. a) 8 days

b) $A(t) = 320\left(2^{-\frac{t}{8}}\right)$; $A(t) = 320\left(\frac{1}{2}\right)^{\frac{t}{8}}$

c)

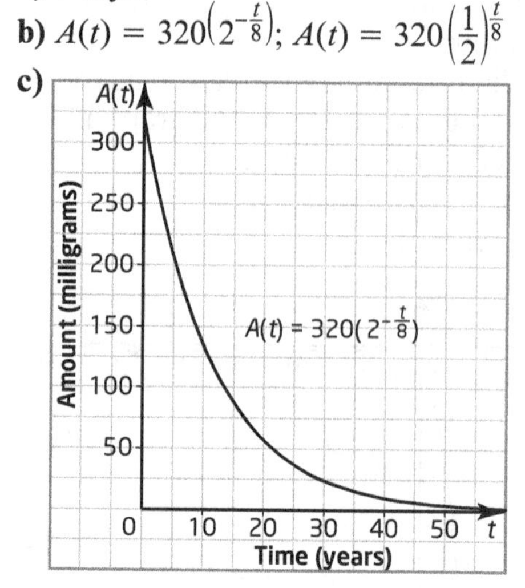

domain $\{t \in \mathbb{R}, t \geq 0\}$, range $\{A \in \mathbb{R}, 0 < A \leq 320\}$

d) 20 days. Answers may vary (estimating from the graph or using systematic trial in the equation).

16. a) $r = \frac{(3V)^{\frac{1}{2}}}{5\pi^{\frac{1}{2}}}$

b) Answers may vary. Sample answer: domain $\{V \in \mathbb{R}, V > 0\}$

c) The radius of the base will increase by a factor of $\sqrt{2}$.

3.5 Transformations of Exponential Functions

1.

The Roles of the Parameters a, k, d, and c in Exponential Functions of the Form $y = ab^{k(x-d)} + c$ ($b > 0$, $b \neq 1$)	
Role of c	**Transformation on Graph of $y = b^x$**
$c > 0$	Translation c units up
$c < 0$	Translation c units down
Role of d	
$d > 0$	Translation d units right
$d < 0$	Translation d units left
Role of a	
$a > 1$	Vertical stretch by a factor of a
$0 < a < 1$	Vertical compression by a factor of a
$-1 < a < 0$	Vertical compression by a factor of $\lvert a \rvert$ and a reflection in the x-axis
$a < -1$	Vertical stretch by a factor of $\lvert a \rvert$ and reflection in the x-axis
Role of k	
$k > 1$	Horizontal compression by a factor of $\frac{1}{k}$
$0 < k < 1$	Horizontal stretch by a factor of $\frac{1}{k}$
$-1 < k < 0$	Horizontal stretch by a factor of $\frac{1}{\lvert k \rvert}$ and a reflection in the y-axis
$k < -1$	Horizontal compression by a factor of $\frac{1}{\lvert k \rvert}$ and a reflection in the y-axis
Domain and Range of $y = ab^{k(x-d)} + c$	
The domain is always $\{x \in \mathbb{R}\}$.	i) When the graph is below its horizontal asymptote the range is $\{y \in \mathbb{R}, y < c\}$. ii) When the graph is above its horizontal asymptote the range is $\{y \in \mathbb{R}, y > c\}$.

2. a) translate $y = 5x$ up 3 units
   b) translate $y = 5x$ right 2 units
   c) translate $y = 5x$ left 1 unit
   d) translate $y = 5x$ right 4 units and down 6 units

3. a)

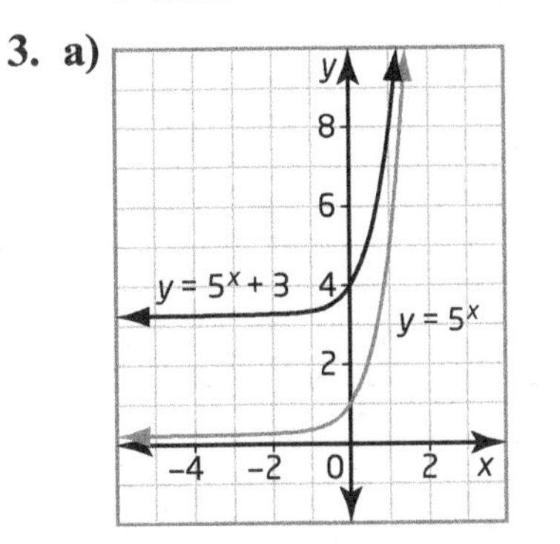

b)

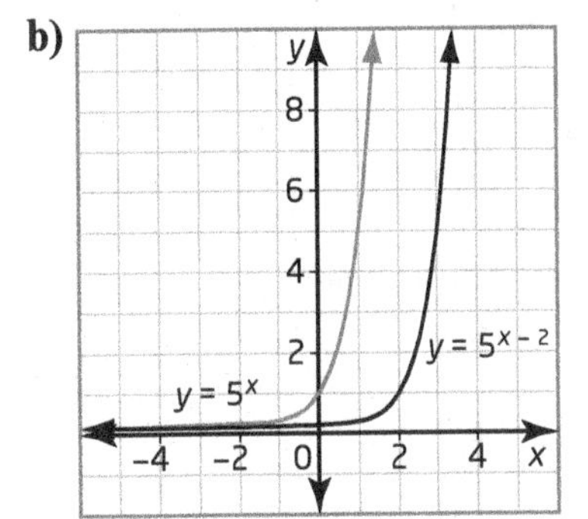

c)

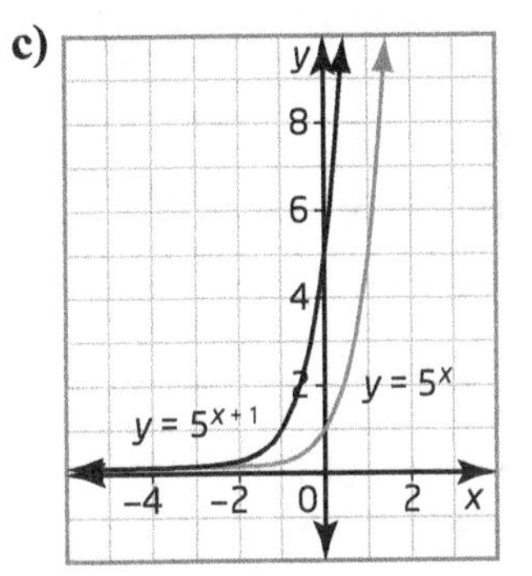

d)

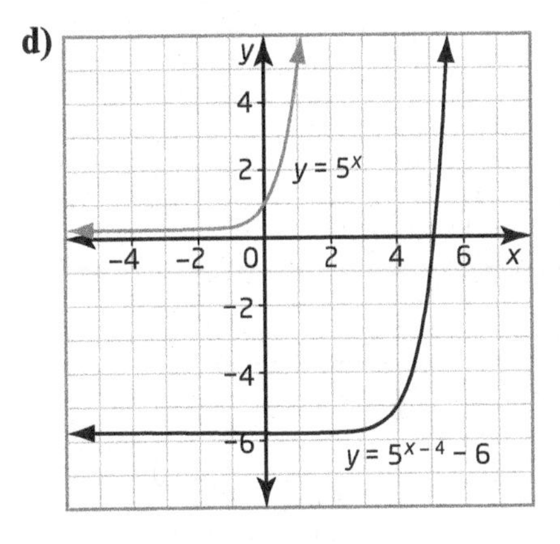

4. a) vertical compression by a factor of $\frac{1}{3}$
   b) horizontal compression by a factor of $\frac{1}{2}$
   c) reflection in the x-axis
   d) horizontal stretch by a factor of 3 and a reflection in the y-axis

5. a)

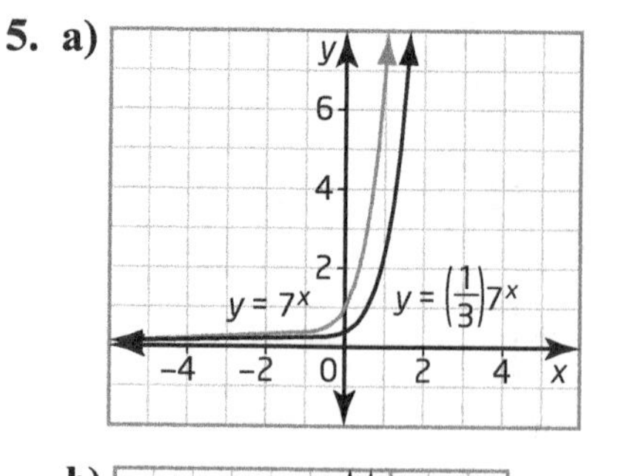

b)

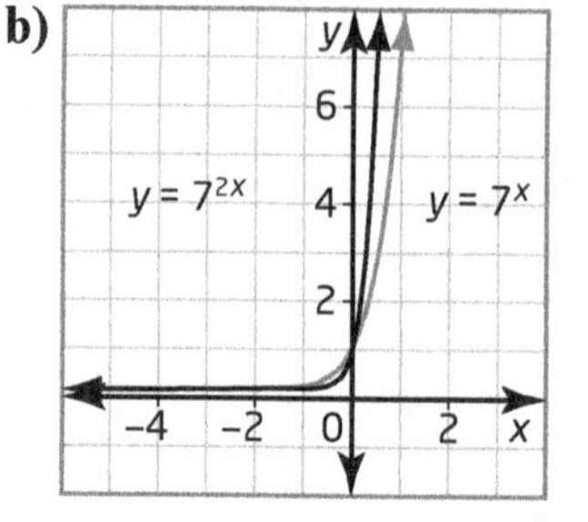

c)

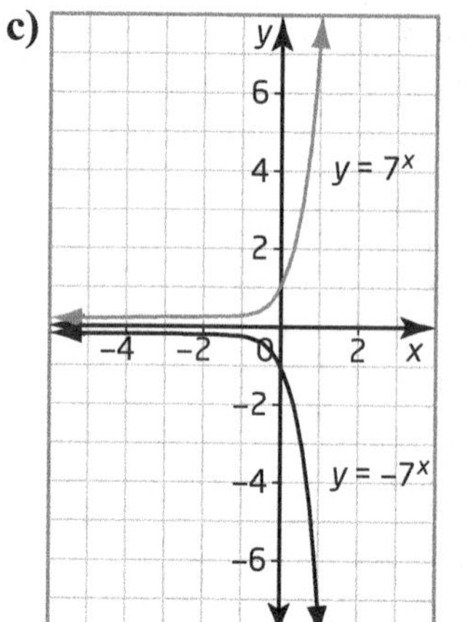

d)

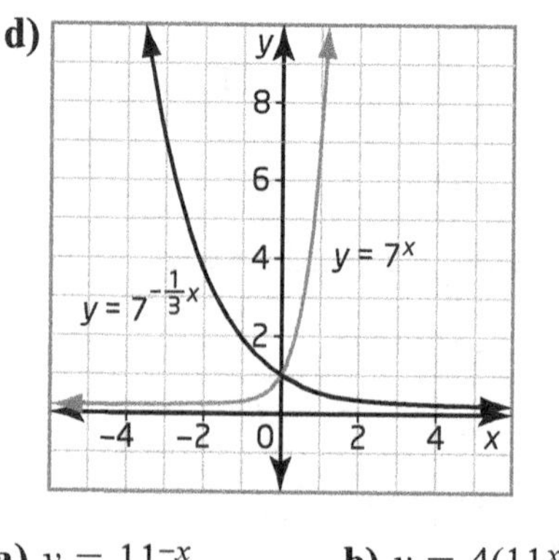

6. a) $y = 11^{-x}$
   b) $y = 4(11^x)$
   c) $y = 11^{\frac{x}{3}}$
   d) $y = -115^x$

7. a) Compare $y = -3[4^{2(x+1)}] + 5$ to $y = ab^{k(x-d)} + c$. The parameters are $a = -3$, $k = 2$, $d = -1$, and $c = 5$.

   i) $k = 2$ corresponds to a horizontal compression by a factor of $\frac{1}{2}$. Divide the x-coordinates of the points in column 1 by 2.

$y = 4^x$	$y = 4^{2x}$
$(-1, 0.25)$	$\left(-\frac{1}{2}, 0.25\right)$
$(0, 1)$	$(0, 1)$
$(1, 4)$	$\left(\frac{1}{2}, 4\right)$
$(2, 16)$	$(1, 16)$
$(3, 64)$	$\left(\frac{3}{2}, 64\right)$

   ii) $a = -3$ corresponds to a vertical stretch by a factor of 3 and a reflection in the x-axis. Multiply the y-coordinates of the points in column 2 by -3.

$y = 4^x$	$y = 4^{2x}$	$y = -3[4^{2x}]$
$(-1, 0.25)$	$\left(-\frac{1}{2}, 0.25\right)$	$\left(-\frac{1}{2}, 0.75\right)$
$(0, 1)$	$(0, 1)$	$(0, -3)$
$(1, 4)$	$\left(\frac{1}{2}, 4\right)$	$\left(\frac{1}{2}, -12\right)$
$(2, 16)$	$(1, 16)$	$(1, -48)$
$(3, 64)$	$\left(\frac{3}{2}, 64\right)$	$\left(\frac{3}{2}, -192\right)$

   iii) $d = -1$ corresponds to a translation of 1 unit to the left, so add -1 to each x-value in column 3. $c = 5$ corresponds to a translation of 5 units up, so add 5 to each y-value in column 3.

$y = 4^x$	$y = 4^{2x}$	$y = -3[4^{2x}]$	$y = -3[4^{2(x+1)}] + 5$
$(-1, 0.25)$	$\left(-\frac{1}{2}, 0.25\right)$	$\left(-\frac{1}{2}, 0.75\right)$	$\left(-\frac{3}{2}, 4.25\right)$
$(0, 1)$	$(0, 1)$	$(0, -3)$	$(-1, 2)$
$(1, 4)$	$\left(\frac{1}{2}, 4\right)$	$\left(\frac{1}{2}, -12\right)$	$\left(-\frac{1}{2}, -7\right)$
$(2, 16)$	$(1, 16)$	$(1, -48)$	$(0, -43)$
$(3, 64)$	$\left(\frac{3}{2}, 64\right)$	$\left(\frac{3}{2}, -192\right)$	$\left(\frac{1}{2}, -187\right)$

To sketch the graph, plot the points in column 4 and draw a smooth curve through them.

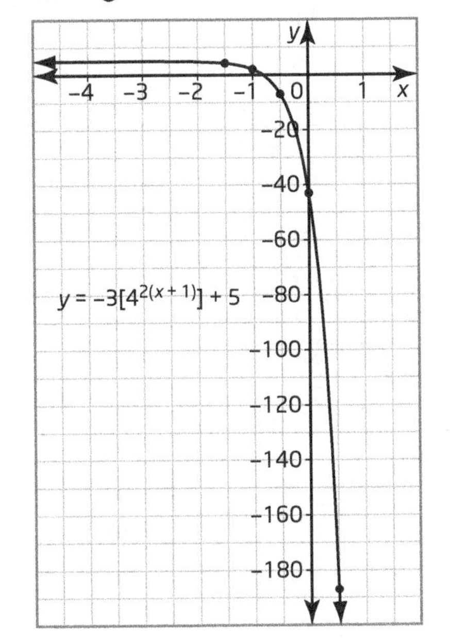

b) The domain is $\{x \in \mathbb{R}\}$. Since the graph is below its horizontal asymptote, which is $y = 5$, the range is $\{y \in \mathbb{R}, y < 5\}$.

8.

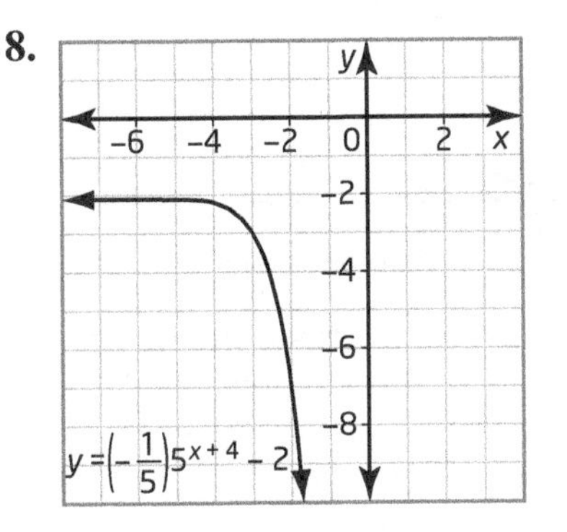

9. a) Compare the transformed equation with $y = ab^{k(x-d)} + c$ to determine the values of a, k, d, and c.
For $y = -f(4x) - 7$ the parameters are $a = -1$, $k = 4$, $d = 0$, and $c = -7$.
The function $f(x) = 3^x$ is reflected in the x-axis, compressed horizontally by a factor of $\frac{1}{4}$, and shifted down 7 units. The equation of the corresponding transformed function is $f(x) = -(3^{4x}) - 7$.

b) The domain is $\{x \in \mathbb{R}\}$. Since a is negative, the graph will be below its horizontal asymptote, which is $y = -7$, so the range is $\{y \in \mathbb{R}, y < -7\}$.

10. a) $f(x) = -\left(2^{-\frac{1}{5}(x-1)}\right) - 3$

b) domain $\{x \in \mathbb{R}\}$,
range $\{y \in \mathbb{R}, y < -3\}$; The equation of the horizontal asymptote is $y = -3$.

11. a)

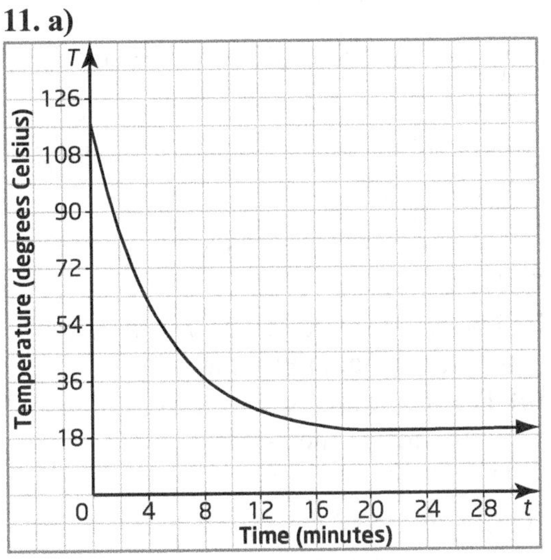

b) $T = 18$, the initial temperature that the bar will cool down to

c) approximately 33 min

12. a) Answers may vary. Sample answer:
$y = 2^{-4x}$; $y = 4^{-2x}$; $y = 16^{-x}$

b) For $y = 2^{-4x}$, the base function $y = 2^x$ is compressed horizontally by a factor of $\frac{1}{4}$ and reflected in the y-axis.
For $y = 4^{-2x}$, the base function $y = 4^x$ is compressed horizontally by a factor of $\frac{1}{2}$ and reflected in the y-axis.
For $y = 16^{-x}$, the base function $y = 16^x$ is reflected in the y-axis.

13. a) Answers may vary. Sample answer:
Equations of the form $y = 8(2^x) - 5$ satisfy the given conditions.

b) No. Equations of the form $y = 8(a^x) - 5$, where $a > 0$, will satisfy the given conditions. The y-intercept indicates that the base function is stretched vertically by a factor of 8, and the asymptote indicates that the base function is translated down 5 units.

14. a) $A = 250\left(\frac{1}{2}\right)^{\frac{t}{138}}$; $A = 175\left(\frac{1}{2}\right)^{\frac{t}{16}}$

b) $A = \left(\frac{1}{2}\right)^t$

c) For $A = 250\left(\frac{1}{2}\right)^{\frac{t}{138}}$, the base function $A = \left(\frac{1}{2}\right)^t$ is stretched vertically by a factor of 250 and stretched horizontally by a factor of 138.

For $A = 175\left(\frac{1}{2}\right)^{\frac{t}{16}}$, the base function $A = \left(\frac{1}{2}\right)^t$ is stretched vertically by a factor of 175 and stretched horizontally by a factor of 16.

d) $A = 250(2)^{\frac{t}{138}}$; $A = 175(2)^{\frac{t}{16}}$

i) $A = 2^t$

ii) The vertical stretch and horizontal stretch remain the same.

iii) The new transformation is a reflection in the y-axis.

e) 123.8 g; 0.4 g

f) 458.4 days; 53.2 days

15. a) $A = A_0\left(\frac{1}{2}\right)^{\frac{t}{h}}$

b) The base function $A = \left(\frac{1}{2}\right)^t$ is stretched vertically by a factor of A_0 and stretched horizontally by a factor of h.

c) $A = A_0(2)^{-\frac{t}{h}}$

3.6 Making Connections: Tools and Strategies for Applying Exponential Models

1. Graph A: $y = 2 \times 2.2^x$; Graph B: $y = 6 \times 1.6^x$; Graph C: $y = 9 \times 0.8^x$

2. Answers may vary.

3. a) Yes. The points increase at a constant ratio.

b) Answers may vary.

c) $V(n) = 150 \times 1.12^n$

d) $584.40

e) approximately 17 years

4. a) $C(t) = 100(0.98)^t$

b) i) 60% ii) 36% iii) 22% iv) 13%

c) The half-life of the battery is 34 days.

5. a)

t	$P(t)$
0	7.4
1	11.8
2	18.7
3	29.8
4	47.3
5	75.2
6	119.6
7	190.2
8	302.3
9	480.6
10	764.2

b)

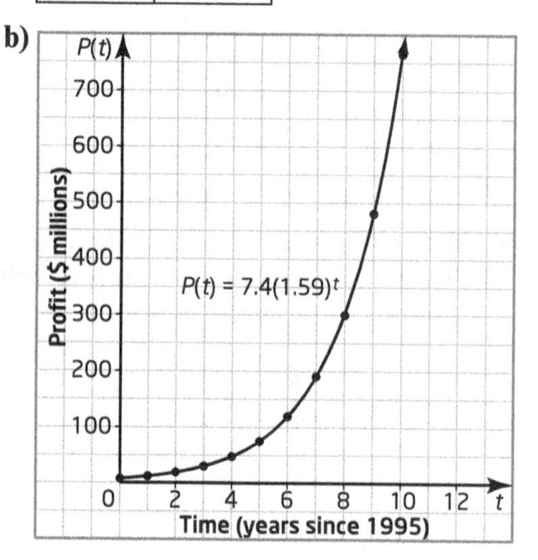

c) The profit in 1995 corresponds to $t = 0$. Substitute $t = 0$ in the equation. Solve for P.

$P(0) = 7.4(1.59)^0$
$= 7.4$

The profit was $7.4 million.

d) 2015 is 20 years from 1995. Substitute $t = 20$ in the equation. Solve for P.

$P(20) = 7.4(1.59)^{20}$
$= 78\,917.66$

In 2015 the predicted profit is $78 917.66 million (or approximately $79 billion).

e) Substitute $P = 500$ in the equation. Solve for t.

$500 = 7.4(1.59)^t$ Divide each side by 7.4.

$67.6 = (1.59)^t$

Use systematic trial to find a value of t so that $(1.59)^t = 67.6$. From the table of values in part a), $h = 500$ lies between $t = 9$ and $t = 10$, so the nearest whole number is $t = 9$.
Add 9 years to 1995 to find the answer.
$1995 + 9 = 2004$
The profit reached $500 million in 2004.

6. a)

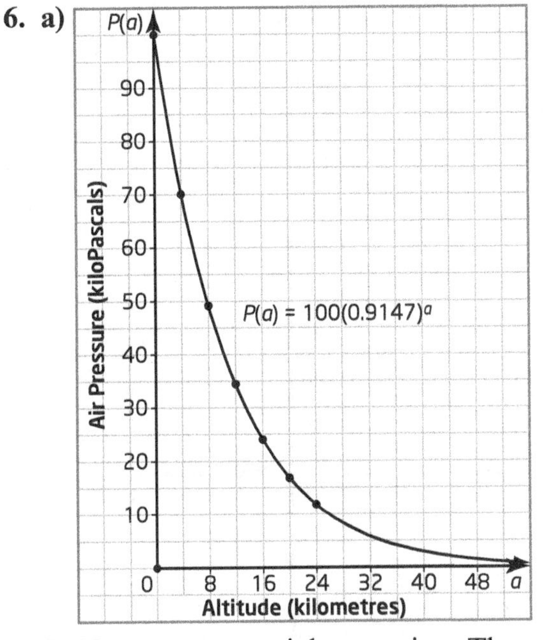

b) Use an exponential regression. The equation $p(a) = 100(0.9147)^a$ represents the air pressure, measured in kiloPascals (kPa), at an altitude of a km above sea level.

c) Use the equation to determine air pressure for each location. Convert each altitude to kilometres. Since 1000 m = 1 km, then $1 \text{ m} = \frac{1}{1000}$ or 0.001 km. Multiply each altitude by 0.001.

i) Mount Logan, 6050 m = 6.050 km

$$p(6.050) = 100(0.9147)^{6.050}$$
$$= 100(0.583\ 090\ 6)$$
$$= 58.309\ 06$$

Therefore, the air pressure on Mount Logan is approximately 58.3 kPa.

ii) Mount Everest, 8848 m = 8.848 km

$$p(8.848) = 100(0.9147)^{8.848}$$
$$= 100(0.454\ 353\ 4)$$
$$= 45.435\ 34$$

Therefore, the air pressure on Mount Everest is approximately 45.4 kPa.

d) To determine the altitude when the air pressure is 20 kPa, substitute $p = 20$ into the equation and solve for a. From the table we know that $p = 24$ when $a = 16$ and also $p = 16.8$ when $a = 20$. Since $p = 20$ is between 16.8 and 24, try values of a between 16 and 20. Try $a = 18$. $100(0.9147)^{18} = 20.09$. This value is very close to 20. Therefore, the air pressure is 20 kPa at an altitude of approximately 18 km above sea level.

7. a)

t (hours)	P (% caffeine remaining)
0	100
2	75.7
4	57.3
6	43.4
8	32.8
10	24.8
12	18.8
14	14.2
16	10.8
18	8.2
20	6.2
22	4.7
24	3.5

b) exponential decay

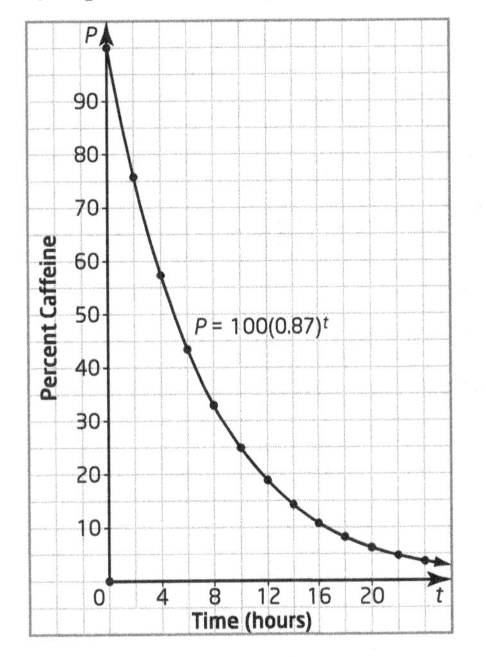

c) i) 87% **ii)** 28.6% **iii)** 12.4%
d) approximately 5 h

8. a) $l = p(1.20)^n$
b) $t = q(0.83)^n$
c) $l = p(1.20)^n$ represents exponential growth; the ratio 1.20 is greater than 1. $t = q(0.83)^n$ represents exponential decay; the ratio 0.83 is between 0 and 1.
d) $l = 2.00(1.20)^n$; $t = 0.50(0.83)^n$
e) $l = 12.38$ m; $t = 0.08$ m
f) 13 passes; approximately 0.04 m
g) 33 passes; approximately 820 m

Chapter 3 Review

1. a) C
b) 85 is the initial population; 3^n represents the constant ratio for tripling

2. a)–c) 1 **d)** −1

3. a) i) exponential **ii)** linear
iii) quadratic
b) i) For exponential functions the constant ratio of the first and second differences is equal.
ii) For linear functions the first differences are equal.
iii) For quadratic functions the second differences are equal.

4. a) $\frac{1}{x^3}$ **b)** $\frac{3}{b^2}$

5. a) w^{-4} **b)** $-3b^{-8}$

6. a) $\frac{1}{216}$ **b)** $\frac{6}{125}$
c) $\frac{1}{12}$ **d)** 8
e) $\frac{125}{216}$ **f)** $\frac{49}{64}$

7. a) $\frac{b^{10}}{9}$ **b)** $-\frac{b^6}{8a^6}$
c) $\frac{x^{18}}{729}$ **d)** $\frac{243d^{10}}{32c^{20}}$

8. a) $\frac{16}{9}$ **b)** $\frac{2187}{128}$
c) −5 **d)** 9

9. a) $(-3125)^{\frac{4}{5}}$ **b)** $32^{\frac{3}{5}}$

10. a) $\sqrt[5]{(-32)^4}$; 16 **b)** $\sqrt[3]{\left(\frac{1}{343}\right)^2}$; $\frac{1}{49}$
c) $\sqrt[3]{(-125)^2}$; 25

11. a) $16^{-\frac{1}{2}}$; $\frac{1}{4}$ **b)** $81^{\frac{3}{2}}$; 729 **c)** $256^{\frac{1}{8}}$; 2

12. a) $s^{\frac{5}{12}}$ **b)** $m^{\frac{2}{7}}n^{\frac{8}{15}}$ **c)** $\frac{1}{k^{\frac{3}{14}}}$
d) $\frac{2}{32}v^{\frac{9}{10}}$

13. a) $s = \frac{2\sqrt{A}}{3^{\frac{1}{4}}}$ **b)** 5.39 m

14. a)

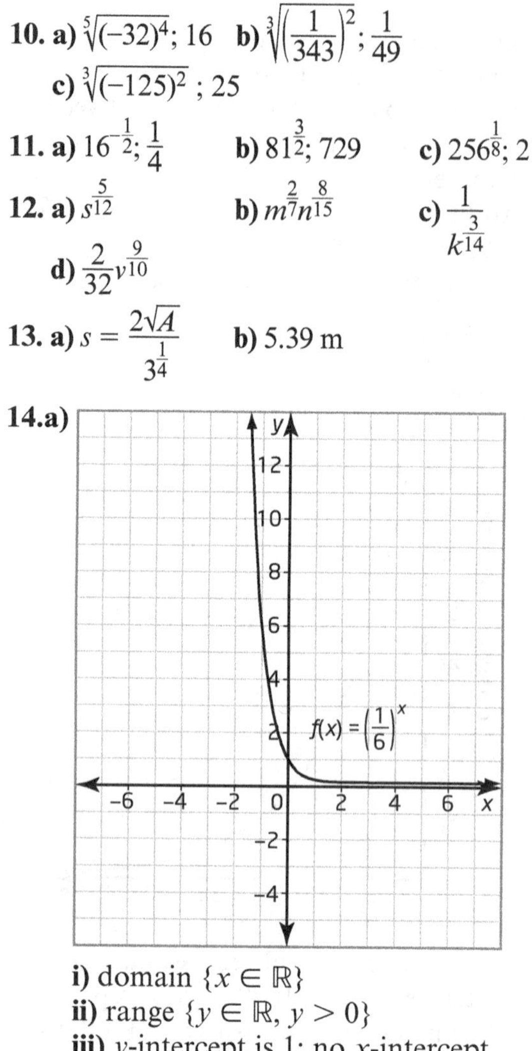

i) domain $\{x \in \mathbb{R}\}$
ii) range $\{y \in \mathbb{R}, y > 0\}$
iii) y-intercept is 1; no x-intercept
iv) decreasing for $x \in \mathbb{R}$
v) horizontal asymptote $y = 0$

b)

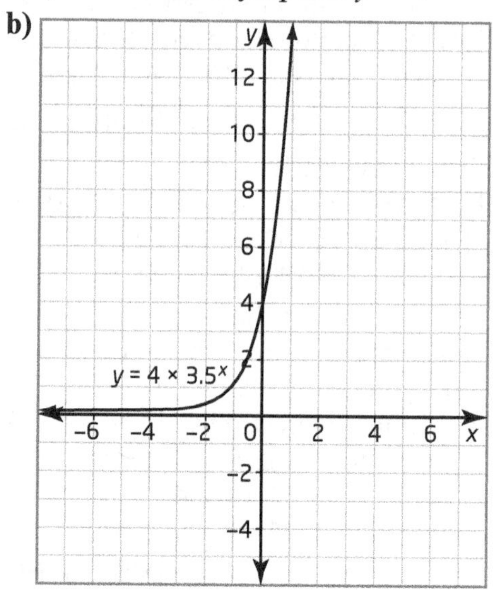

i) domain $\{x \in \mathbb{R}\}$
ii) range $\{y \in \mathbb{R}, y > 0\}$
iii) y-intercept is 4; no x-intercept
iv) increasing for $x \in \mathbb{R}$
v) horizontal asymptote $y = 0$

c)

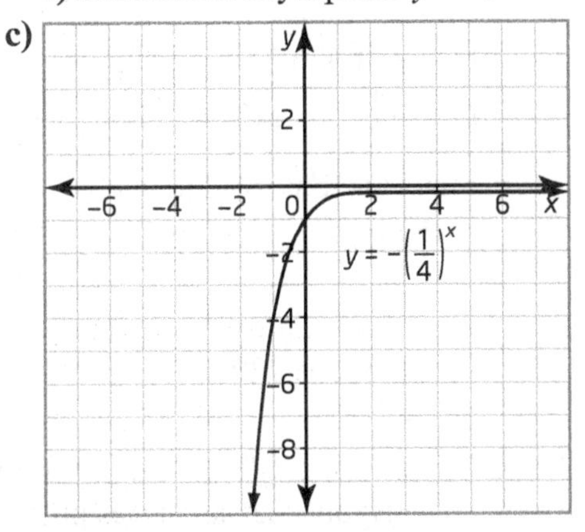

i) domain $\{x \in \mathbb{R}\}$
ii) range $\{y \in \mathbb{R}, y < 0\}$
iii) y-intercept is −1; no x-intercept
iv) increasing for $x \in \mathbb{R}$
v) horizontal asymptote $y = 0$

15.a) $A = 28\left(\frac{1}{2}\right)^{\frac{t}{5}}$

b) Answers may vary. Sample answer: In 5 days half the amount, or 14 grams, of the sample remain. The amount is reduced as time passes.

c) The graph falls to the right, since the amount of radioactive sample decreases. The first point on the graph is (0, 28) and the x-axis, or line $y = 0$, is the horizontal asymptote.
domain $\{t \in \mathbb{R}, t > 0\}$,
range $\{A \in \mathbb{R}, A > 0\}$

d) 4 mg

16.

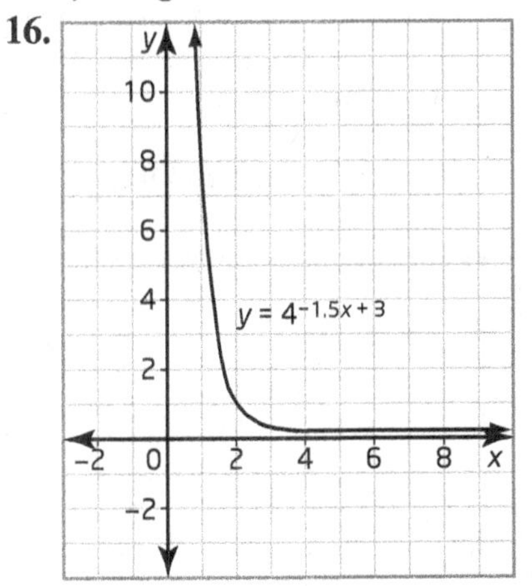

17. a) The function $f(x) = 0.5^x$ is stretched vertically by a factor of 2, stretched horizontally by a factor of 3, and shifted right 5 units. The corresponding transformed equation is $f(x) = 2\left(0.5^{\frac{1}{3}(x-5)}\right)$.

b) domain $\{x \in \mathbb{R}\}$,
range $\{y \in \mathbb{R}, y > 0\}$. The equation of the horizontal asymptote is $y = 0$.

18. a) The equation of the transformed function is

$$f(x) = -\frac{1}{3}\left[\left(\frac{1}{4}\right)^{2(x+4)}\right] + 6$$

b) domain $\{x \in \mathbb{R}\}$,
range $\{y \in \mathbb{R}, y < 6\}$. The equation of the horizontal asymptote is $y = 6$.

19. a)

t (years since 1981)	P (population in millions)
0	24.0
2	24.7
4	25.4
6	26.1
8	26.8
10	27.6
12	28.4
14	29.2
16	30.0
18	30.8
20	31.7

b) $P(t) = 24.0(1.014)^t$ **c)** 31.3 million
d) 36.9 million
e) approximately 2018

Chapter 3 Math Contest

1. D
2. B
3. C
4. D
5. A
6. 6
7. $x = 0, 1$
8. D
9. C
10. −20
11. A
12. D
13. $\{y \in \mathbb{R}, y < 2\}$

Chapter 4 Trigonometry

4.1 Special Angles

1.

θ	$\sin\theta$	$\cos\theta$	$\tan\theta$
0°	0	1	0
30°	$\frac{1}{2}$	$\frac{\sqrt{3}}{2}$	$\frac{1}{\sqrt{3}}$
45°	$\frac{1}{\sqrt{2}}$	$\frac{1}{\sqrt{2}}$	1
60°	$\frac{\sqrt{3}}{2}$	$\frac{1}{2}$	$\sqrt{3}$
90°	1	0	undefined
180°	0	−1	0
270°	−1	0	undefined
360°	0	1	0

2.

θ	$\sin\theta$	$\cos\theta$	$\tan\theta$
0°	0	1	0
30°	0.5000	0.8660	0.5774
45°	0.7071	0.7071	1
60°	0.8660	0.5000	1.7321
90°	1	0	undefined
180°	0	−1	0
270°	−1	0	undefined
360°	0	1	0

3. **a)** 45° **b)** 135°, 315°
   c) $\sin 225° = -\frac{1}{\sqrt{2}}$, $\cos 225° = -\frac{1}{\sqrt{2}}$, $\tan 225° = 1$
   d) $\sin 135° = \frac{1}{\sqrt{2}}$, $\cos 135° = -\frac{1}{\sqrt{2}}$, $\tan 135° = -1$, $\sin 315° = -\frac{1}{\sqrt{2}}$, $\cos 315° = \frac{1}{\sqrt{2}}$, $\tan 315° = -1$

4. **a)** 30° **b)** 210°, 330°
   c) $\sin 150° = \frac{1}{2}$, $\cos 150° = -\frac{\sqrt{3}}{2}$, $\tan 150° = -\frac{1}{\sqrt{3}}$
   d) $\sin 210° = -\frac{1}{2}$, $\cos 210° = -\frac{\sqrt{3}}{2}$, $\tan 210° = \frac{1}{\sqrt{3}}$, $\sin 330° = -\frac{1}{2}$, $\cos 330° = \frac{\sqrt{3}}{2}$, $\tan 330° = -\frac{1}{\sqrt{3}}$

5. **a)** 60° **b)** 120°, 240°
   c) $\sin 300° = -\frac{\sqrt{3}}{2}$, $\cos 300° = \frac{1}{2}$, $\tan 300° = -\sqrt{3}$
   d) $\sin 120° = \frac{\sqrt{3}}{2}$, $\cos 120° = -\frac{1}{2}$, $\tan 120° = -\sqrt{3}$, $\sin 240° = -\frac{\sqrt{3}}{2}$, $\cos 240° = -\frac{1}{2}$, $\tan 240° = \sqrt{3}$

6. Answers may vary. Sample answer: $\sin 70° = 0.94$, $\cos 70° = 0.34$, $\tan 70° = 2.75$

7. Answers may vary. Sample answer: $\sin 220° = -0.64$, $\cos 220° = -0.77$, $\tan 220° = 0.84$

8. **a)** The CAST rule identifies the quadrant in which each trigonometric ratio is positive. In the first quadrant, all the trigonometric ratios are positive. The sine ratio is positive in the second quadrant. The tangent is positive in the third quadrant, and the cosine is positive in the fourth quadrant.
   b)

Ratio	Positive in Quadrants:	Negative in Quadrants:
sin	first and second	third and fourth
cos	first and fourth	second and third
tan	first and third	second and fourth

9. **a)**

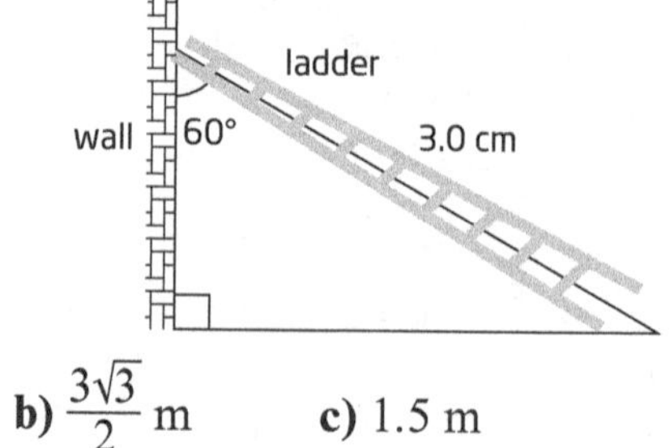

   b) $\frac{3\sqrt{3}}{2}$ m **c)** 1.5 m

10. **a)** $14\sqrt{2}$ km **b)** Pythagorean theorem

11. **a)**

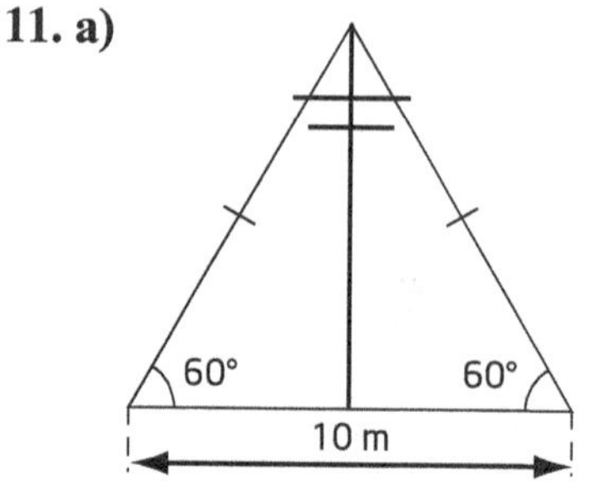

b) Let h represent the height of the hydro pole. The wires are of equal length, so the large triangle formed by the two wires is isosceles. The pole, which represents the altitude of the triangle, is halfway between the two points where the wires are secured to the ground. Therefore, the distance from the bottom of the pole to one of the secured points is 5 m.

Solve $\tan 60° = \frac{h}{5}$.

Substitute $\tan 60° = \sqrt{3}$.

$\sqrt{3} = \frac{h}{5}$

$h = 5(\sqrt{3})$

The pole is $5(\sqrt{3})$ m tall.

c) Let w represent the length of each wire. To determine the length of each wire, find the length of the hypotenuse of one of the right triangles. From part a) we now know the height of the pole.

Solve $\sin 60° = \frac{h}{w}$.

Substitute $\sin 60° = \frac{\sqrt{3}}{2}$ and $h = 5(\sqrt{3})$.

$\sqrt{3} = \frac{5\sqrt{3}}{w}$ Multiply each side by $2w$.

$\sqrt{3}w = 10(\sqrt{3})$ Simplify.

Each wire is 10 m long.

12. $96\sqrt{3}$ cm^2

13. a) $\frac{-(1+\sqrt{3})}{2}$ **b)** $\frac{1}{2\sqrt{3}}$ **c)** $3\sqrt{3} + \frac{1}{\sqrt{2}}$

14. Answers may vary.

15. a) 60°, 120° **b)** 45°, 135°, 225°, 315° **c)** 150°, 330°

16. $15 + 5\sqrt{3}$ m

17. b) i) $A = s^2$ **ii)** $A = \frac{3\sqrt{3}}{2}s^2$ **iii)** $A = \frac{\sqrt{3}}{4}s^2$

4.2 Co-terminal and Related Angles

1. a) $\sin\theta = \frac{4}{5}$, $\cos\theta = \frac{3}{5}$, $\tan\theta = \frac{4}{3}$

b) $\sin\theta = -\frac{2}{\sqrt{53}}$, $\cos\theta = -\frac{7}{\sqrt{53}}$, $\tan\theta = \frac{2}{7}$

c) $\sin\theta = \frac{3}{\sqrt{45}}$, $\cos\theta = -\frac{6}{\sqrt{45}}$, $\tan\theta = -\frac{1}{2}$

d) $\sin\theta = -\frac{5}{\sqrt{29}}$, $\cos\theta = \frac{2}{\sqrt{29}}$, $\tan\theta = -\frac{5}{2}$

2. a) $\sin\theta = \frac{5}{\sqrt{34}}$, $\cos\theta = -\frac{3}{\sqrt{34}}$, $\tan\theta = -\frac{5}{3}$

b) $\sin\theta = \frac{8}{17}$, $\cos\theta = -\frac{15}{17}$, $\tan\theta = -\frac{8}{15}$

c) $\sin\theta = -\frac{4}{5}$, $\cos\theta = -\frac{3}{5}$, $\tan\theta = \frac{4}{3}$

d) $\sin\theta = \frac{12}{13}$, $\cos\theta = -\frac{5}{13}$, $\tan\theta = -\frac{12}{5}$

e) $\sin\theta = \frac{3}{\sqrt{58}}$, $\cos\theta = \frac{7}{\sqrt{58}}$, $\tan\theta = \frac{3}{7}$

f) $\sin\theta = -\frac{9}{\sqrt{82}}$, $\cos\theta = \frac{1}{\sqrt{82}}$, $\tan\theta = -9$

3. a) $\sin A = \frac{15}{17}$, $\tan A = -\frac{15}{18}$

b) $\cos B = -\frac{3}{5}$, $\tan B = \frac{4}{3}$

c) $\sin C = -\frac{12}{13}$, $\cos C = \frac{5}{13}$

d) $\cos D = -\frac{6}{\sqrt{85}}$, $\tan D = \frac{7}{6}$

e) $\sin E = \frac{4\sqrt{10}}{13}$, $\tan E = -\frac{4\sqrt{10}}{3}$

f) $\sin F = -\frac{8}{\sqrt{233}}$, $\cos F = \frac{13}{\sqrt{233}}$

4. Answers may vary. Sample answers:

a) sin 120°, sin (−240°)

b) cos 150°, cos (−210°)

c) tan 135°, tan (−45°)

d) sin 40°, sin (−220°)

e) cos 75°, cos (−75°)

f) tan 10°, tan (−170°)

5. a) To determine three positive angles that are co-terminal with 205°, add multiples of 360° to 205°. The expression $205° + n360°$, where n is a positive integer, will result in positive co-terminal angles.

Let $n = 1$ to obtain one angle:
$205° + (1)360° = 565°$.

Let $n = 2$ to obtain a second angle:
$205° + (2)360° = 925°$.

Let $n = 3$ to obtain a third angle:
$205° + (3)360° = 1285°$.

b) To determine three negative angles that are co-terminal with 310°, subtract multiples of 360° from 310°. The expression $310° - n360°$, where n is a positive integer, will result in negative co-terminal angles.

Let $n = 1$ to obtain one angle:
$310° - (1)360° = -50°$.

Let $n = 2$ to obtain a second angle:
$310° - (2)360° = -410°$.

Let $n = 3$ to obtain a third angle:
$310° - (3)360° = -770°$.

6. **a)** not co-terminal; Their difference is not a multiple of 360°.
   b) co-terminal; Their difference is 360°.
   c) co-terminal; Their difference is a multiple of 360°.
   d) not co-terminal; Their difference is not a multiple of 360°.
   e) co-terminal; Their difference is 360°.
   f) co-terminal; Their difference is a multiple of 360°.
   g) not co-terminal; Their difference is not a multiple of 360°.
   h) co-terminal; Their difference is 360°.

7. **a)** $\sin A = -\frac{1}{2}$, $\cos A = \frac{\sqrt{3}}{2}$, $\tan A = -\frac{1}{\sqrt{3}}$
   b) $\sin B = \frac{\sqrt{3}}{2}$, $\cos B = -\frac{1}{2}$, $\tan B = -\sqrt{3}$
   c) $\sin C = 0$, $\cos C = -1$, $\tan C = 0$
   d) $\sin D = \frac{1}{\sqrt{2}}$, $\cos D = \frac{1}{\sqrt{2}}$, $\tan D = 1$
   e) $\sin E = \frac{1}{2}$, $\cos E = \frac{\sqrt{3}}{2}$, $\tan E = \frac{1}{\sqrt{3}}$
   f) $\sin F = -\frac{1}{2}$, $\cos F = -\frac{\sqrt{3}}{2}$, $\tan F = \frac{1}{\sqrt{3}}$

8. From the CAST rule we know that sine is negative in the third and fourth quadrants. From our special triangles we know that $\sin 45° = \frac{1}{\sqrt{2}}$.
   In the third quadrant, the angle A that results in $\sin A = -\frac{1}{\sqrt{2}}$ is $A = 225°$.
   In the fourth quadrant, the angle B that results in $\sin B = -\frac{1}{\sqrt{2}}$ is $B = 315°$.

9. 45°, 225°

10. 240°, 300°

11. 0°, 180°, 360°; sine

12. **a)** $\sin A = -\frac{7}{\sqrt{74}}$, $\cos A = \frac{5}{\sqrt{74}}$, $\tan A = -\frac{7}{5}$;
    $\sin B = -\frac{7}{\sqrt{74}}$, $\cos B = -\frac{5}{\sqrt{74}}$, $\tan B = \frac{7}{5}$
    b) $\angle A = 306°$, $\angle B = 234°$

13. **a)** $\sin C = -\frac{1}{\sqrt{37}}$, $\cos C = -\frac{6}{\sqrt{37}}$, $\tan C = \frac{1}{6}$;
    $\sin D = \frac{1}{\sqrt{37}}$, $\cos D = -\frac{6}{\sqrt{37}}$, $\tan D = -\frac{1}{6}$
    b) $\angle C = 189°$, $\angle D = 171°$

14. **a)** $\sin E = \frac{3}{\sqrt{13}}$, $\cos E = -\frac{2}{\sqrt{13}}$, $\tan E = -\frac{3}{2}$;
    $\sin F = -\frac{3}{\sqrt{13}}$, $\cos F = \frac{2}{\sqrt{13}}$, $\tan F = -\frac{3}{2}$
    b) $\angle E = 124°$, $\angle F = 304°$

15. **a)** $\theta = 229°$ or $\theta = 311°$
    b) $\theta = 66°$ or $\theta = 294°$
    c) $\theta = 144°$ or $\theta = 324°$

16. **a)** 27.7 square units
    b) 304.0 square units
    c) 1383.9 square units

17. 146.3°

18. **a)** $P\left(-\frac{3}{\sqrt{58}}, -\frac{7}{\sqrt{58}}\right)$
    b) $\sin \theta = -\frac{7}{\sqrt{58}}$, $\cos \theta = -\frac{3}{\sqrt{58}}$
    c) The corresponding trigonometric ratios are equal.

4.3 Reciprocal Trigonometric Ratios

1. $\sin C = \frac{7}{25}$, $\csc C = \frac{25}{7}$, $\cos C = \frac{24}{25}$,
   $\sec C = \frac{25}{24}$, $\tan C = \frac{7}{24}$, $\cot C = \frac{24}{7}$

2. $\sin A = \frac{24}{25}$, $\cos A = \frac{7}{25}$, $\tan A = \frac{24}{7}$,
   $\csc A = \frac{25}{24}$, $\sec A = \frac{25}{7}$, $\cot A = \frac{7}{24}$

3. **a)** $\csc \theta = \frac{5}{3}$ **b)** $\sec \theta = \sqrt{2}$
   c) $\cot \theta = \frac{3}{7}$ **d)** $\sec \theta = -\frac{\sqrt{61}}{6}$
   e) $\cot \theta = -\frac{1}{5}$ **f)** $\csc \theta = -\frac{13}{12}$
   g) $\sec \theta =$ undefined
   h) $\csc \theta = 1$

4. **a)** $\cos \theta = \frac{3}{8}$ **b)** $\sin \theta = \frac{4}{5}$
   c) $\tan \theta = -\sqrt{3}$ **d)** $\cos \theta = -\frac{15}{17}$
   e) $\csc \theta = \frac{1}{\sqrt{2}}$ **f)** $\tan \theta = -\frac{4}{9}$
   g) $\cos \theta = -1$ **h)** $\sin \theta = 0$

5. **a)** $\sin 40° = 0.643$, $\cos 40° = 0.766$, $\tan 40° = 0.839$, $\csc 40° = 1.556$, $\sec 40° = 1.305$, $\cot 40° = 1.192$
   b) $\sin 36° = 0.588$, $\cos 36° = 0.809$, $\tan 36° = 0.727$, $\csc 36° = 1.701$, $\sec 36° = 1.236$, $\cot 36° = 1.376$

c) $\sin 88° = 0.999$, $\cos 88° = 0.035$, $\tan 88° = 28.636$, $\csc 88° = 1.001$, $\sec 88° = 28.654$, $\cot 88° = 0.035$

d) $\sin 110° = 0.940$, $\cos 110° = -0.342$, $\tan 110° = -2.747$, $\csc 110° = 1.064$, $\sec 110° = -2.924$, $\cot 110° = -0.364$

e) $\sin 237° = -0.839$, $\cos 237° = -0.545$, $\tan 237° = 1.540$, $\csc 237° = -1.192$, $\sec 237° = -1.836$, $\cot 237° = 0.649$

f) $\sin 319° = -0.656$, $\cos 319° = 0.755$, $\tan 319° = -0.869$, $\csc 319° = -1.524$, $\sec 319° = 1.325$, $\cot 319° = -1.150$

g) $\sin 95° = 0.996$, $\cos 95° = -0.087$, $\tan 95° = -11.430$, $\csc 95° = 1.004$, $\sec 95° = -11.474$, $\cot 95° = -0.087$

h) $\sin 67° = 0.921$, $\cos 67° = 0.391$, $\tan 67° = 2.356$, $\csc 67° = 1.086$, $\sec 67° = 2.559$, $\cot 67° = 0.424$

i) $\sin 124° = 0.829$, $\cos 124° = -0.559$, $\tan 124° = -1.483$, $\csc 124° = 1.206$, $\sec 124° = -1.788$, $\cot 124° = -0.675$

6. **a)** 38° **b)** 56° **c)** 19° **d)** 61° **e)** 41° **f)** 50° **g)** 15° **h)** 74°

7. $\sin 210° = -\frac{1}{2}$, $\cos 210° = -\frac{\sqrt{3}}{2}$, $\tan 210° = \frac{1}{\sqrt{3}}$, $\csc 210° = -2$, $\sec 210° = -\frac{2}{\sqrt{3}}$, $\cot 210° = \sqrt{3}$

8. $\sin 225° = -\frac{1}{\sqrt{2}}$, $\cos 225° = -\frac{1}{\sqrt{2}}$, $\tan 225° = 1$, $\csc 225° = -\sqrt{2}$, $\sec 225° = -\sqrt{2}$, $\cot 225° = 1$

9. $\sin 90° = 1$, $\cos 90° = 0$, $\tan 90° =$ undefined, $\csc 90° = 1$, $\sec 90° =$ undefined, $\cot 90° = 0$

10. 240°, 300°

11. **a)** 33° **b)** 37° **c)** 69° **d)** 44° **e)** 51° **f)** 33° **g)** 71° **h)** 35°

12. 45°, 225°

13. **a)** $\sin\theta = \frac{4}{5}$, $\csc\theta = \frac{5}{4}$, $\cos\theta = -\frac{3}{5}$, $\sec\theta = -\frac{5}{3}$, $\tan\theta = -\frac{4}{3}$, $\cot\theta = -\frac{3}{4}$

b) $\sin\theta = -\frac{5}{13}$, $\csc\theta = -\frac{13}{5}$, $\cos\theta = -\frac{12}{13}$, $\sec\theta = -\frac{13}{12}$, $\tan\theta = \frac{5}{12}$, $\cot\theta = \frac{12}{5}$

c) $\sin\theta = \frac{15}{17}$, $\csc\theta = \frac{17}{15}$, $\cos\theta = -\frac{8}{15}$, $\sec\theta = -\frac{15}{8}$, $\tan\theta = -\frac{15}{8}$, $\cot\theta = -\frac{8}{15}$

d) $\sin\theta = \frac{1}{\sqrt{10}}$, $\csc\theta = \sqrt{10}$, $\cos\theta = \frac{3}{\sqrt{10}}$, $\sec\theta = \frac{\sqrt{10}}{3}$, $\tan\theta = \frac{1}{3}$, $\cot\theta = 3$

e) $\sin\theta = -\frac{3}{\sqrt{13}}$, $\cos\theta = \frac{2}{\sqrt{13}}$, $\tan\theta = -\frac{3}{\sqrt{13}}$, $\csc\theta = -\frac{3}{\sqrt{13}}$, $\sec\theta = \frac{\sqrt{13}}{2}$, $\cot\theta = -\frac{2}{3}$

f) $\sin\theta = -\frac{12}{\sqrt{193}}$, $\cos\theta = -\frac{7}{\sqrt{193}}$, $\tan\theta = \frac{12}{7}$, $\csc\theta = -\frac{\sqrt{193}}{12}$, $\sec\theta = -\frac{\sqrt{193}}{7}$, $\cot\theta = \frac{7}{12}$

g) $\sin\theta = \frac{5}{\sqrt{26}}$, $\cos\theta = \frac{1}{\sqrt{26}}$, $\tan\theta = 5$, $\csc\theta = \frac{\sqrt{26}}{5}$, $\sec\theta = \sqrt{26}$, $\cot\theta = \frac{1}{5}$

h) $\sin\theta = \frac{11}{\sqrt{157}}$, $\cos\theta = \frac{6}{\sqrt{157}}$, $\tan\theta = \frac{11}{6}$, $\csc\theta = \frac{\sqrt{157}}{11}$, $\sec\theta = \frac{\sqrt{157}}{6}$, $\cot\theta = \frac{6}{11}$

i) $\sin\theta = \frac{1}{\sqrt{2}}$, $\cos\theta = -\frac{1}{\sqrt{2}}$, $\tan\theta = -1$, $\csc\theta = \sqrt{2}$, $\sec\theta = -\sqrt{2}$, $\cot\theta = -1$

j) $\sin\theta = -\frac{3}{\sqrt{73}}$, $\cos\theta = \frac{8}{\sqrt{73}}$, $\tan\theta = -\frac{3}{8}$, $\csc\theta = -\frac{\sqrt{73}}{3}$, $\sec\theta = \frac{\sqrt{73}}{8}$, $\cot\theta = -\frac{8}{3}$

14. **a)** $\csc\theta = \sqrt{37}$, $\sec\theta = \frac{\sqrt{37}}{6}$, $\cot\theta = 6$; $\theta = 9°$

b) $\csc\theta = \frac{\sqrt{29}}{5}$, $\sec\theta = \frac{\sqrt{29}}{2}$, $\cot\theta = \frac{2}{5}$; $\theta = 68°$

c) $\csc\theta = \frac{\sqrt{113}}{7}$, $\sec\theta = \frac{\sqrt{113}}{8}$, $\cot\theta = \frac{8}{7}$; $\theta = 41°$

d) $\csc\theta = \frac{\sqrt{73}}{3}$, $\sec\theta = \frac{\sqrt{73}}{8}$, $\cot\theta = \frac{8}{3}$; $\theta = 21°$

e) $\csc\theta = \frac{\sqrt{202}}{11}$, $\sec\theta = \frac{\sqrt{202}}{9}$, $\cot\theta = \frac{9}{11}$; $\theta = 51°$

f) $\csc\theta = \frac{\sqrt{65}}{4}$, $\sec\theta = \frac{\sqrt{65}}{7}$, $\cot\theta = \frac{7}{4}$; $\theta = 30°$

15. First determine the value of the smallest positive angle θ such that $\csc \theta = 3.5$.

Solve $\sin \theta = \frac{1}{3.5}$ to get $\theta = 17°$. Using the CAST rule we know that cosecant is negative where sine is negative, that is, in the third and fourth quadrants.
In the third quadrant, the angle is $180° + 17° = 197°$.
In the fourth quadrant, the angle is $360° - 17° = 343°$.
The two angles are 197° and 343°.

16. 99°, 261°

17. 14°, 194°

18. $\sin \theta = -\frac{24}{25}$, $\cos \theta = \frac{7}{25}$, $\csc \theta = -\frac{25}{24}$, $\sec \theta = \frac{25}{7}$, $\cot \theta = -\frac{7}{24}$

19. $\sin \theta = \frac{4}{5}$, $\cos \theta = -\frac{3}{5}$, $\tan \theta = -\frac{4}{3}$, $\sec \theta = -\frac{5}{3}$, $\cot \theta = -\frac{3}{4}$

20. $\sin \theta = -\frac{\sqrt{8}}{3}$, $\tan \theta = \sqrt{8}$, $\csc \theta = -\frac{3}{\sqrt{8}}$, $\sec \theta = -3$, $\cot \theta = \frac{1}{\sqrt{8}}$

21. $\sin \theta = \frac{\sqrt{33}}{7}$, $\cos \theta = \frac{4}{7}$, $\tan \theta = \frac{\sqrt{33}}{4}$, $\csc \theta = \frac{7}{\sqrt{33}}$, $\cot \theta = \frac{4}{\sqrt{33}}$

22. a) $\sec 48° = \frac{w}{16.7}$, where w represents the length of the wire
b) 25.0 m

23. a) $\csc 14.5° = \frac{r}{1.3}$, where r represents the length of the ramp
b) 5.2 m, or 5 m and 20 cm

24. a) $\frac{171}{196}$
b) $\frac{16}{153}$
c) $\frac{25}{169}$
d) $\frac{153}{16}$

25. Substitute $\sin \theta = \frac{y}{r}$ and $\cos \theta = \frac{x}{r}$ into the left side of the given equation.

$$\begin{aligned} \text{L.S.} &= \sin^2 \theta + \cos^2 \theta \\ &= \left(\frac{y}{r}\right)^2 + \left(\frac{x}{r}\right)^2 \\ &= \frac{y^2}{r^2} + \frac{x^2}{r^2} \\ &= \frac{x^2 + y^2}{r^2} \\ &= \frac{r^2}{r^2} \\ &= 1 \\ &= \text{R.S.} \end{aligned}$$

Substitute $x^2 + y^2 = r^2$ in the numerator.

The name is appropriate because the identity represents the Pythagorean theorem in terms of the trigonometric ratios.

b) Substitute $\sin \theta = \frac{1}{\cos \theta}$ and $\cos \theta = \frac{1}{\sec \theta}$ in $\sin^2 \theta + \cos^2 \theta = 1$.

An equivalent equation is $\frac{1}{\cos^2 \theta} + \frac{1}{\sec^2 \theta} = 1$.

26. $\sin \theta = -\frac{\sqrt{a^2 - b^2}}{a}$, $\cos \theta = -\frac{b}{a}$, $\tan \theta = \frac{\sqrt{a^2 - b^2}}{b}$, $\csc \theta = -\frac{a}{\sqrt{a^2 - b^2}}$, $\cot \theta = \frac{b}{\sqrt{a^2 - b^2}}$

27. $\csc \theta = \frac{\sqrt{5x^2 + 2x + 1}}{x + 1}$, $\sec \theta = \frac{\sqrt{5x^2 + 2x + 1}}{2x}$

4.4 Problems in Two Dimensions

1. a) Because ΔABC is a right triangle, use the cosine ratio.
b) Because ΔPQR is a right triangle, use the tangent ratio.
c) ΔABC is an oblique triangle where three sides are known, so use the cosine law.
d) ΔDEF is an oblique triangle where two sides and the contained angle are known, so use the cosine law.
e) ΔXYZ is a right triangle, so use the tangent ratio.

2. a) $a = 10.6$ cm b) $r = 7.3$ m
c) ∠B = 44.0° d) $d = 16.3$ cm
e) ∠Y = 51.7°

3. 61.1°

4. a) $a = 8.6$ cm, ∠B = 85°, ∠C = 60°
b) ∠A = 117.3°, ∠B = 26.4°, ∠C = 36.3°
c) $b = 19.8$ m, $c = 17.7$ m, ∠C = 63°

5. 4.7 m

6. 6.0 km

7. a) 4.5 km b) 92.4°

8. **a)** This triangle has only one solution, $a = 14.7$ cm.

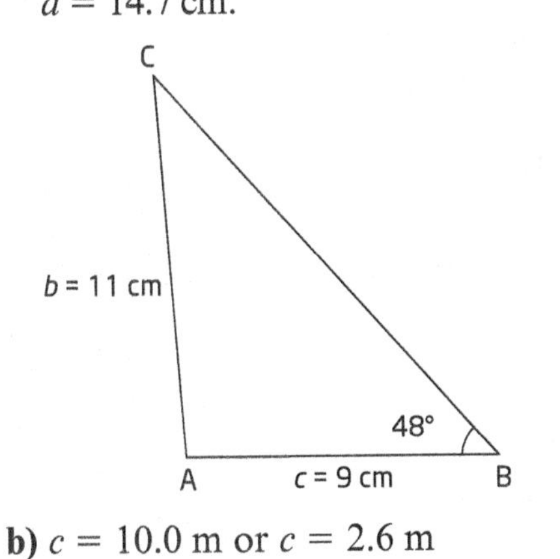

b) $c = 10.0$ m or $c = 2.6$ m

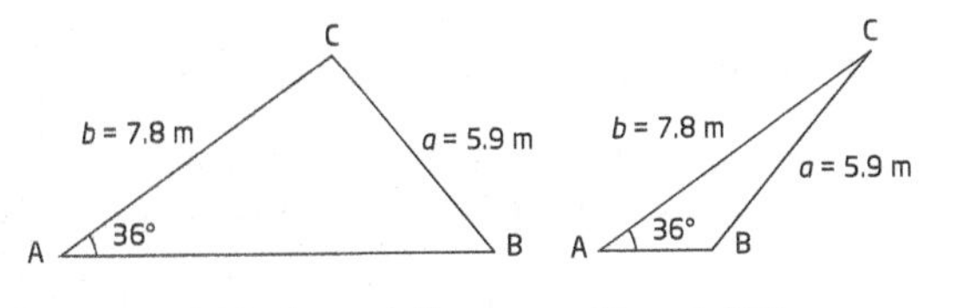

9. **a)** $\angle C = 39°$, $b = 4.7$ cm, $\angle C = 141°$, $b = 1.0$ cm
   b) $\angle F = 56°$, $e = 6$ cm, $\angle F = 124°$, $e = 2.7$ cm

10. **a)** $b \sin A = 2.7 \sin 32°$
    $= 1.4$
    b) Since $a = 1.2$ and $1.2 < 1.4$, then $a < b \sin A$, so there is no solution.

11. **a)** 2.4 **b)** one solution

12. **a)** 4.3 **b)** two solutions

13. 8.1 km

14. 147.5 km or 64.4 km

15. 122 m

16. Aqua: 31.6 km; Belli: 22.8 km

17. 5.8 km or 50.1 km

18. 9.2 units, 12.4 units

19. $\angle A = 49°$, $\angle C = 101°$, $AB = 7.8$ cm OR $\angle A = 131°$, $\angle C = 19°$, $AB = 2.6$ cm

20. Answer may vary.

21. **a)** Two solutions will occur when $a < b$ and $a > b \sin A$. Substitute $\angle A = 40°$ and $b = 50.0$ to get $a > 50 \sin 40°$, where $50 \sin 40° = 32.1$. Note, however, that since $b = 50.0$ and $a < b$, then $a < 50$. The range of values for a is $32.1 < a < 50.0$.
    b) $a < 104.2$ **c)** $a = 61.8$ or $a > 73.7$

4.5 Problems in Three Dimensions

1. 43°

2. **a)** 18.8 m **b)** 74.4°

3. **a)** 3.4 m **b)** 6.8 m **c)** 9.6 m

4. 14.8 cm

5. 4.2 km

6. **a)** 13.7 cm **b)** 21°

7. **a)**

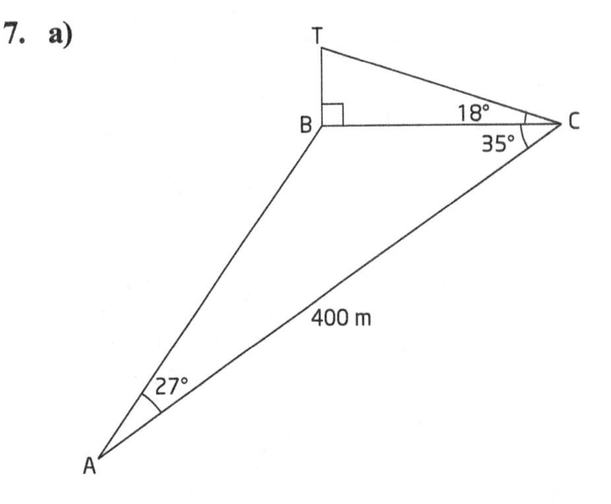

b) There is insufficient information in $\triangle TBC$ to find the height TB directly; however, since BC is in common to $\triangle ABC$ and $\triangle TBC$, use $\triangle ABC$ to find the length of BC. Then, find the height TB in $\triangle TBC$.

In $\triangle ABC$, $\angle B = 180° - 27° - 35°$
$= 118°$

Use the sine law to find the length of BC.

$$\frac{BC}{\sin 27°} = \frac{400}{\sin 118°}$$

$$BC = \frac{400 \sin 27°}{\sin 118°}$$

$$BC \doteq 205.7$$

$\triangle TBC$ is a right triangle. Use the tangent ratio to determine the height TB.

$$\tan 18° = \frac{TB}{205.7}$$

$$TB = 205.7 \tan 18°$$

$$\doteq 66.8$$

The height of the cliff is approximately 67 m.

8. 120 m

9. First draw a diagram to represent this situation.

Let P_1 represent the initial position of the balloon before it rises.
Let P_2 represent the balloon's position after it rises vertically.
Let B represent the barn and let F represent the farmhouse.
Mark the angles of depression.
Use parallel lines to determine that $\angle BFP_2 = 42°$ and $\angle BFP_1 = 28°$.
Subtract 42° − 28° to determine that $\angle P_1FP_2 = 14°$.

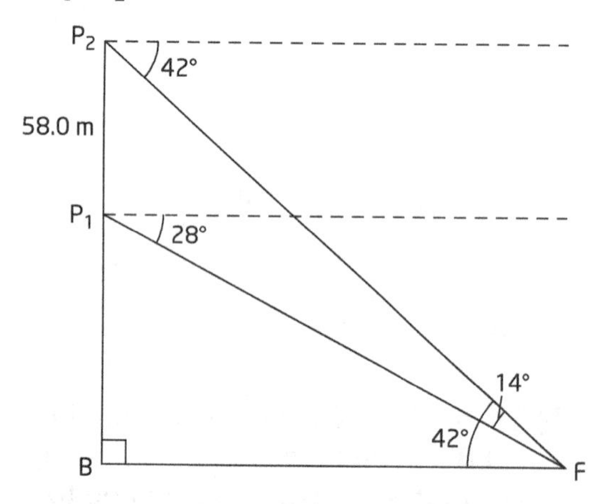

a) There is insufficient information to determine the initial height of the balloon, P_1B.
In ΔP_1P_2F,

$$\angle P_2P_1F = 90° + 28° \doteq 118°$$

Determine the distance P_2F by using the sine law in ΔP_1P_2F.

$$\frac{58}{\sin 14°} = \frac{P_2F}{\sin 118°}$$

$$P_2F = \frac{58 \sin 118°}{\sin 14°} = 211.7$$

ΔP_2BF is a right triangle. Use the sine ratio to determine the distance P_1B.

$$\sin 42° = \frac{P_1B + 58}{211.7}$$

$$P_1B = 211.7 \sin 42° - 58 \doteq 83.7$$

The balloon is at a height of approximately 83.7 m before it rises.

b) ΔP_1BF is a right triangle. Use the cotangent ratio to determine the distance BF.

$$\cot 28° = \frac{BF}{83.7}$$

$$BF \doteq 157.4$$

The barn is approximately 157.4 m from the farmhouse.

10. 37.1 m

11. 37.4 m

12. 43.7 m

13. 1.36 km

4.6 Trigonometric Identities

1. Answers may vary. Sample answers:
a) $1 - \cos^2 \theta$ **b)** $\sec^2 \theta - 1$ **c)** $1 + \tan^2 \theta$
d) $\cos^2 \theta$ **e)** $-\cot^2 \theta$ **f)** -1
g) $\frac{-1}{1 + \cot^2 \theta}$ **h)** $\cot^2 \theta$

2. **a)** 1 **b)** $\sin \theta$ **c)** $\frac{1}{\sin \theta \cos \theta}$
d) $|\sin \theta|$ **e)** -1 **f)** $\frac{2}{\cos \theta}$

3. **a)** $\sin^2 \theta$
b) $\tan^2 \theta + \sin^2 \theta$
c) $4(1 + 2 \cos \theta \sin \theta)$
d) $\sin^2 \theta - \cos^2 \theta$ or $1 - 2 \cos^2 \theta$ or $2 \sin^2 \theta - 1$

4.– 5. Answer may vary.

6. Technology may be used to graph each side of the identity. If the graphs are the same, then the identity is verified.

7. Answer may vary.

8. $$\text{L.S.} = \frac{1 + \cot \theta}{\csc \theta} = \frac{1 + \frac{\cos \theta}{\sin \theta}}{\frac{1}{\sin \theta}} = \frac{\sin \theta}{1} \times \left(\frac{\sin \theta + \cos \theta}{\sin \theta}\right) = \sin \theta + \cos \theta$$

Therefore, L.S. = R.S., and the statement is true for all θ.

9. Answers may vary.

10. Prove $\sin^4\theta + 2\cos^2\theta - \cos^4\theta = 1$ for all θ.

$$\begin{aligned} \text{L.S.} &= \sin^4\theta + 2\cos^2\theta - \cos^4\theta \\ &= (\sin^2\theta)^2 + 2\cos^2\theta - \cos^4\theta \\ &= (1-\cos^2\theta)^2 + 2\cos^2\theta - \cos^4\theta && \text{Substitute } \sin^2\theta = 1-\cos^2\theta. \\ &= 1 - 2\cos^2\theta + \cos^4\theta + 2\cos^2\theta - \cos^4\theta && \text{Expand } (1-\cos^2\theta)^2. \\ &= 1 && \text{Simplify.} \end{aligned}$$

Therefore, L.S. = R.S., and the statement is true for all θ.

11. Answers may vary.

12. $1 + \cot^2\theta$

13.–14. Answers may vary.

15. When $\theta = 90°$, $\sin 90° = 1$, so $\frac{\cos\theta}{1-\sin\theta}$ has a value of 0 in the denominator. Therefore, this part of the expression is undefined. Similarly, when $\theta = 270°$, $\sin 270° = -1$, so $\frac{\cos\theta}{1+\sin\theta}$ has a value of 0 in the denominator. Therefore, this part of the expression is undefined.

16.–25. Answers may vary.

26. a) No **b)** Yes **c)** Yes **d)** No

27. b) Answers may vary. Sample answer: Substitute an angle value and show that the left side is not equal to the right side.

28.–34. Answers may vary.

35. $\cot^2\theta(1 + \tan^2\theta) = \csc^2\theta$

36.–39. Answers may vary.

40. 1

Chapter 4 Review

1. Answers may vary.

2. a) $-\frac{1}{2\sqrt{6}}$ **b)** $1 - \sqrt{3}$ **c)** $\sqrt{3} + 1$

3. a) i) $6\sqrt{2}$ m **ii)** 6 m
b) i) $\frac{12}{\sqrt{3}}$ m **ii)** $\frac{6}{\sqrt{3}}$ m
c) i) 12 m **ii)** $6\sqrt{3}$ m

4. $\sqrt{\frac{20}{\sqrt{3}}}$ cm

5. a) $\sin\theta = \frac{12}{13}$, $\cos\theta = -\frac{5}{13}$, $\tan = -\frac{12}{5}$
b) $\sin = -\frac{3}{5}$, $\cos = \frac{4}{5}$, $\tan = -\frac{3}{4}$

6. a) $\cos G = -\frac{\sqrt{96}}{11}$, $\tan G = \frac{5}{\sqrt{96}}$
b) $\sin E = \frac{\sqrt{33}}{7}$, $\tan E = \frac{\sqrt{33}}{4}$

7. a) $\theta = 39°$ or $\theta = 141°$
b) $\theta = 110°$ or $\theta = 250°$
c) $\theta = 24°$ or $\theta = 204°$

8. $\sin 120° = \frac{\sqrt{3}}{2}$, $\cos 120° = -\frac{1}{2}$, $\tan 120° = -\sqrt{3}$, $\csc 120° = \frac{2}{\sqrt{3}}$, $\sec 120° = -2$, $\cot 120° = -\frac{1}{\sqrt{3}}$

9. a) $\sin\theta = -\frac{7}{25}$, $\csc\theta = -\frac{25}{7}$, $\cos\theta = \frac{24}{25}$, $\sec\theta = \frac{25}{24}$, $\tan\theta = -\frac{7}{24}$, $\cot\theta = -\frac{24}{7}$
b) $\sin\theta = -\frac{3}{\sqrt{34}}$, $\csc\theta = -\frac{\sqrt{34}}{3}$, $\cos\theta = -\frac{5}{\sqrt{34}}$, $\sec\theta = -\frac{\sqrt{34}}{5}$, $\tan\theta = \frac{3}{5}$, $\cot\theta = \frac{5}{3}$
c) $\sin\theta = -\frac{9}{\sqrt{97}}$, $\csc\theta = -\frac{\sqrt{97}}{9}$, $\cos\theta = \frac{4}{\sqrt{97}}$, $\sec\theta = \frac{\sqrt{97}}{4}$, $\tan\theta = -\frac{9}{4}$, $\cot\theta = -\frac{4}{9}$
d) $\sin\theta = \frac{3}{\sqrt{10}}$, $\csc\theta = \frac{\sqrt{10}}{3}$, $\cos\theta = \frac{1}{\sqrt{10}}$, $\sec\theta = \sqrt{10}$, $\tan\theta = 3$, $\cot\theta = \frac{1}{3}$

10. a) one solution; $\angle B = 62°$, $\angle C = 47°$, $c = 9.4$ m
b) no solution
c) two solutions; $\angle B = 67°$, $\angle C = 69°$, $c = 12.5$ mm *or* $\angle B = 113°$, $\angle C = 23°$, $c = 5.2$ mm
d) one solution; $\angle E = 103°$, $\angle F = 35°$, $e = 12.4$ km
e) two solutions; $\angle D = 50°$, $\angle F = 92°$, $f = 21.8$ mm *or* $\angle D = 130°$, $\angle F = 12°$, $f = 4.5$ mm
f) no solution

11. 10.3 km or 1.0 km

12. **a)** 9.2 m **b)** 49°

13. 97.6 m

14. 111.0 km

15. 84 km

16. **a)** $1 - \sin^2 \theta$ **b)** $1 + \cot^2 \theta$
c) $\csc^2 \theta - 1$ **d)** $\tan^2 \theta$
e) 1 **f)** $\frac{1}{1 + \tan^2\theta}$

17. Answers may vary.

Math Contest

1. 2:1
2. $3\sqrt{3}:4\pi$
3. $\frac{10\sqrt{3}}{3}$ cm
4. D
5. B
6. C
7. B
8. A
9. B
10. D
11. C

Chapter 5 Trigonometric Functions

5.1 Modelling Periodic Behaviour

1. **a)** periodic; pattern of y-values repeats at regular intervals
b) non-periodic; pattern of y-values does not repeat at regular intervals
c) non-periodic; pattern of y-values does not repeat at regular intervals
d) periodic; pattern of y-values repeats at regular intervals
e) periodic; pattern of y-values repeats at regular intervals
f) non-periodic; pattern of y-values does not repeat at regular intervals
g) periodic; pattern of y-values repeats at regular intervals
h) non-periodic; pattern of y-values does not repeat at regular intervals

2. **a)** period is 6; amplitude is 1.5
c) period is 360; amplitude is approximately 5
e) period is 6; amplitude is 3.5
g) period is 3; amplitude is 3.5

3.–5. Answers may vary.

6. **a)** 6
b) −4
c) 3
d) 2

7. Answers may vary.

8. No, the period is not necessarily 6. For instance, the following graph shows a periodic function with $f(3) = f(9) = 2$, but the period is 10.

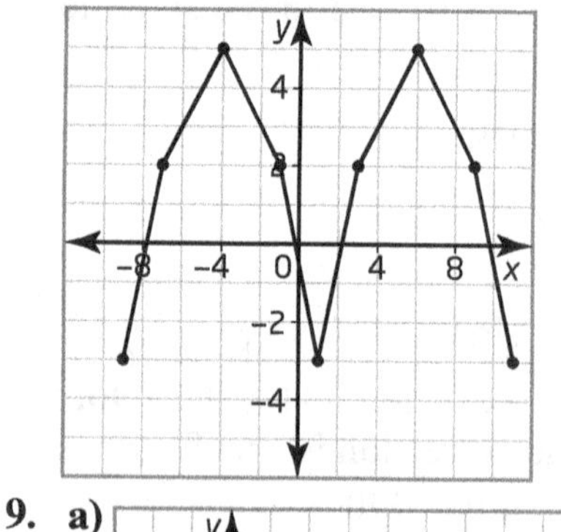

9. **a)**

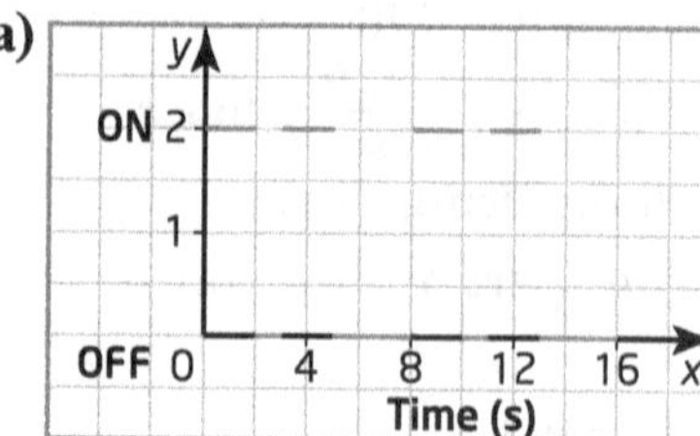

b) It is periodic because the pattern for the length of the flashes repeats at regular intervals.
c) 8 s
d) 1

10. **a)** No
b) Yes
c) Yes

11. Answers may vary.

12. **a)**

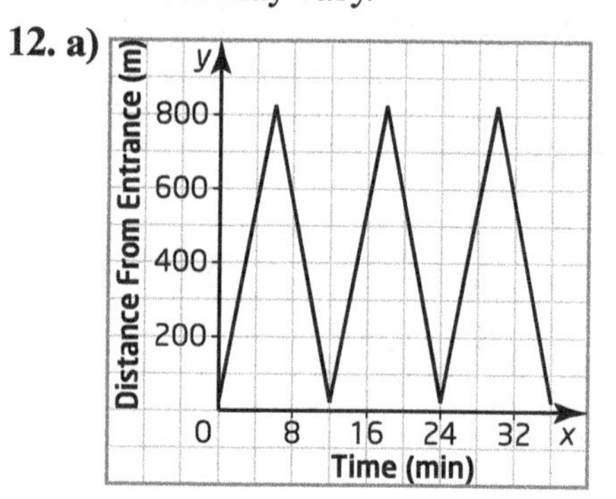

b) period is 12 min; amplitude is 400 m

c) Let t represent the time, in minutes, and let d represent the distance from the entrance, in metres.
The domain is $\{t \in \mathbb{R}, 0 \leq t \leq 36\}$.
The range is $\{d \in \mathbb{R}, 25 \leq d \leq 825\}$.

13. The length of the interval that gives the domain is a whole number multiple of the period. Examples may vary.

14. The amplitude is half the length of the interval that gives the range. Examples may vary.

15. Yes; period is 10

5.2 The Sine Function and the Cosine Function

1. a)

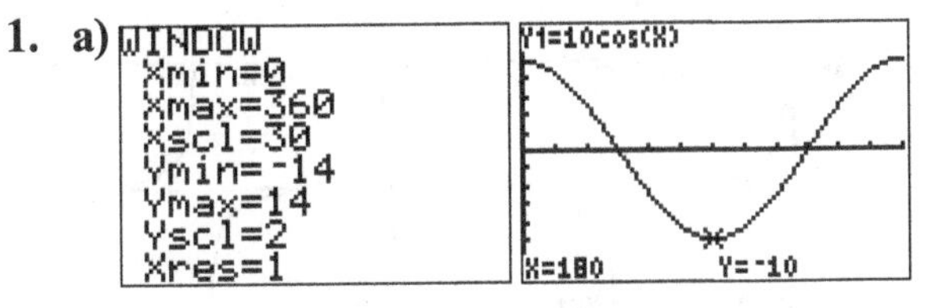

A cosine function models the horizontal displacement, because the horizontal displacement starts at 10 m and decreases to 0 m at 90°, a characteristic of the cosine function.

b)

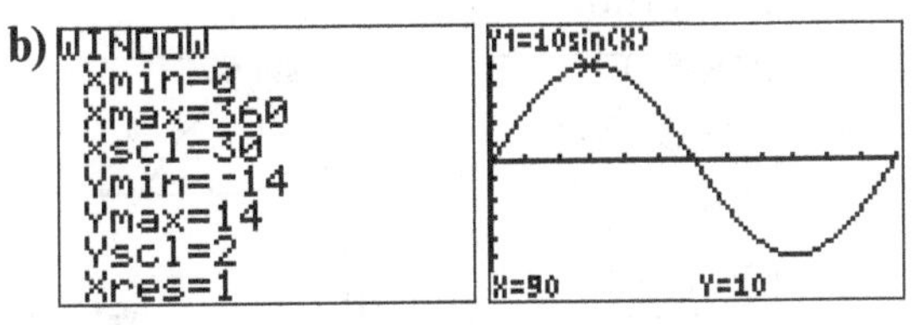

A sine function models the vertical displacement, because the vertical displacement starts at 0 m and moves through to a maximum at 90°, a characteristic of the sine function.

2. The graph has zeros at 0°, 180°, and 360°, and reaches the highest point, 10, at 90°, and the lowest point at 270°, so a sine function models the vertical distance.

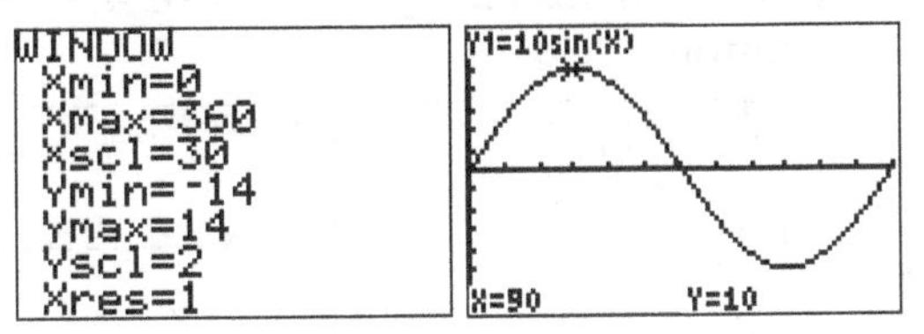

3. a) **b)**

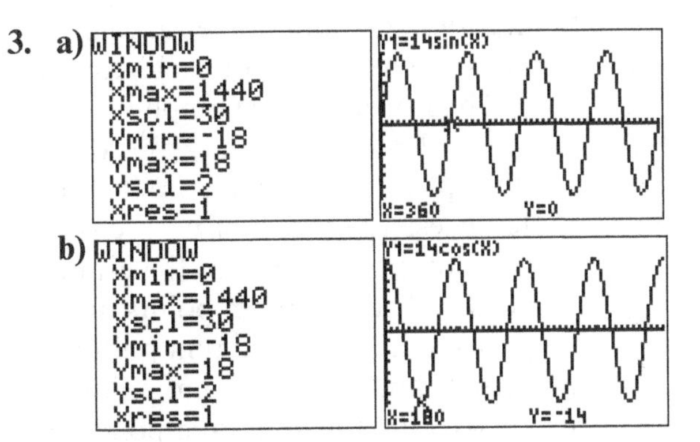

c) 4 cycles

d) 48 cycles

4. a)

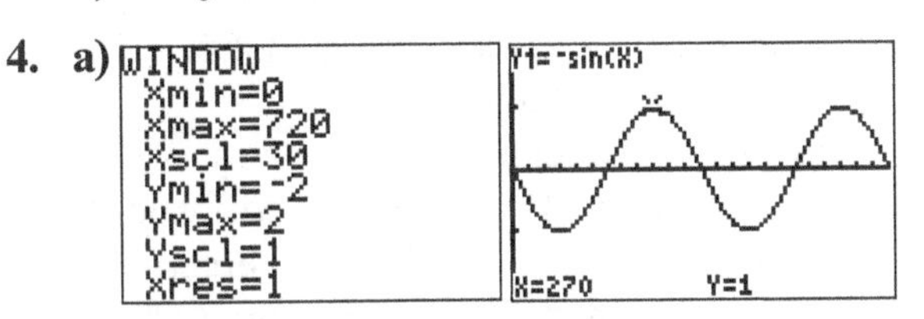

b)

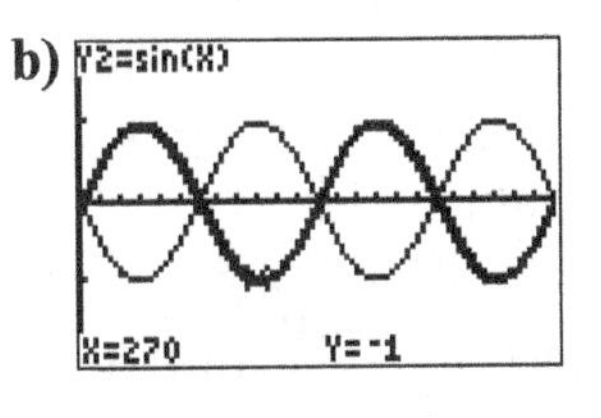

c) Similarities: The amplitude for each graph is 1. The period for each graph is 360°. The range for each graph is $\{y \in \mathbb{R}, -1 \leq y \leq 1\}$. The zeros, or x-intercepts, of each graph are the same.

Differences: The graph of $y = -\sin x$ is a reflection in the x-axis of the graph of $y = \sin x$. The minimum points on $y = -\sin x$ are the maximum points on $y = \sin x$, and the maximum points on $y = -\sin x$ are the minimum points on $y = \sin x$.

5. a) **b)**

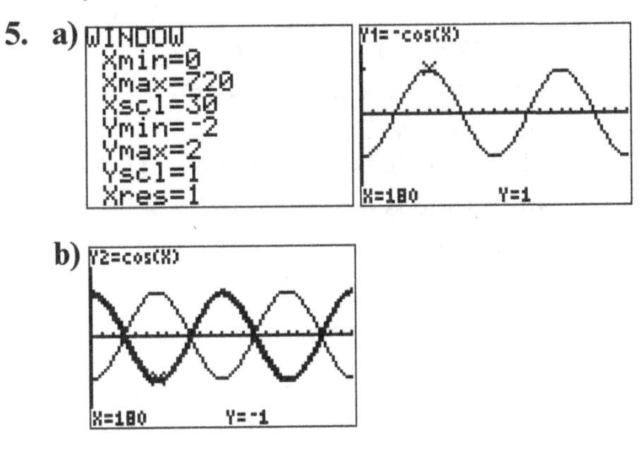

c) Similarities: The amplitude for each graph is 1. The period for each graph is 360°. The range for each graph is $\{y \in \mathbb{R}, -1 \le y \le 1\}$. The zeros, or x-intercepts, of each graph are the same.
Differences: The graph of $y = -\cos x$ is a reflection in the x-axis of the graph of $y = \cos x$. The minimum points on $y = -\cos x$ are the maximum points on $y = \cos x$, and the maximum points on $y = -\cos x$ are the minimum points on $y = \cos x$.

6. a) The y-intercept of the function $y = (\sin x)^2$ is the same as that of $y = \sin x$, which is 0.

b) The x-intercepts occur when $y = 0$. Solve $(\sin x)^2 = 0$. This is equivalent to solving $\sin x = 0$. The x-intercepts are $x = 0°, 180°, 360°, 540°$, and $720°$.

c) Since $(\sin x)^2$ is always positive, the minimum value of $y = (\sin x)^2$ is 0 and the maximum value is 1.

d) The range is $\{y \in \mathbb{R}, 0 \le y \le 1\}$. The amplitude is half of $\frac{1-0}{2}$, or 0.5.

e) 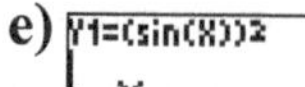
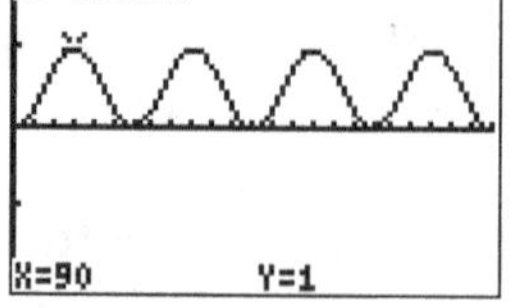

f) Similarities: The graphs of the two functions both begin at 0, they have a maximum of 1, and they have the same x-intercepts.
Differences: The amplitude, range, and period of the two function are different.

7. a) 1

b) 90°, 270°, 450°, and 630°

c) The minimum value is 0 and the maximum value is 1.

d) The range is $\{y \in \mathbb{R}, 0 \le y \le 1\}$. The amplitude is 0.5.

e) 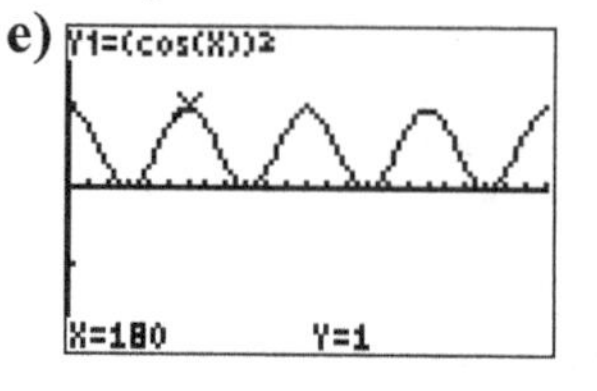

f) Similarities: The graphs of the two functions both begin at 1. They have a maximum of 1 and the same x-intercepts.
Differences: The amplitude, range, and period of the two functions are different.

8. a) Answers may vary. Sample answer: The graphs are the same because $\frac{\sin x}{\cos x} = \tan x$.

b) 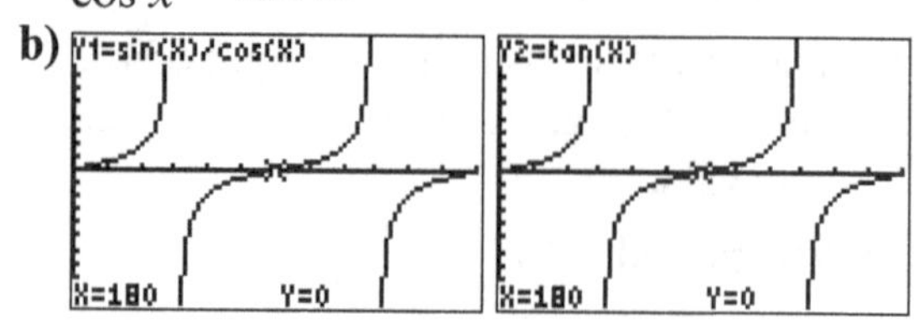

9. a) Answers may vary. Sample answer: The graphs are the same because $\frac{\cos x}{\sin x} = \cot x$.

b) 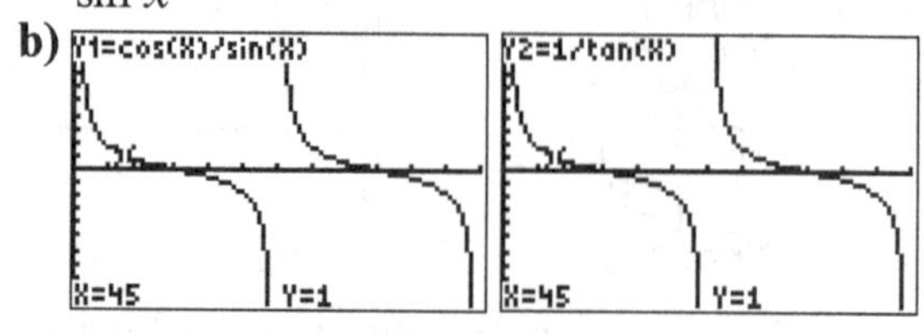

5.3 Investigate Transformations of Sine and Cosine Functions

1. a) vertical stretch by a factor of 5, amplitude 5

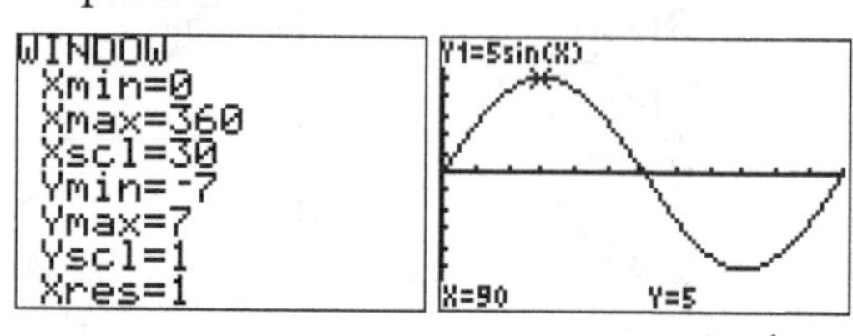

b) vertical compression by a factor of $\frac{4}{5}$, amplitude $\frac{4}{5}$

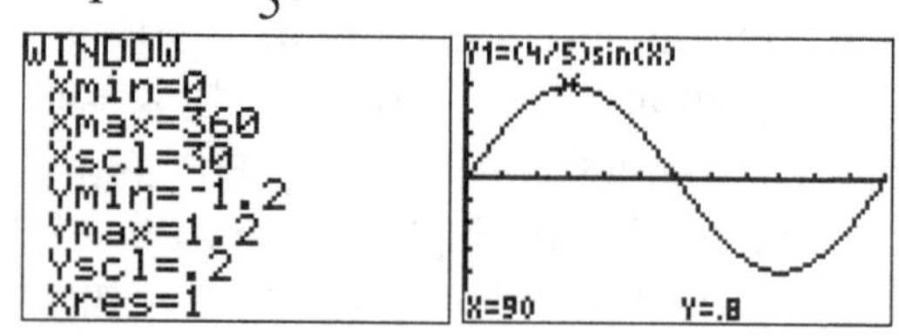

c) vertical stretch by a factor of 4, amplitude 4

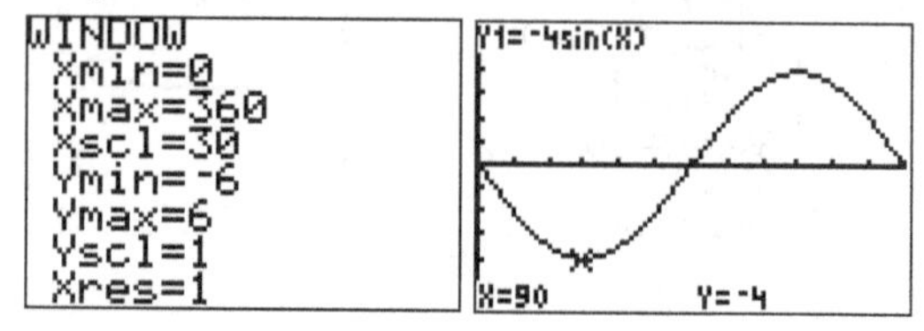

d) vertical stretch by a factor of $\frac{4}{3}$, amplitude $\frac{4}{3}$

WINDOW Xmin=0 Xmax=360 Xscl=30 Ymin=-1.6 Ymax=1.6 Yscl=.2 Xres=1

Y1=(-4/3)sin(X) X=90 Y=-1.333333

2. a) vertical stretch by a factor of 6, amplitude 6

WINDOW Xmin=0 Xmax=360 Xscl=30 Ymin=-8 Ymax=8 Yscl=1 Xres=1

Y1=6cos(X) X=180 Y=-6

b) vertical stretch by a factor of $\frac{3}{2}$, amplitude $\frac{3}{2}$

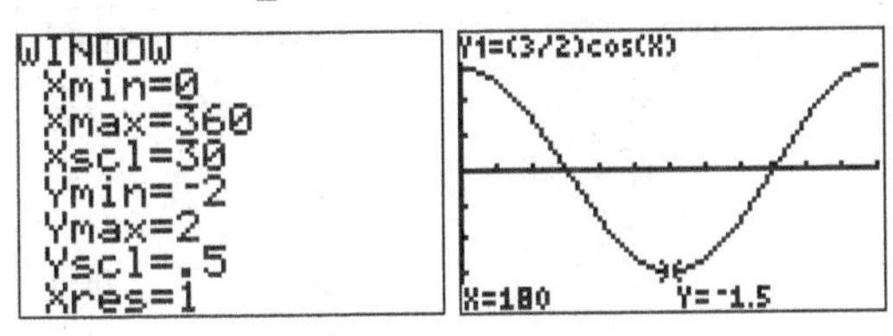

c) vertical stretch by a factor of 3, amplitude 3

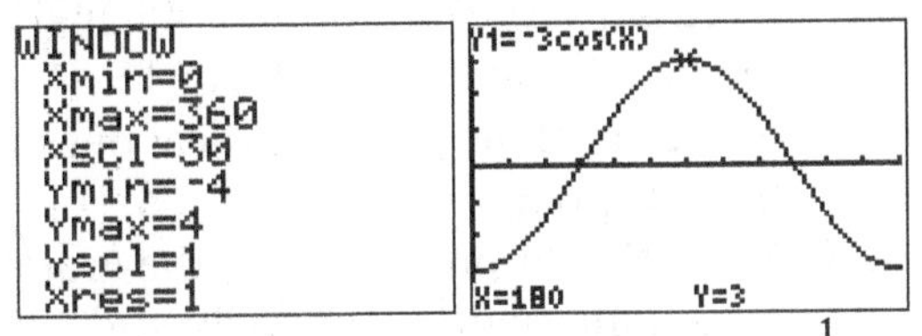

d) vertical compression by a factor of $\frac{1}{2}$, amplitude $\frac{1}{2}$

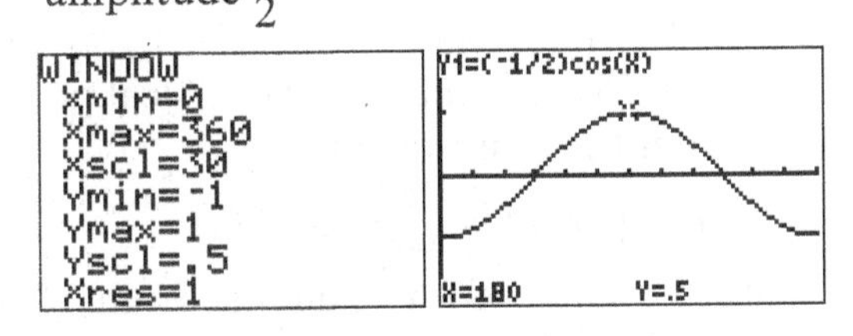

3. a) horizontal compression by a factor of $\frac{1}{2}$, period 180°

b) horizontal stretch by a factor of 2, period 720°

c) horizontal stretch by a factor of $\frac{3}{2}$, period 540°

d) horizontal stretch by a factor of 4, period 1440°

e) horizontal compression by a factor of $\frac{1}{3}$, period 120°

f) horizontal compression by a factor of $\frac{1}{5}$, period 72°

g) horizontal stretch by a factor of $\frac{4}{3}$, period 480°

h) horizontal compression by a factor of $\frac{2}{3}$, period 240°

4. a) The amplitude of the graph is 1, since this is half the difference between the maximum value of −2 and the minimum value of −4. The graph of $y = \sin x$ has a maximum value of 1 and a minimum value of −1, so this graph represents a vertical shift down of 3 units of the graph of $y = \sin x$. The equation that matches this graph is B, $y = \sin x - 3$.

b) The amplitude of the graph is 1, since this is half the difference between the maximum value of 3.5 and the minimum value of 1.5. The graph of $y = \sin x$ has a maximum value of 1 and a minimum value of −1, so this graph represents a vertical shift up of 2.5 units of the graph of $y = \sin x$. The equation that matches this graph is A, $y = \sin x + 2.5$.

5. a) Since the point (0°, 1) on the graph of $y = \cos x$ is now located at (−60°, 1), the equation that matches this graph is B, $y = \cos (x + 60°)$.

b) Since the point (0°, 1) on the graph of $y = \cos x$ is now located at (30°, 1), the equation that matches this graph is A, $y = \cos (x - 30°)$.

6. a) phase shift right 40°; vertical shift up 2 units

b) phase shift left 60°; vertical shift down 3 units

c) phase shift right 38°; vertical shift up 5 units

d) phase shift left 30°; vertical shift down 6 units

7. **a)** phase shift left 70°; no vertical shift
   b) phase shift right 82°; vertical shift up 8 units
   c) phase shift left 100°; vertical shift down 1 unit
   d) phase shift right 120°; vertical shift up 9 units

8. Answers may vary. Sample answers:
   a) $y = 4 \sin 2x$; $y = 4 \cos [2(x - 45°)]$
   b) $y = -2 \sin 3x$; $y = -2\cos [3(x - 30°)]$
   c) $y = 8 \sin 6x$; $y = 8 \cos [6(x - 15°)]$

9. Answers may vary. Sample answers:
   a) $y = 5 \cos 3x$; $y = 5 \sin [3(x - 90°)]$
   b) $y = -4 \cos 2x$; $y = 4 \sin [2(x - 45°)]$
   c) $y = 10 \cos 8x$; $y = 10 \sin [8(x + 11.25°)]$

10. **a) i)** phase shift left 140°, vertical shift up 5 units
   ii) no phase shift, vertical shift up 2 units
   iii) phase shift left 55°, vertical shift down 8 units
   iv) phase shift right 90°, vertical shift up 7 units

   b) i) **ii)** **iii)** **iv)**

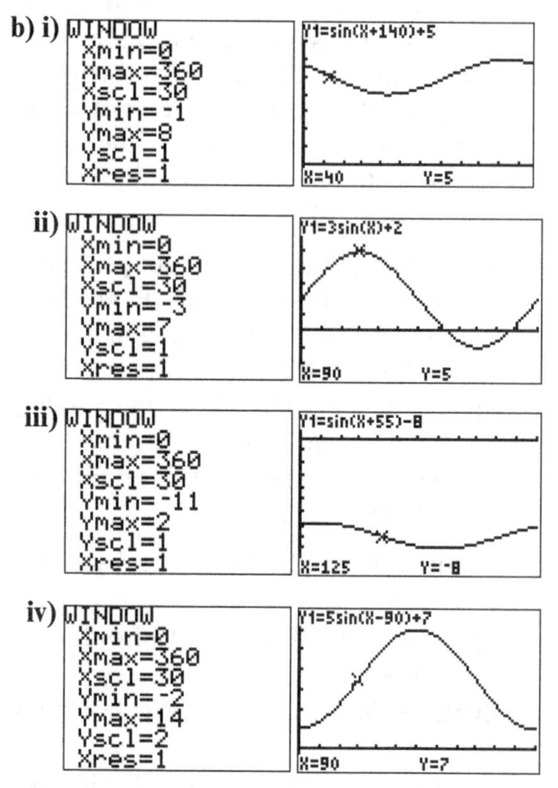

11. **a) i)** no vertical shift, amplitude 1
   ii) vertical shift down 2 units, amplitude 3

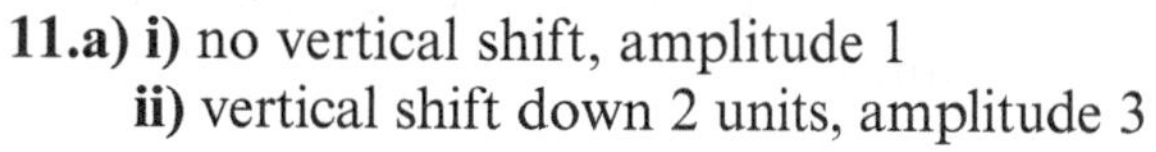

   iii) vertical shift up 1 unit, amplitude 1
   iv) vertical shift down 4 units, amplitude 5

   b) i) **ii)** **iii)** **iv)**

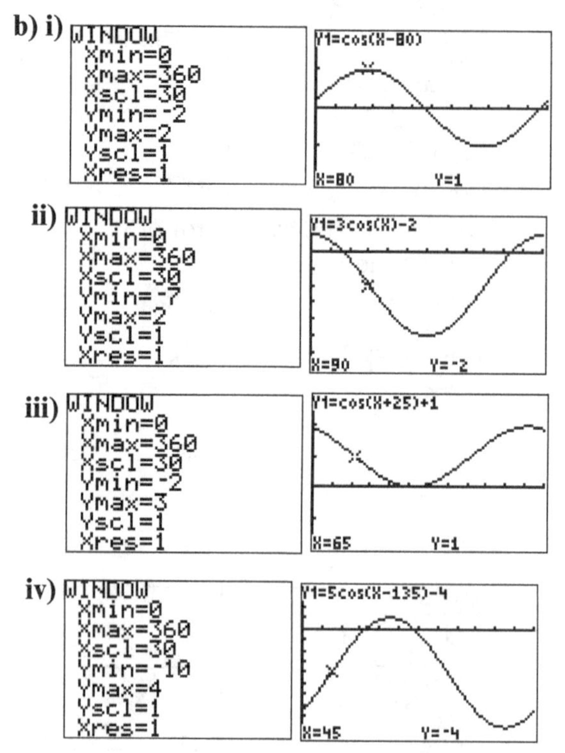

12. **a)** Since the amplitude is 30, the graph would fluctuate between 30 and −30. However, there is a vertical shift up of 45, making the lowest value −30 + 45, or 15.
   So, 15 cm is the lowest vertical position that the point reaches.
   b) Since the amplitude is 30, the graph would fluctuate between 30 and −30. However, there is a vertical shift up of 45, making the highest value 30 + 45, or 75.
   So, 75 cm is the highest vertical position that the point reaches.
   c) The period is $\frac{360}{540}$, or $\frac{2}{3}$ s.
   d) The value of k will change from 540 to 270, so the equation becomes $y = 30 \sin (270t) + 45$.

13. **a)** Since $d = -90°$ and $c = -2$, the graph of $y = \sin x$ must be shifted left 90° and down 2 units.
   b) Since $a = -1$, $d = 60°$, and $c = 4$, the graph of $y = \sin x$ must be reflected in the x-axis, and shifted right 60° and up 4 units.

14. a) The horizontal shift is 25° to the left, so $d = -25°$. The vertical shift is 5 units up, so $c = 5$. The equation of the transformed graph is $y = \sin(x + 25°) + 5$.

b) The graph is reflected in the x-axis, so $a = -1$. The horizontal shift is 42° to the right, so $d = 42°$. The vertical shift is 2 units down, so $c = -2$. The equation of the transformed graph is $y = -\sin(x - 42°) - 2$.

15. a) amplitude 3, period 180°, phase shift right 30°, vertical shift up 1 unit

b) amplitude $\frac{1}{2}$, period 120°, phase shift left 120°, vertical shift down 6 units

c) amplitude 4, period 1440°, phase shift left 45°, vertical shift down 3 units

d) amplitude 0.6, period 300°, phase shift right 90°, vertical shift up 2 units

16. $f = 490 \cos(90°t) + 610$

17. a) 2.7 m

b) 0.3 m

c) 1.2 s

d) 2.1 m

18. a) 25 cm

b) 5 cm

c) 1 s

d) at approximately 0.5 s, 1.0 s, 1.5 s, 2.0 s, etc.

5.4 Graphing and Modelling with $y = a \sin[k(x - d)] + c$ and $y = a \cos[k(x - d)] + c$

1. a) amplitude 2, period 120°, phase shift 15° right, vertical shift 4 units up

b) amplitude 5, period 30°, phase shift 60° left, vertical shift 2 units down

c) amplitude 6, period 20°, phase shift 45° left, vertical shift 1 unit up

d) amplitude $\frac{2}{3}$, period 600°, phase shift 30° right, vertical shift $\frac{4}{5}$ units up

2. a) amplitude $\frac{4}{7}$, period 36°, phase shift 16° left, vertical shift 9 units up

b) amplitude 11, period 10°, phase shift 75° left, vertical shift 3 units down

c) amplitude 8, period 6°, phase shift 12° right, vertical shift 7 units up

d) amplitude $\frac{5}{9}$, period 900°, phase shift 85° right, vertical shift $\frac{3}{8}$ units up

3. a) Answers may vary. Sample answer: Apply the amplitude of 5, apply the vertical shift of 3 units down, and apply the horizontal compression by a factor of $\frac{1}{3}$.

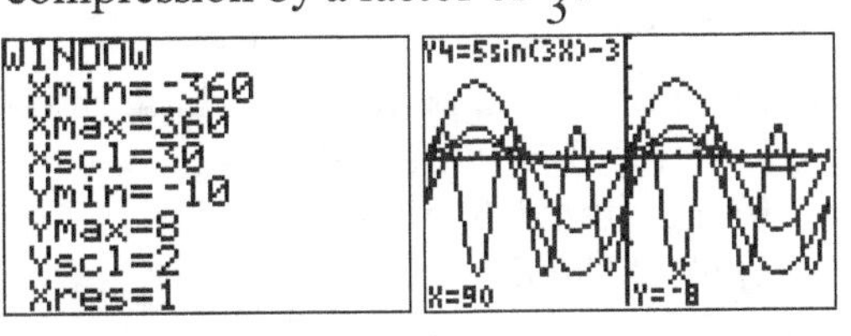

b) $f(x)$: domain $\{x \in \mathbb{R}\}$, range $\{y \in \mathbb{R}, -1 \le y \le 1\}$; $g(x)$: domain $\{x \in \mathbb{R}\}$, range $\{y \in \mathbb{R}, -8 \le y \le 2\}$

c) $h(x) = 5 \sin[3(x + 45°)] - 3$

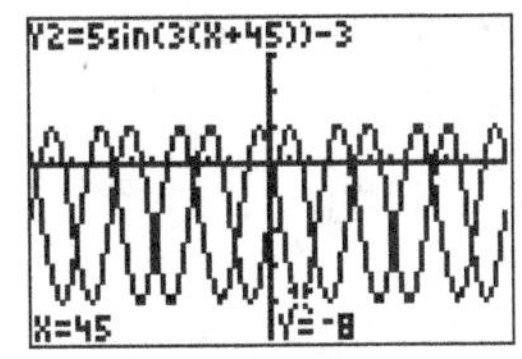

4. a) Answers may vary. Sample answer: Apply the amplitude of 3, apply the vertical shift of 1 unit up, and apply the horizontal compression by a factor of $\frac{1}{4}$.

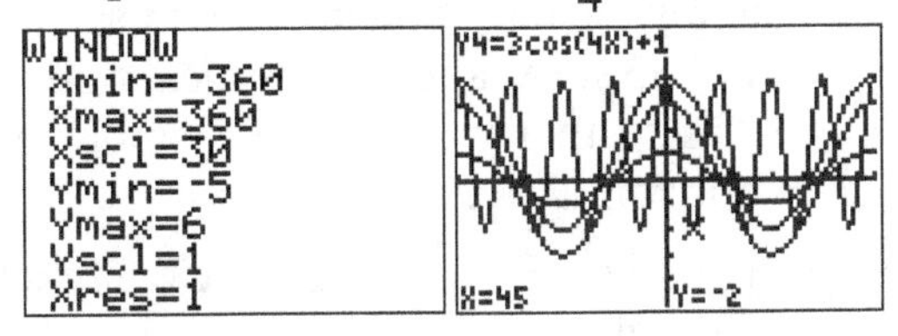

b) $f(x)$: domain $\{x \in \mathbb{R}\}$, range $\{y \in \mathbb{R}, -1 \le y \le 1\}$; $g(x)$: domain $\{x \in \mathbb{R}\}$, range $\{y \in \mathbb{R}, -2 \le y \le 4\}$

c) $h(x) = 3 \cos[4(x - 45°)] + 1$

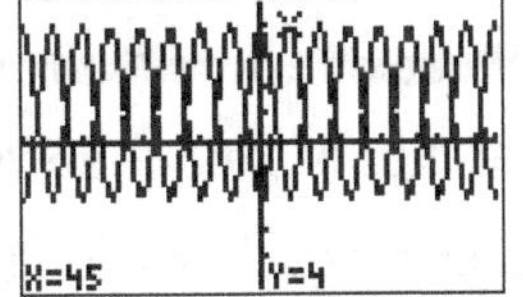

5. Answers may vary. Sample answers:

a) $y = 6 \sin[2(x + 45°)] - 4$

b) $y = 6 \cos 2x - 4$

6. Answers may vary. Sample answers:

   a) $y = \frac{3}{4}\sin\left[\frac{1}{3}(x + 270°)\right] + 2$

   b) $y = \frac{3}{4}\cos\frac{1}{3}x + 2$

7. a) amplitude 8, period 120°, phase shift 20° left, vertical shift down 8 units

   b) maximum 0, minimum −16

   c) 10°, 130°, 250°

   d) −1.07

8. a) amplitude 6, period 72°, phase shift 60° right, no vertical shift

   b) maximum 6, minimum −6

   c) 6°, 42°, 78°

   d) 3

9. Answers may vary.

10. The graph is reflected in the x-axis, and vertically stretched by a factor of 3, so $a = -3$.
    The graph is horizontally compressed by a factor of $\frac{1}{4}$, so $k = 4$.
    The graph is shifted 35° to the left, so $d = -35°$.
    The vertical shift is 8 units down, so $c = -8$.
    The equation of the transformed graph is $y = -3\sin[4(x + 35°)] - 8$.

11. a) Apply the amplitude of 3, $y = 3\sin x$; apply the reflection in the x-axis, $y = -3\sin x$; apply the vertical shift of 7 units up, $y = -3\sin x + 7$; apply the horizontal stretch of factor 4, $y = -3\sin\frac{1}{4}x + 7$; translate the function 50° right, $g(x) = -3\sin\left[\frac{1}{4}(x - 50°)\right] + 7$.

    b) $f(x)$: domain $\{x \in \mathbb{R}\}$, range $\{y \in \mathbb{R}, -1 \le y \le 1\}$; $g(x)$: domain $\{x \in \mathbb{R}\}$, range $\{y \in \mathbb{R}, 4 \le y \le 10\}$

12. a) Apply the amplitude of $\frac{3}{4}$, $y = \frac{3}{4}\cos x$; apply the vertical shift of 2 units down, $y = \frac{3}{4}\cos x - 2$; apply the horizontal compression of factor $\frac{1}{6}$, $y = \frac{3}{4}\cos 6x - 2$; translate the function 45° left, $g(x) = \frac{3}{4}\cos[6(x + 45°)] - 2$

    b) $f(x)$: domain $\{x \in \mathbb{R}\}$, range $\{y \in \mathbb{R}, -1 \le y \le 1\}$; $g(x)$: domain $\{x \in \mathbb{R}\}$, range $\left\{y \in \mathbb{R}, \frac{5}{4} \le y \le \frac{11}{4}\right\}$

13. The equation of the cosine function is of the form $g(x) = a\cos[k(x - d)]$, since the sine function does not have a vertical shift. The cosine function will have the same amplitude and period as the sine function, so $a = 6$ and $k = 5$. Thus far the equation is $y = 6\cos[5(x - d)]$.
    Determine the phase shift. Sketch a graph of the sine function to find d.

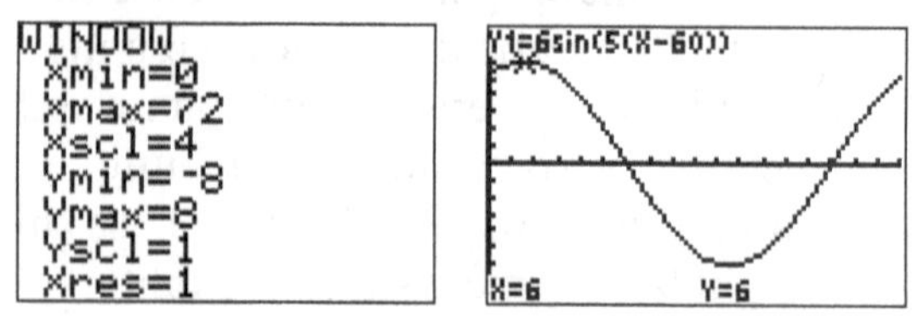

Since the first maximum occurs at 6°, the phase shift is 6° to the right, so $d = 6°$. A cosine equation that models this function is $y = 6\cos[5(x - 6°)]$.

14. a) $y = 4\sin[3(x - 30°)] + 1$

    b) $y = 4\cos[3(x - 60°)] + 1$

15. Answers may vary. Sample answers:

    a) $y = 5\cos 30x + 11$

    b) $y = 5\sin[30(x + 3)] + 11$

    c) $y = 5\sin[30(x - 3)] + 11$

    d) $y = 5\cos[30(x - 6)] + 11$

    e) Answers may vary.

16. Answers may vary. Sample answers:

    a)

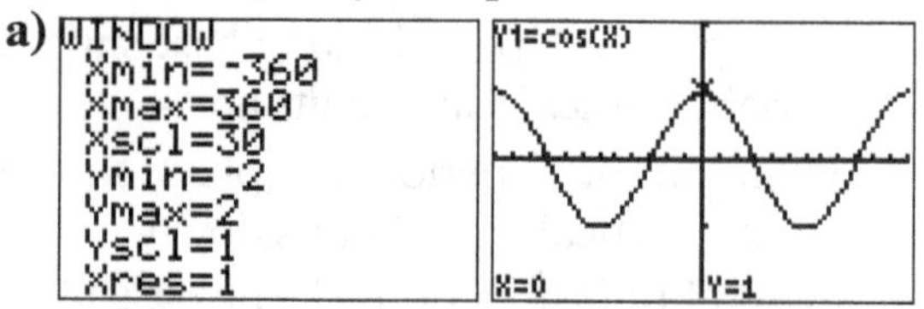

    b), c) The square root function will produce only positive y-values, so the graph of $y = \sqrt{\cos x}$ will have missing sections where the graph of $y = \cos x$ has negative y-values.

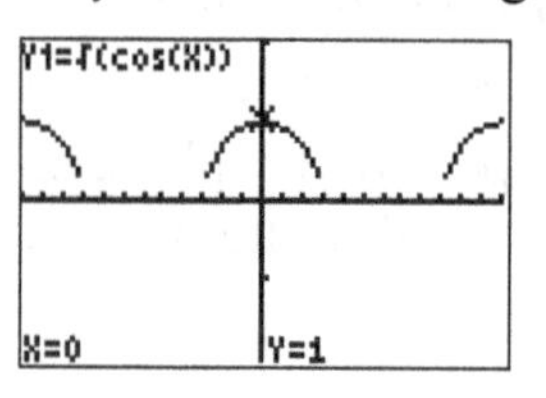

d) The graph of $y = \sqrt{\cos x + 1}$ will not have any missing parts, since no part of the graph will be below the x-axis.

e) 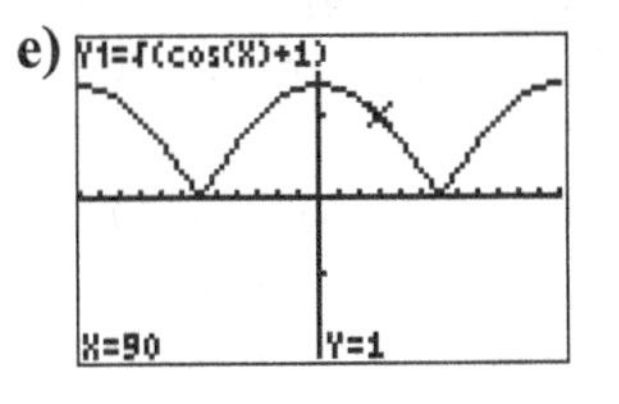

17. a) maximum: $y = a + c$ for $x = d + \frac{90°(1 + 4n)}{k}$, where n is an integer

b) minimum: $y = c - a$ for $x = d + \frac{90°(3 + 4n)}{k}$, where n is an integer

18. a) maximum: $y = a + c$ for $x = d + \frac{n360°}{k}$, where n is an integer

b) minimum: $y = c - a$ for $x = d + \frac{180°(1 + 2n)}{k}$, where n is an integer

5.5 Data Collecting and Modelling

1. a) maximum 10.5 m, minimum 1.5 m

b) high tide at 7 a.m. and 7 p.m.; low tide at 1 a.m. and 1 p.m.

c) 3.75 m

d) 4 a.m., 10 a.m., 4 p.m., 10 p.m.

2. a) maximum 9100 tourists; minimum 2100 tourists

b) maximum in November, at $t = 11$; minimum in May, at $t = 5$

c) 3850

d) March 18 (3 months, 18 days), June 12 (6 months, 12 days)

3. Answers may vary. Sample answers:

a) maximum 3.5 m, minimum 0.5 m, $a = 1.5$

b) $c = 2$

c) $d = 0$

d) period 2.4 s, $k = 150$

e) $y = 1.5 \sin 150x + 2$

f) $y = 1.5 \cos [150(x - 0.6)] + 2$

g) 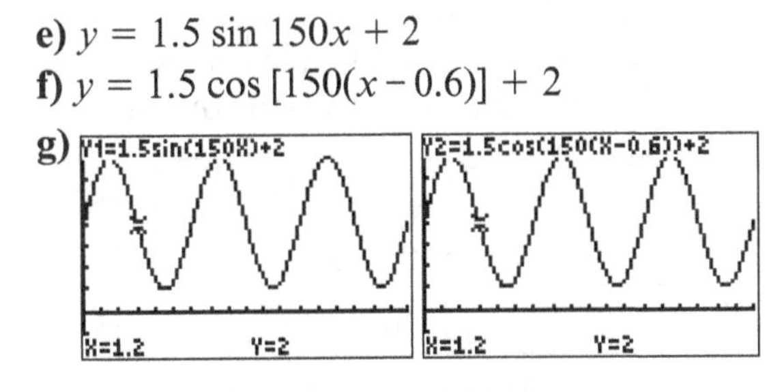

4. Answers may vary. Sample answers:

a) The maximum value on the graph is 8 m and the minimum value is 2 m. Subtract and divide by 2 to find the amplitude, $\frac{8 - 2}{2}$, or 3.

b) Since the amplitude is 3, the horizontal reference line is $y = 5$, which is 3 below the maximum and 3 above the minimum. The value of the horizontal reference line indicates that the graph has been shifted up 5 units, so $c = 5$.

c) Since the y-intercept is at (0, 5) and the points (6, 5) and (12, 5) are all on the horizontal reference line, there is no phase shift, so $d = 0$.

d) Since the period is 12 s, $\frac{360}{k} = 12$ and $k = 30$.

e) Substitute the values $a = 3$, $k = 30$, $d = 0$, and $c = 5$ in $y = a \sin [k(x - d)] + c$. A sine equation that models the motion is $y = 3 \sin 30x + 5$.

f) The part of the graph from 3 s to 12 s represents a cosine function. The values of a, k, and c remain the same but $d = 3$, since the first maximum occurs at (3, 8). A cosine equation that models the motion is $y = 3 \cos [30(x - 3)] + 5$.

g) 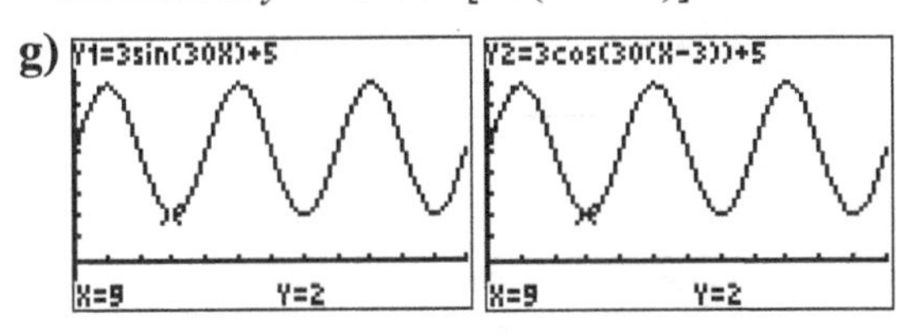

5. **a)** Substitute each value of x from the first column to determine the corresponding *height* value in the second column.

x	$h(x) = 25 \sin (x - 90°) + 27$
0°	$25 \sin (0° - 90°) + 27 = 2$
30°	$25 \sin (30° - 90°) + 27 = 5.35$
60°	$25 \sin (60° - 90°) + 27 = 14.50$
90°	$25 \sin (90° - 90°) + 27 = 27$
120°	$25 \sin (120° - 90°) + 27 = 39.50$
150°	$25 \sin (150° - 90°) + 27 = 48.65$
180°	$25 \sin (180° - 90°) + 27 = 52$
210°	$25 \sin (210° - 90°) + 27 = 48.65$
240°	$25 \sin (240° - 90°) + 27 = 39.50$
270°	$25 \sin (270° - 90°) + 27 = 27$
300°	$25 \sin (300° - 90°) + 27 = 14.50$
330°	$25 \sin (330° - 90°) + 27 = 5.35$
360°	$25 \sin (360° - 90°) + 27 = 2$

b) The cycle will repeat itself after 1 revolution, so the values will follow the pattern in the above table.

x	$h(x) = 25 \sin (x - 90°) + 27$
390°	5.35
420°	14.50
450°	27
480°	39.50
510°	48.65
540°	52
570°	48.65
600°	39.50
630°	27
660°	14.50
690°	5.35
720°	2

c)

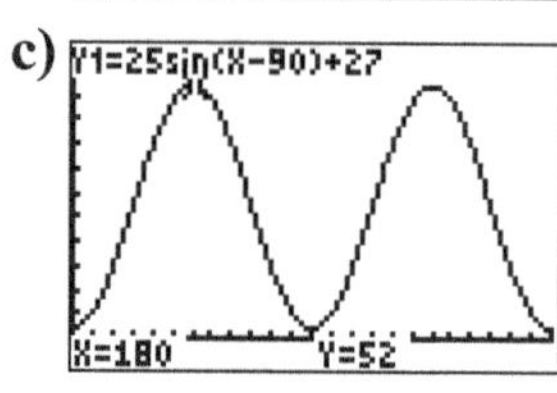

d) From the graph and the table, the maximum height of the rider is 52 m and the minimum height of the rider is 2 m.

e) From the graph, the height of the rider is 40 m in 4 places: approximately 120°, 240°, 480°, and 600°.

f) The start of the first cosine wave is at 180°, so the phase shift is 180° to the right. The period, amplitude, and vertical shift remain the same as in the given sine function. A cosine equation that models the height is $h(x) = 25 \cos (x - 180°) + 27$.

6. **a)** $\sqrt{3}$
b) multiply by a factor of 4

7. **a)** The period of the graph is 360 days, so the equation will be of the form $y = a \sin (x - d) + c$. The maximum value is 20 and the minimum value is 16. So, $a = 2$. The horizontal reference line is $y = 18$, which means there is a vertical shift of 18 units up, so $c = 18$. There is no phase shift, since the first point is at (0, 18), on the horizontal reference line. A sine equation that models the time of sunset in Saskatoon is $y = 2 \sin x + 18$.
b) The first point on the cosine wave is at 90 days, so a cosine equation that models the time of sunset in Saskatoon is $y = 2 \cos (x - 90) + 18$.
c) The range of the function is $\{y \in \mathbb{R}, 16 \leq y \leq 20\}$.

8. **a)** $y = 9 \sin (x + 230°) + 12$
b) $y = 9 \cos (x + 140°) + 12$
c) The phase shift of the curves will be altered by an additional 10°; $y = 9 \sin (x + 220°) + 12$; $y = 9 \cos (x + 130°) + 12$

9. **a)** $y = 9 \sin (x + 230°) + 14.5$
b) $y = 9 \cos (x + 140°) + 14.5$

10. **a)** $\frac{1}{25}$ s
b) maximum 63 cm, minimum −27 cm, amplitude 45
c) maximum at $\frac{1}{100}$ s, minimum at $\frac{3}{100}$ s
d) 63 cm

11. 59.8 cm

12. $h(t) = 8 \cos (19.9t) + 9.5$

13. a) $y = 1100 \sin (93\,600t)$
b) $y = 550 \sin (70\,200t)$

5.6 Use Sinusoidal Functions to Model Periodic Phenomena Not Involving Angles

1. a) maximum height 7 m, minimum height −7 m
b) high tide at 5:30 a.m. and 5:30 p.m.; low tide at 11:30 a.m. and 11:30 p.m.
c) $h(t) = 7 \cos [30(t + 6.5)]$

2. a) $h(t) = 4.5 \sin [30(t + 4)]$
b) low tide at 5 p.m.; high tide at 11 a.m. and 11 p.m.
c) $h(t) = 4.5 \sin [30(t + 3.5)]$
d) $h(t) = 4.5 \cos [30(t + 0.5)]$

3. a) maximum 1050, minimum 250, amplitude 400
b) $c = 650$
c) $d = 0$
d) 5 years, $k = 72$
e) $y = 400 \sin 72x + 650$
f) Answers may vary, but all graphs should match the shape of the graph given.

4. For 8 years, $k = 45$. The new equation is $y = 400 \sin 45x + 650$.

5. a) The graph begins at March 21. There are 31 days in March, so April 1 occurs 11 days after March 21. Substitute $x = 11$ into $y = 4.5 \sin \frac{72}{73}x + 12$ to find y.

$$y = 4.5 \sin \frac{72}{73}(11) + 12$$
$$= 4.5 \sin \frac{792}{73} + 12$$
$$\doteq 12.8$$

Convert 12.8 h to hours and minutes.
$0.8 \times 60 = 48$
There are about 12.8 h, or 12 h 48 min of daylight on April 1.

b) First, determine how many days September 1 falls after March 21.

March 21–31	= 10 days
April	= 30 days
May	= 31 days
June	= 30 days
July	= 31 days
August	= 31 days
September	= 1 day
Total	= 164 days

Substitute $x = 164$ in $y = 4.5 \sin \frac{72}{73}x + 12$ to find y.

$$y = 4.5 \sin \frac{72}{73}(164) + 12$$
$$= 4.5 \sin \frac{11\,808}{73} + 12$$
$$\doteq 13.4$$

Determine the number of minutes.
$0.4 \times 60 = 24$
There are approximately 13.4 h, or 13 h 24 min of daylight on September 1.

6. a) The amplitude is $\frac{12 - 2}{2}$, or 5. So, $a = 5$.
The period is 12 h.

$$\frac{360}{k} = 12$$
$$k = 30$$

The vertical shift is $2 + 5$, or 7.
So, $c = 7$.
Since x represents the hours after midnight, the first maximum point is (6, 12) and the point at the beginning of the first sine wave is (3, 7), so the phase shift is $d = 3$.
Substitute the values $a = -5$, $k = 30$, $d = 3$, and $c = 7$ into the equation $y = a \sin [k(x - d)] + c$.
A sinusoidal equation that represents the depth of the water is
$y = 5 \sin [30(x - 3)] + 7$.

b) 4:15 a.m. occurs 4.25 h after 12 midnight. Substitute $x = 4.25$ into the equation and solve for y.

$$y = 5 \sin [30(4.25 - 3)] + 7$$
$$\doteq 10.0$$

At 4:15 a.m., the depth of the water is approximately 10.0 m.

3:30 p.m. occurs 15.5 h after 12 midnight. Substitute $x = 15.5$ into the equation and solve for y.

$y = 5 \sin [30(15.5 - 3)] + 7$
$\doteq 8.3$

At 3:30 p.m. the depth of the water is approximately 8.3 m.

c) 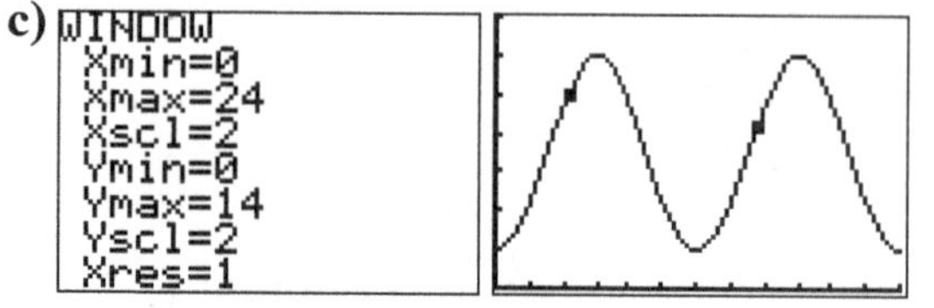

7. a) maximum 18 m, minimum 4 m
   b) 12 h
   c) 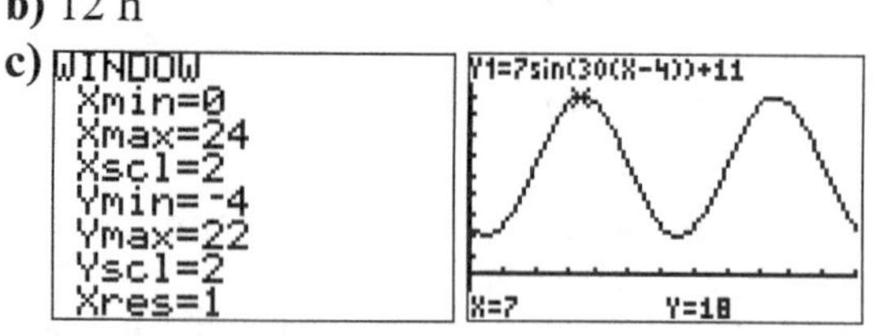

   d) midnight, 2 a.m., 12 noon, and 2 p.m.

8. a) $\frac{1}{5}$ s
   b) $k = 1800$
   c) 8 V
   d) $V = 8 \sin 1800t$

9. a) Answers may vary. Sample answer:
   $y = 3 \cos \left[\frac{72}{73}(x - 172)\right] + 12.3$
   b) 12.8 h
   c) Answers may vary. Sample answer: April 26

10. a) period 0.017 s, amplitude 160 V
    b) 160 V
    c) $V = 160 \sin \frac{360}{0.017}t$

11. a) $y = 6.9 \sin [15(x + 4)] + 22$
    b) Plot the points in the table and sketch a graph of the equation on the same set of axes. Then, check to see if the points lie on the graph of the equation.
    c) i) 15.3 °C
       ii) 28.7 °C
       iii) 22.9 °C

12. a) $y = 3.5 \sin 7200x + 11.5$
    b) 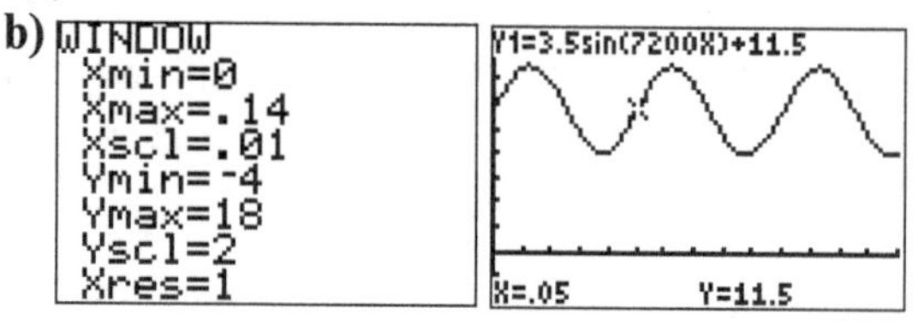

    c) 0.029 min, 0.046 min

13. a) Graph ①: $y = 10 \sin 2400x + 12$
    Graph ②:
    $y = 10 \sin [2400(x - 0.05)] + 12$
    Graph ③:
    $y = 10 \sin [2400(x - 0.1)] + 12$
    b) 0.15 cycles per second

Chapter 5 Review

1. a) Yes; pattern of y-values repeats at regular intervals
   b) No; pattern of y-values does not repeat at regular intervals
   c) No; pattern of y-values does not repeat at regular intervals

2. Answers may vary.

3. a)

x	$2x$	$y = \sin 2x$
0°	0°	0
45°	90°	1
90°	180°	0
135°	270°	−1
180°	360°	0
225°	450°	1
270°	540°	0
315°	630°	−1
360°	720°	0

   b) 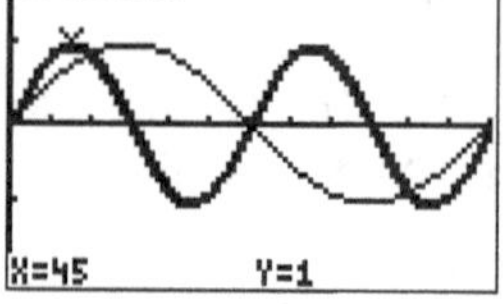

   c) Similarities: The amplitude for each graph is 1. The range for each graph is $\{y \in \mathbb{R}, -1 \leq y \leq 1\}$.
   Differences: The period for $y = \sin x$ is 360°, but the period for $y = \sin 2x$ is 180°. The zeros, or x-intercepts, of $y = \sin x$ are 0°, 180°, and 360°. The x-intercepts of $y = \sin 2x$ are 0°, 90°, 180°, 270°, and 360°.

4. a) 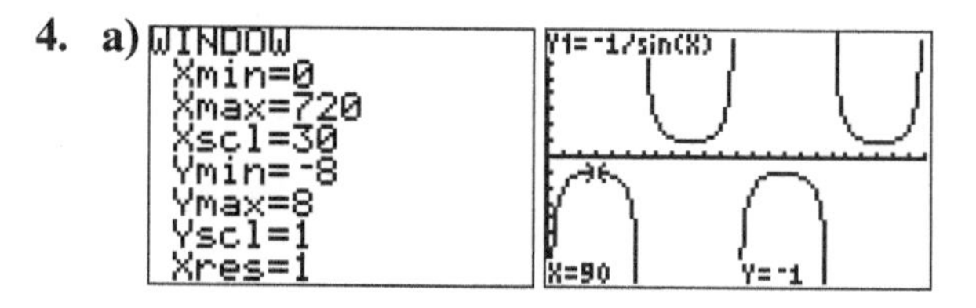

b) 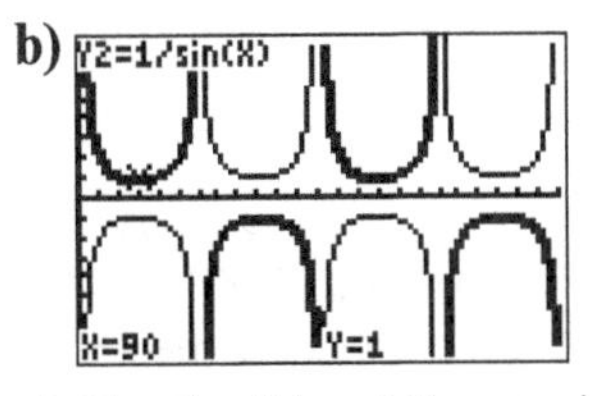

c) Similarities: The period of each graph is 360°. The vertical asymptotes for each graph are $x = n180°$, where n is an integer. The range for each graph is $\{y \in \mathbb{R}, y \leq -1 \text{ or } y \geq 1\}$.
Differences: The graph of $y = -\csc x$ is a reflection of the graph of $y = \csc x$ in the x-axis, so each branch of the graph opens in the opposite direction.

5. Answers may vary. Sample answers:
$y = \frac{3}{4}\sin 4x$; $y = \frac{3}{4}\cos[4(x - 22.5°)]$

6. Answers may vary. Sample answers:
$y = 6\cos 4x$; $y = 6\sin[4(x - 67.5°)]$

7. a) amplitude 5, period 120°, phase shift right 40°, vertical shift up 6 units

b) amplitude $\frac{1}{4}$, period 90°, phase shift left 100°, vertical shift down 2 units

c) amplitude 7, period 540°, phase shift left 75°, vertical shift down 1 unit

d) amplitude 0.4, period $\frac{720°}{7}$, phase shift right 60°, vertical shift up 5.6 units

8. a) Apply the amplitude of 7, $y = 7\sin x$; apply the reflection in the x-axis, $y = -7\sin x$; apply the vertical shift of 1 unit up, $y = -7\sin x + 1$; apply the horizontal stretch by a factor of 2, $y = -7\sin\frac{1}{2}x + 1$; translate the function 30° right,
$g(x) = -7\sin\left[\frac{1}{2}(x - 30°)\right] + 1$.

b) $f(x)$: domain $\{x \in \mathbb{R}\}$, range $\{y \in \mathbb{R}, -1 \leq y \leq 1\}$;
$g(x)$: domain $\{x \in \mathbb{R}\}$, range $\{y \in \mathbb{R}, -6 \leq y \leq 8\}$

9. a) Apply the amplitude of $\frac{2}{3}$, $y = \frac{2}{3}\cos x$; apply the vertical shift of 4 units down, $y = \frac{2}{3}\cos x - 4$; apply the horizontal compression by a factor of $\frac{1}{5}$, $y = \frac{2}{3}\cos 5x - 4$; translate the function 28° left, $g(x) = \frac{2}{3}\cos[5(x + 28°)] - 4$.

b) $f(x)$: domain $\{x \in \mathbb{R}\}$, range $\{y \in \mathbb{R}, -1 \leq y \leq 1\}$;
$g(x)$: domain $\{x \in \mathbb{R}\}$, range $\left\{y \in \mathbb{R}, -\frac{14}{3} \leq y \leq -\frac{10}{3}\right\}$

10. Answers may vary. Sample answers:
a) $y = -7\sin[2(x - 30°)]$
b) $y = -7\cos[2(x - 75°)]$

11. Answers may vary. Sample answers:
a) $y = 18\sin[30(x - 4.4)] + 8$

b) 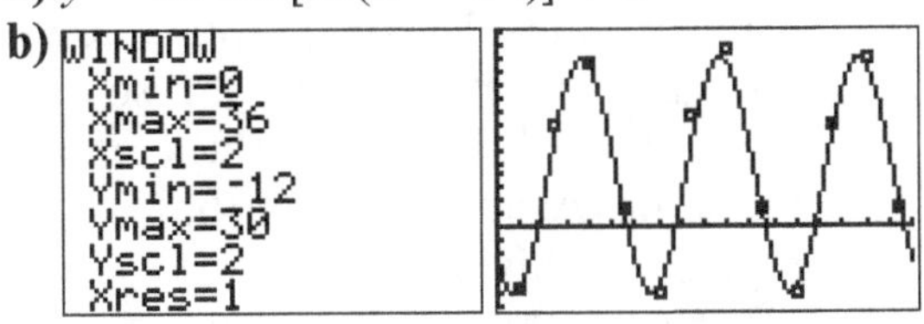

c) There is a good fit because the graph passes through most of the points.

12. a) Answers may vary. Sample answer:
The depth of the water at low tide is a minimum of 2 m, which is 6 m below average sea level. So, average sea level is 2 + 6, or 8 m. This represents the horizontal reference line of the graph.
At high tide the maximum depth of the water is 14 m.
Since the maximum and minimum values are 6 m from the horizontal reference, the amplitude is $a = 6$.
The cycle takes 12 h to complete, so the period is 12 h and $k = 30$. At times 0 h, 6 h, and 12 h, the water depth is 8 m.
Since the tide is coming in, it is high tide 3 h past midnight, so the water depth is 14 m. Low tide occurs 3 h before the end of the 12-h cycle, so at 9 h the water depth is 2 m. The graph represents a 24-h period, so there will be 2 cycles on the graph.
Points on the graph will be (0, 8), (3, 14), (6, 8), (9, 2), (12, 8), (15, 14), (18, 8), (21, 2), (24, 8). Plot these points and draw a sine curve to obtain the following graph.

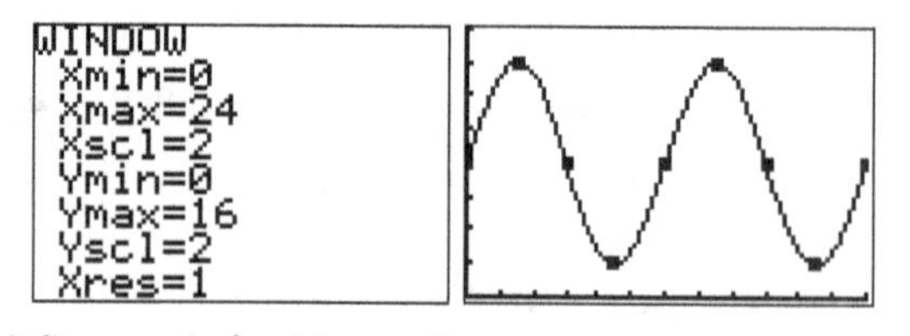

b) i) $y = 6 \sin 30x + 8$
ii) $y = 6 \cos [30(x - 3)] + 8$

c) Answers may vary. Sample answer: In this situation the depth of the water at 3 a.m. is 8 m, the average sea level, and the tide is coming in, so the maximum will occur 3 h later at 6:00 a.m. This indicates that the graph is now translated 3 units to the right, so $d = 3$, but all the other values remain the same. A sine equation that represents this situation is $y = 6 \sin [30(x - 3)] + 8$, and a cosine equation is $y = 6 \cos [30(x - 6)] + 8$.

Math Contest

1. B
2. D
3. $x = 3, y = 2, z = 5$
4. A
5. 8, 9, 10
6. C
7. D
8. C
9. A
10. B
11. A
12. D
13. $3\sqrt{2}$
14. B

Chapter 6 Discrete Functions

6.1 Sequences as Discrete Functions

1. **a)** 3, 5, 7
   b) 1, −2, −5
   c) −1, 1, 3
   d) 9, 11, 13
   e) 1, 2, 4
   f) −18, −54, −162
2. **a)** −27
   b) 50
   c) 6
   d) $\frac{1}{64}$
3. **a)** The first term is 5. Multiply each term by 5 to get the next term. Next three terms: 3125, 15 625, 78 125
   b) The first term is 9. Subtract 2 from each term to get the next term. Next three terms: 1, −1, −3
   c) The first term is −4. Multiply each term by 2 to get the next term. Next three terms: −64, −128, −256
   d) The first term is 300. Divide each term by 10 to get the next term. Next three terms: 0.03, 0.003, 0.0003
   e) The first term is 3. Multiply each term by 3 to get the next term. Next three terms: 729, 2187, 6561
   f) The first term is ar^3. Divide each term by r to get the next term. Next three terms: $\frac{a}{r}, \frac{a}{r^2}, \frac{a}{r^3}$
   g) The first term is 0.11. Multiply each term by −3 to get the next term. Next three terms: 8.91, −26.73, 80.19
4. **a)** $f(n) = 6n$; domain $\{n \in \mathbb{N}\}$

Term Number, n	Term, t_n	First Differences
1	6	
		6
2	12	
		6
3	18	
		6
4	24	

b) $f(n) = 10 - 3n$; domain $\{n \in \mathbb{N}\}$

Term Number, n	Term, t_n	First Differences
1	7	
		−3
2	4	
		−3
3	1	
		−3
4	−2	

c) $f(n) = n^2 + 1$; domain $\{n \in \mathbb{N}\}$

Term Number, n	Term, t_n	First Differences	Second Differences
1	2		
		3	
2	5		2
		5	
3	10		2
		7	
4	17		

d) $f(n) = 2n^2 + 3n - 1$; domain $\{n \in \mathbb{N}\}$

Term Number, n	Term, t_n	First Differences	Second Differences
1	4		
		9	
2	13		4
		13	
3	26		4
		17	
4	43		

5. a) $f(n) = 15n$; domain $\{n = 1, 2, 3, 4\}$
   b) $f(n) = n^2 - 3$; domain $\{n = 1, 2, 3, 4\}$
   c) $f(n) = 1 - \frac{1}{2}n$; domain $\{n = 1, 2, 3, 4\}$
6. a) $f(n) = -\frac{1}{4}n^2$; domain $\{n = 1, 2, 3, 4\}$
   b) $f(n) = n^2 + 3n$; domain $\{n = 1, 2, 3, 4\}$
   c) $f(n) = -3^n$; domain $\{n = 1, 2, 3, 4\}$
7. a) discrete; set of disconnected points
   b) continuous; line is made up of connected points
   c) discrete; set of disconnected points
   d) continuous; curve is made up of connected points
8. a) The first term is 2 and further odd terms are multiples of 2. The second term is −5 and further even terms are multiples of −5. The next four terms are −25, 12, −30, 14.
   b) The first term is −7 and further odd terms increase by 6. The second term is 9 and further even terms decrease by 7. The next four terms are −12, 17, −19, 23.
   c) The first term is 4 and further odd terms increase by 5. The second term is $\frac{1}{27}$ and further even terms are multiplied by 3. The next four terms are 1, 24, 3, 29.
   d) The first term is 8 and further odd terms are multiplied by 0.1. All even terms are −1. The next four terms are 0.008, −1, 0.0008, −1.
9. a) Yes; a multiple of 9
   b) No; not a multiple of 9
   c) No; not a multiple of 9
   d) Yes; a multiple of 9
10. a) $t_n = -16(-2)^{-n+1}$ or $t_n = \frac{-16}{(-2)^{n-1}}$; $t_{15} = \frac{-16}{(-2)^{15}}$
    b) $t_n = \frac{n}{2n-1}$; $t_{15} = \frac{15}{29}$
    c) $t_n = \frac{2}{\sqrt{n}}$; $t_{15} = \frac{2}{\sqrt{15}}$
    d) $t_n = 3^{n-1}$; $t_{15} = 3^{15}$
    e) $t_n = \frac{n+1}{n}$; $t_{15} = \frac{16}{15}$
11. Answers may vary. Sample answers:
    a) 9, 5, 1, −3; $f(n) = 13 - 4n$
    b) −3, 9, −27, 81; $f(n) = -3(-3)^{n-1}$
12. a) The sales on the first day are \$20, so the first term is 20.
    Since the sales triple each day, multiply the first term and subsequent terms by 3 to obtain the sequence 20, 60, 180, 540, 1620.
    b) Since 20 is repeatedly multiplied by 3, the explicit formula is $f(n) = 20(3^{n-1})$.
    c) Substitute $n = 14$ to obtain the 14th term.
    $f(14) = 20(3^{14-1})$
    $= 31\ 886\ 460$
    Since this is a new small business, it is unreasonable to expect sales of \$31 886 460 on the 14th day. It is unlikely that sales will triple every day for 2 weeks. Most likely sales will level off at a certain amount.
13. a) $f(n) = 3400 - 260(n - 1)$
    b) $f(6) = 2100$
    c) 9 years
14. a) $\sqrt{\sqrt{\sqrt{\sqrt{5}}}}$, $\sqrt{\sqrt{\sqrt{\sqrt{\sqrt{5}}}}}$
    b) $5^{\frac{1}{2}}, 5^{\frac{1}{4}}, 5^{\frac{1}{8}}, 5^{\frac{1}{16}}, 5^{\frac{1}{32}}$
    c) $f(n) = 5^{\frac{1}{2^n}}$
    d) $f(n) = 5^{2^{-n}}$
    e) $f(50) = 5^{2^{-50}}$

15. a) $t_n = (2n - 1) \times (3n - 2)$

b) $t_n = \dfrac{(2n - 1) \times (2n + 1)}{(2n) \times (2n + 2)}$

6.2 Recursive Procedures

1. a) 2, 8, 14, 20 **b)** 4, 10, 28, 82
c) −1, 0, 0.5, 0.75 **d)** 500, 100, 20, 4
e) 3, 0, 9, −6 **f)** 90, 120, 160, $\frac{640}{3}$

2. a) −3, 1, 5, 9 **b)** 0.25, −0.50, 1.0, −2.0
c) $4, \frac{4}{3}, \frac{1}{3}, \frac{1}{15}$ **d)** −7, 10, −7, 10
e) −1.5, 0.5, 3.5, 7.5

3. a) $f(1) = 2, f(n) = 2f(n - 1) + 1$
b) $f(1) = 3, f(n) = f(n - 1) - 2n$
c) $f(1) = -2, f(n) = f(n - 1) - n + 1$

4. a) 32, 16, 8, 4; $f(1) = 32$; $f(n) = 0.5f(n - 1)$
b) 2, −3, 7, −13; $f(1) = 2$; $f(n) = 1 - 2f(n - 1)$

5. a) $f(n) = 3.14$
b) 3.14, 3.14, 3.14, 3.14, 3.14

6. a) 0.035

b)

Year	House Value ($)
0	275 000
1	275 000 + 0.035 × 275 000 = 284 625
2	284 625 + 0.035 × 284 625 = 294 586.88
3	294 586.88 + 0.035 × 294 586.88 = 304 897.42
4	304 897.42 + 0.035 × 304 897.42 = 315 568.83
5	315 568.83 + 0.035 × 315 568.83 = 326 613.74
6	326 613.74 + 0.035 × 326 613.74 = 338 045.22
7	338 045.22 + 0.035 × 338 045.22 = 349 876.80
8	349 876.80 + 0.035 × 349 876.80 = 362 122.49

c) 275 000, 284 625, 294 586.88, 304 897.42, 315 568.83, 326 613.74, 338 045.22, 349 876.80, 362 122.49
d) $t_1 = 275\,000,\ t_n = 1.035t_{n-1}$
e) $547 191.94

7. a) 42, 51, 65, 84
b) Answers may vary. Sample answer: There are 42 seats in the row 1. The number of seats in row 2 is equivalent to the number of seats in row 1 reduced by 1 and then increased by 5 times the row number. The number of seats in each subsequent row is found by taking the number of seats of the previous row, reduced by 1, and then increased by 5 times the row number.
c) $t_1 = 42,\ t_n = t_{n-1} + 5n - 1$

8. a) The number of bacteria doubles every hour. Multiply each term by 2 to obtain the next term, starting with 12. The first seven terms of the sequence are 12, 24, 48, 96, 192, 384, and 768.
b) Since each term is multiplied by 2 to get the next term, the terms of the sequence may be written as follows:
$t_1 = 12(2^0), t_2 = 12(2^1), t_3 = 12(2^2), t_4 = 12(2^3), \ldots$
By following the above pattern, the explicit formula for the nth term is $t_n = 12(2^{n-1})$.
c) Each subsequent term is found by multiplying each preceding term by 2, so the recursion formula is $t_1 = 12$, $t_n = 2t_{n-1}$.
d) Answers may vary. Sample answer: It is easier to find the recursion formula because the pattern depends on the preceding term.
e) Answers may vary. Sample answer: Substitute $n = 12$ in the explicit formula.
$t_{12} = 12(2^{12-1})$
$= 12(12^{11})$
$= 24\,576$
After 12 h, there are 24 576 bacteria.
I used the explicit formula because the number of bacteria can be found by substituting $n = 12$. To use the recursion formula it is necessary to find the previous 11 terms.
f) Since the number of bacteria is known, find n.
Substitute $t_n = 1\,572\,864$ into $t_n = 12(2^{n-1})$ and solve for n.

$1\,572\,864 = 12(2^{n-1})$
$131\,072 = 2^{n-1}$
Use systematic trial to find n.
When $n = 18$, $2^{18-1} = 2^{17} = 131\,072$.
There are 1 572 864 bacteria after approximately 18 h.

9. **a)** 1, 7, 13, 19, 25; $t_1 = 1$, $t_n = t_{n-1} + 6$
b) 2, 5, 8, 11, 14; $t_1 = 2$, $t_n = t_{n-1} + 3$
c) $-\frac{1}{2}, \frac{1}{4}, -\frac{1}{8}, \frac{1}{16}, -\frac{1}{32}$; $t_1 = -\frac{1}{2}$, $t_n = -\frac{1}{2}t_n - 1$
d) −1, 0, 3, 8, 15; $t_1 = -1$, $t_n = t_{n-1} + 2n - 3$

10. **a)** 1, 1, 2, 3, 5
b) It is given that $f(1) = 4$ and $f(2) = -1$, so the first two terms are 4, −1.
To find the third term, substitute $n = 3$ into $f(n) = f(n-1) - 2f(n-2)$.

$f(3) = f(3-1) - 2f(3-2)$
$= f(2) - 2f(1)$ — Substitute $f(2) = -1$ and $f(1) = 4$.
$= -1 - 2(4)$
$= -9$

To find the fourth term, substitute $n = 4$ into $f(n) = f(n-1) - 2f(n-2)$.

$f(4) = f(4-1) - 2f(4-2)$
$= f(3) - 2f(2)$ — Substitute $f(3) = -9$ and $f(2) = -1$.
$= -9 - 2(-1)$
$= -9 + 2$
$= -7$

To find the fifth term, substitute $n = 5$ into $f(n) = f(n-1) - 2f(n-2)$.

$f(5) = f(5-1) - 2f(5-2)$
$= f(4) - 2f(3)$ — Substitute $f(4) = -7$ and $f(3) = -9$.
$= -7 - 2(-9)$
$= -7 + 18$
$= 11$

The first five terms of the sequence are 4, −1, −9, −7, and 11.
c) 2, 3, 3, 6, 3 **d)** −1, 4, 6, −2, −14
e) 3, −2, −3, 10, −25 **f)** 5, 1, −1, 2, 5

11. **a)** 1, 0, 1, 0 **b)** 64, −16, 4, −1
c) −3, 15, −75, 375
d) −2, 5, 26, 89
e) $\frac{1}{8}, -\frac{1}{2}, -3, -13$
f) $a - 2b, a + b, a + 4b, a + 7b$
g) $2c + 3d, c + 3d, 3d, 3d - c$
h) $m - 5n, 3m - 4n, 5m - 3n, 7m - 2n$

12. **a)** 4, −3, −10, −17; $t_n = 11 - 7n$
b) 81, −27, 9, −3; $t_n = 81(-3)^{1-n}$
c) 0, 3, 8, 15; $t_n = n^2 - 1$
d) −5, −2, 1, 4; $t_n = 3n - 8$

13. **a)** 2, −5, 16, −47, 142
b) 17, 13, 7, −1, −11

14. Yes. Examples may vary. Sample answer:
Example: 2, 4, 8, 16, 32, …
$t_1 = 2$, $t_n = 2t_{n-1}$ or $t_1 = 2$, $t_n = t_{n-1} + 2^{n-1}$

6.3 Pascal's Triangle and Expanding Binomials

1. **a)** Due to the symmetry of Pascal's triangle, there is an equivalent hockey stick pattern that begins with the first 1 in row 3 and ends with the first 35 in row 7, as shown.

1
1 1
1 2 1
1 3 3 1
1 4 6 4 1
1 5 10 10 5 1
1 6 15 20 15 6 1
1 7 21 35 35 21 7 1
1 8 28 56 70 56 28 8 1

b)

1
1 1
1 2 1
1 3 3 1
1 4 6 4 1
1 5 10 10 5 1
1 6 15 20 15 6 1
1 7 21 35 35 21 7 1
1 8 28 56 70 56 28 8 1
1 9 36 84 126 126 84 36 9 1
1 10 45 120 210 252 210 120 45 10 1

i) $84 = 56 + 21 + 6 + 1$
ii) $120 = 84 + 28 + 7 + 1$
iii) $56 = 35 + 15 + 5 + 1$
iv) $252 = 126 + 70 + 35 + 15 + 5 + 1$

2. a) 2048 b) 524 288
c) 4 194 304 d) 1 073 741 824
e) 2^{n+1}

3. a) $t_{6,8}$ b) $t_{10,3}$
c) $t_{4,5}$ d) $t_{11,8}$
e) $t_{16,10}$ f) $t_{a+2,b+1}$

4. a) $t_{18,10} + t_{18,11}$ b) $t_{24,15} + t_{24,16}$
c) $t_{13,6} + t_{13,7}$ d) $t_{a-1,1} + t_{a-1,2}$
e) $t_{x+1,x-4} + t_{x+1,x-3}$

5. a) $(x + 1)^8 = x^8 + 8x^7 + 28x^6 + 56x^5 + 70x^4 + 56x^3 + 28x^2 + 8x + 1$
b) $(y - 2)^7 = y^7 - 14y^6 + 84y^5 - 280y^4 + 560y^3 - 672y^2 + 448y - 128$
c) $(2 + t)^6 = 64 + 192t + 240t^2 + 160t^3 + 60t^4 + 12t^5 + t^6$
d) $(1 - m^2)^4 = 1 - 4m^2 + 6m^4 - 4m^6 + m^8$
e) $(a + 2b)^3 = a^3 + 6a^2b + 12ab^2 + 8b^3$

6. a) 8 b) 21 c) 2 d) 39
e) 55 f) $n + 2$ g) 1

7. a) 1 b) 5 c) 3
d) 210 e) 45 f) 4

8. a) 15 b) 7 c) 17 d) 10
e) 20 f) 13 g) 9 h) 12

9. a) $t_{8,3} - t_{7,2}$ b) $t_{10,5} - t_{9,4}$
c) $t_{14,2} - t_{13,1}$ d) $t_{27,17} - t_{26,16}$
e) $t_{25,3} - t_{24,2}$ f) $t_{11,0} - t_{10,9}$
g) $t_{n+1,r} - t_{n,r-1}$

10. a) Refer to Pascal's triangle. Look for the row where the number 28 appears. This is in row 8. The number 28 is the 3rd entry and the 7th entry. To decide which is accurate for the given diagram, note that in the diagram the last number is 1. So, use the 28 in row 8 that is the 7th entry. It is followed by an 8, so in the middle position, write the number 8. Find the numbers in row 7 of Pascal's triangle to insert in the top two hexagons. These are 7 and 1. Use row 9 of Pascal's triangle to find the values that belong in the bottom two hexagons. These are 36 and 9.

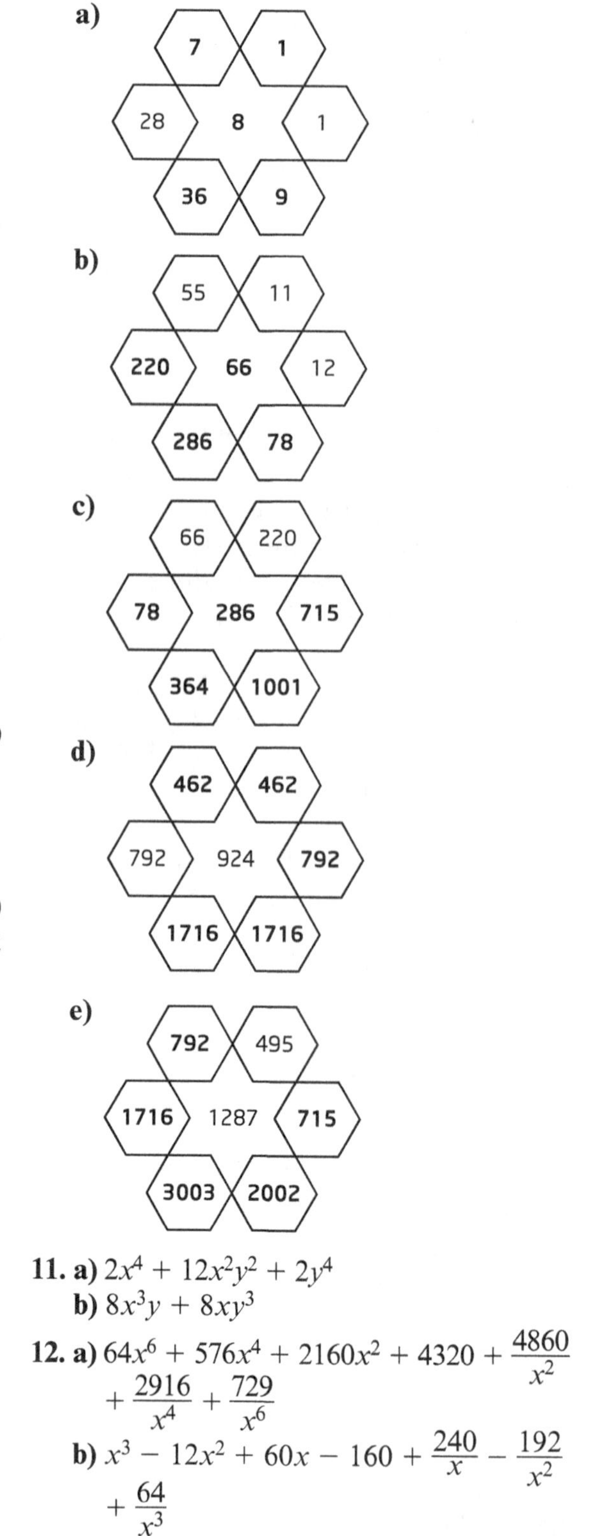

11. a) $2x^4 + 12x^2y^2 + 2y^4$
b) $8x^3y + 8xy^3$

12. a) $64x^6 + 576x^4 + 2160x^2 + 4320 + \frac{4860}{x^2} + \frac{2916}{x^4} + \frac{729}{x^6}$
b) $x^3 - 12x^2 + 60x - 160 + \frac{240}{x} - \frac{192}{x^2} + \frac{64}{x^3}$

13. Since Pascal's triangle is for binomials, group together two of the three terms to express the trinomial as a binomial, and then expand.

Use $(a + b + c)^3 = [(a + b) + c]^3$ and treat $(a + b)$ as a single term, such as x. To expand $[(a + b) + c]^3$ think of this as $[x + c]^3$. Once this is expanded using Pascal's triangle, replace x with $(a + b)$ and further expand and simplify.

b) $(a + b + c)^3$
$= [(a + b) + c]^3$
$= (a + b)^3 + 3(a + b)^2c + 3(a + b)c^2 + c^3$
$= a^3 + 3a^2b + 3ab^2 + b^3 + 3(a^2 + 2ab + c^2)c + 3ac^2 + 3bc^2 + c^3$
$= a^3 + 3a^2b + 3ab^2 + b^3 + 3a^2c + 6abc + 3ac^2 + 3bc^2 + c^3$

14. $a = b = 2$

15. –467

16. a) The coefficients of the expansion of $(a + b)^5$ are 1, 5, 10, 10, 5, 1.

$\binom{5}{0} = \frac{5!}{0!(5-0)!} = 1, \binom{5}{1} = 5, \binom{5}{2} = 10,$
$\binom{5}{3} = 10, \binom{5}{4} = 5, \binom{5}{5} = 1$

b) $\binom{10}{0} = 1, \binom{10}{1} = 10, \binom{10}{2} = 45,$
$\binom{10}{3} = 120, \binom{10}{4} = 210, \binom{10}{5} = 252,$
$\binom{10}{6} = 210, \binom{10}{7} = 120, \binom{10}{8} = 45,$
$\binom{10}{9} = 10, \binom{10}{10} = 1$

6.4 Arithmetic Sequences

1. a) $a = 5, d = 3$; 14, 17, 20, 24
b) $a = -3, d = 5$; 12, 17, 22, 27
c) $a = 1.5, d = -0.8$; –0.9, –1.7, –2.5, –3.3
d) $a = 33, d = -1.8$; 27.6, 25.8, 24, 22.2
e) $a = \frac{1}{4}, d = \frac{1}{4}$; $1, \frac{5}{4}, \frac{3}{2}, \frac{7}{4}$
f) $a = 0.25, d = 0.01$; 0.28, 0.29, 0.30, 0.31

2. a) arithmetic; $a = 1, d = 3$
b) not arithmetic; no common difference between terms
c) arithmetic; $a = -12, d = 7$
d) arithmetic; $a = 0.41, d = -0.09$
e) not arithmetic; no common difference between terms
f) arithmetic; $a = \frac{19}{12}, d = -\frac{1}{3}$

3. a) 12, 7, 2; $t_n = -5n + 17$
b) –9, –7, –5; $t_n = 2n - 11$
c) $11, \frac{81}{8}, \frac{37}{4}$; $t_n = -\frac{7}{8}n + \frac{95}{8}$
d) $-\frac{2}{3}, -\frac{1}{6}, \frac{1}{3}$; $t_n = -\frac{1}{2}n - \frac{7}{6}$
e) $x^2, 2.3x^2, 3.6x^2$; $t_n = 1.3x^2n - 0.3x^2$

4. a) 39 **b)** –77 **c)** –9
d) –28.8 **e)** 75 **f)** –173

5. a) 3, 7, 11, 15, 19

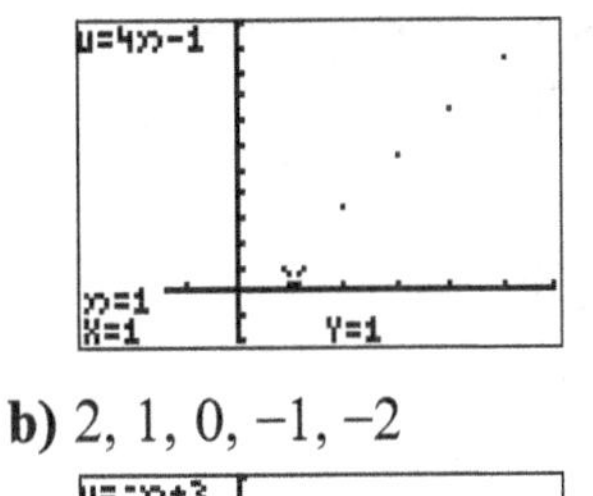

b) 2, 1, 0, –1, –2

c) –8, –18, –28, –38, –48

d) 11, 5, –1, –7, –13

e) 2.5, 4, 5.5, 7, 8.5

f) 1.2, 2.1, 3, 3.9, 4.8

g) 0.5, 0.7, 0.9, 1.1, 1.3

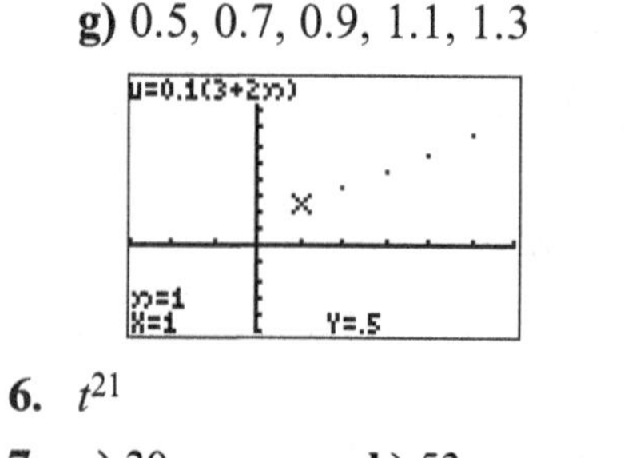

6. t^{21}

7. a) 30 b) 53 c) 86
d) 33 e) 65 f) 38

8. a) Find the terms of the sequence using the recursion formula $t_1 = -5, t_n = t_{n-1} + 3$.
$t_1 = -5$
$t_2 = -5 + 3 = -2$
$t_3 = -2 + 3 = 1$
$t_4 = 1 + 3 = 4$
The sequence is −5, −2, 1, 4, ...
The first term is −5 and the common difference is 3, so this is an arithmetic sequence.

b) Substitute $a = -5$ and $d = 3$ into $t_n = a + (n - 1)d$.
$t_n = -5 + (n - 1)(3)$
$= -5 + 3n - 3$
$= 3n - 8$

9. a) $a = \frac{1}{5}, d = \frac{4}{15}; 1, \frac{19}{15}, \frac{23}{15}$
b) $a = -1, d = -\frac{2}{3}; -3, -\frac{11}{3}, -\frac{13}{3}$
c) $a = 2, d = -\frac{3}{4}; -\frac{1}{4}, -1, -\frac{7}{4}$
d) $a = -\frac{3}{8}, d = \frac{7}{8}; \frac{9}{4}, \frac{25}{8}, 4$
e) $a = -4x + y, d = x + 4y; -x + 13y, 17y, x + 21y$
f) $a = 3m - \frac{5}{6}n, d = -6m + \frac{1}{6}n; -15m - \frac{1}{3}n, -21m - \frac{1}{6}n, -27m$

10. a) $a = -3, d = 7; t_n = 7n - 10$
b) $a = -3, d = 5; t_n = 5n - 8$
c) $a = 42, d = 2; t_n = 2n + 40$
d) $a = -3, d = 3; t_n = 3n - 6$
e) $a = 4.5, d = 1.5; t_n = 1.5n + 3$
f) $a = 16.2, d = -6; t_n = -6n + 22.2$
g) $a = x + 29, d = 5x; t_n = 5nx - 4x + 29$
h) $a = 3x^3 - 2, d = -x^3 - 1; t_n = 4x^3 - nx^3 - n - 1$

11. a) $t_1 = -3, t_n = t_{n-1} + 7$
b) $t_1 = -3, t_n = t_{n-1} + 5$
c) $t_1 = 42, t_n = t_{n-1} + 2$
d) $t_1 = -3, t_n = t_{n-1} + 3$
e) $t_1 = 4.5, t_n = t_{n-1} + 1.5$
f) $t_1 = 16.2, t_n = t_{n-1} - 6$
g) $t_1 = x + 29, t_n = t_{n-1} + 5x$
h) $t_1 = 3x^3 - 2, t_n = t_{n-1} - x^3 - 1$

12. a) 13 m
b) 0, 13, 26, 39, 52, 65, 78, 91, 104, 117
c) $t_n = 13n - 13$
d) 13 is the common difference, d

13. a) The salary the first 6 months is \$73 000. Add \$2275 for each subsequent 6-month period.
The sequence is 73 000, 75 275, 77 550, 79 825, ...
The sequence is arithmetic because there is a common difference of 2275 between each term, beginning with the first term, 73 000.

b) Substitute $a = 73\,000$ and $d = 2275$ into $t_n = a + (n - 1)d$.
$t_n = 73\,000 + (n - 1)(2275)$
$= 2275n + 70\,725$
The general term is $t_n = 2275n + 70\,725$.

c) Since each term is 2275 greater than the previous term, the recursion formula is $t_1 = 73\,000, t_n = t_{n-1} + 2275$.

d) 8 years is equivalent to 16 6-month periods. Substitute $n = 16$ into $t_n = 2275n + 70\,725$.
$t_{16} = 2275(16) + 70\,725$
$= 107\,125$
After 8 years, the architect's salary will be \$107 125.

e) Substitute $t_n = 127\,600$ into $t_n = 2275n + 70\,725$ and solve for n.
$127\,600 = 2275n + 70\,725$
$56\,875 = 2275n$
$n = 25$
25 6-month periods is equivalent to 12.5 years.
The architect's salary will be \$127 600 after 12.5 years.

14. a) 15
b) 9, 13, 17, 21, 25

15. $t_n = 5n - 2$

16. a) \$786.60
b) 21 years

17. 8, 3, −2 and −2, 3, 8

18. 11, 5, −1 or −1, 5, 11

6.5 Geometric Sequences

1. a) arithmetic; The first term is $a = 7$ and the common difference is $d = -2$.
b) geometric; The first term is $a = 4$ and the common ratio is $r = -4$.
c) geometric; The first term is $a = 3$ and the common ratio is $r = 0.1$.
d) neither; The first term is $a = 8$, but there is no common difference or common ratio between the consecutive terms.
e) geometric; The first term is $a = 1$ and the common ratio is $r = 3$.
f) geometric; The first term is $a = ab$ and the common ratio is $r = b$.

2. a) 2; 48, 96, 192
b) −4; −1280, 5120, −20 480
c) −2; 8, −16, 32 **d)** 0.1; 0.8, 0.08, 0.008
e) 3; $-\frac{27}{2}, -\frac{81}{2}, -\frac{243}{2}$
f) 0.2; 0.004, 0.0008, 0.000 16
g) $\frac{(x+3)^3}{4}$; $\frac{(x+3)^{14}}{768}, \frac{(x+3)^{17}}{3072}, \frac{(x+3)^{20}}{12\,288}$

3. a) $t_n = 4096\left(\frac{1}{4}\right)^{n-1}$; $\frac{1}{4}$
b) $t_n = 12\left(\frac{1}{2}\right)^{n-1}$; $\frac{3}{512}$
c) $t_n = 6\left(-\frac{1}{3}\right)^{n-1}$; $-\frac{2}{729}$
d) $t_n = 13.45(0.2)^{n-1}$; 0.000 006 886 4
e) $t_n = \frac{1}{32}(4)^{n-1}$; 524 288
f) $t_n = \frac{a^2}{b}\left(\frac{a}{2}\right)^{n-1}$; $\frac{a^{17}}{32\,768b}$

4. a) 3, −3, 3, −3 **b)** 22, −44, 88, −176
c) $\frac{1}{3}, \frac{2}{3}, \frac{4}{3}, \frac{8}{3}$, **d)** $4, 4\sqrt{5}, 20, 20\sqrt{5}$
e) $-2, -\frac{4}{3}, -\frac{8}{9}, -\frac{16}{27}$
f) −1111, 333.3, −99.99, 29.997

5. a) 8 **b)** 15 **c)** 8
d) 7 **e)** 13

6. a) arithmetic; $a = 3m$, $d = 4m$
b) geometric; $a = -1$, $r = \frac{2}{x}$
c) arithmetic; $a = 3x - 4y$, $d = 2x - 2y$
d) geometric; $a = 5.440$, $r = 10$
e) neither
f) arithmetic; $a = 7$, $d = -3 + s$

7. a) $m = 21, n = 189$ or $m = -21, n = -189$
b) $m = -50, n = -250$
c) $m = \frac{1}{3}, n = \frac{3}{4}$
d) $m = 1, n = 36$
e) $m = 32, n = 8$
f) $m = 20, n = 100$

8. First determine a and r to find the general term.
$a = \frac{2}{81}$
Divide the second term by the first term to find r.
$$r = \frac{\frac{4}{27}}{\frac{2}{81}} = \frac{4}{27} \times \frac{81}{2} = 6$$
$$t_n = \frac{2}{81}(6)^{n-1}$$
To determine the n-value that results in 6912, solve $6912 = \frac{2}{81}(6)^{n-1}$.
$$6912 = \frac{2}{81}(6)^{n-1}$$
$$\frac{6912(81)}{2} = 6^{n-1}$$
$$279\,936 = 6^{n-1}$$
Use systematic trial to find n. Since $6^7 = 279\,936$, $n - 1 = 7$ and $n = 8$. Therefore, 6912 is eighth term in the sequence.

9. 9

10. In each recursion formula the first term, t_1, corresponds with the value of a in the formula for the general term of a geometric sequence, and the coefficient of t_{n-1} corresponds with the value of r.
a) Since $t_1 = 4$, then $a = 4$. The coefficient of t_{n-1} is $-3x$, so $r = -3x$. Substitute a and r into $t_n = ar^{n-1}$. The general term is $t_n = 4(-3x)^{n-1}$.

b) Since $t_1 = -28m^3$, then $a = -28m^3$. The coefficient of t_{n-1} is $\frac{1}{2}$, so $r = \frac{1}{2}$. Substitute a and r in $t_n = ar^{n-1}$. The general term is $t_n = -28m^3\left(\frac{1}{2}\right)^{n-1}$.

c) Since $t_1 = \frac{5}{3}$, then $a = \frac{5}{3}$. The coefficient of t_{n-1} is $\frac{3}{4} + c$, so $r = \frac{3}{4} + c$. Substitute a and r in $t_n = ar^{n-1}$. The general term is $t_n = \frac{5}{3}\left(\frac{3}{4} + c\right)^{n-1}$.

11. a) $t_n = 2(2)^{n-1}$
b) i) 64 **ii)** 1024 **iii)** 16 384
c) 13 generations

12. a) 2048 bacteria **b)** $t_{72} = 8(2)^{71}$

13. a) 20 **b)** 32

14. a) 24 m **b)** 13th bounce

15. a) 0 or $-\frac{19}{3}$ **b)** −9

16. $p = \frac{1}{3}, q = 2, r = 12, s = 72$

17. a) $t_n = 9\left(\frac{1}{3}\right)^{n-1}$ **b)** t_9

18. 2, 6, 18

19. a) $\frac{9}{5}, \frac{6}{5}, \frac{4}{5}, \frac{8}{15}, \frac{16}{45}$ or $9, -6, 4, -\frac{8}{3}, \frac{16}{9}$
b) 1, −2, 4, −8, 16 or $\frac{3}{7}, \frac{6}{7}, \frac{12}{7}, \frac{24}{7}, \frac{48}{7}$

6.6 Arithmetic Series

1. a) 72 **b)** −136 **c)** −240
d) 105 **e)** $\frac{53}{3}$ **f)** $331.5x$

2. a) $a = 3, d = 4; S_{10} = 210$
b) $a = 5, d = 7; S_{10} = 365$
c) $a = 2, d = 6; S_{10} = 290$
d) $a = 6, d = 12; S_{10} = 600$
e) $a = \frac{3}{2}, d = -1; S_{10} = -30$
f) $a = 5.6, d = 0.3; S_{10} = 69.5$

3. a) $\frac{8752}{3}$ **b)** 510 **c)** −1368
d) −151.8 **e)** $168\sqrt{5}$ **f)** $\frac{3280}{81}$

4. a) 1 001 000 **b)** 20 200 **c)** −1430
d) 399 **e)** 416 **f)** −383.5

5. a) 7155 **b)** −110 **c)** −137.6
d) $\frac{55}{6}$ **e)** $210\sqrt{3}$ **f)** 780

6. a) 528 **b)** −850 **c)** 462
d) 235 **e)** −40 **f)** −285
g) 63 **h)** $231a + 210b$ **i)** 495

7. a) 12 **b)** 30 **c)** 20
d) 25 **e)** 6 or 10 **f)** 15
g) 7 or 22 **h)** 12 **i)** 21

8. a) 10 000 **b)** 4 002 000 **c)** 9560

9. a) 25 **b)** 1111

10. −1575

11. 1035

12. a) $286\sqrt{6}$ **b)** $-19x$
c) $1479a + 261b$
d) $\frac{1520}{x^2}$

13. a) not arithmetic; The sequence of terms does not have a common difference.
b) arithmetic; The sequence of terms has a common difference of $-4x^2$.
c) arithmetic; The sequence of terms has a common difference of $2m - b$.
d) not arithmetic; The sequence of terms does not have a common difference.

14. 1540

15. a) The profit in the first week is \$350. This is the first term of the series.
The profit in the second week is \$350 + \$75, or \$425. This is the second term of the series.
The profit in the third week is \$425 + \$75, or \$500. This is the third term of the series.
Each term is \$75 more than the previous term. The constant difference between terms is 75. Therefore, the terms form an arithmetic sequence and the sum of the terms form an arithmetic series. The last term represents the profit in the 16th week. The last term is \$350 + 15(\$75), or \$1475.
The arithmetic series that represents the total profit is
$350 + 425 + 500 + \cdots + 1475$.

b) Substitute $a = 350$, $t_{16} = 1475$, and $n = 16$ into the formula $S_n = \frac{n}{2}(a + t_n)$.

$$S_{16} = \frac{16}{2}(350 + 1475)$$
$$= 8(1825)$$
$$= 14\,600$$

The total profit for the season is $14 600.

16. Since there are 8 two-week periods in 16 weeks, in Job A Bashira would earn $450 × 8, or $3600. In Job B, Bashira would earn $100 the first week, $125 the second week, $150 the third week, and so on until week 16 when he earns $100 + 15($25), or $475.
The total amount of money is represented by the arithmetic series
$100 + 125 + 150 + \cdots + 475$.
The sum of the series is $\frac{16}{2}(100 + 475)$, or 4600.
Bashira should accept Job B since he would earn $4600, which is $1000 more than the amount he would earn in Job A.

17. a) $n^2 + 4n$ **b)** $2n^2 + 3n$
c) $\frac{5n^2 + n}{2}$ **d)** $\frac{7n^2 + 15n}{2}$
e) $\frac{-3n^2 + 21n}{2}$

18. a) $n^2 + n$ **b)** n^2

19. $28 + 25 + 22 + 19 + \cdots$

20. $t_n = 4n + 3$

21. 5, 7, 9, 11

22. $2 + 5 + 8 + 11 + 14 + \cdots$

23. $t_n = 3n - 2$

6.7 Geometric Series

1. a) geometric; The first term is $a = 1$ and the common ratio is $r = 10$.
b) arithmetic; The first term is $a = 6$ and the common difference is $d = 6$.
c) geometric; The first term is $a = -4$ and the common ratio is $r = -2$.
d) neither; The first term is $a = 7$ and there is no common ratio or common difference.
e) neither; The first term is $a = 6571$ and there is no common ratio or common difference.
f) neither; The first term is $a = \frac{1}{8}$ and there is no common ratio or common difference.

2. a) $a = 3, r = 2; S_9 = 1533$
b) $a = 5, r = 2; S_{12} = -6825$
c) $a = \frac{1}{8}, r = 2; S_8 = \frac{255}{8}$
d) $a = -0.2, r = -3; S_{13} = -79\,716.2$
e) $a = 9, r = -1; S_{50} = 0$
f) $a = 2, r = 0.1; S_{17} = \frac{20}{9}$

3. a) $\frac{1093}{81}$ **b)** $\frac{2049}{512}$ **c)** -1364
d) $-524\,286$ **e)** $1\,562\,496$ **f)** $-16\,382$
g) $\frac{133}{16}$ **h)** 0 **i)** 31 100

4. a) 3906 **b)** 88 572
c) $\frac{29\,524}{3}$ **d)** 27 305
e) 6560 **f)** 2999.9997
g) $\frac{9841}{27}$

5. a) $\frac{511}{128}$ **b)** 9840 **c)** $\frac{8525}{64}$
d) $\frac{5115}{512}$ **e)** $\frac{1705}{512}$

6. a) $\frac{-624\sqrt{5}}{\sqrt{5} + 1}$
b) The first term is $a = x$. The common ratio is $r = \sqrt{7}$. To find S_{13}, $n = 13$. Substitute these values in the formula

$$S_n = \frac{a(r^n - 1)}{r - 1}.$$
$$S_{13} = \frac{x[(\sqrt{7})^{13} - 1]}{\sqrt{7} - 1}$$

First, simplify $(\sqrt{7})^{13}$.

$$(\sqrt{7})^{13} = (\sqrt{7})^{12 + 1}$$
$$= (\sqrt{7})^{12}\sqrt{7}$$
$$= 117\,649\sqrt{7}$$

Then,

$$S_{13} = \frac{x(117\,649\sqrt{7} - 1)}{\sqrt{7} - 1}$$

c) $\frac{4(x^{14} - 1)}{x - 1}$
d) $\frac{2(x^{22} - 1)}{x^2 - 1}$

7. a) $\frac{25\,999}{64}$

b) $\frac{3\sqrt{6}(279\,936\sqrt{6} + 1)}{\sqrt{6} + 1}$

c) 19 790.251 12 or $2500(1.2^{12} - 1)$

d) $\frac{8(8192x^{39} - 1)}{2x^3 - 1}$

8. a) From the general term $t_n = -2(3)^{n-1}$, $a = -2$ and $r = 3$. Substitute these values in $S_n = \frac{a(r^n - 1)}{r - 1}$ and simplify, if possible.

$$S_n = \frac{-2(3^n - 1)}{3 - 1}$$
$$= \frac{-2(3^n - 1)}{2}$$
$$= 1 - 3^n$$

Therefore, an expression for the sum of the series is $S_n = 1 - 3^n$. Substitute $n = 9$ to obtain $S_9 = 1 - 3^9$, or $-19\,682$.

b) $S_n = 54\left(1 - \left(\frac{2}{3}\right)^n\right)$, $S_9 = \frac{38\,342}{729}$

c) $S_n = \frac{x^2(x^{2n} - 1)}{x^2 - 1}$, $S_9 = \frac{x^2(x^{18} - 1)}{x^2 - 1}$

9. $\frac{1023}{32}$

10. $a = 13$

11. 27

12. 717 km

13. 10 prizes

14. $10 737 418.23; Answers may vary. Sample answer: Her dad would probably not be able to afford this amount.

15. $t_n = 3(5)^{n-1}$ or $t_n = 75\left(\frac{1}{5}\right)^{n-1}$

16. Answers may vary.

17. 9841

18. a) $S_n = 2(2^n - 1) - \frac{1}{2}(3^n - 1)$
b) −238

Chapter 6 Review

1. a) $\frac{1}{3}, \frac{1}{9}, \frac{1}{27}$ b) $\frac{5}{2}, \frac{7}{3}, \frac{9}{4}$

2. a) 250 b) $\frac{7}{8}$

3. a) The first term is 7. Add 7 to the absolute value of each term and then multiply the result by $(-1)^{n+1}$ to get the next term. Next three terms: 35, −42, 49

b) The first term is $-\frac{1}{2}$. Divide each term by −2 (or multiply by $-\frac{1}{2}$) to get the next term. Next three terms: $-\frac{1}{32}, \frac{1}{64}, -\frac{1}{128}$

c) The first term is $3x$. Multiply each term by $2x$ to get the next term. Next three terms: $48x^5, 96x^6, 192x^7$

4. a) $f(n) = -5n$, domain $\{n \in \mathbb{N}\}$

Term Number, n	Term, t_n	First Differences
1	−5	
		−5
2	−10	
		−5
3	−15	
		−5
4	−20	

b) $f(n) = -3n^2 + 10n + 15$, domain $\{n \in \mathbb{N}\}$

Term Number, n	Term, t_n	First Differences	Second Differences
1	22		
		1	
2	23		−6
		−5	
3	18		−6
		−11	
4	7		

5. a) 2, 8, 7, 13 b) 5, 2, 0.8, 0.32
c) 10, −10, 5, $-\frac{5}{3}$

6. a) $f(1) = 1, f(n) = 3f(n - 1) + 1$
b) $f(1) = 3, f(n) = f(n - 1) + 2$
c) $f(1) = -2, f(n) = -4 - 3f(n - 1)$

7. a) $\frac{1}{8}, -\frac{1}{2}, -3, -13$
b) $a - 2b, a + b, a + 4b, a + 7b$

8. a) 5, 5.60, 6.27, 7.02
b) $t_1 = 5, t_n = 1.12t_{n-1}$
c) $t_n = 5(1.12)^{n-1}$
d) $13.87
e) 25 weeks

9. a) $210 = 126 + 56 + 21 + 6 + 1$
b) $70 = 35 + 20 + 10 + 4 + 1$
c) $126 = 70 + 35 + 15 + 5 + 1$

10. a) 2 097 152 b) 262 144

11. a) $t_{9,7}$ b) $t_{13,3}$ c) $t_{24,22}$

12. a) $a^5 + 5a^4 + 10a^3 + 10a^2 + 5a + 1$
b) $256x^8 - 786x^6y^3 + 864x^4y^6 - 432x^2y^9 + 81y^{12}$
c) $1 - \frac{5}{x} + \frac{10}{x^2} - \frac{10}{x^3} + \frac{5}{x^4} - \frac{1}{x^5}$

13. a) $a = -19, d = -6, t_n = -13 - 6n$; $-37, -43, -49, -55$
b) $a = \frac{8}{3}, d = -\frac{2}{5}, t_n = \frac{46}{15} - \frac{2}{5}n$; $\frac{22}{15}, \frac{16}{15}, \frac{2}{3}, \frac{4}{15}$

14. a) 9 b) 52

15. a) $t_n = 437 - 14n$ b) 269 m
c) 20th minute

16. a) neither; The first term is $a = \frac{3}{5}$, but there is no common difference or common ratio between successive terms.
b) geometric; The first term is $a = 2$ and the common ratio is $r = \sqrt{3}$.
c) arithmetic; The first term is $a = x + 7y$ and the common difference is $d = x + 3y$.

17. a) $t_n = -3(-5)^{n-1}$; $-1\ 171\ 875$
b) $t_n = -\frac{2}{625}(-5)^{n-1}$; $-31\ 250$

18. 1 171 875 e-mail messages

19. a) $a = 21, d = -6; -60$
b) $a = -4, d = -5; -265$

20. a) 42 b) 3604

21. 420 m

22. $2 + 6 + 10 + \cdots$

23. $a = 100, r = -2; S_8 = -8500$

24. a) 2186 b) $\frac{14\ 762}{19\ 683}$

25. $2 + 10 + 50 + \cdots$ or $72 - 60 + 50 - \cdots$

Math Contest

1. B
2. D
3. $8x^2 - 10x + 5$
4. $x = 4, y = 5$
5. C
6. A
7. D
8. B
9. A
10. $t_n = 1$ and $t_n = 4(-2)^{1-n}$
11. $x = -16, y = -\frac{128}{3}$
12. A
13. $1, -2, 4, -8, \ldots$ and $\frac{3}{7}, \frac{6}{7}, \frac{12}{7}, \frac{24}{7}, \ldots$
14. A
15. C
16. B

Chapter 7 Financial Applications

7.1 Simple Interest

1. a) \$108 b) \$33.25
c) \$18.17 d) \$24.09

2. a) \$535, \$570, \$605, \$640, \$675
b) $a = 535, d = 35$
c) $t_n = 500 + 35n$; The nth term is the linear model that represents the amount of the \$500 investment at the end of the nth year.

3. a) All first differences are \$40, representing the amount of simple interest added to the GIC each year.
b) \$1000; $t = 0$ is the start of the investment
c) 4%

4. a) $A = 1000 + 40t$
b) Answers may vary. Sample answer: This is a partial variation since the initial amount is not \$0. The linear model contains a fixed part and a variable part; fixed part = 1000, variable part = $40t$.
c) 25 years

5. The principal is $P = 2100$.
The interest rate is 18%, so $r = 0.18$.
The time is 23 days. Since there are 365 days in a year, then in days, $t = \frac{23}{365}$.
Substitute these values into the formula $I = Prt$ and solve for I.
$I = 2100 \times 0.18 \times \frac{23}{365}$
$\doteq 23.82$
The company would charge \$23.82 in interest.

6. **a)** \$800 **b)** 5%
   c) $A = 800 + 40t$ **d)** 20 years
7. **a)** $I = 40t$
   b) 20 years, the same as in 6d)
8. Determine the principal, P.
   The interest rate is $2\frac{3}{4}$%. So, $r = 0.0275$.
   The time is $t = 4$.
   The interest is $I = 165$.
   Substitute these values into the formula $I = Prt$ and solve for P.
   $165 = P \times 0.0275 \times 4$
   $165 = 0.11P$
   $P = \frac{165}{0.11}$
   $P = 1500$
   Katio borrowed \$1500.
9. **a)** $A = 320 + 17.60t$
   b) 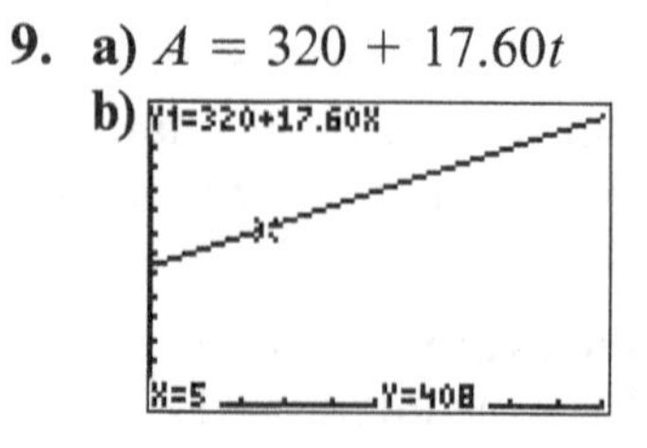

   c) 7 years 5 months **d)** 7.54%
10. Determine the interest rate, r.
    The principal is $P = 1350$.
    The time is 8 months. Since there are 12 months in a year, then in years,
    $t = \frac{8}{12}$, or $\frac{2}{3}$.
    The interest is $I = 38.50$.
    Substitute these values into the formula $I = Prt$ and solve for r.
    $38.25 = 1350 \times r \times \frac{2}{3}$
    $38.25 = 900r$
    $r = \frac{38.25}{900}$
    $r = 0.0425$
    The annual rate of interest of Lorilo's loan was 4.25%.
11. **a)** \$4213.25 **b)** \$413.25
    c) Rosalie should repay the loan 6 months sooner, that is, in approximately 1 year.
12. 8 years
13. **a)** Option 1: $A = 4500 + 382.50t$;
    Option 2: $A = 4650 + 360t$
    b) 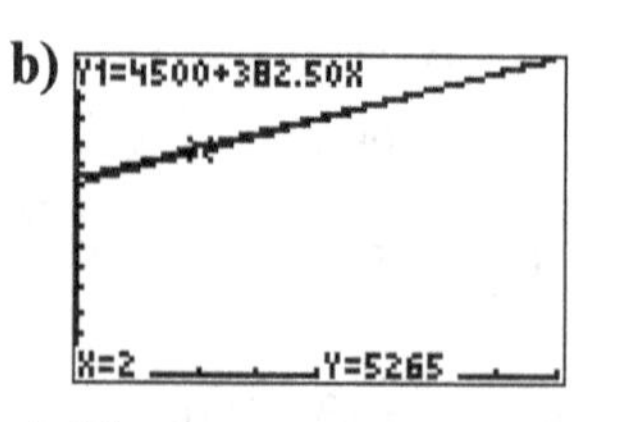

    c) The loan payment for the two options is equal at 6 years 8 months. Option 1 is less costly, so it is the better option if Arash pays the loan in less than 6 years 8 months. For a longer repayment period, Option 2 is the better option.
14. **a)** \$63.75 **b)** \$850 **c)** 7.5%
15. \$611.76
16. \$2400
17. **a)** \$1419.01 **b)** \$56.61
    c) Answers may vary. Sample answer: The interest is "compounded" on the previous interest as well as the initial principal.

7.2 Compound Interest

1. **a)** \$914.62 **b)** \$264.62
2. **a)** \$1466.07 **b)** \$491.07
3. **a)** 0.005 83 **b)** 0.0225
   c) 0.04 **d)** 0.0042
4. **a)** 16 **b)** 10 **c)** 8
   d) 21 **e)** 7
5. **a)** $n = 4$, $i = 0.085$ **b)** $n = 20$, $i = 0.0175$
   c) $n = 36$, $i = 0.003$ **d)** $n = 13$, $i = 0.0275$
   e) $n = 730$, $i = 0.000\ 169\ 86$
6. **a)** \$1601.59 **b)** \$301.59
   c) simple interest is \$273; compound interest earns \$28.59 more
7. \$8.81
8. **a)** The principal is \$6800, so $P = 6800$.
   When the interest is compounded semi-annually, it is added twice a year.
   The semi-annual rate is $\frac{5.2\%}{2}$, or 2.6%.
   So, $i = 0.026$.
   i) In 4 years, there are 4×2, or 8 compounding periods. So, $n = 8$.
   Substitute the known values into the compound interest formula.

$A = P(1 + i)^n$
$= 6800(1 + 0.026)^8$
$= 6800(1.026)^8$
$\doteq 8350.03$

The amount after 4 years is \$8350.03.

ii) In 7 years, there are 7 × 2, or 14 compounding periods.
Substitute the known values into the compound interest formula.
$A = P(1 + i)^n$
$= 6800(1 + 0.026)^{14}$
$= 6800(1.026)^{14}$
$\doteq 9740.29$
The amount after 7 years is \$9740.29.

b) Determine the difference between the amounts for the 4th year and 7th year.
\$9740.29 − \$8350.03 = \$1390.26
Therefore, \$1390.26 was earned in interest between the 4th year and the 7th year.

9. a) i) \$555
ii) \$700.31
iii) \$720.39
iv) \$730.97
v) \$738.24
vi) \$741.82

b) The best scenario for Kara is simple interest, since this is the least interest payment. The worst is the daily compounded interest, since this is the greatest interest payment.

c) The shorter the compounding period, the greater the interest.

10. The principal is $P = 5000$.
Since Isabella wants her investment to double, then $A = 10\,000$.
The daily interest rate is $\frac{6\%}{365}$, so $i \doteq 0.000\,164$.
Let x represent the number of years it takes for the investment to double in value.
In x years, there are $365x$ compounding periods. So, $n = 365x$.
Use the compound interest formula.
$A = P(1 + i)^n$
$10\,000 = 5000(1 + 0.000\,164)^{365x}$
$2 = (1.000\,164)^{365x}$
Use systematic trial to find the value of $365x$.
Since $(1.000\,164)^{4230} \doteq 2.001$, then $x \doteq 11.6$.
Convert to years and months.
$0.6 \times 12 = 7.2$
Therefore, it takes approximately 11 years and 7 months for Isabella's investment to double.

11. a) The best choice is the one that earns the most interest. Determine the amount at the end of 7 years for each option. The principal is $P = 8000$.

Option 1:
When the interest is compounded semi-annually, it is added twice a year.
The semi-annual rate is $\frac{6\%}{2}$, or 3%. So, $i = 0.03$.
In 7 years, there are 7 × 2, or 14 compounding periods. So, $n = 14$.
Substitute the known values into the compound interest formula.
$A = P(1 + i)^n$
$= 8000(1 + 0.03)^{14}$
$= 8000(1.03)^{14}$
$\doteq 12\,100.72$
If Meg invests her money in Option 1, she will have \$12 100.72 after 7 years.

Option 2:
Calculate the interest first. Substitute $P = 8000$, $r = 0.075$, and $t = 7$ into $I = Prt$.
$I = 8000(0.075)(7)$
$= 4200$
Now, find the amount.
$A = P + I$
$= 8000 + 4200$
$= 12\,200$
If Meg invests her money in Option 2, she will have \$12 200 after 7 years.
Therefore, Meg should choose Option 2 because she will earn more interest.

b) In Option 1, the investment earns compound interest. This represents an exponential function because interest is earned on interest. The amount grows exponentially because it is multiplied by

1.03 for each compounding period. In Option 2, the investment earns simple interest. This is a constant amount paid out at the end of each year, so it represents a linear function.

12. 7.25%

13. 5.8%

14. a) i) 18 years

ii) 24 years

iii) 12 years

b) Answers may vary. Sample answer: The Rule of 72 is close but not exact. The results using the compound interest formula are

i) 17 years 8 months

ii) 23 years 5 months

iii) 11 years 11 months

15. 7 years

16. Maxime should choose Option 1 because the amount at the end of 4 years is \$6194.12, whereas the amount at the end of 4 years with Option 2 is \$6189.87.

17. Answers may vary. Sample answer: James takes out a \$1200 loan at 6.5% per year, compounded annually.

18. 17 years 6 months

19. \$5420.75

20. a) i) 6.09% **ii)** 8.24%

b) Answers may vary. Sample answer: No, the principal amount does not influence the effective rate. However, the effective rate of interest is higher the more often the nominal rate is compounded.

7.3 Present Value

1. a) \$633.67 **b)** \$950

2. \$47.21

3. a) \$1100 **b)** \$514.63

4. a) \$2000 **b)** \$1151.68

5. The future value of the investment is \$10 000. So, $FV = 10\ 000$.

The monthly rate is $\frac{6.3\%}{12}$, or $i = 0.005\ 25$.

In 5 years there are 5×12, or 60 compounding periods. So, $n = 60$.

Substitute the known values into the formula $PV = \frac{FV}{(1+i)^n}$.

$$PV = \frac{10\ 000}{(1 + 0.005\ 25)^{60}}$$
$$= \frac{10\ 000}{(1.005\ 25)^{60}}$$
$$\doteq 7303.90$$

Therefore, Tara should invest \$7303.90 at 6.3% today to have \$10 000 in 5 years.

6. quarterly

7. 7 years

8. a) Investment A:

Substitute $FV = 8000$, $n = 24$, and $i = 0.013\ 75$ into $PV = \frac{FV}{(1+i)^n}$.

$$PV = \frac{8000}{(1 + 0.013\ 75)^{24}}$$
$$= \frac{8000}{(1.013\ 75)^{24}}$$
$$\doteq 5764.33$$

With Investment A, Paula would have to invest \$5764.33 to have \$8000 in 6 years.

Investment B:

Substitute $FV = 8000$, $n = 72$, and $i \doteq 0.004\ 417$ into $PV = \frac{FV}{(1+i)^n}$.

$$PV = \frac{8000}{(1 + 0.004\ 417)^{72}}$$
$$= \frac{8000}{(1.004\ 417)^{72}}$$
$$\doteq 5824.76$$

With Investment B, Paula would have to invest \$5824.76 to have \$8000 in 6 years.

b) Investment A is the better choice for Paula since she would have to invest less money to reach her goal of \$8000 in 6 years.

9. a) \$4083.50 **b)** \$4053.39 **c)** \$4037.83

10. \$757.88

11. 6%

12. a) \$3759.68 **b)** 9.7%

13. a) \$2.63 **b)** \$0.45

14. \$49 295.23

15. \$7651.41

16. $16 137.80

17. $473.06

7.4 Annuities

1. a) semi-annually; The annual interest is 10%, but in the time line, $(1.05)^n$ indicates that for each payment period, 5% interest is paid. This means that interest is paid twice a year.
   b) 6 years; The time line shows 12 payments, with payments made twice a year.
   c) $4775.14
2. a) quarterly; The annual interest is 8%, but in the time line, $(1.02)^n$ indicates that for each payment period, 2% interest is paid. This means that interest is paid four times a year.
   b) 5 years; The time line shows 20 payments, with payments made four times a year.
   c) $9718.95
3. a) a time line for the future value of an annuity with $R = 1200$, $n = 10$, and $i = 0.0375$
   b), c) $14 241.41 d) $2241.41
4. a) a time line for the future value of an annuity with $R = 40$, $n = 24$, and $i = 0.005$
   b) $1017.28 c) $57.28
5. $899.65
6. $560.19
7. a) $174.48 b) 10%
8. a) 3 years b) $86.95
9. 170 weeks, or 3 years 4 months
10. Substitute $A = 500\ 000$, $i \doteq 0.004\ 667$, and $n = 420$ into $A = \frac{R[(1 + i)^n - 1]}{i}$, and then solve for R.

$$500\ 000 = \frac{R[(1 + 0.004\ 667)^{420} - 1]}{0.004\ 667}$$

$$2333.5 = R[(1.004\ 667)^{420} - 1]$$

$$R = \frac{2333.5}{(1.004\ 667)^{420} - 1}$$

$$R \doteq 384.56$$

Daniel should make monthly deposits of $384.56 so that he will have $500 000 at retirement.

11. a) $24 000 b) Answers may vary.
    c) Anna: $27 908.01; Donella: $32 775.87; Tina: $46 204.09
12. a) Option A: $480 000; Option B: $960 000
    b) Mick should choose Option A. When he is 65, the value of Option A will be $3 491 007.83, which is $1 143 926.17 more than Option B, which will be worth $2 356 081.66.
13. i) Substitute $R = 1000$, $n = 45$, and $i = 0.06$ into $A = \frac{R[(1 + i)^n - 1]}{i}$.

$$A = \frac{1000[(1 + 0.06)^{45} - 1]}{0.06}$$

$$= \frac{1000[(1.06)^{45} - 1]}{0.06}$$

$$\doteq 212\ 743.51$$

In this situation, the amount at age 65 is $212 743.51.
A total of $1000 × 45, or $45 000, was deposited into the account.

ii) Substitute $R = 3000$, $n = 15$, and $i = 0.06$ into $A = \frac{R[(1 + i)^n - 1]}{i}$.

$$A = \frac{3000[(1 + 0.06)^{15} - 1]}{0.06}$$

$$= \frac{3000[(1.06)^{15} - 1]}{0.06}$$

$$\doteq 69\ 827.91$$

In this situation, the amount at age 65 is $69 827.91.
A total of $3000 × 15, or $45 000, was deposited into the account.
In each situation, the deposit amount is equal but the final amount is much higher for the $1000 deposited since age 20 than for the $3000 deposited since age 50.

14. a) $13 971.65 b) $13 180.79
    c) $A = \frac{R(1 + i)[(1 + i)^n - 1]}{i}$
15. $3799.47

16. $4199.32

17. $1230.17

7.5 Present Value of an Annuity

1. **a)** 14%; The time line shows an interest rate of 7%, which is paid every 6 months.
   b) 4; There are 4 compound interest periods.
   c) $10 161.63

2. **a)** $200 159.61

3. **a)** a time line for present value of an annuity with $R = 500$, $n = 5$, and $i = 0.09$
   b) $1944.83

4. **a)** a time line for the present value of an annuity with $R = 300$, $n = 36$, and $i = 0.005\ 75$
   b) $9730.34 **c)** $1069.66

5. $361.52

6. **a)** $2766.21 **b)** $50 648.40

7. **a)** Substitute $PV = 12\ 000$, $i \doteq 0.006\ 667$, and $n = 60$ into $PV = \frac{R[1 - (1 + i)^{-n}]}{i}$.

$$12\ 000 = \frac{R[1 - (1 + 0.006\ 667)^{-60}]}{0.006\ 667}$$

$$80.004 = R[1 - (1.006\ 667)^{-60}]$$

$$R = \frac{80.004}{1 - (1.006\ 667)^{-60}}$$

$$R \doteq 243.32$$

Therefore, Jessica's monthly payments are $243.31.

   b) To calculate the interest paid, multiply the amount of the payments by the number of payments and subtract the amount borrowed.

$$I = n \times R - PV$$
$$= 60 \times 243.32 - 12\ 000$$
$$= 14\ 599.20 - 12\ 000$$
$$= 2599.20$$

Jessica is paying $2599.20 in interest on the loan.

8. **a)** $33 982.11
   b) $26 017.89

9. **a)** Substitute $R = 100$, $i = 0.005$, and $n = 120$ into $PV = \frac{R[1 - (1 + i)^{-n}]}{i}$.

$$PV = \frac{100[1 - (1 + 0.005)^{-120}]}{0.005}$$
$$= \frac{100[1 - (1.005)^{-120}]}{0.005}$$
$$\doteq 9007.35$$

The charitable organization needs $9007.35 to fund this prize.

   b) $A = n \times R$
$$= 120 \times 100$$
$$= 12\ 000$$

The winner receives $12 000.

   c) $I = A - PV$
$$= 12\ 000 - 9007.35$$
$$= 2992.65$$

Therefore, $2992.65 of the winnings was earned as interest.

10. Substitute $PV = 7500$, $i \doteq 0.002\ 417$, and $n = 36$ into $PV = \frac{R[1 - (1 + i)^{-n}]}{i}$.

$$7500 = \frac{R[1 - (1 + 0.002\ 417)^{-36}]}{0.002\ 417}$$

$$18.1275 = R[1 - (1.002\ 417)^{-36}]$$

$$R = \frac{18.1275}{1 - (1.002\ 417)^{-36}}$$

$$R \doteq 217.78$$

The customer's monthly payment will be $217.78.

11. 9.8% compounded monthly

12. $498.43

13. 7.93%

14. **a)** $854.45 at 8%; $846.26 at 7.5%
    b) $41 013.60 at 8%; $40 620.48 at 7.5%
    c) $393.12

15. $3260.67

16. 10 years

17. $4866.72

Chapter 7 Review

1.

Principal, P	Interest Rate, r	Time, t	Simple Interest, I
\$627.00	6.5%	2 months	\$6.79
\$389.15	9.25%	58 days	\$5.72
\$270.00	8%	3 years	\$64.80
\$425.00	$7\frac{1}{2}$%	145 days	\$12.66
\$380.21	$4\frac{3}{4}$%	6 months	\$9.03
\$178.50	8.6%	245 days	\$10.30
\$3200.00	11.5%	4.5 months	\$138.00

2. \$29.07
3. **a)** \$960 **b)** \$4960
4. Answers may vary. Sample answer: Simple interest is paid annually on the principal and is not reinvested. Compound interest is earned annually but is reinvested with the principal, so interest is earned on interest. Simple interest accumulates at the same rate and represents linear growth. Compound interest accumulates at a rate that has a constant ratio and represents exponential growth.
5. **a)** \$750.00 **b)** \$936.28 **c)** \$186.28 **d) i)** \$2250 **ii)** \$2436.28
6. **a)** \$1773.95 **b)** \$173.95
7. \$1432.49
8. 7.72%
9. 15 years 1 month
10. 10.78%
11. **a)** \$12 918.79 **b)** \$1918.79
12. \$933.09
13. 8.14%
14. **a)** \$2896.99 **b)** \$3000 **c)** \$103.01
15. \$26 050.33
16. 3.5%

Math Contest

1. B
2. C
3. B
4. $-\frac{1}{8}$
5. A
6. D
7. 12
8. $\frac{9}{49}$
9. 0, 3, −7
10. $t_n = 1$ and $t_n = 4(-2)^{1-n}$
11. 30°
12. B

Practice Exam

1. $\frac{81}{625}$
2. $(-7)^{65}$
3. $\frac{x^{28}}{y^{42}}$
4. $\frac{1}{(5)^9}$
5. $48^{\frac{1}{5}}$
6. −8
7. exponential
8. 1
9. $y = 0$
10. $\{y \in \mathbb{R}, y > 0\}$
11. $y = 2^{x-3}$
12. $y = 6^{2x}$
13. increasing
14. $y = 2^{-3x}$
15. $y = -1$
16. **a)** $y = 7 \sin [2(x - 30°)]$ **b)** $y = -4 \sin 3x + 2$
17. $\frac{5x^2 + 44x}{(x-2)(x-3)(x+4)}$; the restrictions are $x \neq -4, x \neq 2, x \neq 3$
18. When simplified, $f(x) = 11(x + 4)$ and $g(x) = 11(x - 4), x \neq -1$. Therefore, $f(x)$ is not equivalent to $g(x)$.

19. a) $a = -1$; this is a reflection in the x-axis
$k = 4$; this is a horizontal compression by a factor of $\frac{1}{4}$
$d = -3$; this is a horizontal translation of 3 units to the left
$c = -1$; this is a vertical translation of 1 unit down
The equation is $y = -\sqrt{4(x + 3)} - 1$.

b) $a = \frac{1}{2}$; this is a vertical compression of factor $\frac{1}{2}$
$k = -1$; this is a reflection in the y-axis
$d = -5$; this is a horizontal translation of 5 units to the left
$c = 2$; this is a vertical translation of 2 units up
The equation is $y = \frac{-1}{2(x + 5)} + 2$.

20. a) base function $f(x) = \frac{1}{x}$; transformed function $g(x) = \sqrt{x - 2} - 5$

b) base function $f(x) = \frac{1}{x}$; transformed function $g(x) = \frac{1}{x - 1} + 4$

21. i) a) domain $\{x \in \mathbb{R}, x \neq 2\}$, range $\{y \in \mathbb{R}, y \neq 0\}$

b) $f(-5) = \frac{1}{7}$

c) $f^{-1}(x) = \frac{2x - 1}{x}$

ii) a) domain $\{x \in \mathbb{R}\}$, range $\{y \in \mathbb{R}, y \geq 1\}$

b) $f(-5) = 76$

c) $f^{-1}(x) = \pm\sqrt{\frac{x - 1}{3}}$

22. a) $f(x) = -3(x - 1)^2 + 7$; V(1, 7) is a maximum

b) $f(x) = 2(x - 2)^2 - 1$; V(2, −1) is a minimum

23. $f(x) = 2x^2 - 12x + 8$

24. a) The value of the discriminant is 17, which is greater than zero, so the line and the quadratic function intersect at two points.

b) The value of the discriminant is −27, which is less than zero, so the line and the quadratic function do not intersect.

25. Ambiguous case; there are two answers: 21.9 km or 12.7 km

26. 4.2 m

27. a) amplitude is 5, period is 90°, horizontal translation is 30° to the right, range $\{y \in \mathbb{R}, -7 \leq y \leq 3\}$

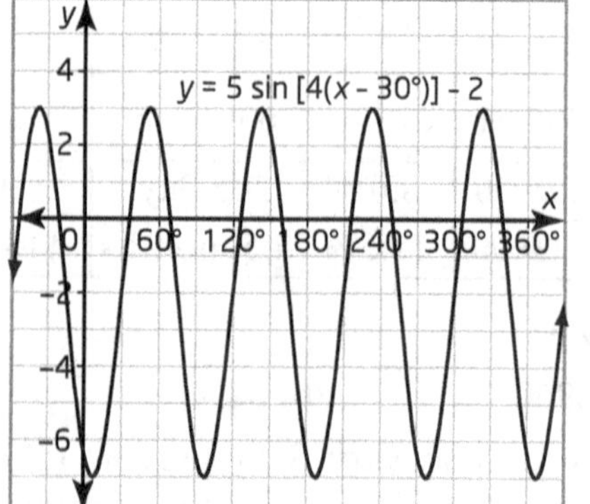

b) amplitude is 2, period is 120°, horizontal translation is 45° to the left, range $\{y \in \mathbb{R}, 3 \leq y \leq 7\}$

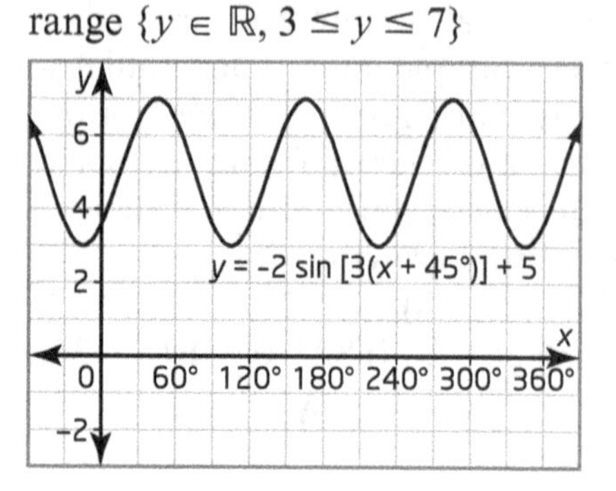

28. $10\sqrt{3} + 40$ m

29. Answers may vary.

30. a) maximum: 29 °C, in July

b) minimum: −7 °C, in January

c) 36 °C

d) twice the value of 18, the coefficient of the sine term

e) 22

f) twice the amount of 11, the constant term

g) October is month 10; substitute $t = 10$ in equation to get 11 °C

h) month 5, May, and month 9, September

31. $t_{19, 8} - t_{18, 7}$

32. $(4x - y)^5 = 1024x^5 - 1280x^4y + 640x^3y^2 - 160x^2y^3 + 20xy^4 - y^5$

33. a) 82 **b)** 19

34. $a = -5, d = 12; t_n = 12n - 17$

35. 10

36. $3 + 10 + 17 + 24 + 31 + 38 + \cdots$

37. 180 m

38. a) approximately 13.4 m
b) approximately 201.2 m

39. $S_{64} = 2^{64} - 1$

40. a) arithmetic; $a = 100, d = -10$; sum $= -1980$
b) geometric; $a = 1, r = 3$; sum $= 3280$

41. $t_4 = 250; S_6 = 7812$

42. a) 24 800 is the purchase value of the car; 0.78 is the constant factor or ratio as the value depreciates 22% each year
b) i) \$15 088.32 **ii)** \$7160.19
c) The initial value of the car depreciates by a constant factor each year.
d) 3.7 years or approximately 3 years 8 months

43. \$131.25

44. a) \$2030 **b)** \$7030

45. \$8121.66

46. 9.51% per annum, compounded quarterly

47. \$801.40

48. approximately 12.3 years

49. \$1799.05